ELECTRONICS

A Textbook for Students in
Science and Engineering

ELECTRONICS

A Textbook for Students in
Science and Engineering

THOMAS BENJAMIN BROWN

Professor of Physics
The George Washington University

New York · JOHN WILEY & SONS, Inc.
London · CHAPMAN & HALL, Ltd.

Library of Congress Catalog Card Number: 54-6683

PRINTED IN THE UNITED STATES OF AMERICA

To my wife
LEA

Preface

Why another book in Electronics? No field of science is better represented by books than this one. And what are the special qualifications of its author? These questions will be asked by the prospective users of this book, and I shall try to answer them by explaining as best I can my reasons for writing it.

First of all, it is a *textbook*. Textbook is an old-fashioned term, at the present time used mostly in a generic sense to comprise all books for instruction, and one rarely seen in book titles. In a narrower sense, however, and in a sense I am pleased to call more exact, a textbook is one in which the content, the order of its arrangement, and the mode of its presentation are planned to meet most effectively the needs of the classroom and the laboratory; this is the aim of this textbook in Electronics. It has been written first of all to meet the needs of a basic course which is given at George Washington University for students in physics, engineering, and other sciences. This is a practical course in electron-tube theory, in which the emphasis is placed upon physical analysis of the performance of electron tubes and circuits, rather than upon study of all possible types. For example, in each amplifier experiment the gain, which is measured experimentally, is checked against theory by analytical or graphical methods. Although this limits the number of types of amplifiers studied, it trains the student in methods of analysis applicable to *any* type.

The present course has evolved from a beginning made over 35 years ago, with a handful of tubes from World War I. At no time in this period have I found a book which satisfied me as a textbook. In the earlier years, when classes were small (principally physics students, with a few electrical engineering students), it was possible to base the course upon lectures, with one or more books assigned for reference and collateral reading. Instructions for experiments were mimeographed. This arrangement became less satisfactory as classes became larger, and in 1949 the need for a suitable textbook was met by a mimeographed book which was the forerunner of this one.

As indicated above, the order of presentation here is that of a textbook for students; it is the order which I have found, in years of experimentation, to be most satisfactory for teaching the fundamentals of Electronics. It is not always the strictly "logical" order. An illustration is the treatment of electron emission theory, which here is delayed to Chapter 7. The first six chapters consider the properties and fundamental applications of thermionic tubes in which current is space-charge limited, and for these tubes it is sufficient to know that their cathodes emit electrons copiously enough to meet the requirements of the space-charge law. The advantages gained are, first, the student makes earlier contact with practical applications, an important point in gaining his interest, and second, he appreciates better the theory of electron emission after he has become acquainted with these applications. Descriptions of laboratory and demonstration experiments are made an integral part of the text, in accord with my conviction that personal experience with the phenomena studied is essential to their full understanding. For the most part the equipment required for these experiments is simple and relatively inexpensive. Even if the experiments are not performed their descriptions may be studied with profit, as specific examples of the topics represented. All circuits are kept as simple as possible, so that basic electronic theory will not be confused with circuit theory. On the other hand, theories concerning the physical processes taking place *inside* electron tubes, such as space-charge effects, the functioning of grids, and the effect of gas in gas-type tubes, are developed more fully than is usual in books at this level. An outline of this book is given in Secs. 9 to 12 of the *Introduction*.

I am indebted to many in the preparation of this book. First to my own teachers, beginning with Earnest Merritt of Cornell University, whose Friday lectures gave me my first insight into this subject, and including E. L. Chaffee of Harvard University, whose lectures I attended during a sabbatical year and whose book, *Theory of Thermionic Vacuum Tubes*, I still regard as a classic. I must include also my many students, whose questions and comments have repeatedly challenged my ideas and helped me to develop new ones. I owe particular thanks to Dr. L. R. Koller for most helpful advice and criticism concerning gaseous conduction, and to Dr. C. L. Andrews for valuable help in connection with microwaves. I thank also the Radio Corporation of America, the General Electric Company, and the Bell Telephone Laboratories for permission to use diagrams and charts as noted elsewhere. Finally, I acknowledge with thanks that the *Bell System Technical Journal* has been my principal source of information for Appendix 6, *Crystal Rectifiers and Transistors;* specific references are listed at the end of this appendix.

THOMAS B. BROWN

Washington, D. C.
February, 1954

Contents

Laboratory Experiments

INTRODUCTION

1. Electronics. "Electronics" is a very popular term, and almost everything electrical, from electric blankets to radar, tends to assume the electronics label. Even in its more scientific usage this word is employed with many gradations of meaning. At one extreme we find included all engineering applications, such as radio and radar, which utilize electron tubes in any way whatsoever; at the other extreme we find this field limited to the most fundamental physical aspects of electron emission, electron dynamics, and kindred phenomena, excluding all applications. Textbooks in electronics represent many variations between these two extremes.

To clarify this situation somewhat we must first specify what we mean by electronic phenomena. Here we shall define electronic phenomena as those in which electrical conduction occurs as the motion of "free" electrically charged particles between electrodes in "free" space. The *free particles* generally are electrons, although sometimes they are ions (electrically charged atoms or atomic groups) of either sign. Ordinarily the *free space* is a region so highly evacuated that the residual gas particles have negligible effect upon the particles passing through, although many important electronic phenomena occur when the gas density is far from negligible. In some cases the gas pressure may equal or even exceed atmospheric pressure. Metallic conduction, ionic conduction in electrolytes, and generally all electrical conduction in which Ohm's law is followed are excluded by this definition. Indeed, deviation from Ohm's law may be taken as one of the identifying characteristics of all electronic phenomena.

2. Scope. In this textbook the scope of the field of electronics is limited to the following topics:

(*a*) The manner in which electronic conduction takes place.

(*b*) The control of streams of electrically charged particles.

(*c*) The liberation of electrons from electrodes. This includes thermionic emission, photoelectric emission, and secondary emission.

(*d*) The production of free ions, either at electrodes or by the ionization of gas atoms or molecules.

(*e*) Devices in which these phenomena are utilized, such as electron tubes.

(*f*) Electrical circuits and other applications in which such devices

1

are *essential* elements. Only the *basic* applications are considered here.

(*g*) Certain other devices in which conduction does not follow Ohm's law, such as crystal rectifiers and transistors. These are included primarily because they are able to perform many of the functions of which vacuum tubes are capable. A brief survey of crystal-rectifier and transistor theory and circuits is given in Appendix 6.

3. Mathematics and Physics Background. It is assumed that the user of this textbook has had training in mathematics through calculus, in addition to good training in basic physics and in electric-circuit theory. It is assumed further that he is already familiar with the salient facts concerning electrons, atoms, and ions. Most of these will be reviewed later on, as they are needed. The following may be mentioned here:

(*a*) The electron is a particle having a very small mass and a permanent negative electric charge. Its mass is approximately 9.1×10^{-28} gram, or $\frac{1}{1840}$ times the mass of the smallest atom. Its charge is very small in absolute value (4.80×10^{-10} statcoulomb, or 1.60×10^{-19} coulomb) but very large relative to its mass: the *specific charge*, or ratio of its charge to its mass, is 5.28×10^{17} statcoulombs per gram, or 1.76×10^8 coulombs per gram.

(*b*) Electrons are constituent parts of all atoms and molecules. The massive part of an atom is a very small, very dense *nucleus*, which is positively charged. The number of elementary positive charges on a nucleus equals the *atomic number*, Z, for the chemical element to which it belongs, and determines all the chemical properties of the atom, as well as most of its physical properties. In a neutral atom this nucleus is surrounded by electrons equal in number to Z, such that the net charge on the atom is zero. A *positive ion* has too few electrons to neutralize the nuclear charge, whereas a *negative ion* has an excess. Since the volume of an atom is something like 10^{12} times that of either the nucleus or an electron, the particles making up an atom are relatively very far apart. Molecular structure is comparable in many ways to atomic structure, and molecular ions are similar to atomic ions.

(*c*) These concepts extend also to the structure of solids, where the atoms are crowded so closely together that electrons may no longer be considered the exclusive property of the individual atoms (or molecules). In solids (metals) which are good conductors of electricity a rather simple description often suffices. According to this description the electrons which account for electrical conduction in a metal (one or two for each atom of the metal) are free to move about anywhere

within the volume of the metal; thus they may be regarded as consti-
tuting an *electron gas* whose boundaries are those of the metal.   These
same electrons serve also to make metals good conductors of heat.

Although these electrons may be regarded as free particles within the
volume of the metal, their escape into the region outside the metal
is opposed by strong electrical forces.   Thus the *free* electrons referred
to in Sec. 1 have to be liberated from the electrodes in some special
manner.   In thermionic tubes this liberation is accomplished by heating the electrode to a sufficiently high temperature, and in phototubes
electron emission is produced by the incidence of electromagnetic
radiation such as visible light.   Details of these and other methods are
discussed in Chapter 7.

4. Electron Mechanics.   It will be necessary also to recall from
earlier studies the elementary principles concerning interactions
between electrically charged particles, such as electrons and ions, and
electric and magnetic fields.   For example:

(*a*) When an electrically charged particle is in an electric field it is
acted upon by an electric force equal to the product of its charge, q,
and the strength, E, of the field.   That is,

$$f_E = qE \qquad (1)*$$

On a positive charge this force acts in the direction of E; on a negative
charge, in the opposite direction.   An example is the force which
deflects the electron beam in a cathode-ray tube.

(*b*) If an electrically charged particle is free to move in an electric
field it will gain energy equal to the work done on it by that field, or
work equal to the product of the charge q and the potential difference,
V, through which it moves.   Thus if it starts from rest its kinetic
energy will attain the value given by

$$\tfrac{1}{2}mu^2 = Vq \qquad (2)*$$

Here m is the mass of the particle and u the speed which it attains.
The electrons in the beam of a cathode-ray tube gain their initial speed
by passing through a potential difference of several thousand volts in
the "electron gun."

(*c*) An electrically charged particle which is *at rest* is unaffected
by a magnetic field.   But a charged particle *moving* in a magnetic
field is acted upon by a force which is perpendicular to both its velocity,
u, and the direction of the magnetic induction (flux density), B.   The

---

* Equations 1 and 2 apply to emu, esu, and mks units.   If V is in volts, E in
volts/cm, and q in coulombs, the right-hand side of each equation must be multiplied by 10^7 to give force and energy in cgs units.

magnitude of this force is given by

$$f_B = Bqu \sin \theta \tag{3}$$

The angle θ is the angle between the vectors which represent B and u, as shown in Fig. 1.   The force is in dynes if B is measured in gauss, q in abcoulombs (emu), and u in cm/sec.   (In a vacuum B, in gauss, is numerically equal to H, the field intensity, in oersteds.)   The direction of this force may be figured out from any rule for the force on a conductor carrying electric current.   If the charge is negative, as for an electron, it must be remembered that moving negative charge corresponds to current in the opposite direction.   This magnetic field force is sometimes utilized to deflect an electron beam, especially in certain types of television tubes and radar tubes.

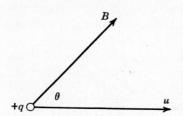

FIG. 1. f_B is normal to the plane of the figure and outward, toward the reader.

5. Electron Tubes. It is assumed also that the reader is familiar with the general aspects of simple electron tubes such as are found in radio sets; cross-sections of two basic types are shown in Figs. 2 and 3.   Such tubes are commonly classified according to the number of electrodes.   Thus the tube of Fig. 2 is a two-electrode tube, or *diode*, whose primary function is to serve as a one-way conductor, or rectifier. Its inner electrode, K, is a thin, cylindrical nickel tube, covered over on the outside with a thin coating of barium and strontium oxides which has had a very special heat treatment.   In use this electrode, which is called the *cathode*, is heated electrically to a temperature a little below 1000 degrees C.   At this temperature it serves as a source of free electrons.   The electric heater is made of resistance wire, looped or coiled inside the cathode tube and insulated from it.   The cold outer electrode, A, which surrounds the cathode, serves to collect electrons and is called the *anode*.   The glass envelop or bulb which encloses these electrodes is highly evacuated.   Wires sealed through the glass make connections from K, A, and the heater to the outside.   In the early electron tubes the heater wires themselves served as the cathode, and such filamentary cathodes are still employed in certain types of power tubes, and also in very small tubes.   There can be no current in the tube of Fig. 2 when the potential of A is negative with respect to K, but when this potential is positive electrons can flow from K to A, corresponding to a conventional current from A to K.   At first thought it might seem that the current should jump to saturation value as soon as this potential becomes positive, the only apparent limit to its value being the rate at which electrons may leave the cathode. In actuality, although the current rises rapidly with anode potential its value does depend upon that potential, being limited by mutual repulsions among the electrons themselves. The functioning of this limiting factor, which is commonly called *space-charge*, is given first consideration in

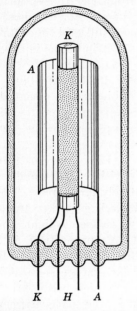

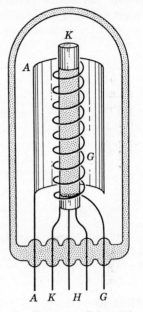

FIG. 2. DIODE. Schematic diagram. Front half of anode removed to show cathode. Mechanical supports for electrodes not shown.

FIG. 3. TRIODE. Schematic diagram. Front half of anode removed to show cathode and grid. Mechanical supports for electrodes not shown.

Chapter 1, since it is of fundamental importance to all applications of electronics.

6. The Grid. The cathode and anode of a diode have been described here in some detail since they are essential elements in all thermionic electron tubes. The introduction of a third electrode, called a *grid*, between the cathode and anode produces a three-electrode tube, or *triode*, as illustrated in Fig. 3. This grid is generally a mesh of wires between which electrons may pass from the cathode to the anode, subject to the control of the potentials of both the grid and the anode. The effect of this grid is, first, to weaken the influence of the anode potential, by standing as a partial electrostatic screen between anode and cathode; and, second, to superimpose the influence of its own potential upon this reduced influence of the anode potential. If the anode potential is sufficiently positive the grid potential may be maintained always negative, so that the electron current to it is zero. The grid then provides an electrostatic control over the current between cathode and anode, and this characteristic makes the triode the most important basic type of electron tube. The insertion of additional electrodes produces tetrodes (four electrodes), pentodes (five electrodes), and even more complex types. For the most part, however, all these multigrid tubes function as special types of triodes, as is explained in Chapter 5.

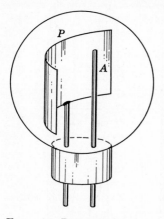

FIG. 4. PHOTOELECTRIC TUBE. *A*—anode *P*—cathode.

7. Phototubes. Phototubes are also fairly familiar objects, as essential elements in electric-eye mechanisms, in the sound-track pick-up for moving pictures, and in many other applications. A simple phototube of the type illustrated in Fig. 4 is a diode with a small anode and a cathode of relatively large area. The surface of the cathode is coated or treated to make it sensitive to visible light, and the saturation electron current from it is directly proportional to the intensity of the incident light. Saturation is attained at quite low anode potentials because the large cathode area and small electron current make the space-charge effect very slight. Since photoelectric currents are generally much smaller than thermionic currents their measurement requires either sensitive meters or some means for amplification.

8. Cathode-Ray Tube. Another familiar type of electron tube is the cathode-ray tube, which is an essential part in laboratory oscilloscopes and in television receivers. We shall find so much need for a cathode-ray oscilloscope in the laboratory and lecture experiments that it is desirable to describe the cathode-ray tube here in some detail. Its essential features are diagrammed in Fig. 5. The cathode is a flat, oxide-coated disk, *K*, on the end of a nickel tube which contains the necessary heater coils. A series of cylindrical electrodes and circular diaphragms in front of *K* serves to accelerate the emitted electrons to several thousand electron-volts energy and to focus the electron beam to a fine point on the fluorescent screen, *S*. These electrodes, which vary in number and form in different types of tubes, are represented in Fig. 5 by *G*, *A*1, and *A*2. The last electrode (*A*2 in Fig. 5) is at ground potential, and the potential of K is negative and equal to the accelerating potential. Focussing is accomplished by varying the potential of one or more of the intermediate electrodes. The intensity of the beam is controlled mainly by the potential of G, the electrode nearest to K.

If a potential difference is set up between plates $P1$ and $P1'$ the electron beam will be deflected up or down; if set up between plates $P2$ and $P2'$ the beam will be deflected to one side or the other. In either

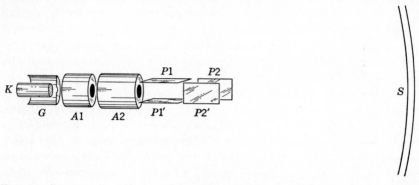

FIG. 5. CATHODE-RAY TUBE. Schematic diagram of electrodes. Front of grid removed to show cathode.

case the deflection of the fluorescent spot upon the screen is proportional to the potential difference. One hundred volts or more may be required for a full-screen deflection. The cathode-ray tube is usually mounted in a metal case which screens it from external electric and magnetic fields, with only the face of the screen showing. This case also contains amplifiers for the vertical and horizontal deflections, a "sweep circuit," and the necessary power supplies. By means of the amplifiers full-screen deflections are possible with only a fraction of a volt input. The "sweep circuit" (see Sec. 23, Chapter 9) provides a time axis by supplying to the horizontal deflector plates a "sawtooth" voltage which increases linearly with time until the beam has been deflected from left to right across the screen; then it drops very suddenly back to the starting point and repeats. The rate of repetition may be varied over wide limits. The motion of the fluorescent spot over the screen plots a curve which represents the relationship between whatever voltages are applied to the horizontal and vertical deflector terminals. When these plots are retraced repeatedly (by periodic voltages) they appear as continuous lines, owing to persistence of vision. If the sweep circuit is connected to the horizontal deflectors the screen displays a time plot of the voltage applied to the vertical deflectors.

Descriptions of other, less familiar types of electron tubes are left to later chapters.

9. Outline. A brief outline of the contents of this book will now be given. The greater part of it has to do with thermionic tubes, that is, tubes having hot cathodes as sources of electrons, and throughout the early part of the book it will be assumed that all thermionic cathodes emit electrons at a rate which greatly exceeds the demand of the largest currents required. Considerations relating to the design of such cathodes are postponed to Chapter 7. We then are concerned here with only the other factors which determine the magnitude of the electron current, namely, the electrode configuration and the *space-charge* distribution.

Unless the reader has a clear comprehension of the physical nature of space-charge, and of its effect upon the flow of the electron stream, he cannot understand properly the operation of any electron tube. Hence Chapter 1 starts off with a thorough treatment of this topic. General diode theory, together with the principal diode applications, makes up the rest of this chapter. Chapter 2 gives detailed consideration to the effect of the grid in a triode, and to triode theory generally. These topics are fundamental to almost everything which follows. In Chapters 3 and 4 this theory is applied to amplifiers. Analysis is made both for small-output ("linear") operation, which may be treated by means of equivalent circuits, and for operation with larger output, where graphical methods are required. This amplifier analysis is limited at first to circuits which employ triodes. Then, in Chapter 5, tetrodes and pentodes are considered. The functions performed by the several grids are thoroughly analyzed, and the advantages and disadvantages of multigrid tubes in amplifier circuits are studied by detailed consideration of typical circuits. Feedback circuits are considered in Chapter 6, the general treatment of feedback theory being preceded by detailed analysis of typical feedback circuits. Particular attention is given to cathode-follower circuits.

10. Physical Electronics. In the next few chapters we are concerned to a greater extent than before with what goes on *inside* electron tubes. Chapter 7 deals with the fundamental processes of electron emission, including photoelectric emission and its applications, and with the physical theories which account for these phenomena. The next two chapters take up the effects produced by gas atoms in an electron tube when enough gas is present to cause the electrical conduction to differ appreciably from that in corresponding types of high vacuum tubes.   Since in general the physical processes involved are very complex, the considerations here are limited to the several processes which are less difficult to explain.   Luckily, these are also the processes which correspond to the principal applications.   This presentation departs radically from the usual approach to this topic, which starts with the very complicated "glow" discharge between cold electrodes.

11. Radiofrequency Electronics.   Chapters 10 through 13 are concerned principally with electron circuits designed to operate at single frequencies, or in very narrow frequency bands, circuits generally encountered in the radiofrequency range.   Another characteristic of the topics here treated, and a more important characteristic from the point of view of the physics involved, is their predominant concern with the *non-linear* operation of electron tubes and with non-linear devices.   Class C operation, detection, modulation, and frequency conversion are examples of this characteristic.   The presentation emphasizes the physical performance of the electron tubes which makes such operation possible.   Special tubes such as the pentagrid converter, klystron and magnetron oscillators, and the traveling-wave tube are included.

12. Instrumentation.   Among the most valuable contributions of electronics to science and technology are the instruments and instrumental methods which have been made possible by the applications of electronics to problems of measurement.   These range from the familiar cathode-ray oscillograph and vacuum-tube voltmeter to the giant "electronic brain" computers.   In the last chapter this topic is surveyed and typical examples are analyzed.

13. Laboratory.   Electronics is an outstanding example of a laboratory science.   It had its start from discoveries made in the physics laboratory, a large part of its development has been carried out in the physics and engineering laboratories, and most of its applications are laboratory developments.   Workers in this field must be trained in the laboratory.   In all fields of physics this is so, but it is particularly true in the field of electronics.   For this reason laboratory experiments have been made an integral part of this book, and the sequence of topics has been arranged so as to make this laboratory work most effective.   It is assumed that the student has been trained in the methods of good laboratory work by earlier physics courses.   A summary of these methods is given in Appendix 1.   In Appendix 2 will be found some suggestions for setting up a laboratory in which to perform these experiments.   Also in Appendix 2 are given several suggested experiment sequences.   More than enough experiments for a year's work are included in the book, to allow the instructor to plan his laboratory work according to his own preferences or the limitations of his equipment.

The effectiveness of laboratory work depends upon the point of view from which the student approaches it. The most obvious purposes for performing an experiment are (*a*) to obtain first-hand acquaintance with the phenomena being studied, and (*b*) to obtain familiarity with the methods of observation and measurement which apply to those phenomena. Even these purposes are defeated by a "cook-book" approach to the work. Experimental work is a waste of time if the student performs it as a routine task, following detailed instructions without any particular understanding of what he is doing.* A still more important aim of laboratory work is to enable the student to discover and to verify for himself the laws and principles studied. Although many students will miss this aim entirely, the alert and observant student will discover much he has not yet learned from his books. This is training in research, even when the facts learned in this way are already known to others. The student should never be discouraged if an experiment involves something he has not yet studied in the classroom, since this gives him opportunity to approach the experiment from a research point of view. It is very desirable that provisions be made for students to investigate further, on a voluntary basis, any topic which especially arouses their interest.

14. Problems. Next in importance to work in the laboratory is the working of many problems. Good problems provide practice in the application of principles and ideas, practice which the student must have if he is to appreciate fully the significance of his study and gain confidence in his knowledge. They provide also a simple and effective means by which he can *examine himself*, to discover his strength or weakness in the topic represented. Difficulties encountered in working a problem point the way to missing knowledge.

Problems are of value, however, only when they are worked in the proper way, and solution by formula is *not* the correct method. Indeed, the formula itself must be regarded as an *algebraic* solution to the problem, with numerical evaluation of the answer representing only a minor step in the process. A profitable solution starts with a qualitative analysis of the problem, to learn what conditions and what

---

* This is an obvious and hackneyed statement, but it needs constant repetition. It is possible to buy laboratory manuals and apparatus kits which leave little to the intelligence of the student. Even when instructions are sufficiently meager to require intelligent work, a student may still by-pass them by following the guidance of a fellow student, or by patterning his work upon the reports of former students.

situations are represented and what procedures must be followed to obtain an answer: this may be called a *physical* solution to the problem. Then the necessary computations may be made, in accordance with this analysis, starting from fundamental principles. It is often easier to compute numerical values for each step, rather than to carry through the computations algebraically. This method has the added advantage that it enables one to check the work step by step. Many errors may be caught by watching out for unreasonable magnitudes among these intermediate values. The only truly satisfactory solution is one which the student has verified by at least one other independent method of analysis, rather than by comparison with an answer obtained by someone else. The student will have no answer-book for the practical problems he will meet in later life, and he should practice this method of checking now.

Representative problems are included in each chapter. Other problems may be set up by the instructor or by the student himself. Still other problems arise in the laboratory. Students should always be urged to approach whatever they do analytically, rather than by the cut-and-try method of the "gadgeteer," and this approach requires setting up problems and solving them.

15. Collateral Reading. The primary purpose of this book is to acquaint the reader with the fundamental principles in this field of electronics. The reader will wish to know about many details, and many related topics, which are not touched upon here; for these he must turn to the many books and periodicals which represent this field, and this book will have served its purpose if it has prepared him to read and understand this extensive literature.

CHAPTER 1

Thermionic Diodes

1. Thermionic Electron Tubes. An electron tube is an evacuated vessel or bottle enclosing two or more electrodes, in which there can be a current only when electrons pass from one electrode to another. To make this possible one electrode, which is then called the *cathode*, is in some manner made capable of emitting electrons. The vessel may be made of glass or other insulating material, with the electrodes supported by wires sealed through the glass to make connections to the outside. It may also be made of metal, with the electrodes supported by non-conducting bushings passing through the metal walls. In *thermionic* electron tubes the cathode is made a source of free electrons by heating it electrically to a sufficiently high temperature. It may be a simple filament of tungsten or other suitable metal wire, or, as shown in Fig. 2 of the Introduction, it may be a hollow tube or box of metal which is heated indirectly, by conduction and radiation from an electrically heated wire coiled or looped inside it. The temperature at which a thermionic cathode must be operated depends upon the nature of the emitting surface. It may be as high as 3000 degrees C for pure tungsten, or as low as 750 degrees C for a nickel surface coated with barium oxide which has been rendered emissive, or *activated*, by special heat treatment. The reasons for these differences will be discussed in Chapter 7.

2. Thermionic Current. When a thermionic tube contains only one cold electrode, or two electrodes in all, it is called a *diode*. Let us connect a thermionic diode in series with a d-c battery of variable emf and a current meter, as shown in Fig. 1. *Let us also consider that the potential of the cathode is always zero.* This *convention* does not require that the cathode be at ground potential, or at the potential of its surroundings, but only that the potential of the cold electrode, or *anode*, be specified as equal to the potential difference from anode to cathode. This convention is generally followed in electronic literature, since it makes possible clearer and more concise specifications of anode potentials. It may be extended to tubes having any number of electrodes. As we vary the potential of the anode, represented by P in Fig. 1, the current will be found to change as indicated schematically

12

in the plot of Fig. 2. Obviously this plot does not follow Ohm's law. Indeed, the relationship here represented is quite complex. However, we may distinguish three separate regions, represented in Fig. 2 by the three sections designated by A, B, and C, for each of which it is possible to find a relatively simple law which fits quite well. Section A may

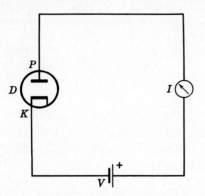

FIG. 1. DIODE CIRCUIT. D is the conventional symbol for a diode. P—anode. K—cathode.

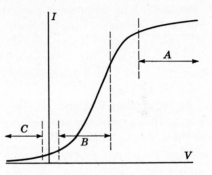

FIG. 2. DIODE CURRENT. A—saturation region. B—space-charge region. C—Maxwell region.

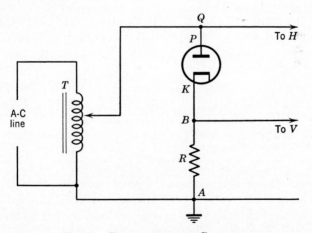

FIG. 3. DEMONSTRATION CIRCUIT.

be called the *saturation* region, Sec. B the *space-charge* region, and Sec. C the thermal distribution or *Maxwell* region.

3. Demonstration Experiment 1. The characteristic curve for a diode may be traced upon a cathode-ray oscilloscope screen by use of the circuit shown in Fig. 3. Point A is the common ground connection. Point B is connected to the V (vertical-deflection) terminal of the oscilloscope, point Q to the H (horizontal-deflection) terminal. The vertical deflection is then proportional to the current in the small, fixed resistor, R, and the horizontal deflection to the anode potential, V_p, plus the small potential drop across R. If R is small enough this potential drop may be neglected in comparison with V_p. Any diode will serve, as will any triode with the anode and grid connected together. The value of R should be only as big as required with the vertical amplifier set for full gain. The saturation region, A in Fig. 2, will not be reached if the cathode is operated at normal heater voltage and the cathode current kept within the limits specified for the tube. Saturation may be demonstrated by operating the cathode heater at a reduced voltage.

4. Saturation Region. In the saturation region represented by A, Fig. 2, the current has reached a value which is relatively independent of the anode potential. For this region the current value is determined solely by the *rate of emission* of electrons from the cathode, since the high potential values which characterize this region produce electric fields capable of carrying all electrons over to the anode, as fast as they are emitted from the cathode. If, as is sometimes assumed, the electron emission were determined by cathode temperature alone, this *saturation current* would become constant whenever the anode potential exceeded the saturation value, and the plot for this region would be a horizontal line in Fig. 2. Experimentally, there is found to be a slight increase of this saturation current with anode potential, as represented in Fig. 2, and this rise may be explained as due to an increase in the rate of emission with anode potential, produced by the electric field at the surface of the cathode. This effect is called the *Schottky effect*. If we neglect it we may represent the value of the saturation current density, or saturation current per unit area of cathode surface, by

$$J = A T^2 \epsilon^{-b/T} \tag{1}$$

The values of the constants A and b depend upon the physical characteristics of the cathode surface. Theoretical explanations for this equation, and for the Schottky effect, are given later on, in Chapter 7.

5. Maxwell Region. When the anode potential is negative the electron current may be considered zero for most purposes. If, however, the current meter is a sensitive galvanometer, it is found that some electrons are able to reach the anode even when its potential is negative by several volts. The current scale of Sec. C, Fig. 2, has been greatly exaggerated to represent this region. Electrons which are able to reach the anode against a negative potential do so because they possess some kinetic energy as they escape from the cathode.

The average value of this thermal energy corresponds to the cathode temperature and is quite low. According to the kinetic theory it equals $\frac{3}{2}kT$, where T is the absolute temperature of the cathode and k is Boltzmann's constant (1.38×10^{-16} erg/degree). If we equate this energy to the electrical work, $V_T e$, required to produce it we obtain a value for the potential, $-V_T$, which would keep *all* electrons from the anode if all had the same energy.

$$V_T e = \tfrac{3}{2}kT \qquad \text{or} \qquad V_T = (3k/2e)T \tag{2}$$

In numerical value,

$$V_T = 0.129 \times 10^{-3} T \text{ volt} \tag{2a}$$

Electron speeds, instead of being all the same, are distributed statistically from zero to very high values, in the manner demonstrated by Maxwell for gas molecules. The evidence for this distribution is given by the form of the current plot for this region which we have called the Maxwell region. Indeed, it is possible to obtain an excellent value for the cathode temperature from a current plot for this region, as will be explained in Chapter 7.

6. Space-Charge Region. The space-charge region, represented by Sec. *B*, Fig. 2, is the one in which most electron tubes operate. Here the primary controlling factor is potential, not temperature, as shown by Fig. 4, in which current, I, is plotted as a function of potential, V, for several different temperature values. It is evident that, within this space-charge range of potential values, only a fraction of the electrons emitted thermionically are able to reach the anode; the rest must return again to the cathode. The theoretical reasons for this current limitation we shall examine shortly. First let us try to find an empirical equation to fit this upward-curving line, by finding a set of variables which will yield a straight-line plot for the experimental data. When the electrodes are symmetrical (e.g., concentric cylinders, or plane-parallel plates close together) so that the *electric field is uniform over the surface of the cathode*, it has been found that a straight-line is obtained by plotting the two-thirds power of I as ordinates, V as abscissae. See Fig. 5. From this plot we may deduce the equation

$$I^{2/3} = B(V + V_i) = BV' \tag{3}$$

The constant B equals the slope of the plotted line, while V_i is the negative of the x-intercept. The potential V', equal to $(V + V_i)$, may be called the *effective value* of the anode potential. If the curves of Fig. 4 are replotted with V' as abscissae they will almost (but not quite) coincide over the space-charge region.

By an obvious transformation Eq. 3 may be converted into

$$I = GV'^{3/2} \tag{4}$$

This equation represents the three-halves power law, or Child's law. It was derived theoretically by Child, for plane-parallel electrodes. His proof is reproduced in Sec. 11. Later Langmuir proved it for cylindrical electrodes, and proved that it must follow for any symmetrical electrode structure.

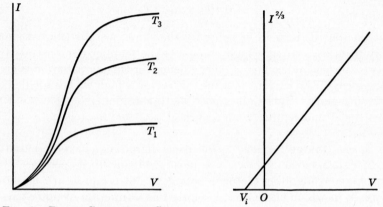

Fig. 4. Diode Current at Several Temperatures.

Fig. 5.

7. Perveance. The constant, G, in Eq. 4 is called the *perveance* of the tube. Its value, which depends upon the "geometry" (size, shape, and placement) of the electrodes, may be determined experimentally, as from the plot of Fig. 5. For simple geometries it may be computed from theoretical equations. Thus for large, plane electrodes, each of area A cm^2, placed parallel to one another and separated by a distance b cm,

$$G = \frac{2.33 \times 10^{-6} A}{a^2} \text{ amp/volt}^{3/2} \tag{5}$$

For electrodes which are concentric cylinders, b cm long and having radii r_A cm and r_K cm, respectively,

$$G = \frac{14.65 \times 10^{-6} b}{r_A \beta^2} \text{ amp/volt}^{3/2} \tag{6}$$

The factor β^2 is a function of r_A/r_K which is given by a power series.* A few values of β^2 are given in Table 1.

TABLE 1

r_A/r_K	1.000	1.500	2.000	2.500	3.000
β^2	0.000	0.116	0.275	0.405	0.512

8. Internal Bias. The difference, V_i, between the effective value of the anode potential, V', and the voltmeter reading, V, is often called contact potential, although this term is incorrect.   Another name for it is Edison voltage.   *Internal bias* is a better name, since it implies nothing concerning its origins.   These origins are several, including

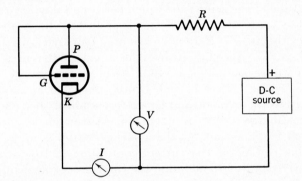

Fig. 6.   Experiment 1.   Direct-current source may be batteries with a voltage-divider (see Appendix 2) or a power supply.   The value of R depends upon the range of the d-c source.

true contact potential, initial electron energies (see Sec. 5), and thermal emf's.   The value of V_i is a function of cathode temperature, and generally less than a volt.

9. Experiment 1.   Three-halves Power Law.   The law expressed by Eq. 4 may be tested experimentally for a commercial diode, or for a diode formed by connecting together the plate and grid terminals of a triode as indicated in Fig. 6.   The tube chosen should have a symmetrical electrode structure.   The range of data here given applies to triode types 6P5-G and 76.   It may be modified to apply to any other suitable type which may be available.

Set up the circuit as shown in Fig. 6 and take two sets of data, one with the cathode operated at normal heater power, the other with the heater power reduced sufficiently to cause appreciable saturation.   For

* See E. L. Chaffee, *Theory of Thermionic Vacuum Tubes*, p. 72; W. G. Dow, *Fundamentals of Engineering Electronics*, First Ed., p. 106; F. E. Terman, *Radio Engineers' Handbook*, p. 288.

the type 6P5-G or 76 tube the current range may be from 0 to 15 ma
at normal heater operation (6.3 volts). For the second set of data
the plate potential should be limited to 15 or 20 volts, even though this
does not bring the current to the top value obtained in the first set.
Ten or fifteen evenly spaced observations of both V and I should be
made for each set.

For each set plot $I^{2/3}$ vs. V as indicated by Fig. 5. It is advisable
to plot both sets on the same sheet, to the same axes, for comparison.
Explain carefully whether or not your results verify the three-halves
power law, and why. Measure the slopes of the linear parts of both
plots, and obtain the corresponding values of G and of V_i. If there is
available a tube of the same type which has been taken apart, a rough
check for the value of G may be made from the dimensions of the
electrodes of this tube. If a triode has been employed, use the radius
of the grid as r_A. Account, if possible, for the differences observed
between the values of G and of V_i obtained for the two sets of data.

Explain why the voltmeter in Fig. 6 is connected as shown rather
than directly to the cathode and anode terminals of the tube.

10. Space-Charge. Why is it that the electron current does not go
to saturation value as soon as the anode potential is made positive?
In a metallic conductor the current-controlling factor is resistance,
and the power required to maintain the current is expended in heating
the conductor throughout its volume. (According to the electron
theory for metallic conduction, mentioned in Sec. 3 of the Introduction,
this energy is transferred to the atoms of the metal by frequent collisions among electrons and atoms.) In an electron tube the electron
stream meets no such opposition. Electrons encounter no collisions
until they reach the anode, and the kinetic energy gained by each
electron is not lost until the electron strikes the anode. The energy
required to maintain the current appears as heating of the anode
only. What then does limit the electron current in this space-charge
region?

*The controlling factor in this case is the mutual repulsions among the
electrons themselves.* To simplify the explanation which follows, let
us consider a tube having electrodes which are large, plane plates, close
together and parallel to one another, as in Fig. 7a. When both electrodes are cold a positive anode potential will set up an electric field
which is of constant value everywhere, except for negligible differences
near the edges of the plates. When, however, the cathode is hot
enough to emit electrons at a rate greatly exceeding the requirements
of the electron current, the electric field is quite different because of
the electrons which then stream from cathode to anode. Since elec-

trons are negatively charged particles which repel one another, those electrons which are nearer the anode push back on those following behind, causing the resultant electric field to be less and less as we go back toward the cathode. The electron current builds up until the number of electrons *in transit* between the electrodes is sufficient to reduce the electric field at the cathode to zero value, or slightly below zero. At the same time the value of the field at the anode is increased considerably.

This stream of moving electrons which accounts for the electron current thus *limits itself* to a current value which depends upon the anode potential in the manner represented by Sec. *B* of the plot of Fig. 2. The electric charge distribution which is maintained by this stream is the *space-charge* from which this region is named. It is also the "space-charge" referred to whenever this term is found in electronic literature. This space-charge is not to be confused with the charge distribution produced by the cloud of electrons immediately surrounding the cathode, as a result of thermionic emission. This electron cloud always exists, whether there is current or not. Indeed, its density is greatest when the current is zero. When there is current a fraction of these electrons enters the electron stream and travels to the anode, thus becoming a part of the *space-charge* in our technical use of this term. The remainder re-enter the cathode. When there is no current all the electrons return to the cathode, at the same average rate at which they leave it. Conditions then are strictly analogous to the evaporation-condensation balance in a saturated vapor.

11. Derivation of Child's Law. If mathematical analysis is now applied to the premises stated in Sec. 10 a theoretical equation is obtained which agrees with the empirical equation (Eq. 4) obtained experimentally. This equation was first derived by Child, for plane-parallel electrodes, and the law expressed by it is sometimes called Child's law. More often it is named the three-halves power law or the space-charge law. It is also sometimes called Langmuir's law, since Langmuir derived it for concentric cylindrical electrodes, and showed that the $3/2$ power applies whenever the electrodes are symmetrical.

We shall now reproduce Child's proof, starting with the conditions specified in Sec. 10 and represented by Fig. 7. As usual, the cathode potential is considered zero, and the elementary electric charge is represented by e. At any distance x from the cathode we shall designate the electric field intensity by E, the electric potential by V, the electron density (electrons per unit volume) by n, and the electron speed by u. These quantities are of course not independent, but directly related, and each is a function of x. Thus, at any distance x

the law of conservation of energy gives us, for electrons which start from the cathode with zero initial speed,

$$\tfrac{1}{2}mu^2 = Ve \tag{7}$$

Later on we shall consider how to take account of the small but finite initial speeds which do exist; for now we shall assume that these may be neglected, and Eq. 7 holds true.

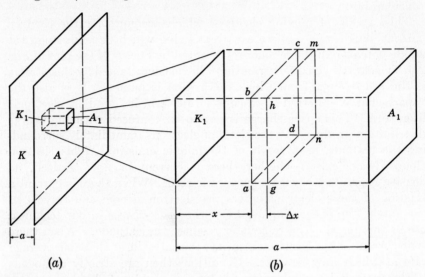

Fig. 7. Diagram for Child's Law Proof. K_1 and A_1 are each 1 cm square.

Quantities n and u are related through the current density, J, which equals the quantity of electric charge crossing unit area per unit time. That is,

$$J = neu \tag{8}$$

If the current is steady J must have the same value everywhere. Combining Eqs. 7 and 8 gives

$$ne = J/u = J \sqrt{m/2Ve} \tag{9}$$

Next, the electric field, E, which is in the x-direction only, is related to V by the definition of V, which gives

$$E = -dV/dx \tag{10}$$

Finally, from Gauss's law, which states that the net outward electric flux from any volume inclosing a charge q equals $4\pi q$, we have

$$k(dE/dx) = -4\pi ne \tag{11}$$

The dielectric constant, k, is unity if electrostatic units* are employed.

Equation 11 is derived as follows. Consider a region K_1A_1, of unit cross-section and extending from cathode to anode, as represented to an enlarged scale in Fig. 7b. In it take the volume represented by the broken lines in Fig. 7, of unit height ab, unit width ad, and thickness Δx. Since E is in the x-direction only, there is no flux through the narrow top, bottom, and side areas. In the x-direction the flux density, D, equals kE. The flux *out* of this volume is then $-kE$ through the unit area $abcd$, and $+k(E + \Delta E)$ through the unit area $ghmn$. The inclosed charge is $-\bar{n}e\,\Delta x$, where $\bar{n}$ represents the *average* value of n over the distance Δx. Gauss's law then gives

$$-kE + k(E + \Delta E) = k\,\Delta E = -4\pi\bar{n}e\,\Delta x \tag{12}$$

If Eq. 12 is now divided by Δx and the limit taken as Δx approaches zero, Eq. 11 results.

Substitution into Eq. 11 of the value of ne given by Eq. 9, and the value of E given by Eq. 10, gives

$$k\,\frac{d^2V}{dx^2} = \frac{4\pi}{k}\,J\,\sqrt{\frac{m}{2e}}\,V^{-\frac{1}{2}} \tag{13}$$

An integrating factor is $2\,dV/dx$. Multiplying by it and integrating, we get

$$\left(\frac{dV}{dx}\right)^2 - \left(\frac{dV}{dx}\right)_0^2 = \frac{16\pi}{k}\,J\,\sqrt{\frac{m}{2e}}\,V^{\frac{1}{2}} \tag{14}$$

Now, if the emission of electrons from the cathode is sufficiently copious, the current builds up until the electric field has zero value at the surface of the cathode, where x is zero. Then $(dV/dx)_0$ equals zero and Eq. 14 may be solved for dV/dx.

$$\frac{dV}{dx} = \sqrt{\frac{16\pi}{k}\,J\,\sqrt{m/2e}}\;V^{\frac{1}{4}} \tag{15}$$

Separation of variables gives

$$V^{-\frac{1}{4}}\,dV = \sqrt{\frac{16\pi}{k}\,J\,\sqrt{m/2e}}\;dx \tag{16}$$

Equation 16 integrates to

$$\frac{4}{3}\,V^{\frac{3}{4}} = x\,\sqrt{\frac{16\pi}{k}\,J\,\sqrt{m/2e}} \tag{17}$$

or

$$J = \frac{k}{9\pi x^2}\,\sqrt{\frac{2e}{m}}\,V^{\frac{3}{2}} \tag{18}$$

* Electrostatic units are most convenient for this problem. See Appendix 3.

When $x = a$, $V = V_p$, and

$$J = \frac{k}{9\pi a^2} \sqrt{\frac{2e}{m}} \, V_p^{\frac{3}{2}} \qquad (19)$$

Figure 8 shows plots of the potential, V, the positive value of the electric field, $-E$, and the space-charge density, ne. These plots should be studied carefully. Note that $-E$ starts from zero at the cathode, and that this quantity corresponds, as it should (see Eq. 10),

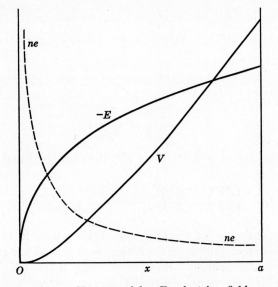

Fig. 8. Child's Law. V—potential. E—electric field. ne—space-charge density.

to the upward curvature of the plot for V. Note particularly that the most important part of the space-charge is close to the cathode.

12. Initial Electron Speeds. In the proof of Sec. 11 we have assumed that the electrons leave the cathode with zero speed, whereas, as has been mentioned in Sec. 5, they are emitted actually with speeds which range from zero up to very high values. Fortunately, most thermally emitted electrons have very low speeds, the average value corresponding to an accelerating potential, V_T, given by Eq. 2a. Values of V_T vary from about 0.4 volt for a pure tungsten cathode to about 0.1 volt for an oxide cathode.

When we take account in our theory of these initial electron speeds we find that the electric field at the surface of the cathode must have a small *reverse* value when the current is steady. The point of zero field then lies a very small distance in front of the cathode, as indicated by x_0 in Fig. 9. It then follows that the potential near the cathode must be negative, with a minimum value (maximum *negative* value) at the point x_0. This also is shown in Fig. 9. If the average energy for the emitted electrons were the actual energy of all, then this minimum potential would have the value V_r. Since the actual energy distribu-

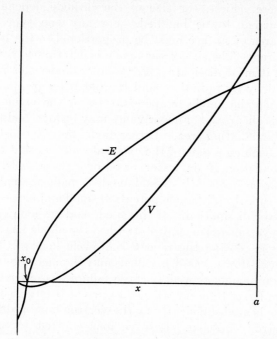

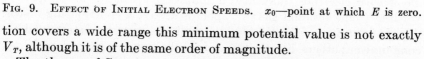

Fig. 9. Effect of Initial Electron Speeds. x_0—point at which E is zero.

tion covers a wide range this minimum potential value is not exactly V_r, although it is of the same order of magnitude.

The theory of Sec. 11 now applies quite closely if we consider that the *effective* cathode ("virtual" cathode) is located at x_0 and that the effective anode potential is the potential difference from the anode to the point x_0. The distance to x_0 from the cathode is not fixed, but varies somewhat with the current. However, this variation is not enough to be very noticeable, except at quite low potentials. It should be noted that displacement of the virtual cathode to x_0 causes a small change in the perveance, G, since it in effect moves the cathode a little closer to the anode. This factor accounts for the small difference observed in Exp. 1, between the perveance values for two different temperatures.

13. Commercial Diodes. Commercial diodes range in size from very small ones such as the miniature type 1A3 and the standard type 6H6 detector tubes, having peak current values of only a few milliamperes, up to the very large rectifier tubes employed in big a-c to d-c power supplies, which have peak current capacities of many amperes. Several of the factors involved in the design of such tubes may be mentioned here. First, the size of the cathode depends upon the maximum current to be handled. For any one type of cathode surface, the area of surface must be proportional to the *peak* value of current required. The size of the anode is determined by the *average* power which it must dissipate. For smaller diodes this power leaves the anode chiefly by radiation, and the radiating area must be large enough to keep the anode temperature below the value at which it begins to emit electrons. Fins or vanes may be attached to the anode to increase the radiating area. Larger diodes may be constructed with their anodes forming a part of the external walls, so that they may be cooled by circulation of air, water, or oil over these walls.

The spacing between cathode and anode is made as small as possible to keep the "tube drop" (anode potential) small and hence to minimize the plate power dissipation. If the anode and cathode are too close, however, a reverse current may start when the anode has a high negative value (e.g., during the reverse half-cycle in a rectifier circuit), and this "break-down," as it is called, may damage the tube and the associated equipment, as well as cause failure of the circuit. Breakdown is more likely to occur when the current is large, since then the anode may be heated sufficiently by the electron bombardment to have a weak electron emission. Positive ions emitted by the cathode, along with electrons, may also account for break-down. Imperfect vacuum (some residual gas or vapor) is always a contributing factor. Some of the factors in the design of diodes may be determined by computation; others, like the anode to cathode spacing, are determined largely by cut-and-try methods.

14. Diode as a Circuit Element. Figure 10 represents a circuit which includes a diode, D, in series with a d-c battery, E, a resistor, R, and a current meter, I. Figure 11 represents a similar circuit in which the d-c battery is replaced by an a-c source of emf equal to $E_1 \cos \omega t$. When a diode is made part of such a circuit, in which all other circuit elements are linear, a first rough estimate of the performance of the circuit may be made by assuming that the diode is a *short circuit* when the anode potential is positive (relative to the cathode), but an *open circuit* when the anode potential is negative. Thus for Fig. 10 the current I is approximately equal to E/R for the polarity shown, but zero when the battery is reversed.   For Fig. 11 the current is approximately equal to $E_1/R \cos \omega t$ for the half-cycle when the cosine is positive, but zero for the reverse half-cycle.

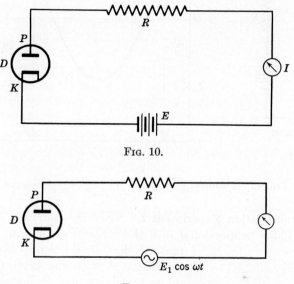

Fig. 10.

Fig. 11.

Figure 12a represents a circuit in which both a d-c battery and an a-c source are in series with a diode and a resistor.   For this circuit the resultant emf is

$$e = E_1 \cos \omega t - E \qquad (20)$$

The current is zero when e is negative.   When e is positive the current may again be taken as approximately equal to e/R, or

$$i = \frac{E_1 \cos \omega t - E}{R} \qquad (21)$$

Oscillograms for e and for i are shown in Fig. 12b.   The fraction of the cycle during which there is current is measured by the angle $2\theta_i$, as indicated in this figure, and θ_i may be evaluated by putting i equal to zero, and ωt_i equal to θ_i, in Eq. 21.   That is,

$$\cos \theta_i = E/E_1 \qquad (22)$$

Sometimes such an approximate analysis is satisfactory, but more often a better one is needed.

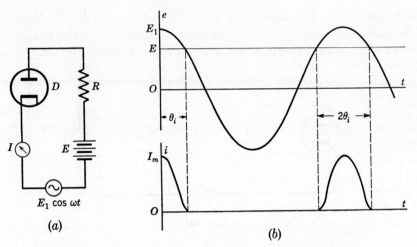

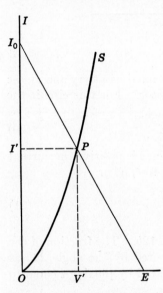

FIG. 12.   DIODE CIRCUIT WITH A-C AND D-C SOURCES.

15. Demonstration Experiment 2.   Since the potential drop across R in Fig. 12a is proportional to i, the current oscillogram of Fig. 12b may be demonstrated by connecting the terminals of R to the vertical-deflection input terminals of a cathode-ray oscilloscope.   If the a-c source is a variable output transformer (as in Fig. 3), it may be shown that i is zero until E_1 exceeds E. With the battery removed the current oscillogram for the circuit of Fig. 11 may also be shown.

16. Graphical Analysis.   An exact analysis of the circuit of Fig. 10 may be made by the procedure indicated in Fig. 13. The line OS is the characteristic plot of I against V, as obtained experimentally for the diode.   On this diagram the point E is plotted on the x-axis to represent the emf of the battery, and the point I_0 on the y-axis represents the current I_0 in the circuit if the diode is by-passed or shorted out.   The value of I_0 is E/R; note that this is the approximate value computed in Sec. 14.   The points E and I_0 are now joined by a straight line called the *load-line*, whose slope is evidently equal to $-1/R$.   Now

FIG. 13.   GRAPHICAL ANALY-
SIS: CIRCUIT OF FIG. 10.

this load-line is in a sense the characteristic line for the resistor R, since the ordinate for any point on this line represents the current in R when the potential drop across R equals the abscissa value *measured from E in the negative direction.* (Proof for this is that the ratio of ordinate to abscissa as measured in this way is $-1/R$, which is the slope of this line.)

For the point P where the load-line intersects OS the current in R thus has the value I' when the potential difference across R equals

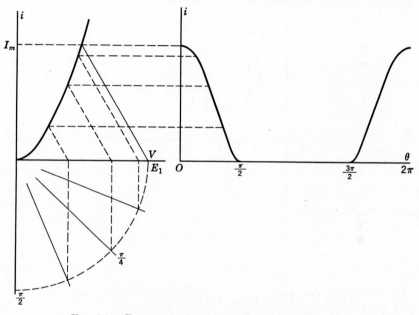

Fig. 14.   Graphical Analysis: Circuit of Fig. 11.

$(E - V')$. But since P lies also upon the diode characteristic, OS, I' is also the current in the diode when the anode potential is V'. These, however, are the conditions represented in Fig. 10. Hence this diagram gives the values I' and V' for the current and the anode potential which actually exist in this circuit.

Extension of this method to the a-c circuit of Fig. 11 is fairly obvious, as shown in Fig. 14. The process described above for Fig. 13 is repeated for a series of values for e, corresponding to a sequence of equally spaced values for ωt, here represented by θ. In Fig. 14 these values for e are obtained by a circle diagram: the quadrant of a circle having a radius E_1 is drawn as shown by the broken line, and divided into equal parts (four as shown) corresponding to equal increments of

θ.   Each division point on this circle is then projected vertically upon the x-axis to give the corresponding values of e.   Through these points on the x-axis are then drawn parallel lines as shown, each line having a slope equal to $-1/R$.   Finally the current values determined by the intersections of these lines with OS, the diode characteristic, are plotted against θ to represent i as a function of time, as shown to the right of the figure.

Figure 15 illustrates similarly a graphical analysis for the circuit of Fig. 12a.   It will be observed that the origin of the circle diagram has

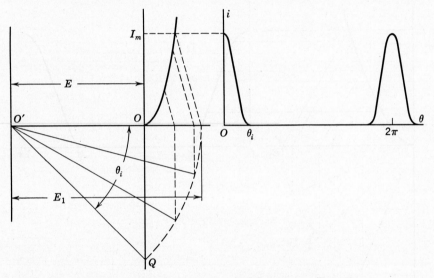

Fig. 15.   Graphical Analysis: Circuit of Fig. 12.

been displaced to the *left* by the amount representing the battery emf, E, since e now equals $E_1 \cos \theta - E$.   Otherwise the analysis is carried out in the same manner as for Fig. 14.   Note that Eq. 22, which evaluates θ_i, the half-angle of operation, is here represented graphically by the triangle $OO'Q$.

17. Rectifier Circuits.   The commonest use for a diode is for current and voltage rectification.   We have already considered two examples, represented by Fig. 11 and Fig. 12a.   Figure 11 represents a simple half-cycle or "half-wave" rectifier.   Current in the load, R, is always in the same direction and pulsating, being zero for alternate half-cycles.   Figure 12a illustrates a similar circuit for charging a storage battery; for this service a pulsating current is practically as good as a steady direct current.

Figure 16a illustrates a method whereby two diodes may be combined to make rectification more effective. Each diode is served by a separate a-c source (obtained from the center-tapped secondary of a transformer), the emf's of the two sources differing in phase by 180 electrical degrees. Rectification is obtained for each half-cycle, the diodes conducting alternately. Each diode may be considered to be in an independent circuit, which may be analyzed separately by the method illustrated in Fig. 14 if the load is a pure resistance, or by the

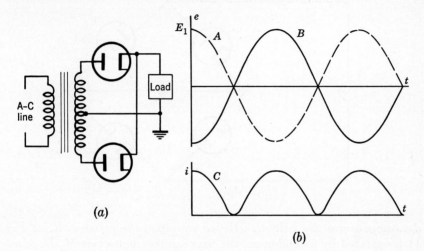

FIG. 16.   FULL-CYCLE RECTIFIER.

method of Fig. 15 if the load includes a battery. The currents then may be combined in a time plot as shown in Fig. 16b. The resultant current is pulsating, with a pulse frequency which is twice the frequency of the a-c source.

Another possible circuit, utilizing a single a-c source with four diodes, is diagrammed in Fig. 17. It is sometimes called a rectifier bridge, since it appears similar to a Wheatstone bridge. When the upper terminal is positive, diodes A and C conduct; when the lower terminal is the positive one the conducting path passes through diodes D and B. The current in the load has the same direction in either case, and is pulsating, with a pulse frequency which is twice the source frequency, just as for the circuit of Fig. 16. Two-phase and three-phase circuits provide even smoother rectification.*

* For more extended treatments of filter circuits for power supplies, see L. B. Arguimbau, *Vacuum-Tube Circuits*, Chapter II; F. E. Terman, *Radio Engineers' Handbook*, Sec. 8.

18. Reactances in Diode Circuits. In the diode circuits which have been considered so far the impedance in series with the diode has always been *resistive*, so that it may be represented graphically by a straight line as in Figs. 13, 14, and 15. Analysis is far less simple when a diode circuit includes *reactances*, although a few general conclusions may be drawn. First of all, a condenser cannot be put in series with a diode unless a resistance is in parallel with the condenser to *by-pass the*

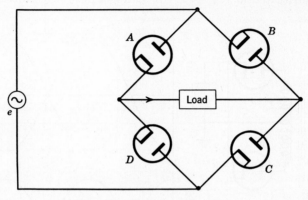

Fig. 17.   Rectifier Bridge.

d-c component of the current. If, for example, the resistor, R, in Fig. 11 is replaced by a condenser, the first positive half-cycle of the alternating potential will charge the condenser up to peak value. Thereafter the anode potential (relative to the cathode) will be zero or negative and the current will be zero. *Always a complete d-c path must pass through a diode,* to pass the d-c component of the current. This is a very important fundamental rule.

When the capacitance in a diode circuit is very large (its reactance practically zero) and properly by-passed by a fairly high resistance, some fairly simple approximate analyses may be made. Several practical examples will be considered in the next few sections. Likewise, we may analyze fairly simply certain special cases involving very large inductive reactances. For the more general cases some very useful but laborious step-by-step graphical methods have been developed.

19. A-C to D-C Power Supplies. The introduction of a large condenser across the output terminals of a rectifier, as shown in Fig. 18, makes possible the conversion of a-c power into quite steady d-c power. During the fraction of each cycle when the diode conducts, electric charge flows into the condenser, C, as well as through the resistor, R. During the rest of the cycle the current in R is supplied from C. If C is large enough (more exactly speaking, if the product RC is very much larger than the time of one a-c cycle) the condenser will charge up to a potential, V_0, not much below the peak value of the alternating emf, and this value will change but slightly thereafter. From then on the condenser resembles the storage battery of Fig. 12a, and the circuit may be analyzed in like manner. As a rough approximation we might assume that V_0 equals the peak value of the alternating emf; this is often done, although it gives relatively poor results.

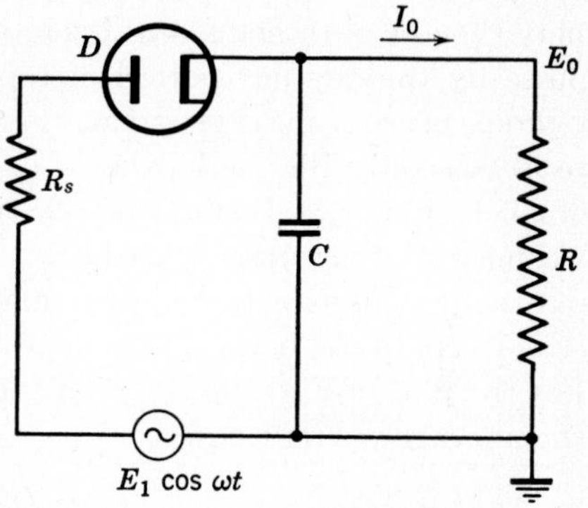

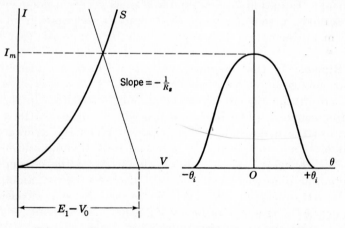

FIG. 18.   HALF-CYCLE POWER SUPPLY.

A better analysis is shown by Fig. 19. First a *guess* is made as to the value of V_0, the average potential difference across C. (If this analysis is made to check the results of an experiment, V_0 is given by the experiment.) Then it is assumed that the potential difference

FIG. 19.   GRAPHICAL ANALYSIS: CIRCUIT OF FIG. 18.

across C remains constant at this value throughout the cycle. Finally it is assumed that, when the diode is conducting, the impedance of the circuit in series with it is a pure resistance, represented in Fig. 18 by R_s; i.e., that the impedance of C is zero in comparison with R_s. This assumption must be made also to meet other requirements of the circuit. If the impedance of the a-c source is not negligible it must be considered resistive and included in R_s.

We may now proceed to find values of i sufficient to make the current-time plot represented in Fig. 19b. The procedure is indicated by Fig. 19a, and is the same as explained for Fig. 15. The average current may then be obtained from this plot by dividing the area of the current pulse by the angular period of repetition, namely 360 degrees. This tedious process may be greatly shortened, however, by employing it to obtain only the *peak value*, I_m, of the diode current, and the angle of operation, θ_i. Instead of plotting points for the rest of the pulse we may now assume it to be a parabola. Although it is not truly parabolic, this is a fair approximation, and the area of a parabola is easy to compute, being equal to two-thirds of the base times the height. For the plot of Fig. 19b the area then may be taken equal to $\frac{4}{3}I_m\theta_i$, and the average current equals

$$I_0 = (\theta_i/270)I_m \qquad (23)*$$

Since I_0 is the d-c component of the diode current it must equal also the direct current in R, or V_0/R. If the agreement for the first trial value of V_0 is poor, the process must be repeated with a new value, and continued until a value is found which gives sufficiently satisfactory agreement. Equation 23 is valuable also as giving a good value for the peak diode current, I_m, when E_1, I_0, and V_0 are known from experimental measurements. The angle θ_i may be computed from E_1 and V_0.

20. Ripple. In the foregoing analysis we have assumed that V_0 does not change by any noticeable amount. Unless C is exceedingly large there will be a small *ripple*, or periodic fluctuation in V_0, at the *pulse* frequency, f. The following procedure will give a fairly good estimate of the magnitude of this ripple. When the average direct current is I_0 an electric charge, q, equal to I_0/f, flows through the load, R, each cycle. If this charge flows out of the condenser, C, the potential difference across C will decrease by an amount ΔV equal to q/C or I_0/Cf. Since ΔV is the peak-to-peak variation the ripple, or the swing above or below V_0, is half this amount, or $I_0/2Cf$. The percent ripple is then given by

$$100(\Delta V/2V_0) = 100/2CfR \qquad (24)$$

* Equation 23 gives a value for the ratio of I_0 to I_m which is always somewhat too high. When R_s is very small, so that most of $(E_1 - V_0)$ falls across the diode, this value may be as much as 15 percent too high. Nevertheless, the value given by Eq. 23 is a very useful first approximation, since in general no simple means exist for obtaining a better one, short of the graphical method represented in Fig. 15.

This analysis is best for very narrow pulses. When the pulses are fairly broad the ripple is less than here computed, since C discharges only while the tube current is zero. It is not applicable to output circuits such as those shown in Figs. 22 and 23. For these circuits Fourier series methods must be employed, as explained in Sec. 23.

21. Demonstration Experiment 3. The manner in which a condenser modifies a rectifier circuit may be demonstrated very convincingly with the circuit of Fig. 20 and a cathode-ray oscilloscope. The output, from point H to ground, is connected to the vertical-deflection terminals, with the internal sweep circuit producing a suit-

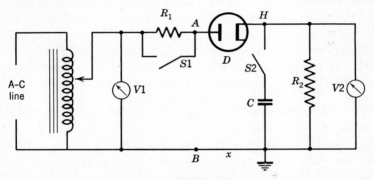

FIG. 20. EXPERIMENT 2.

able time axis. With $S1$ closed and $S2$ open the half-cycle peaks of Demonstration Experiment 2 are observed. Closing $S2$ causes these peaks to level off to a nearly horizontal line with a small ripple. Increased gain for the vertical deflection shows that the ripple is essentially "saw-tooth" in form, as it should be to agree with the analysis of Sec. 20. It is equally interesting to observe the change in diode current when C is inserted. For this demonstration a small resistor is inserted at x, Fig. 20, and the potential drop across it supplied to the vertical-deflection terminals. Without C the current pulses extend over a full half-cycle and have a low peak value. When C is inserted they become much narrower and higher. It is interesting also to repeat these observations with $S1$ open, when the ripple is less and the current pulses are broader. (Values for the circuit elements in Fig. 20 are given in Sec. 22.)

22. Experiment 2. Diode Rectifier Circuits. The purpose of this experiment is to study several typical rectifier circuits. The circuit of Fig. 20 may be modified by means of switches $S1$ and $S2$ to represent these several types. Any suitable diode, such as type 5Y3-G or type 80 rectifier tubes, will serve. Use only one plate of a "full-wave" tube, and make the cathode connection to the filament terminal next to the plate chosen. (Check this when the filament is hot. A low-range d-c voltmeter will show a larger reading between the wrong terminals than between the right ones.) The value for R_2 depends upon the value available for C. The product, CR_2f, should not be less than 12 ($\sec^{-1} \times$ ohms $\times$ farads). Thus R_2 should be at least 10,000 ohms if C is 20 μf. The ratio of R_1 to R_2 may be about $\frac{1}{20}$. Voltmeter $V2$ must be of the high-resistance type (1000 ohms per volt or higher).

Part I. With $S1$ closed and $S2$ open we have a simple rectifier circuit as shown in Fig. 11, connected to an a-c source of practically zero impedance. Take 8 or 10 evenly spaced observations from zero up to the maximum voltage output of the auto-transformer, reading both voltmeters very carefully. For each observation compute the *average* value of the alternating emf, assuming that $V1$ reads rms values. Represent your results by two plotted curves, plotted on the same sheet and to the same coordinates, with readings of $V1$ as abscissae. The ordinates for one plot should be the readings of $V2$, for the other, one-half the average value of the alternating emf. According to very elementary theory these plots should coincide; explain carefully why they do not. From the data taken when $V1$ reads 100 volts compute the average value of the direct current, remembering that the resistance of $V2$ is part of the load. Then compute the peak value of the current pulses, assuming them to be sinusoidal.

Part II. With both switches closed the circuit is a simple a-c to d-c power supply, the same as shown in Fig. 18. Consider carefully the difference that closing $S2$ will make in the readings of $V2$. Then proceed to take data as in Part I. Read the meters with special care when $V1$ reads 100 volts. Plot the readings of $V2$ as ordinates with readings of $V1$ as abscissae. For comparison, plot on the same sheet and to the same coordinates a line representing the *peak* values of the alternating emf. Explain why these two plots do not coincide. From the data taken when $V1$ reads 100 volts compute: (*a*) the direct current; (*b*) the angle of operation for the diode; (*c*) the peak value of the current pulses in the diode, from Eq. 23; (*d*) the tube drop for peak current. As a check, compute the peak current from the perveance of the tube (see Appendix 5) and the potential drop computed for (*d*). Discuss any discrepancies. Compute the percent ripple for your circuit.

Part III. With $S1$ open and $S2$ closed the impedance of the a-c source is increased from practically zero to the value of R_1. The effect of this a-c source impedance may now be investigated by taking a set of data under these conditions, following the same procedure as in Part II. Note that the a-c voltmeter, $V1$, still reads the *emf* of the a-c source, which is now greater than the potential difference at the input terminals, A and B, because of the current in R_1. Again take very careful readings when $V1$ reads 100 volts. Plot these data on the same sheet and to the same axes with the results for Part II. Repeat for these data the computations made for Part II. Compare these results with those found for Part II, and explain the differences. The surprisingly large drop in the d-c output which occurs when the

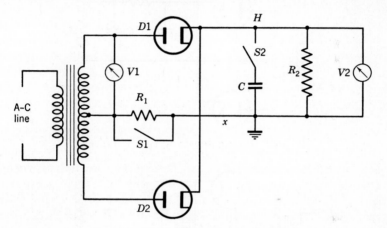

FIG. 21.   FULL-CYCLE POWER SUPPLY.

input impedance is not negligible may be accounted for if it is remembered that the diode current consists of narrow pulses having high peak values.

This experiment may be modified to employ the full-cycle circuit of Fig. 21. It is left to the instructor to modify the instructions accordingly. Demonstration Experiment 3 may also be repeated with this circuit.

23. Filter Circuits. The combination of a condenser C with a resistor R, in Fig. 18, constitutes a very simple filter circuit. Its d-c (zero frequency) impedance is R. Its a-c impedance is approximately that of the condenser, C, and may be made of negligible value by making C large enough. When this requires C to have an inconveniently large value, other means for accomplishing the same end are desirable.

One way to meet this difficulty is to increase the frequency, and the circuit of Fig. 21 does just that; indeed, this might be called a frequency-doubler circuit. As was pointed out in Sec. 17, in connection with Fig. 16, the pulse frequency from this combination of two diodes with a center-tapped transformer is twice the a-c supply frequency. Figure 22 shows an improved output circuit.   The second condenser and resistor, C_2 and R_2, serve to attenuate further the a-c components of the pulses, so that smaller condensers will suffice.   This gain, however, is at the expense of a loss in output potential, due to the potential drop in R_2.   To avoid most of this loss, R_2 may be replaced

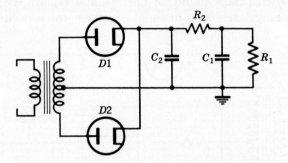

FIG. 22.   POWER SUPPLY WITH R-C FILTER.

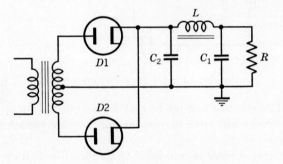

FIG. 23.   POWER SUPPLY WITH L-C FILTER.

by a suitable inductance, as shown in Fig. 23, which represents a very common type of "low-pass" filter circuit.   Many other low-pass circuits are possible.

The requirements for such a filter circuit are determined by the a-c characteristics of the current which is supplied to it from the rectifier tubes.   When the input impedance of the filter is capacitative, as in Figs. 18, 21, 22, and 23, this current consists of quite narrow, high pulses whose pulse frequency may be the a-c frequency, as in Fig. 18, or some multiple of it, as in Figs. 21, 22, and 23.   Harmonic analysis (Fourier analysis) shows that such a pulse has many harmonic components, the amplitude of the fundamental, or pulse frequency, component being approximately twice the steady d-c value.   The amplitudes of the components of higher frequencies (multiples of the fundamental frequency) decrease slowly from that value, but these components are of less importance, since attenuation for them is much more rapid than for the fundamental component.   The corresponding output components may be computed separately, by the usual a-c circuit methods, and then combined.   For the circuits of Figs. 18 to 23 the fundamental component is the only one of much importance.

24. Demonstration Experiment 4.   The performance of the filter circuits of Figs. 22 and 23 may be demonstrated with the oscilloscope,

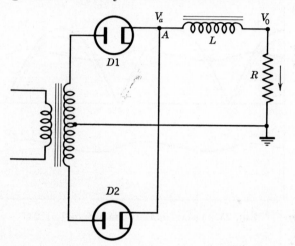

FIG. 24.   POWER SUPPLY WITH CHOKE-COIL FILTER.

following the procedure outlined in Sec. 21.   A suitable value for R_1 is 10,000 ohms, for C_1 and C_2, 8 μf each.   In the circuit of Fig. 22, R_2 should be variable from 0 to 5000 ohms, so that it may be demonstrated how the ripple decreases as R_2 is increased.   A milliammeter in series with R_1 will show how this improvement is accompanied by decreased output.   Note not only the decrease in ripple, but also the change in its waveform.   Choke-coils of several values of inductance should be tried in the circuit of Fig. 23.   The primary or secondary winding of a transformer will serve in place of a regular choke-coil. It may be possible to find one which will make the ripple greater instead of less, because of resonance.

25. Filter Circuits with Choke-Coil Input.   In the filter circuits heretofore considered the first element is a comparatively large shunt capacitance, and the input current consists of high, narrow pulses. Whenever the output current is large a better filter circuit is one in which the first element is a large series inductance or choke-coil, as represented in Fig. 24, which shows the simplest filter of this type.

With this type of filter circuit it is quite essential that the diode input be full-cycle (full-wave) as shown: then the current in the inductance is continuous, and nearly constant if the inductance is sufficiently large. Let us now consider the circuit of Fig. 24, and assume a very large inductance. The current, I, in L and R, and the output potential, V_0, are then nearly constant, as represented in the oscillograms of Fig. 25. The small variations in I now cause the potential difference across L to vary above and below V_0 in the manner represented in

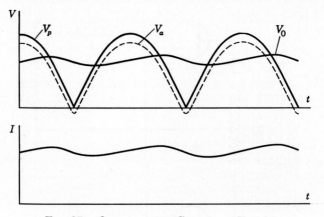

FIG. 25.   OSCILLOGRAM: CIRCUIT OF FIG. 24.

Fig. 25, so that V_a, the potential at the point A, Fig. 24, closely follows the potential, V_p, of the anode of the *conducting* diode. (This potential, V_p, is always positive, since it switches from one diode to the other with the current.) The difference between V_p and V_a is the potential drop across the conducting diode, and remains nearly constant, as it must do if I is to be nearly constant.

As a first approximation, which neglects the potential drop across the diodes, we may take the input potential to the filter to be equal to V_p. If we then assume an ideal choke-coil, having infinite reactance and zero resistance, the output potential, V_0, will equal the average value of V_p. Since each loop of V_p is sinusoidal in form, with a peak value E_1, it is easy to figure this approximate value for V_0 to be $2E_1/\pi$, or 0.90 times the rms value of the a-c input. Actual values are considerably below this ideal value. For the same a-c input the choke-input filter has a lower output potential than the condenser-input type, but the output potential changes less with current. The greatest advantage of the choke-input type is that larger direct current is possible without exceeding the allowable peak current for the diodes, since the peak diode current for this type is comparable with the output current.

A more effective circuit than shown in Fig. 24 is made by adding shunt condensers and another choke-coil, as in Fig. 26. Then it is

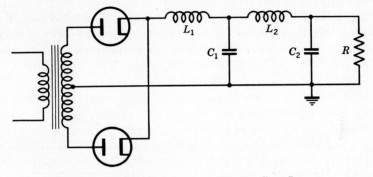

FIG. 26. POWER SUPPLY WITH CHOKE-COIL INPUT.

usual to make the first inductance rather small, so that the operating conditions are intermediate between the choke-input and condenser-input types here considered. Experimental methods of analysis are quicker than theoretical ones for these circuits.

26. Crystal Rectifiers. When suitable contact is made between a metallic conductor and any one of a variety of crystalline substances, a very slight potential difference in one direction will cause electrons to move readily across the boundary, whereas few electrons will move in the opposite direction unless the potential difference is very much larger. This characteristic is represented in Fig. 27. The resemblance of this figure to the characteristic curve for a thermionic diode (see Fig. 4) explains why such *crystal rectifiers* may be used in place of thermionic diodes for many applications. Substances which possess this rectifying property include selenium, germanium, and copper oxide, as well as the silicon, Carborundum, and galena (lead sulfide) crystals of early radio days. The characteristic curve of Fig. 27 may be reproduced on the screen of a cathode-ray oscilloscope by replacing

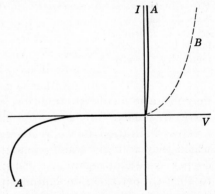

FIG. 27. CRYSTAL-RECTIFIER CHARACTERISTIC.

the diode in Demonstration Experiment 2 with the crystal rectifier under examination.   One of the type found in a-c, d-c radio sets will serve very well.   In early radio detectors the galena or silicon crystal was mounted in a metal cup, and a wire, called a "cat-whisker," was adjusted manually until its sharpened point rested with the right pressure upon a sensitive area of the crystal.   Modern crystal detec-

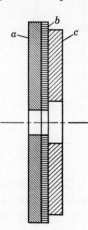

tors are similar except that the crystal is generally silicon or germanium, and the adjustment is made at the factory.   The assembly is then sealed into a ceramic or glass case.

Crystal rectifiers for larger currents must possess larger areas of contact.   The elements designed to serve as power-supply rectifiers are generally metal disks upon which a thin film of the crystal substance has been formed by very special processes. Copper oxide on copper disks, and selenium on iron disks, are common types.   Rectification occurs at the boundary layer between the film and the metal disk.   Electrical connection to the film is made by means of another disk of metal pressed against it, as represented schematically in Fig. 28.

Fig. 28.   Crystal Rectifier. Cross-section.   *a* —metal disk.   *b*— crystal film, firmly bonded to *a*.   *c*— metal disk pressed against *b*.

When crystal rectifiers may be employed they possess certain definite advantages over thermionic diodes.   Thus they require no heater power, are small in size, and are instantly ready to use. Moreover, they do not set up internal bias currents, an advantage which makes them particularly useful for rectifier-type voltmeters.   (See Sec. 27.)   They may be also made to function as detectors at very high (microwave) frequencies by making the contact area extremely small.   Their greatest limitation is the relatively low reverse potential difference which they will withstand without appreciable reverse current.   For copper oxide and selenium rectifiers this limit varies roughly from 10 to 40 volts per disk, depending upon the type and the perfection of fabrication.   To accommodate greater potential differences a number of disks may be connected in series, by stacking them up.   Projecting metal vanes help to cool the stack.   Figure 29 represents another type of rectifier assembly; four disks are stacked with polarities as shown to form a full-cycle, "bridge"-type rectifier similar to the one of Fig. 17.

27. "Average-Value" A-C Voltmeter.   The circuit of Fig. 29 is employed in a very common type of a-c voltmeter whose readings are proportional to the *average* value of the a-c voltage, although such meters are always calibrated to read the equivalent rms value (for sinusoidal voltage).   The circuit of this meter is diagrammed in Fig. 30.   The range of the milliammeter, M, is generally one milliampere for full-scale reading.   The rectifier is very small.   The value of R depends upon the scale of the voltmeter; taps on R may provide several scales.   At low voltages the scale is not quite uniform, because

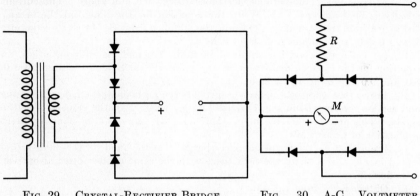

FIG. 29.   CRYSTAL-RECTIFIER BRIDGE.   FIG.   30.   A-C   VOLTMETER, RECTIFIER TYPE.

of the non-linear characteristics of the rectifier.   At higher voltages, when R is large in comparison with the impedance of the rectifier, the scale is quite linear.   Several other types of electronic voltmeters are described in Chapter 14.

PROBLEMS

1. The current in an electronic diode is 50 ma with an effective anode potential of 18.0 volts.   Compute the perveance.

2. The current in a diode is 9.5 ma when the effective anode potential is 7.0 volts.   Compute the anode potential required to make the current 20.0 ma.

3. The current in a diode is 470 ma when the effective anode potential is 50 volts.   Compute the current if the anode potential is raised 40 volts higher.

4. Compute the perveance of a diode whose electrodes are flat, circular plates, 13.0 mm in diameter and 0.45 mm apart.

5. The electrodes of a diode are coaxial cylinders, the diameters being 2.0 mm for the cathode, 3.0 mm for the anode.   Both electrodes are 12.5 mm long. (*a*) Compute the perveance of this tube.   (*b*) Compute the current when the effective anode potential is 18.2 volts.

6. At 2.00 volts anode potential the current in a diode is 2.30 ma; at 10.00 volts it is 19.8 ma.   Compute the internal bias.

7. Two large, plane plates are placed parallel and 4.20 mm apart.   One is at zero potential, the other at 92 volts.   Compute the electric field between these plates, in the following units: (*a*) dynes per statcoulomb, (*b*) kilodynes per coulomb.

8. Compute the speed of an electron which, starting from rest, moves through a potential difference of 8.00 volts. Explain the units employed.

9. An electron tube has plane-parallel electrodes each 15.0 mm square. The current in this tube is 45.0 ma. (a) Compute the speed of the electrons at a point where the potential is 20.0 volts. (b) Compute the electron density, n, at this point.

10. Compute the electric field gradient, dE/dx, in a uniform electron stream where the current density is 50.0 ma/cm^2 and the electron speed is 2.35×10^8 cm/sec. Suggestion: reduce data to esu first.

11. A diode has plane-parallel electrodes spaced 9.0 mm apart. The current density is 35.0 ma/cm^2. (a) Write the equation for the potential, V, at any distance x from the cathode. (This may be obtained from Eq. 14.) (b) Compute V at 1.0, 5.0, and 9.0 mm from the cathode.

12. (a) From the equation obtained in Prob. 11a find, by differentiation, an equation for the electron density, n, at any point x. (b) Evaluate n at points 1.0, 5.0, and 9.0 mm from the cathode.

13. Prove that the total space-charge between cathode and anode within the unit section represented in Fig. 7 equals $kE_a/4\pi$, where E_a is the value of E at the anode. This may be done by integration of Eq. 11, but *should* be done by direct application of Gauss's law.

14. Prove that, as the result of space-charge, E at the anode of the diode represented in Fig. 7 is $\frac{4}{3}$ times the field there with the same anode potential but the cathode cold.

15. Obtain Eq. 5 from Eq. 19.

The characteristic curve for a 5Y3-G diode, which is needed for the solutions of the following problems, may be plotted for the perveance value given in Appendix 5, and an internal bias of 1.0 volt.

16. A 5Y3-G diode is connected in series with a resistance R to a 92-volt battery of negligible resistance. (a) Compute R if the current is 75 ma. (b) Compute the current if R is 260 ohms. Solve graphically.

17. A 5Y3-G diode is connected in series with a 750-ohm resistor to an a-c source of 200 volts rms emf and negligible impedance. (a) Following the graphical method of Fig. 14, obtain and plot current values for one a-c cycle. (b) From this plot obtain, by graphical integration, the *average* current.

18. In the circuit of Fig. 12a the alternating emf is 220 volts rms, R is 90 ohms, E is 210 volts, and D is a 5Y3-G diode. Compute (a) the angle of operation, (b) the peak value for the diode current, and (c) the approximate value for the average current in the battery, as given by Eq. 23. If time permits, compute the more exact value for the average current by the point-by-point method.

19. In the circuit of Fig. 18 the a-c emf is 240 volts rms at 60 cps, C is 40 μf, R is 8500 ohms, I_0 is 35.0 ma, and R_s is zero. Compute (a) the d-c output voltage, (b) the maximum potential drop across D when it is conducting, (c) the maximum potential difference across D in the reverse (non-conducting) direction, (d) the approximate value of the peak diode current, from Eq. 23, and (e) the percent ripple.

Solution: The peak value of the alternating emf $= 240 \sqrt{2} = 340$ volts. (a) $E_0 = RI_0 = 8.5 \times 35.0 = 297$ volts. (b) $340 - 297 = 43$ volts. (c) $340 + 297 = 637$ volts. (d) $\cos \theta_i = \frac{297}{340} = 0.875$; $\theta_i = 29$ degrees. $I_0 = 35.0$ ma, and $I_m = 326$ ma, from Eq. 23. (e) See Sec. 20: $q = I_0/f = 35,000 \ (\mu a)/60 = 583$ microcoulombs. $\Delta V = q/C = \frac{583}{40} = 14.6$ volts. Ripple $= 14.6/2 = 7.3$ volts, and percent ripple $= 7.3/297 = 2.5$ percent.

20. The circuit of Fig. 21 is set up with 350 volts rms input to each diode, at 60 cps, and the d-c output is 375 volts, 80 ma. Compute (a) the angle of operation for each diode, (b) the approximate value of the peak current for each diode, and (c) the percent ripple if C is 16.0 μf.

21. The filter circuit of Fig. 24 is made with 1.00 henry for L and 30.0 ohms for R. The resistance of L is 1.0 ohm. The a-c input to each diode is 120 volts rms, at 60 cps. Make the approximations suggested in Sec. 26. (a) Compute the direct-current component in R. Remember that for this current the filter circuit is only a resistance. (b) Harmonic analysis of the plot for V_p in Fig. 25 gives the first-harmonic component an amplitude $4E_1/3\pi$. Explain why the frequency of this component is 120 cps and compute the impedance of the filter at this frequency. Then compute the rms value of the corresponding current component in R.

22. What value must be given to R in Fig. 30 in order that an a-c input of 100 volts rms will give 1.00 ma direct current in the meter? Neglect the impedances of the rectifier units.

CHAPTER 2

Triodes

1. The Grid.   A triode is formed by introducing a third electrode *between* the cathode and anode of a diode.   This electrode, which is

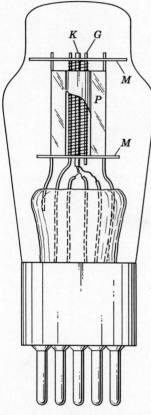

called a *grid,* may have any form providing it has apertures through which electrons can move.   Usually it is composed of fine wires running parallel to one another and equally spaced, as shown in Fig. 1.   The primary function of this grid is to serve as an *electrostatic screen* which partially shields the cathode from the anode.   To simplify the explanation of how a grid functions, let us consider first a triode having as cathode and anode two large, plane plates, parallel to one another and close together.   The grid then may consist of parallel wires lying in a plane which is between these plates and parallel to them.   Figure 2 represents a cross-section for a small portion of this electrode structure.

The shielding effect of the grid may now be considered as a problem in electrostatics, with the cathode cold and no electrons present.   Before the grid is inserted the electric field between the cathode, K, and the anode, P, is the same everywhere (except for negligible differences near the edges of the plates).   If the anode potential is V_p, the cathode potential is zero as always (see Sec. 2, Chapter 1), and the separation of the plates is a, the intensity, E_0, of this uni-

FIG. 1.   TRIODE.   Type 6P5-G (76) tube. K —cathode. G—grid. P—anode or plate.   Front of P is cut away to show G and K.

44

form field is given by

$$E_0 = -V_0/a \qquad (1)$$

If now the grid is inserted and set at zero potential the field between K and G, Fig. 2, is greatly reduced, to some value E', and the field between G and P is increased to some other value, E''. Most of the electric flux from P now terminates upon G, and only a small fraction of it passes between the grid wires to reach K. The finer the mesh of the grid the smaller is the value of E', whereas the value of E'' does not change appreciably with grid mesh, but remains nearly equal to $-V_p/b$ unless the grid is very coarse.

2. The Field Tank. It is possible to demonstrate these phenomena in a tank of some poorly conducting electrolyte. The electric field and potential distribution between electrodes immersed in this tank are identical with the distribution of field and potential for the same electrodes in air, or in a vacuum, provided that the glass walls of the tank and the free surface of the liquid are parallel to lines of force; since lines of flow correspond to lines of force in a conductor, there can be no flow of charge across these surfaces.

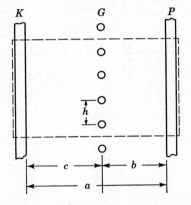

FIG. 2. TRIODE STRUCTURE. Cross-section near center of triode having plane-parallel electrodes. K—cathode. G—grid. P—anode.

Advantage may be taken of this condition to represent the whole of an electrode structure by only a small portion of it. Thus the field for plane-parallel electrodes of infinite area may be represented by plane electrodes at the ends of a rectangular glass tank, and the triode structure diagrammed in Fig. 2 may be exactly simulated if the tank boundaries correspond to the broken lines in this figure. A practical apparatus for this purpose is shown in Fig. 3.

For demonstration purposes the field tank should be quite deep, so that it may be viewed from the side. The one used by the author is a rectangular glass aquarium tank, 8 inches by 12 inches by 8 inches deep. The cathode and anode are copper plates covering the ends of the tank on the inside, with the top edges bent over so as to hang from the edge of the tank. The grid elements are copper tubes ⅜ inch in diameter, drilled transversely at the top so they may be strung on a horizontal metal rod which rests on the sides of the tank, as seen in

Fig. 3. They hang at equal distances apart, with half this distance from each wall to the nearest rod, and are almost but not quite long enough to touch the bottom. The grid spacing may be varied by changing the number of grid rods. The distance between grid and anode may be changed by moving the grid back and forth, or by hanging the anode from another rod and moving it toward the grid

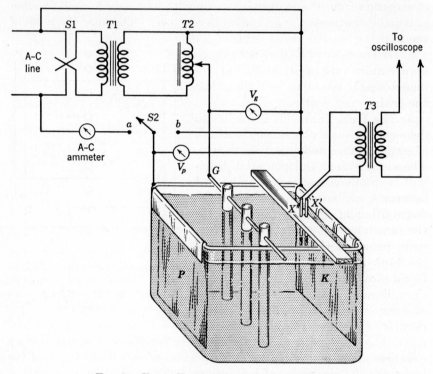

Fɪɢ. 3.   Fɪᴇʟᴅ-Tᴀɴᴋ Aᴘᴘᴀʀᴀᴛᴜs.   See Sec. 2.

The tank is filled with a very dilute aqueous solution of copper sulfate (one or two grams is sufficient for the whole tank).

The circuit is shown schematically in Fig. 3. The use of a-c power avoids trouble due to electrolysis, and permits us to employ a cathode-ray oscilloscope to measure the field intensity. The "anode" and "cathode" electrodes, P and K, are connected directly to the a-c line. If the current exceeds $\frac{1}{2}$ amp the tank overheats; this governs the dilution of the solution. Power is supplied to the grid through an isolation transformer, $T1$, and the magnitude of the grid potential may be varied with the variable-output transformer, $T2$. Its phase may be reversed with the switch $S1$. The field is explored with the double probe, $X'X''$, two copper rods about 1 mm in diameter, supported about 1 cm apart by a strip of wood or plastic. These probes dip 1 or 2 cm below the surface, and the potential difference between them at any point is a measure of the field strength at that point, along the line joining the probes. Since only the potential *difference* is to be observed, regardless of the actual potential of either probe, these probes must be connected to the oscilloscope through another isolation transformer, $T3$, which should have low capacity between windings.

3. Demonstration Experiment 1. Set the oscilloscope gain to give about half-screen deflection with switch $S2$ closed to point a, and with the grid removed from the tank. The same deflection will be observed for any location of the probes, thus demonstrating that the field represented by E_0 in Sec. 1 is uniform between K and P. Then assemble a three-rod grid, insert it half-way between K and P, and make its potential zero by moving the contact on $T2$ to the zero end, so that G is connected directly to K. (Merely opening $S1$ will not insure that G is at the same potential as K, since there is current in any impedance between G and K.) The probes now show that the field (E'') between P and G is about doubled, whereas the field (E') between G and K is very much reduced. Both fields are quite uniform except close to the grid rods.

With the probes between G and K increase the oscilloscope gain to give a good-sized deflection and note the value of the anode potential, V_p. Then throw $S2$ to point b, so as to "ground" P, close $S1$, and raise the grid potential, V_g, until the *same* deflection is produced. This value for V_g will be very much smaller than the corresponding value of V_p.

4. Geometric Amplification Factor. Since the cathode, K, is so well shielded from the anode, P, but not shielded at all from the grid, G, the field between K and G is affected to a much greater extent by V_g than by V_p. The fact that G is nearer to K than P gives an added advantage to V_g, but this factor is far less important than the *shielding* effect of G. The influence of V_g relative to V_p has been demonstrated in the experiment described above. If V_1 and V_2 are the values of V_g and V_p respectively which give the *same* value of the field, E', between K and G, then the ratio of V_2 to V_1 is a constant, μ_0, called the *geometric amplification factor* for this triode structure.

$$\mu_0 = V_2/V_1 \qquad (2)$$

For a more precise determination of μ_0 with the field tank we may apply both V_g and V_p simultaneously, with opposite signs, and adjust their values until E' is zero. This is accomplished by closing $S2$ to point a, and $S1$ so that V_g and V_p are opposed; the probes are placed close to K and V_g is varied until the deflection is zero. The ratio of these values of V_p and V_g is then $-\mu_0$, the minus sign indicating the opposing directions of V_g and V_p. For plane-parallel electrodes such as represented in Fig. 2 an approximate value for μ_0 is

$$\mu_0 = \frac{2.7b}{h \log (h/2\pi r)} \tag{3}$$

The distances b and h are indicated in Fig. 2; r is the radius of the grid rods. It is very interesting to note that the distance from K to G does not affect the value for μ_0 for plane electrodes.

5. Experiment 3. Geometric Amplification Factor. Equation 3 may be checked experimentally with the field-tank apparatus. The procedure is the *null* (zero deflection) method described above for demonstration.

Part I. With one grid (the three-rod grid for the apparatus here described) placed $0.4a$ or $0.5a$ from K, take readings for several positions of P. Take care that the current does not exceed the safe value (specified by the instructor for the apparatus at hand). Compute μ_0 and plot its values as ordinates with b as abscissae.

Part II. Repeat these observations for a distance of $0.2a$ or $0.3a$ between G and K. Plot these results on the same sheet and to the same axes as for Part I. Interpret these results for Parts I and II.

Part III. With P and K at the ends of the tank and G about halfway between, take data for several grid spacings. From two to five grid rods may be used with the apparatus here described. To space the rods correctly, divide the distance between side walls into equal parts, then put a rod in the *middle* of each part. Be very careful to put every grid structure in the same position. For each gird structure compute μ_0 from Eq. 3 and compare the result with the experimental value. Analyze the discrepancies as far as possible.

All kinds of electrode structures may be studied with field-tank apparatus, which has become a very valuable aid to the design of new tubes. Electric fields may be measured by means of the double probe here described, or lines of constant potential may be plotted with a single probe. The single probe is connected, through the detector, to a point of known potential, and an equipotential line is traced by moving the probe so that the detector reading remains zero. By means of a mechanical linkage called a pantograph this line may be automatically plotted on a chart.*

* For further details, consult V. K. Zworykin and G. A. Morton, *Television*, p. 73.

6. Equivalent Diode. In most triodes the electric field, in the absence of space-charge (with the cathode cold), is uniform over the surface of the cathode, as in the triode of Fig. 2. For lack of a better name we shall speak of all such triodes as *symmetrical triodes*. The theory developed above for the special case of plane electrodes may be modified to apply to any symmetrical triode, and the geometric amplification factor, μ_0, defined for it by Eq. 2 is a constant determined by its electrode structure. It follows that a potential V_p at the anode of such a triode produces an electric field at its cathode which is the same as that produced by a potential V_p/μ_0 applied to its grid. If then its anode and grid potentials have independent, arbitrary values V_p and V_g respectively, the electric field at the cathode is determined by the composite voltage, V, which is the sum of V_g and V_p/μ_0.

$$V = V_g + \frac{V_p}{\mu_0} \tag{4}$$

An *equivalent diode* now may be constructed, such that equal electric fields are produced at the cathodes of both tubes with the anode and grid of the triode at potentials V_p and V_g respectively, and the anode of the diode at the potential V given by Eq. 4. The cathode of this equivalent diode is identical with that of the triode, and its anode has almost the same size, shape, and position relative to the cathode as the *grid* of the triode.

This equivalence is easily established for a triode having plane electrodes, such as represented in Fig. 2. First let the potential of G, Fig. 2, be V_g while that of P is zero. Then E_g, the electric field next to the cathode, is approximately equal to V_g divided by c. The true value of E_g is not quite this large, since a grid is less effective than a solid plate when employed as an electrode. A more exact value is

$$E_g = V_g/c' \tag{5}$$

in which c' is a distance slightly greater than c.* Next let the potentials be zero for G, and V_p for P. Since the field produced by V_p is equivalent to that produced by a grid potential of only V_p/μ_0, the field at the cathode is now

$$E_p = V_p/c'\mu_0 \tag{6}$$

If the potentials of G and P are simultaneously V_g and V_p, the resultant

---

* The difference between c' and c is comparable with c/μ_0. See E. L. Chaffee, *Theory of Thermionic Vacuum Tubes*, Sec. 74, and W. G. Dow, *Fundamentals of Engineering Electronics*, First Ed., Sec. 19. The presence of space-charge reduces this difference somewhat.

field at the cathode must be

$$E = E_g + E_p = \frac{1}{c'}\left(V_g + \frac{V_p}{\mu_0}\right) = \frac{V}{c'} \tag{7}$$

In the equivalent diode the anode is at a distance c' from the cathode, and the electric field next the cathode is the same as given by Eq. 7, if its anode has the potential V.

The same equivalence may be established for any other symmetrical triode.

7. Equivalent-Diode Theorem.   The equivalent-diode concept developed in Sec. 6 for conditions of zero space-charge (cold-cathode) may be extended to hot-cathode conditions.   In a thermionic triode the electron current, I_k, depends upon the potentials of both plate and grid, in a manner which may be expressed most generally by saying that I_k is *some function* of V_p and V_g.   Mathematically expressed,

$$I_k = I_k(V_p, V_g) \tag{8}$$

This current is of course limited by space-charge, just as in a diode (see Sec. 10, Chapter 1).   Furthermore, all the space-charge of any significance in a triode lies between the cathode and the grid.   Outside the grid there is little space-charge, since the electron speeds there are quite high, and this small amount is almost entirely screened from the cathode by the grid.   Thus the space-charge conditions which determine I_k in a symmetrical triode correspond very closely to those in the equivalent diode defined in Sec. 6, and I_k is not only a function of V_p and V_g but of the particular combination of these potentials given by Eq. 4.

$$I_k = I_k\left(V_g + \frac{V_p}{\mu_0}\right) \tag{9}$$

Thus, when Child's law applies, we may write

$$I_k = G\left(V_g + \frac{V_p}{\mu_0}\right)^{3/2} \tag{10}$$

where G is the perveance of the equivalent diode.

These deductions are confirmed, with only slight modifications, by experimental measurements for actual electronic triodes.   Equation 10 may be written also as

$$I_k = \frac{G}{\mu_0^{3/2}}(V_p + \mu_0 V_g)^{3/2}$$

$$= B(V_p + \mu_0 V_g)^{3/2} \tag{11}$$

This combination of V_g and V_p is better known than the one in Eq. 10.

8. Triode Characteristics. Since the cathode current, I_k, is a function of both V_p and V_g, the relationships among these quantities might be represented by a three-dimensional plot. It is more practi-

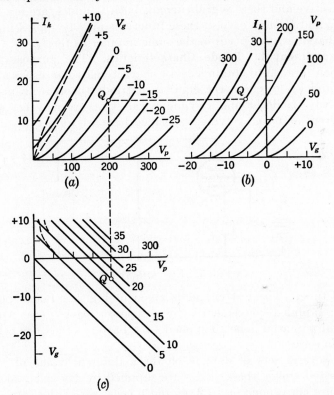

FIG. 4. CHARACTERISTIC CURVES FOR A TRIODE. V_p—anode or plate potential. V_g—grid potential. I_k—cathode current. The point Q represents the *same* set of values for I_k, V_p, and V_g in each of the three plots. The dotted lines represent the *anode* current when V_g is positive.

cal, however, to represent them by *families* of curves, plotted to coordinates which represent two of the three variables. Each curve in this family is plotted for a different fixed value of the third quantity, which is then called a parameter. For example, I_k may be plotted as y with V_p as x, each separate plot representing a different fixed value of V_g. Alternate possibilities are I_k plotted as y with V_g as x and V_p as parameter, and V_g as y with V_p as x and I_k as parameter. All three families are represented in Fig. 4. Such plots are called *characteristic curves*.

When V_g is negative there is no grid current; all the cathode current goes between the grid wires to the anode or *plate*. The same characteristic curves then represent both I_k and I_p. In a very large share of their applications triodes are operated with negative grids. When V_g is positive and there is grid current, both I_p and I_g are functions of both V_p and V_g, and each of these functions may be represented by a set of characteristic curves in the same manner as for I_k.

9. Experiment 4. Triode Characteristics. The purposes of this experiment are (1) to obtain a set of characteristic curves for a typical triode, and (2) to check the equivalent-triode theorem against these data. Any triode having a symmetrical structure may be studied. The current and voltage values specified here are for a type 6P5-G or

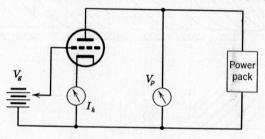

FIG. 5. EXPERIMENT 4.

type 76 tube. The test circuit is given in Fig. 5. Plate potential may be supplied conveniently by a "power pack" (see Appendix 2). Grid potential is best supplied by a battery of six dry cells connected in series.

Take several sets of data, each for a different value of V_g. If, as suggested above, these values are supplied by dry cells, take negative values corresponding to 2, 4, and 6 cells, zero value, and a positive value produced by 2 cells. Measure the emf's of these cells carefully with a voltmeter reading to 0.05 volt. For each set observe I_k and V_p for the *same* regularly spaced series of values for I_k: values 0, 1, 3, 5, 7, 9, 11, 13, and 15 ma are suggested. As the grid potential is made more negative it will be necessary to leave off one or more of the top values, to keep the plate potential within a top limit of 250 volts. In taking data for a triode there are two limitations to be observed. The first is an upper limit to the cathode current, which is set by the emission of the cathode. The other is the power which may be dissipated safely by the plate. A similar limitation exists for the grid power when there is grid current. For the type 6P5-G tube these limits may be considered to be 15 ma maximum current and 2.5 watts maximum plate power.

Plot these data as a family of curves having I_k as ordinates and V_p as abscissae, with V_g as parameter; see Fig. 4a. The lines which represent these plots should be drawn with great care: first sketch them in free-hand with a pencil, then ink them. The pen may be steadied by a "french curve" only as long as it follows the pencil line. Plot another family of curves having V_g as ordinates and V_p as abscissae, each curve representing a different value of I_k. See Fig. 4c. According to the theory given in Sec. 7 each plot of this family should be a straight line with a slope equal to $-\mu_0$. Explain why this is so.

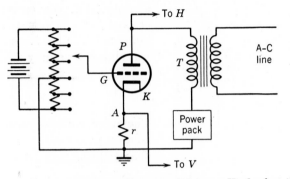

FIG. 6. TRIODE CHARACTERISTICS DEMONSTRATION. H—horizontal-deflection terminal. V—vertical-deflection terminal.

Measure the slopes of these lines and average them for a value of μ_0 for use in the next plot.

To check the equivalent-diode theorem, compute the equivalent-diode potential, V, for all your data, by means of Eq. 4, and put all these data into a single plot having I_k as ordinates and V as abscissae. This is the equivalent-diode characteristic. Draw a smooth line to fit these plotted points and try to account for any points which do not fall near this line.

10. Demonstration Experiment 2. The circuit of Fig. 5 may be modified as in Fig. 6 so that characteristic curves for a triode may be traced upon the screen of an oscilloscope. The grid potential is varied in steps, as indicated. The plate potential is swung from zero to maximum value by means of the isolation transformer, T, with its secondary in series with a power pack whose emf approximates the peak value of the a-c emf. Horizontal deflection of the cathode-ray beam is caused by the plate potential. Vertical deflection is produced by the amplified value of the potential at A, which is proportional to I_k. A whole family of curves may be made visible at one time by changing the grid potential rapidly through a series of values with a motor-driven switch.*

11. Variational Resistance. In most applications of triodes, and in some applications of diodes as well, we are in one way or another concerned with *changes* of current caused by *changes* of electrode potentials. Consider first a diode. When the anode potential is V the current has a value I which may be found from the characteristic curve for this diode. See Fig. 7. If now V is increased by a small amount, ΔV, the current will also change by a small amount, ΔI, as indicated in Fig. 7. For *infinitesimal* changes we may write

$$dI = \frac{dI}{dV} dV \qquad (12)$$

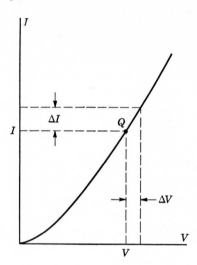

The same equation will give also a good approximation for small finite changes; this may be written

$$\Delta I \cong \frac{dI}{dV} \Delta V \qquad (13)†$$

Fig. 7. Variational Resistance.
$r = \Delta V / \Delta I$.

If it is now recalled that dI/dV represents the slope of a line drawn tangent to the characteristic curve at Q, Fig. 7, it may be seen that the error introduced by this approximation is measured by the deviation of the tangent line from the curve when x equals $(V + \Delta V)$. Thus if the curvature of the diode characteristic is small in the neighborhood of Q the approximation may be satisfactory for relatively large changes of V.

It is evident from these equations that dI/dV has the dimensions of conductance. Indeed, if we regard ΔI and ΔV as *variational* values of current and potential, superimposed upon the steady values of V and I at Q, then Eq. 13 expresses Ohm's law for these variational values if we define the *variational conductance* as

$$g = \frac{dI}{dV} \qquad (14)$$

* An all-electronic circuit is described by R. S. Mackay in the *American Journal of Physics,* Vol. 16 (1948), p. 46.

† The equals sign with a wavy line above it is read "approximately equal to."

The reciprocal of g is r, the *variational resistance*. Since potential variations are produced most often by superimposing small a-c voltage upon a steady d-c potential, the variational resistance is usually called the "a-c resistance."

For a triode we have to consider in general two potentials, V_p and V_g, as well as three currents, I_k, I_p, and I_g. For the present we shall limit our attention to I_p. Any set of steady conditions may be represented by a point such as Q in Fig. 4.* Any finite changes of V_p and I_p, without any change in V_g, then are represented by other points along the curve passing through Q in Fig. 4a. For infinitesimal change of V_p, with V_g held constant, the corresponding infinitesimal change of I_p is given by

$$dI_p = \frac{\partial I_p}{\partial V_p}\bigg)_{V_g} dV_p \qquad (15)$$

The subscript V_g reminds us that V_g is held constant in taking this *partial* derivative. Hereafter it will be taken for granted that the third variable is held constant, and this cumbersome subscript will be omitted. For small but finite changes or variations we may then write, just as for the diode,

$$\Delta I_p \cong \frac{\partial I_p}{\partial V_p} \Delta V_p \qquad (16)$$

We may now follow the example set for the diode, and define a variational conductance, g_p, and a variational resistance, r_p, by

$$\frac{\partial I_p}{\partial V_p} = g_p = \frac{1}{r_p} \qquad (17)$$

This partial derivative equals the slope of the straight line drawn through Q, Fig. 4a, and tangent to the characteristic curve through Q. Since partial derivatives are not always familiar concepts it is best to state the *physical* definition for r_p.

The variational ("a-c") plate resistance is the ratio of a very small change in plate potential to the very small change of plate current which it produces, with the grid potential held constant.

---

* Note that, when V_g is negative, Fig. 4 represents I_p as well as I_k, since I_g is then zero. When V_g is positive, I_p is represented by the dotted lines.

12. Transconductance (Mutual Conductance). When V_p is held constant and V_g is varied we obtain in similar manner the equations

$$dI_p = \frac{\partial I_p}{\partial V_g}\, dV_g \tag{18}$$

and

$$\Delta I_p \cong \frac{\partial I_p}{\partial V_g}\, \Delta V_g \tag{19}$$

The partial derivative appearing in these equations equals the slope of a line drawn through Q, Fig. 4b, and tangent to the corresponding I_p, V_g curve. It has the dimensions of conductance. Since it relates current at one electrode to potential at another electrode it is a *trans-*conductance. The common name is "mutual conductance," with the symbol g_m.

$$g_m = \frac{\partial I_p}{\partial V_g} \tag{20}$$

Again a physical definition is preferable.

> Transconductance (mutual conductance) for a triode is the ratio of a very small change of plate current to the very small change of grid potential which causes it, with the plate potential held constant.

13. Amplification Factor. A third factor, called the *amplification factor*, may be defined for a triode. The physical definition may be stated as

> Amplification factor for a triode is the ratio of a very small change of plate potential to a very small change of grid potential which is so chosen that *each* change in potential, acting *by itself* with the other potential held constant, will cause the *same* change in plate current.

This amplification factor, which is represented by μ, is not the same as μ_0, the geometric amplification factor, although it has close to the same value for a symmetrical triode. (It is assumed equal to μ_0 in Exp. 4.) Although μ may be made a variable quantity in tubes of special (unsymmetrical) design, it is very close to constant for most triodes.

This amplification factor may also be defined by a partial derivative. When plate potential and grid potential are changed simultaneously by infinitesimal amounts δV_p and δV_g respectively, so chosen that *no* change in I_p results, it follows that

$$\frac{\delta V_p}{\delta V_g} = \frac{\partial V_p}{\partial V_g}\bigg)_{I_p} = -\mu \tag{21}$$

This partial derivative is the slope of the corresponding line through Q in Fig. 4c. The negative sign is needed since μ is positive, whereas this slope is negative. The physical definition is preferable to this one.

14. Tube Factors. The quantities μ, g_m, and r_p are called tube factors. In general all three are variable factors which may be represented as functions of the independent variables, V_p and V_g. For a symmetrical triode operated with negative grid, however, μ is practically a constant and nearly equal to μ_0, as has been stated in Sec. 13, and the other two factors depend chiefly upon I_p. Indeed, for such a tube both g_m and g_p are nearly proportional to the cube-root of I_p, as may be demonstrated from the equivalent-diode equation, Eq. 10. If we add the internal bias, V_i, which is always present in a real tube, and remember that I_k equals I_p when the grid potential is negative, we may write Eq. 10 as

$$I_p = G\left(V_g + \frac{V_p}{\mu} + V_i\right)^{3/2} \tag{22}$$

Then, from the definition of g_m given by Eq. 20,

$$g_m = \frac{3}{2}G\left(V_g + \frac{V_p}{\mu} + V_i\right)^{1/2} \tag{23}$$

If we now eliminate the quantity in parentheses between Eqs. 22 and 23, we obtain

$$g_m = (\tfrac{3}{2}G^{2/3})I_p{}^{1/3} \tag{24}$$

The factors which determine the constant G are chiefly the structural characteristics of the cathode and grid, such as size and shape. The value of g_m depends very little upon the size and position of the plate, or the mesh of the grid. This is an important fact to remember. The value of r_p, on the contrary, does depend upon grid mesh and the geometry of the plate, *in exactly the same manner that μ depends upon these factors*. Thus, if the value of $1/r_p$ is derived from Eq. 22 by means of the definition given in Eq. 17, this value is the same as Eq. 24 except for a factor μ in the denominator. That is,

$$1/r_p = g_m/\mu \qquad \text{or} \qquad g_m = \mu r_p \tag{25}$$

As will be proved in Sec. 16, the relationship stated in Eq. 25 holds for *any* triode. It may be interpreted by saying that the grid gains most of its advantage over the plate (this advantage being represented by μ) by reducing the effectiveness of the plate, that is, by increasing r_p.

15. The Small-Variations Equation. When V_p and V_g change simultaneously by infinitesimal amounts, we may compute the changes in I_p produced by each potential change alone, then add to obtain the total change. This may be expressed as

$$dI_p = \frac{\partial I_p}{\partial V_p} dV_p + \frac{\partial I_p}{\partial V_g} dV_g \qquad (26)$$

or

$$dI_p = g_p \, dV_p + g_m \, dV_g \qquad (27)$$

If the changes are small but finite, we may represent them in the approximate equation

$$\Delta I_p \cong g_p \, \Delta V_p + g_m \, \Delta V_g \qquad (28)$$

or

$$\Delta I_p \cong \frac{\Delta V_p}{r_p} + g_m \, \Delta V_g \qquad (28a)$$

Equation 28 (or 28a) is the basic equation from which many circuit analyses start.

16. The Tube-Factor Equation. A very fundamental relationship among μ, g_m, and r_p may be derived from Eq. 27. If we choose the infinitesimal changes in V_p and V_g to be δV_p and δV_g such that dI_p is zero, Eq. 27 becomes

$$dI_p = 0 = g_p \, \delta V_p + g_m \, \delta V_g \qquad (29)$$

or

$$\delta V_p / \delta V_g = - g_m/g_p = -g_m r_p \qquad (30)$$

But, according to Eq. 21, this ratio equals $-\mu$. Hence, for *any* triode,

$$\mu = g_m r_p \qquad (31)$$

17. Commercial Triodes. Triodes vary in size over wide limits, and serve many functions. Design principles are similar to those for diodes. Thus the comments made in Sec. 13, Chapter 1, concerning the design of cathodes apply equally well for triodes, and the principles involved in the design of anodes are the same also, but generally the power which must be dissipated at the plate of a triode is much greater than for the same current in a diode. Grid design involves most of the factors of plate design. Thus, when there is grid current the problem arises of keeping the grid cool enough, and since it is composed of fine wires and lies between the cathode and the plate, close to the cathode, this is sometimes a troublesome problem. Generally the design of a triode is directed first toward making g_m large enough. Then consideration is given to making the value of μ suitable to the application intended for the tube. These two factors fix the value for r_p. If this value for r_p is too high it may be necessary to compromise on a lower value of μ. The same principles govern the choice of a suitable tube from among the many types available. Tube capacitances, that is, electrostatic capacitances between electrodes, are other factors which must be considered for certain applications.

18. Triode as a Circuit Element. Figure 8 shows a very simple circuit which includes a triode as a means for controlling the current

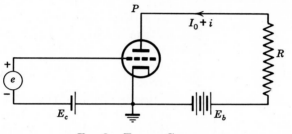

FIG. 8. TRIODE CIRCUIT.

in the load, R. Assume that the biasing emf, E_c, is made large enough to maintain the grid potential always negative, and that E_b, the emf of the plate supply, is high enough to produce the current I_0 when the grid potential is $-E_c$. If now we are interested in the change in I_p which is caused by introducing a small additional voltage, e, in series with $-E_c$, as shown in Fig. 8, we may obtain an approximate value for this change by means of the small-variations equation, Eq. 28a. For this example, ΔV_g is $+e$, ΔI_p may be considered to be a small current, i, superimposed upon I_0, and ΔV_p becomes $-iR$. Equation 28a then becomes

$$i \cong -iR/r_p + g_m e \qquad (32)$$

or

$$(r_p + R)i \cong g_m r_p e \qquad (33)$$

Since $g_m r_p$ equals μ (Eq. 31)

$$(r_p + R)i \cong \mu e \qquad (34)$$

If e is an added direct voltage, i is an additional direct current; if e is a variable voltage, for example an alternating voltage, then i varies accordingly.

If we keep the values of e and of i small enough to make this a good approximation we may, for practical purposes, write Eq. 34 with an equals sign. This is commonly done, even when e and i are quite large. The error resulting from the approximation may be checked by graphical methods, such as are described in Chapter 4.

19. Principle of Superposition. When all the elements in a circuit are *linear* the resultant current in any part may be found by computing the current produced by each source separately (the other sources being replaced by equivalent impedances), then adding these several currents. This principle of superposition does not apply to a circuit which includes non-linear elements such as electron tubes.

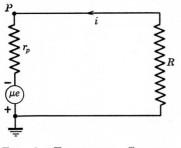

Nevertheless, we have employed it in Sec. 18, and the success of our venture there depends upon the smallness of the variations which are superimposed upon the steady potentials and currents, and upon our tolerance of errors introduced by the approximations involved. What has been done in Sec. 18 is to consider that the variations occur along a straight, tangent line instead of along the curve which represents the true relationship among them. We are often willing to tolerate considerable error for the advantages gained by this procedure.

Fig. 9. Equivalent Circuit. for Fig. 8.

20. Equivalent Variational (A-C) Circuit. When our chief concern is for the variations of current and potential we may reduce many electronic circuits to equivalent, or approximately equivalent, linear circuits in which only the variations occur. Thus, in the example cited in Sec. 18, all d-c sources might be removed, and the electron tube replaced by a linear generator having an emf equal to μe and internal resistance r_p. The rest of the circuit remains the same. The result is represented in Fig. 9. For this circuit Ohm's law gives the equation

$$(r_p + R)i = \mu e \qquad (35)$$

But this equation is identical with Eq. 34, except that it is exact whereas Eq. 34 is an approximation. Hence, in so far as the *variational* current, i, and the variational voltage, e, are concerned, the circuit of Fig. 9 is a good approximation, electrically, to the one in Fig. 8. The circuit of Fig. 9 may be called the *equivalent variational circuit*. Note particularly the polarity of the emf, μe, relative to e, which is required to make the current i have the same direction in R for both circuits. When e is an a-c voltage, this circuit is called the equivalent a-c circuit.   Note that the grid part of the circuit does not appear in the equivalent circuit, since there is current in the plate part only. Circuits in which there is grid current will not be considered until a later chapter.

In the example of Fig. 8 the plate circuit includes only a single element, the resistor R.   In general it may include any combination of linear elements—resistors, inductors, and condensers.   The procedure for constructing the equivalent circuit is always the same: (a) omit all d-c sources, (b) leave out the grid part of the circuit, and (c) replace each triode by an equivalent generator having an emf equal to its

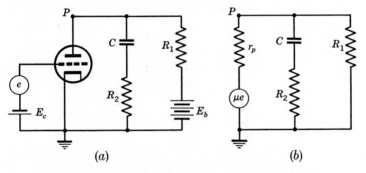

FIG. 10.   (a) Triode circuit.   (b) Equivalent circuit.

amplification factor times the variational part of its grid potential, and internal impedance equal to its variational plate resistance. Another example is illustrated in Fig. 10.   It must be remembered always that this method for solving triode circuits gives approximate results only.   When the variations are so large that the approximations are unsatisfactory, graphical methods must be employed.   These are considered in Chapter 4.

21. Evaluation of μ, g_m, and r_p.   In order to analyze triode circuits by the method described in Sec. 20 we need values for the tube factors μ, g_m, and r_p, for the conditions existing before the variations are introduced.   For most triodes the value given for μ in the tube maker's data is quite satisfactory, since μ changes very little with operating conditions.   Sometimes the values given for g_m and r_p also are suitable; generally they are not, because of different operating conditions.   If a complete set of characteristic curves (as in Fig. 4) is available, values for these tube factors may be obtained graphically, as explained in Secs. 11, 12, and 13.   Thus, if the point Q, Fig. 4a, represents the initial conditions, the corresponding value for r_p may be obtained from the curve through Q by drawing a straight line tangent to it at Q.

The slope of this line equals $1/r_p$.   Similar procedures give values for g_m and μ from the curves represented in Figs. 4b and 4c respectively. The tangent line must always be drawn very carefully and its slope computed from points taken on it as far apart as practicable.   Even then the values obtained are not very exact.

Since the tube maker's data do not often include more than one set of characteristic curves, usually those represented in Fig. 4a, it is customary to accept the value of μ given in the table, obtain r_p graphically from these curves, and compute g_m from the tube-factor equation,

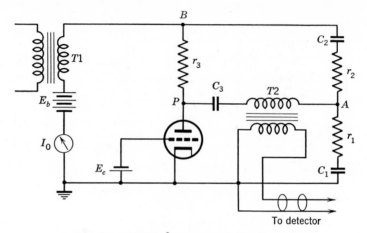

FIG. 11.   A-C BRIDGE FOR r_p.   See Sec. 22.

Eq. 31.   An alternate procedure, not so well known, is to accept the value given for μ and to compute the desired value for g_m from the given value by assuming that g_m is proportional to the cube-root of the current.   See Sec. 14.

22. Bridge Measurement of r_p. Tube factors may be measured with greater precision by means of special *null* circuits which somewhat resemble bridge circuits for measuring a-c impedances.   Indeed, the circuit for measuring r_p is a modified a-c impedance bridge, as shown in Fig. 11.   A small alternating test voltage, e, is introduced in series with the d-c supply voltage, E_b, by means of transformer $T1$.   A frequency of several hundred cps is desirable.   The detector may be a telephone receiver or a cathode-ray oscilloscope, and may be aided by an amplifier of one or two stages.   Transformer $T2$ allows the detector to be operated with one terminal grounded.   All resistors must be suitable for a-c operation, and r_3 must be capable of dissipating considerable power without overheating, since it carries the plate current.

When the bridge is balanced,

$$r_p : r_3 = r_1 : r_2 \tag{36}$$

Condensers C_1 and C_2 are needed to block direct current from r_1 and r_2, and C_3 blocks the d-c potential of P from r_1 and r_2, for the protection of the operator. If C_1 and C_2 have large capacitance they will not sensibly affect the balance. For best results, however, one condenser should be variable, so that an exact phase balance may be made. The condition is that

$$C_1 r_1 = C_2 r_2 \tag{37}$$

Exact balance is attained by adjusting the resistances and capacitances alternately until the best values are found.

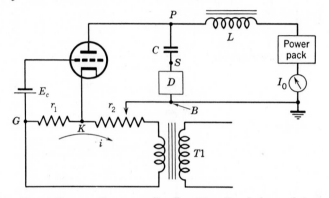

FIG. 12. μ-FACTOR BRIDGE. See Sec. 23. D —balance detector.

If the test voltage, e, is too strong, curvature of the tube characteristics will introduce a second-harmonic component into the circuit, and this component will not balance out. With an oscilloscope detector the balance will be shown clearly by absence of the *fundamental* component. The value of e should be kept as low as possible, to minimize this harmonic production. A filter circuit will remove the second-harmonic component, and is desirable when the detector is a telephone receiver.

23. Amplification Factor "Bridge." The amplification factor, μ, may be measured with high precision by means of the null circuit shown in Fig. 12. When the alternating current, i, set up by the transformer, $T1$, has the direction shown it produces in r_1 and r_2 the potential increments $+ir_1$ at the grid, and $-ir_2$ at the anode. If the value of r_2 is varied until the detector, D, shows no current in the plate circuit,

$$\mu = ir_2/ir_1 = r_2/r_1 \tag{38}$$

Equation 38 follows from the definition of μ given in Sec. 13. Note that, when the circuit is unbalanced, the detector carries practically all the a-c component of the plate current, because of the very high a-c impedance of the choke-coil, L. The condenser, C, is needed to block direct current from D; otherwise D would practically short-circuit the battery E_b.

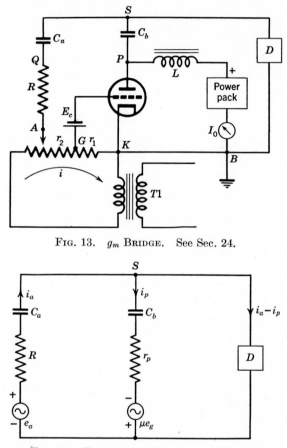

FIG. 13. g_m BRIDGE.   See Sec. 24.

FIG. 14.   EQUIVALENT CIRCUIT FOR FIG. 13.

24. Transconductance "Bridge." The circuit of Fig. 13 provides a null method for measuring the transconductance, g_m, for a triode. When the alternating current, i, set up by the transformer $T1$ is in the direction shown it produces at the grid of the tube an a-c increment of potential, e_g, equal to $+ir_1$, and at the point A an a-c potential, e_a, equal to $+i(r_1 + r_2)$. Let us now consider the equivalent a-c circuit of Fig. 14. If we assume that the reactances of condensers C_a and C_b

are negligibly small the a-c potential of the point S is, for the left-hand branch in Fig. 14, represented by

$$V_s = e_a - i_a R = i(r_1 + r_2) - i_a R \tag{39}$$

For the middle branch,

$$V_s = -\mu e_g + i_p r_p = -\mu i r_1 + i_p r_p \tag{40}$$

When the circuit is balanced, so that the detector current $(i_a - i_p)$ is zero, V_s is zero and $i_a = i_p$. From Eqs. 39 and 40 it then follows that

$$i(r_1 + r_2) = i_a R \quad \text{and} \quad i r_1 = i_p r_p / \mu = i_p / g_m \tag{41}$$

Hence $$g_m = (r_1 + r_2)/r_1 R \tag{42}$$

Condenser C_b and choke-coil L serve the same functions here as in the circuit of Fig. 12. Condenser C_a may be needed to obtain a good phase balance, and should be variable, as explained in Sec. 22. If C_b is large enough, however, it may be possible to omit C_a. In this circuit, as in the circuit of Fig. 11, it is necessary to keep the a-c components as small as possible, since the assumption is made that they are infinitesimal. The presence of a large second-harmonic component is an indication that they are too large, as has been explained in Sec. 22.

25. Experiment 5. Measurement of μ and g_m. Since μ equals the product of g_m and r_p it is necessary to measure but two of these three tube factors. In this experiment we measure μ and g_m since, as may be seen by comparing Figs. 12 and 13, both may be measured with the same equipment, by making a few changes in circuit. The fixed resistors r_1 and R, the condenser C_b, and the amplifier for the detector may be mounted together on a board as shown in Fig. 15. Corresponding junction points in Figs. 12, 13, and 15 are indicated by capital letters. The amplifier may be built as indicated, or it may be a commercial unit. The plate-to-grid transformer in Fig. 15 must be well shielded. Suitable values for the fixed resistors are 50 ohms for r_1 and 5000 ohms for R. The range of the voltage-divider, r_2, depends upon the tube under test; 1000 ohms will cover values of μ up to 20, and values of g_m up to 2100 micromhos. A wire-wound resistor of the "potentiometer" type will serve, if it is supplied with a finely graduated dial and is calibrated with an a-c bridge at the frequency employed. It must have a current capacity equal to the largest d-c plate current encountered, since it carries plate current in Part I. If condenser C_b is 20 mf or over, C_a may be omitted. Electrolytic condensers will not serve for C_a and C_b. The choke-coil, L, should be quite large.

Grid bias is best supplied with dry cells; 3 volts is a suitable value for the observations described below.   The d-c plate power is supplied most conveniently by a power pack.   It is best to supply the cathode heaters for both the tube under test and the amplifier tube from a storage battery, and B-batteries are best for the amplifier plate power, since this circuit is very sensitive to "pick-up" from a-c power circuits.   The a-c test source should have an emf of 2 to 5 volts, at a frequency between 400 and 2000 cps.   It is supplied most conveniently

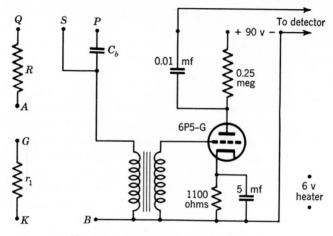

Fig. 15.   Circuit Board for Exp. 5.

by a plate to voice-coil output transformer having several secondary taps.

Part I.   Make up the circuit of Fig. 12 and measure μ with it for the same tube studied in Exp. 4.   Balance the circuit for a set of current values spread well over the range for which data were taken in Exp. 4.   Values 1, 2, 4, 7, 10, and 15 ma are suggested for type 6P5-G tubes, with grid bias approximately 3 volts.   Represent your results by a plot having μ as y, I_p as x.   What do your results show?   How does the average value for μ compare with the value obtained graphically in Exp. 4?

Part II.   Change connections to make the circuit of Fig. 13.   (Do this with *all power off*, and have the circuit checked before putting power on again.)   Then measure g_m for plate-current values chosen to give approximately evenly spaced values of $I_p{}^{1/3}$.   For the type 6P5-G tube, values 1, 2, 4, 7, 10, and 15 ma are suggested.   Plot two curves: one with g_m as y, I_p as x; the other with g_m as y and the cube-root of I_p as x.   For a symmetrical triode such as the type 6P5-G tube, the second plot should be close to a straight line. Explain why this is so, and try to account for any discrepancies.

Part III. Compute r_p from the measured values of μ and g_m, and plot these values as y, with I_p as x. Obtain *graphically*, for the curves plotted in Exp. 4, corresponding values of r_p, and plot these values along with those computed for this experiment.* Discuss the agreement, or lack of it, between these two sets of values for r_p.

The circuits for this experiment must be connected up with very careful attention to the wiring and to the location of the various parts. Otherwise, capacitative or inductive couplings may make a good balance difficult if not impossible. Reread carefully the instructions for making circuits given in Appendix 1.

26. Experiment 6. Measurement of r_p. The procedure for this experiment is quite fully described in Sec. 22. The fixed resistor, r_3 in Fig. 11, may be about 5000 ohms, non-inductive, and rated at at least 5 watts. An inexpensive glass-inclosed ferrule type will serve if calibrated with an a-c bridge. Both r_1 and r_2 may be supplied by a well-made linear voltage-divider or "potentiometer" having a finely divided scale. A 20,000-ohm "Helipot" is excellent. The sliding contact is at A. A capacitance of 1 mf will do for C_3, and C_1 and C_2 may be inexpensive two-decade condenser boxes of 1.1-mf range. A plate-to-grid interstage transformer is best for $T2$. The connections from its secondary to the detector amplifier should be shielded, as indicated.

This experiment may be performed independently of Exp. 5, or it may be carried out with the same tube studied in Exp. 5, as a check on that experiment. When this is done, data should be taken over the same range of current values, with several different values of grid bias. Represent results with plots of $1/r_p$ as y, cube-root of I_p as x. In your report derive the balance equations, Eqs. 36 and 37.

The precautions discussed for Exp. 5 apply to this experiment as well.

27. Grid Current. In all discussions of triode circuits earlier in this chapter the assumption has been made that grid current is zero when the grid potential is negative. When the grid potential is negative the grid current is indeed very small; for the most part it is the

---

* Unless the same tube is available for both experiments it will be necessary to take data for a characteristic curve for the tube employed in Exp. 5, by the method of Exp. 4. Only one curve is needed, for the grid bias used in Exp. 5, and the data may be taken with the circuit of Fig. 13 (with a-c power off) if a d-c voltmeter, to measure V_p, is connected between point P and the negative terminal of the power pack.

electron current mentioned in Sec. 5, Chapter 1, which is maintained by electrons having enough thermal energy to reach the grid against the negative potential.   There may also be a small positive-ion current, which may arise from ionization of the residual gas in the tube, or occur as a flow of positive ions emitted from the cathode itself.   Usually these very small currents may be neglected unless the d-c resistance of the circuit connected between grid and cathode is very high.   If this impedance is too high (the safe value depends upon the individual tube) the grid potential will be unsteady or fluctuating.   Thus a "floating" grid, having no external connections, may acquire a relatively high negative potential by catching electrons having high thermal energies.   The negative potential a grid may attain in this manner is limited only by leakage current from grid to cathode, and simultaneous positive-ion current to the grid.   For most purposes, however, we may consider that a triode, when it is operated with negative grid potential, is a device in which current to the plate is controlled by almost purely electrostatic means.

When the grid potential is positive, the grid picks up a small share of the cathode current.   Since it is then necessary to supply power to the grid circuit this condition is avoided unless some considerable advantage may be gained.   Positive grid conditions are rarely found except in certain types of power amplifier circuits.

In addition to these electron and positive-ion currents to the grid there is also a *displacement* current when the grid potential includes an a-c component.   This displacement (condenser) current results from the capacitances between grid and cathode, grid and plate, and would exist even with the cathode cold.   It increases with frequency, and at very high frequencies it may become so large as to render the tube useless, as will be explained in Chapter 13.

PROBLEMS

1. The anode and cathode plates, P and K, in a field-tank apparatus are 24.0 cm apart, with the anode potential 125 volts.   Compute the electric field intensity in dynes per statcoulomb.

2. A grid of rods 6.0 mm in diameter, spaced 65 mm between centers, is placed in the field tank of Prob. 1, 15.0 cm from K, and connected electrically to K. The potential of P is 125 volts.   (a) Compute the geometric amplification factor for this arrangement.   (b) Compute the intensity of the electric field between G and P.   (c) Compute the field intensity between K and G.   Neglect the small correction to the grid-cathode distance mentioned in Sec. 6.

Solution: (a) From Eq. 3, $\mu_0 = 7.0$.   (b) $V_p = \frac{125}{300} = 0.42$ statvolt. $b = 24.0 - 15.0 = 9.0$ cm. $E = V_p/b = 0.42/9.0 = 47 \times 10^{-3}$ dyne/statcoulomb.   (c) Equivalent-diode potential $= V_p/\mu_0 = 125/7.0 = 18$ volts $= 60 \times 10^{-3}$ statvolt. $E = 60 \times 10^{-3}/15.0 = 4.0 \times 10^{-3}$ dyne/statcoulomb.

3. In a field tank the double probe is next to K. The amplitude of the oscilloscope pattern is 40 mm with the anode potential zero, and 20 volts a-c on the grid, and 30 mm with -5.0 volts on the grid and $+150$ volts on the anode. Compute μ_0. HINT: The deflection is proportional to the equivalent-diode potential.

4. A triode has plane-parallel electrodes 12.0 mm square and spaced 0.75 mm from cathode to grid, 0.80 mm from grid to anode. The grid mesh is such as to make μ_0 15.0. (a) Compute the field at the cathode with $V_g = -8.0$ volts, $V_p = 0$. (b) Compute the field when $V_p = 210$ volts, $V_g = -5.0$ volts. Neglect correction to grid-cathode distance.

5. (a) Compute the perveance of the equivalent diode for the triode described in Prob. 4. Neglect correction to grid-cathode spacing. Then write the equation for the electron current in the triode. (b) Compute from this equation values for I_p, g_m, and r_p for the conditions specified in Prob. 4b.

6. The amplification factor for a triode is 18.2, the internal bias is 0.42 volt, and the perveance of the equivalent diode is 480 microamperes/volt$^{3/2}$. (a) Write the equation for the equivalent-diode current, in terms of V_p and V_g. (b) Compute from this equation the values for I_p, g_m, and r_p when $V_g = -3.40$ volts, $V_p = +175$ volts.

7. The current in a triode is 11.8 ma with $V_g = -2.75$ volts and $V_p = 133$ volts. $\mu = 13.7$. If V_p is changed to 195 volts, to what must V_g change to keep the current constant?

8. (a) Find r_p graphically for a type 76 triode, for $I_p = 6.0$ ma and $V_g = 0$, -4.0, -8.0, and -12.0 volts. (b) Compute g_m for each value of V_g. Characteristic curves are given in Appendix 5.

9. For a certain triode, μ is given as 8.00 and g_m as 4700 μ-mhos (micromhos) with $I_p = 40$ ma. Compute g_m at 5.0 ma and at 80 ma, from the relationship given in Sec. 14. Compute r_p for each of these current values.

10. For a certain triode $\mu = 9.5$ and $g_m = 1250$ μ-mhos when $I_p = 5.75$ ma. $V_g = -5.20$ volts, $V_p = 115$ volts. Compute the change in current (a) when V_g changes to -4.80 volts, with V_p unchanged; (b) when V_g is held at -5.20 volts and V_p changes to 110 volts; and (c) when both these changes occur together.

11. For a certain triode $\mu = 24.0$ and $r_p = 15,000$ ohms when $I_p = 3.20$ ma. I_p changes to 3.00 ma when V_g changes from -2.70 volts to -2.55 volts. Compute the change in V_p which must occur at the same time.

12. (a) Compute r_p graphically for a type 76 triode, for $I_p = 6.0$ ma, $V_g = -6.0$ volts. (b) Compute the change in V_p caused by an increase of I_p to 9.0 ma, and by a decrease to 3.0 ma, with V_g held constant. Do this first by the small-variations equation, then read the values from the plots. Note the errors introduced when the equation is used for such large variations. Characteristic curves are given in Appendix 5.

13. For the circuit of Fig. 8 take $\mu = 25.0$, $r_p = 20.8$ K, and $R = 85$ K.* A small change in V_g causes I_p to change by 0.170 ma. (a) Compute the change this makes in V_p. (b) Then compute, from the small-variations equation, the change in V_g required.

14. Solve Prob. 13 by means of the equivalent variational circuit.

Solution: The total resistance of the equivalent circuit is 85 K + 20.8 K = 105.8 K. The emf = 0.170 ma $\times$ 105.8 K = 18.0 volts = μe. Hence $e = 18.0$ volts/25.0 = 0.72 volt.

* The letter K is a symbol standing for 1000 ohms. Thus 85 K means 85,000 ohms.

15. In the circuit of Fig. 8 take $\mu = 13.8$, $g_m = 1900$ μ-mhos, and $R = 14.0$ K. Diagram the equivalent circuit and compute (a) the change in I_p, (b) the change in V_p, when $e = +0.355$ volt.

16. The circuit of Fig. 8 is set up with $E_c = -3.0$ volts, $E_b = 200$ volts, and $I_0 = 5.25$ ma. For the triode, $\mu = 16.0$ and $g_m = 1900$ μ-mhos at $I_p = 9.5$ ma. The characteristic curves give $V_p = 124$ volts with the conditions specified. (a) Compute the value for R. (b) Compute the approximate value for g_m at this current. (c) Diagram the equivalent circuit and compute the a-c component of I_p when e, Fig. 8, is 0.85 volt.

Solution: (a) The potential drop across R is $200 - 124$ or 76 volts. Hence $R = 76$ volts/5.25 ma $= 14.5$ K. (b) $g_m = 1900(5.25/9.5)^{1/3} = 1560$ μ-mhos, from Eq. 24. $r_p = \mu/g_m = 10.3$ K. (c) In the equivalent circuit, the emf $= \mu e = 16.0 \times 0.85 = 13.6$ volts. The total series resistance $= 10.3 + 14.5 = 24.8$ K. Hence $i_p = 13.6$ volts/24.8 K $= 0.55$ ma. (d) $e_p = -i_p R = -0.55$ ma $\times 14.5$ K $= -8.0$ volts. The minus sign here indicates that e_p is 180 degrees out of phase with e.

17. The circuit of Fig. 8 is made up with a triode for which the following data are given: $V_p = 250$ volts, $V_g = -8.0$ volts, $I_p = 8.0$ ma, $\mu = 20.0$, $g_m = 2000$ μ-mhos. It is operated with $I_0 = 4.0$ ma, $E_c = -4.0$ volts, and $R = 44$ K. The characteristic curves show that $V_p = 125$ volts for these conditions. (a) Compute the value of E_b required. (b) Compute g_m and r_p for the operating conditions. (c) Diagram the equivalent circuit and compute the value of e which will produce an a-c component of 0.78 ma. (d) Compute the a-c component of V_p.

18. In the circuit of Fig. 10a, $R_1 = 75$ K, $R_2 = 135$ K, and $C = 0.50$ μf. For the triode, $\mu = 12.5$, $g_m = 1750$ μ-mhos, $E_c = -4.50$ volts, $V_p = 85$ volts d-c, and $I_0 = 2.35$ ma. The a-c component of V_p is -11.8 volts, at 1000 cps. (a) Compute E_b. (b) Diagram the equivalent a-c circuit and compute the alternating currents in R_1, R_2, and in the triode. (c) Compute e.

Solution: (a) The direct current in R_1 is 2.35 ma, in R_2, zero. Hence $E_b = 85$ volts $+ 2.35$ ma $\times 75$ K $= 261$ volts. (b) The alternating current in R_1 is $i_1 = 11.8$ volts/75 K $= 0.118$ ma. The reactance of C at 1000 cps is 320 ohms, and negligible in comparison with R_2. Hence $i_2 = 11.8/135 = 0.087$ ma. In the triode, $i_p = i_1 + i_2 = 0.205$ ma. $r_p = \mu/g_m = 71.5$ K. The equivalent emf $= \mu e = 11.8$ volts $+ 0.205$ ma $\times 71.5$ K $= 26.5$ volts, and $e = 2.12$ volts. Note that e_p and e are opposite in sign, or 180 degrees out of phase.

19. In the circuit of Fig. 10a, $R_1 = 4.20$ K, $R_2 = 50.0$ K, $C = 0.20$ μf. For the triode, $\mu = 9.5$, $g_m = 2400$ μ-mhos, $I_0 = 8.2$ ma, $E_c = -7.50$ volts, and $E_b = 450$ volts. (a) Compute the d-c potential at P. (b) Compute the value of e required to produce alternating current in R_2 of 0.135 ma at 1000 cps.

20. Prove that, for a triode which has characteristics in accord with Child's law,

$$\frac{3}{2} I_p = g_m \left(V_g + \frac{V_p}{\mu} + V_i \right) \qquad (43)$$

CHAPTER 3

Triode Amplifiers

1. Introduction. In many applications an electronic triode functions as a device in which an *emf* introduced into one circuit controls *current* in a second circuit which is otherwise quite independent of the first. This emf, which is generally alternating, will hereafter be referred to as the "signal," signal voltage, or input voltage. The first circuit is the grid circuit, in which the signal is superimposed upon the steady bias potential. The current controlled is in the plate circuit, and may conveniently be regarded as the *change* in plate current which occurs when the signal acts in the grid circuit. If the plate-current changes are large enough to be comparable with the steady current when the signal is zero, graphical methods are necessary to predict or analyze the performance of the circuits. Such high-output circuits will be considered in Chapter 4. In this chapter we shall limit attention to low-output circuits, in which current changes are so small that the portions of the triode characteristics involved are approximately straight lines, and μ, g_m, and r_p are practically constants. Within these limitations it is possible to represent a triode circuit by an approximately equivalent *linear* circuit, as has been explained in Sec. 20, Chapter 2.

2. Voltage Amplifiers. Let us consider in this manner the triode circuit of Fig. 1a, and its equivalent a-c circuit, Fig. 1b. The signal is e, the change of current is i_p, superimposed upon the steady current, I_0. From the equivalent circuit we may obtain for i_p the value

$$i_p = \mu e/(r_p + R) \tag{1}$$

In the equivalent circuit the point P has a potential $-i_p R$ if the current is in the direction indicated. In the actual circuit the point P has the same *change* in potential, superimposed upon the steady value $(E_b - I_0 R)$. This incremental or a-c value we shall call the output voltage, and represent by e_0.

$$e_0 = -i_p R = -\mu e R/(r_p + R) \tag{2}$$

Ordinarily e_0 is greater than e in magnitude; in other respects it is an exact replica of e, for the small a-c values here considered. We say that the circuit has *amplified* the signal, e, and the *gain* of such an amplifier circuit is represented by A and defined as

$$A = e_0/e \qquad (3)$$

For the circuit of Fig. 1 the gain is evidently

$$A = -\mu R/(r_p + R) \qquad (4)$$

The *phase reversal* which is represented by the minus sign must *never* be overlooked; both the gain *and* this phase reversal are fundamental characteristics of all voltage amplifier circuits.

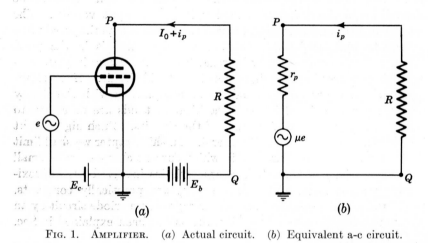

Fig. 1. Amplifier. (a) Actual circuit. (b) Equivalent a-c circuit.

3. A-C Isolation. The simple resistance "load," R, of Fig. 1 may be replaced by many other types of impedances. In any case the gain may be found by first diagramming the equivalent a-c circuit, then solving it for the a-c plate current, i_p, and the output voltage, e_0. One important need for a more complex load impedance is to separate or isolate the a-c output from the d-c potential at the plate of the triode. Figure 2a shows one way this may be done. It is evident that the d-c potential is zero at the point S, Fig. 2a, but that the a-c potential, e_0, is $-i_2R_2$. If the reactance of the condenser, C, is negligible in comparison with R_2 the points S and P have essentially the same a-c potential and C may be omitted from Fig. 2b. Figure 2b then becomes a simple resistive circuit, with R_1 and R_2 in parallel. At low enough frequencies X_C, the reactance of C, is always appreciable and must be considered in the solution for e_0.

When X_C must be included it is usually more practical to assume numerical values before proceeding with the solution for circuit gain. For example, let us consider the following data for Fig. 2b. $\mu = 15$, $r_p = 15$ K, $R_2 = 100$ K, $R_1 = 50$ K, $X_C = -20$ K. (The symbol K stands for 1000 ohms.) It is now easier to start with e_0 and work back to e. That is,

$$i_2 = -e_0/R_2 = -e_0/100 \text{ ma}$$

$$e_p \text{ (at } P) = -i_2(R_2 + X_C) = e_0(1.00 - j0.20) \text{ volts}$$

$$i_1 = -e_p/R_1 = -e_0(1.00 - j0.20)/50 \text{ ma}$$

$$-\mu e = e_p - r_p(i_1 + i_2) = e_0(1.45 - j0.26) \text{ volts}$$

$$= 1.47e_0\underline{/-10.4°} \text{ volts}$$

$$-e = e_0(0.097 - j0.017) \text{ volts} = 0.098e_0\underline{/-10.4°} \text{ volts}$$

Hence

$$A = e_0/e = -10.2\underline{/+10.4°} = 10.2\underline{/-169.6°}$$

When X_C is negligible the value of A is -10.3 for the same circuit values.

As this computation shows, the effect of reactance is to reduce the magnitude of e_0 and to change its phase relative to e. This is repre-

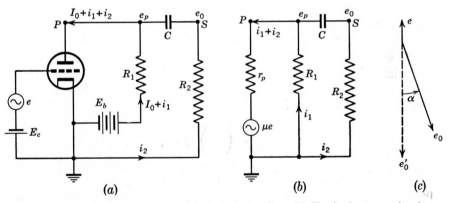

FIG. 2. VOLTAGE AMPLIFIER. (a) Actual circuit. (b) Equivalent a-c circuit.

sented by the vector diagram of Fig. 2c, in which e_0 represents the exact output, and e_0' the output computed by neglecting the reactance, X_C. The phase shift, α, introduced by the reactance must be measured from the vector representing e_0'; that is, it must be added algebraically to the phase *reversal* which is always present. This is illustrated in the example above. As seen also in this example, an appreciable phase shift is produced before any great change in magnitude appears. For this reason it is possible to obtain reasonably good values for the magnitude of the gain, A, without considering X_C, even when the magnitude of X_C is not negligible in comparison with R_2.

4. Transformer Output. The d-c potential at the triode plate may be eliminated from the output also by means of a transformer, as shown in Fig. 3a. The equivalent a-c circuit is given in Fig. 3b. According to a-c circuit theory an ideal transformer (one having no leakage flux and no losses) may be represented by an inductance, L_m, Fig. 3b, in parallel with a resistance, R_2'. The value of L_m is the inductance of the transformer at its primary terminals, with the

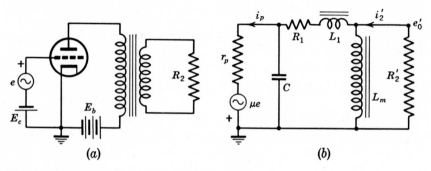

Fig. 3. Amplifier, Transformer Output. (a) Actual circuit. (b) Schematic equivalent circuit.

secondary circuit open, and the value of R_2' is determined by the load resistance, R_2, Fig. 3a, and N_1/N_2, the ratio of turns in the primary and secondary windings. That is,

$$R_2' = \left(\frac{N_1}{N_2}\right)^2 R_2 \tag{5}$$

When the transformer coils have appreciable resistance, that of the primary is represented by R_1, and that of the secondary is added to R_2. Leakage flux and coil capacitance are represented by the small inductance, L_1, and the small capacitance, C, respectively. A good transformer is represented fairly well by L_m alone. For best results with transformer coupling R_2' should be so much smaller than the reactance of L_m that the current in L_m is negligible in comparison with i_2' in R_2'. Then L_m may be left out of the equivalent circuit, which thus becomes a simple series circuit with gain A_0' given by

$$A_0' = \frac{e_0'}{e} = -\frac{\mu R_2'}{R_2' + r_p} \tag{6}$$

For the circuit of Fig. 3a the gain, under these conditions, at the terminals of the transformer secondary is evidently

$$A_0 = \frac{e_0}{e} = \frac{N_2}{N_1}\frac{e_0'}{e} = \frac{N_2}{N_1}A_0' \tag{7}$$

At low frequencies the current in L_m is not negligible and causes the gain to decrease toward zero as the frequency falls. At high frequencies the current in C and the voltage drop across L_1 both become appreciable, and both cause the gain to drop as the frequency increases.

When i_m, the current in L_m, is not negligible the circuit may be analyzed as follows. First it must be noted, in Fig. 3b, that e_0' is opposite in sign to μe and to the currents, and that i_m lags in phase 90 degrees behind i_2'. In complex-number notation we then may write

$$i_p = i_2' + i_m = -\frac{e_0'}{R_2'} + \frac{je_0'}{L_m\omega} \tag{8}$$

and

$$\mu e = -e_0' + i_p r_p = -e_0' - \frac{e_0'r_p}{R_2'} + j\frac{e_0'r_p}{L_m\omega} \tag{9}$$

If A' represents e_0'/e, the gain under these conditions,

$$\frac{1}{A'} = -\frac{R_2' + r_p}{\mu R_2'} + j\frac{r_p}{\mu L_m\omega} \tag{10}$$

or

$$\frac{1}{A'} = \frac{1}{A_0} + j\frac{r_p}{\mu L_m\omega} \tag{10a}$$

The magnitude of A' is given by

$$\left(\frac{1}{A'}\right)^2 = \left(\frac{1}{A_0}\right)^2 + \left(\frac{r_p}{\mu L_m\omega}\right)^2 \tag{11}$$

For output at the terminals of the secondary of the transformer, in Fig. 3a, the gain is evidently A' multiplied by N_2/N_1.

5. Experiment 7. Voltage Amplifier. The common method for determining the gain of an amplifier is to take the ratio of experimentally measured values of e_0 and e. The output, e_0, may be measured with a vacuum-tube voltmeter. The signal, e, is obtained from a calibrated voltage-divider or attenuator. For high precision, the calibration of the voltage-divider should be checked with the voltmeter used to measure e_0. Figure 4 shows a circuit for measuring the gain of an amplifier of the type represented in Fig. 2. Specifications below are given for a type 6P5-G or type 76 triode. They may be modified to suit other tubes.

The signal is supplied from a fixed resistor, g-h, Fig. 4, in series with a voltage-divider, h-k, a variable resistor, R_3, and an a-c source of 5 or 6 volts at 500 to 2000 cps. The fixed resistor must be of good quality (good to $\frac{1}{2}$ percent or better); a suitable value for its resistance, r_1, is 500 ohms. The voltage-divider may be any good wire-wound "potentiometer" with a precisely graduated scale; it should be calibrated to read ohms (or multiples of r_1). An overall resistance for h-k of about 15 times r_1 will serve with the 6P5-G tube. The sliding contact on h-k is adjusted to some resistance value, r_2, such that the

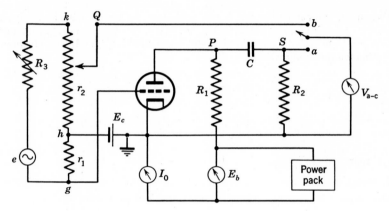

FIG. 4.   VOLTAGE-AMPLIFIER CIRCUIT FOR EXP. 7.

potential of the point Q equals e_0. The gain, A, then equals the ratio of r_2 to r_1. Since both e_0 and the potential at Q are read with the same meter, at the same point on its scale, this meter does not need to be calibrated. Its full-scale range should be 5 volts or less.

Part I. This method is applicable to any amplifier. In this experiment we shall apply it to the one diagrammed in Fig. 4, for various combinations of values for the resistors R_1 and R_2. Ordinary "radio" resistors will serve here, and it is convenient to mount the resistors needed on a board with binding-posts, along with the condenser, C. The value of C should be large enough to make its reactance less than 5 percent of the smallest resistance value for R_2. The following resistance values are suitable.

Case	i	ii	iii
R_1	50 K	100 K	100 K
R_2	250 K	250 K	500 K

These are nominal values: measure the exact values, or obtain them from the instructor. Hold the d-c voltmeter reading at 250 volts for all three cases, and each time read the plate-current value. Likewise keep the grid bias constant, at about 3 volts.

For each case first switch the a-c voltmeter to point a and adjust R_3 to give some fairly large reading of the a-c voltmeter. Then switch to point b and adjust the value of r_2 to give the same reading. Check back to point a to make sure. Compute the gain from these data. Check this value with a second, slightly different, voltmeter reading.

Part II. When these data have been taken, take data for a triode characteristic curve for this tube. The circuit is quickly modified for this purpose by turning off the a-c power, reducing the d-c supply voltage to zero, and shorting out resistor R_1. Leaving the grid bias the same as for Part I, take data for plate-current values from zero to several milliamperes above the highest value observed in Part I. From this characteristic curve obtain values of r_p for each current value used in Part I, by the graphical method described in Sec. 11 of Chapter 2. With these values then compute the gain to be expected from the equivalent a-c circuit. Diagram the equivalent circuit and derive the necessary equations. Include the a-c voltmeter resistance as a part of the load. (If you have not measured μ for this tube, take the value given in Appendix 5.)

Present all data in a carefully planned table, and include percent discrepancies between measured and computed values of gain. Analyze the results for sources of error.

6. Experiment 8. Frequency Characteristics for a Voltage Amplifier.

Part I. If an audiofrequency signal generator is available, Exp. 7 may be repeated for a wide range of frequency values. (The customary range is from 20 to 20,000 cps.) The value of C, Fig. 4, should be low enough to reduce the gain at the lowest frequency to a small fraction of its high-frequency value. For a 6P5-G or 76 triode the following values are suggested: $R_1 = 50$ K, $R_2 = 100$ K, and $C = 0.020$ μf. The results of such measurements should be presented as a plot of gain, A, as ordinates with the logarithm of frequency as abscissae. The experimentally measured values may be checked at several frequencies by computation from the equivalent circuit, following the example given in Sec. 3.

Part II. Experiment 7 does not provide any means for measuring phase angle, but this defect may be corrected by adding to the circuit of Fig. 4 a cathode-ray oscilloscope, with its x and y deflection terminals connected to points Q and S respectively. When the circuit has been adjusted as described in Exp. 7 the alternating potentials at Q and S have the same magnitude, and the oscilloscope may be adjusted so that they produce deflections of equal amplitude. If the phase shifts produced by the tube capacitances and C are negligible and the x and y amplitudes are equal, the pattern on the oscilloscope screen will be a diagonal straight line at an angle of 45 degrees with the horizontal, as shown in Fig. 5a.   In general the pattern on the screen is an ellipse, as in Fig. 5b.   The phase angle, α, now may be determined

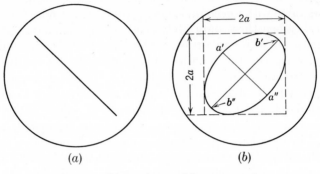

$$(a)\qquad\qquad\qquad\qquad (b)$$

Fig. 5.   Phase-Angle Measurement.

(a) 180° phase difference.   (b) $\tan \dfrac{\alpha}{2} = \dfrac{a'a''}{b'b''}$.

from $a'a''$ and $b'b''$, the lengths of the principal axes of the ellipse. When the x and y deflections are of equal amplitude,

$$\tan \frac{\alpha}{2} = \frac{a'a''}{b'b''} \tag{12}$$

Proof for Eq. 11.   We may write, for x and y,

$$x = a \cos (\omega t - \alpha/2)$$
$$= a \cos \omega t \cos \alpha/2 + a \sin \omega t \sin \alpha/2$$
$$y = a \cos (\omega t + \alpha/2)$$
$$= a \cos \omega t \cos \alpha/2 - a \sin \omega t \sin \alpha/2$$

Now rotate the axes through 45 degrees: the new coordinates are

$$x' = \sqrt{\tfrac{1}{2}}(x + y) = a \sqrt{2} \cos \omega t \cos \alpha/2$$
$$y' = \sqrt{\tfrac{1}{2}}(x - y) = a \sqrt{2} \sin \omega t \sin \alpha/2$$

From these equations it follows that

$$\sin^2 \omega t + \cos^2 \omega t = 1 = \frac{x'^2}{2a^2 \cos^2 \alpha/2} + \frac{y'^2}{2a^2 \sin^2 \alpha/2}$$

This is the equation of an ellipse whose major axes are proportional to $\cos \alpha/2$ and $\sin \alpha/2$ respectively.   Equation 11 then follows.

This method is perhaps the simplest and most precise one for measuring the phase angle between two sinusoidal voltages.

These phase-angle data should be taken along with the amplitude data of Part I. Represent the results by plotting α as ordinates, $\log f$ as abscissae. Check the results at the low-frequency end against the values computed from the equivalent a-c circuit.

7. Demonstration Experiment 1.   Experiment 8 may be performed qualitatively in the lecture; it makes an excellent demonstration experiment.

8. Self-Bias.   In all circuits already considered here the grid bias is produced by a small battery, called the C-battery. Unfortunately, C-batteries deteriorate and must be renewed.   In addition, the available values of grid bias with batteries are practically limited to multiples of the emf of a single cell, and such values are not always suitable.   For these and other reasons it is now almost universal practice in small amplifiers to replace C-batteries with the cathode resistor and condenser combination which is illustrated in Fig. 6.   In

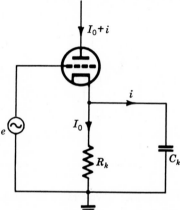

FIG. 6.   SELF-BIAS.

this arrangement the d-c grid potential is zero ("ground" potential), whereas the cathode is at a steady *positive* potential relative to the ground, of value equal to the product of I_0, the d-c component of the cathode current, and the resistance of R_k, a resistor connected between the cathode and the ground.   The a-c component of the cathode current is by-passed by the condenser, C_k, which offers to it a very small impedance at all but the lowest frequencies.   Indeed, if C_k is large enough the alternating potential drop across it will be negligible and the cathode will be effectively at zero potential in so far as a-c components are concerned, except for the lowest frequencies.

We shall continue to follow the custom of referring the potential of all electrodes to that of the cathode, even when the cathode potential is not ground potential.   Thus, in Fig. 8 the potential of the plate, P, equals the difference in potential between P and K, and the potential of the grid, G, is the potential difference between G and K, or $-I_0 R_k$ plus e.

When the capacitance, C_k, is too small, or the frequency too low, so that the reactance of C_k is not negligible, the a-c potential which then appears between K and the ground is in series-opposition with the signal, e. The alternating potential of the grid (relative to the cathode) is then reduced by this amount, the output is likewise reduced, and the effective gain is lowered. This is an example of negative feedback, a topic which will be studied systematically in Chapter 6.

9. Cascade (Multistage) Amplifiers. Greater amplification may be obtained by connecting the point S, Fig. 2, to the grid of a second amplifier tube, as in Fig. 7, thus producing a two-stage amplifier. If

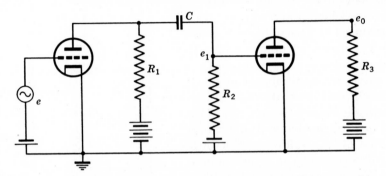

FIG. 7.   TWO-STAGE AMPLIFIER.   Separate B-batteries and battery bias.

the final output voltage is e_0, and the output of the first stage is e_1 when the signal is e, the separate gains for the two stages are

$$A_1 = e_1/e \qquad \text{and} \qquad A_2 = e_0/e_1 \tag{13}$$

The overall gain is then

$$A = e_0/e = A_1 A_2 \tag{14}$$

A multistage or cascade amplifier is made by thus connecting together two or more *stages* (single-tube amplifiers) of any type. For an ideal cascade amplifier it is possible to compute the overall gain by multiplying together the gains computed separately for each stage, as in the example above. A well-designed amplifier, having each stage supplied by its own batteries and very carefully shielded from its neighbors, comes close to being an ideal amplifier in this respect. The input to the following grid is the only interaction factor of any importance, and this may be included as a part of the load for each stage. Thus the equivalent a-c circuit for the first stage in Fig. 7 would include C and R_2, as represented in Fig. 2b.

Most a-c amplifiers are "self-biased" (see Sec. 8) and have a common d-c source for all plate power, as shown in Fig. 8. Such amplifiers are limited to two or three stages, even when well shielded and care-fully designed.   If more stages are added the interaction or "feed-back" among stages which is always present to some degree tends to cause trouble, as will be explained in Chapter 6.

10. Phase Shift in Cascade Amplifiers.   Consider the amplifier of Fig. 7, operated at a frequency for which the reactance of C may be neglected.   When the signal, e, is positive the plate current in the first tube increases and the plate potential drops; in other words e_1, the output from that stage, is negative, as was emphasized in Sec. 2.

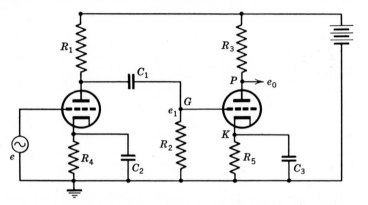

FIG. 8.   TWO-STAGE AMPLIFIER.   Common battery and self-bias.

A similar phase reversal takes place in the second stage so that, when e is positive, e_0 is positive also.   The phase reversal which is produced in each stage of a cascade amplifier in which the reactances may be neglected is represented by a minus sign in the value for the gain of that stage, and the phase of the final output, relative to the signal, is determined by the product of these minus signs.   For an odd number of stages the output is reversed in phase; for an even number it is not.

Additional phase shifts are introduced whenever the reactances in an amplifier circuit may not be neglected, as explained in Secs. 3 and 4.   Such phase changes are computed for each stage separately, then the total phase shift is found by adding their sum to the overall effect of phase *reversal*.   For example, the gains for each stage of a three-stage amplifier might be -12.5, -18.0, and -8.2 respectively, with corresponding phase shifts of $+15°$, $+20°$, and $+4°$.   The overall gain is then -1840, with $+39°$ phase shift.   This result may also be expressed as $+1840$ with $-180° + 39°$, or $-141°$ phase shift.   A very concise representation for this result is

$$A = -1840 \underline{/39°} \qquad \text{or} \qquad A = +1840 \underline{/-141°}$$

It is often convenient to express gain for an amplifier with complex numbers. For the example cited:

$$A_1 = -12.5\epsilon^{j15°} \qquad A_2 = -18.0\epsilon^{j20°} \qquad A_3 = -8.2\epsilon^{j4°}$$

and
$$A = A_1 A_2 A_3 = -1840\epsilon^{j39°}$$

11. Decibel. It is common practice to express amplifier gain in terms of the common (base 10) logarithm of A, multiplied by 20. This quantity is called the gain in decibels, or db.

$$\text{db gain} = 20 \log_{10} A \qquad (15)$$

It is evident that the overall db gain for a cascade amplifier equals the *sum* of the db gains for each stage, and herein lies the greatest advantage of this mode of representing gain.

The reason for the factor 20 is interesting. The decibel unit was invented to measure *power* ratio for losses in telephone cables, to replace an earlier unit representing the power loss in one mile of standard cable. The common logarithm of the ratio of power in to power out for any device is by definition the power loss in *bels*. Since $\frac{1}{10}$ bel, or 1 *decibel*, is nearer to the earlier unit in size, the decibel is the practical unit. Power loss (or gain) in db equals 10 times the common logarithm of the power loss (or gain) ratio. The decibel was later extended to voltage ratio. Since power is proportional to voltage squared (other things being equal) the factor for voltage gain became 20.

12. Experiment 9. Cascade Amplifier. Gain and phase shift for a cascade amplifier may be measured experimentally with the equipment which served for a single stage, in Exp. 8. It will be necessary, of course, to make r_1 much smaller in value, but the procedure is the same. If the point at which e_0 is measured has d-c potential it will be necessary to put a blocking condenser between it and the voltmeter terminal unless, as frequently happens, such a condenser is a part of the voltmeter. It is suggested that the circuit studied be a fairly simple two-stage amplifier, similar to Fig. 7, so that the experimental values for A and α may be checked by computation from the tube data and circuit constants. Measure A and α for as wide a frequency range as possible. Plot db gain and α as ordinates with $\log f$ as abscissae. Compute several values for A and α as suggested above and plot them along with the experimental values, for comparison.

Repeat measurements with the circuit modified so that both tubes are supplied from the same power supply, as shown in Fig. 8. (If the results do not differ greatly from the first set, try putting several thousand ohms in series with the d-c source, to simulate a stale battery or a poor power supply.)

One precaution must be observed in measuring phase angle for a cascade amplifier. It is very unlikely that the phase angle for a single stage will exceed 90 degrees before the gain is almost zero. With several stages, however, the phase angle may be greater and then difficulty may be met in interpreting phase from the oscilloscope pattern: e.g., the same pattern may represent 65 degrees or (180 + 65) degrees. To resolve this difficulty, vary the frequency slowly enough to keep track of the phase angle as it shifts away from zero.

13. Demonstration Experiment 2. Experiment 9 makes an excellent demonstration experiment. The approximate gain may be

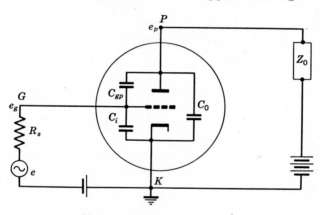

FIG. 9.   TUBE CAPACITANCES.

measured with the oscilloscope, by balancing the circuit to obtain equal horizontal and vertical deflections. It is interesting to study the performance of a commercial audio amplifier in this manner.

14. Grid Input Impedance. When the a-c signal is supplied from a high-impedance source it is necessary to consider the grid input impedance, that is, the impedance between grid and cathode within the tube. As has been stated in Sec. 27, Chapter 2, this input impedance is primarily due to tube capacitances, since electron current to the grid is quite negligible in most a-c amplifiers. If we assume that the cathode is always at ground potential these tube capacitances are equivalent to the three represented in Fig. 9. The input capacitance, C_i, consists of the capacitance between grid and cathode within the tube, plus the capacitance to ground from the grid leads, mostly within the base of the tube. The output capacitance, C_0, represents similarly the capacitance within the tube between plate and cathode, plus lead capacitance. It is interesting to note that C_0 would equal C_i/μ_0 if lead capacitances could be eliminated, since the *shielding* effect of the grid reduces this capacitance in exactly the same way that it reduces the influence of the plate potential upon the electron stream. In UHF (ultra-high-frequency) tubes, where it is required that tube capacitances be as small as possible, the grid and plate leads are brought out through the walls of the tube, well away from all other leads.

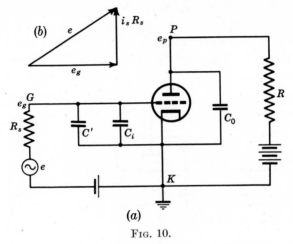

FIG. 10.

The most troublesome tube capacitance is that from grid to plate, C_{gp} in Fig. 9. It is comparable with C_i in magnitude, but has far greater effect upon the grid input impedance because the alternating potential difference across it is relatively large. Consider an amplifier circuit having a pure resistive load, as in Fig. 1. For this circuit the a-c potential difference across C_i equals e_g, whereas the potential difference across C_{gp}, from G to P, equals $e_g - e_p$, or $e_g - Ae_g$. It must now be remembered that the gain, A, for this amplifier is *intrinsically negative*, so that $-A$ is positive. Let us now write A' for $-A$. Then

$$e_g - e_p = (1 + A')e_g \tag{16}$$

In Fig. 10a the capacitance C', connected between G and K, replaces C_{gp}, which is connected between G and P in Fig. 9. If now this circuit is to be the equivalent of Fig. 9, for resistive loads, the electric charge flowing in and out of C' must be the same as for C_{gp} in Fig. 9, and this will be so if

$$C'e_g = C_{gp}(e_g - e_p) = C_{gp}(1 + A')e_g \tag{17}$$

or

$$C' = (1 + A')C_{gp} \tag{18}$$

This equivalent capacitance, C', is usually called the "Miller" capacitance.

The current i_s, in C_i and C_{gp}, causes a potential drop in the source impedance, represented by R_s in Fig. 10a, so that e_g is less than the signal, e. The value of i may be computed from C_i and C'; its magnitude is $\omega(C_i + C')e_g$ and it leads e_g in phase by 90 degrees. In Fig. 10b, e_g, e, and the potential drop, i_sR_s, are represented vectorially,

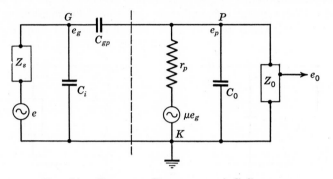

FIG. 11.   COMPLETE EQUIVALENT A-C CIRCUIT.

to show how e is greater than e_g. In complex number notation this same relationship is represented as

$$e = e_g + i_sR_s = e_g + j\omega(C_i + C')e_g$$

or
$$e/e_g = 1 + j\omega(C_i + C') \tag{19}$$

As an example consider a type 6J5 triode, for which the following data are given: $C_i = 3.4$ $\mu\mu$f, $C_0 = 3.5$ $\mu\mu$f, and $C_{gp} = 3.4$ $\mu\mu$f. (1 $\mu\mu$f $= 10^{-6}$ microfarad.) For this tube μ is 20, and A may easily have a value -14. From Eq. 18 the value of C' is then $(1 + 14)3.4$ $\mu\mu$f, or 51 $\mu\mu$f. For a frequency of 10,000 cps, which is still within the audible range, and for a source impedance of 0.25 megohm, the magnitudes for i_s, i_gR_s, and e for this example would be

$$|i|_s = 2\pi\ 10,000(3.4 + 51) \times 10^{-6}e_g = 3.4e_g \text{ microamperes}$$

$$|i_sR_s| = 3.4 \times 0.25e_g = 0.85e_g \text{ volt}$$

$$|e| = \sqrt{(e_g{}^2 + i_g{}^2R_s{}^2)} = 1.32e_g \text{ volts}$$

The magnitude of the gain is reduced from 14 to 14/1.32 or 10.6.

Because of tube capacitances the gain of an amplifier of this type thus falls off at the high-frequency end of its range. At very high frequencies the net "gain" may become less than unity.

15. Complete Equivalent A-C Circuit. When tube capacitances must be included in the equivalent a-c circuit for a triode this circuit appears as represented in Fig. 11. Since C_0 may be included in the output impedance, Z_0, this circuit reduces to three meshes and may be solved by usual circuit methods. It is necessary, of course, to express all impedances in complex form. Fortunately the current in the part of this circuit to the right of the dotted line is very often much larger than the currents elsewhere; then this circuit may be solved in two simple steps which are diagrammed in Fig. 12. Step one is solution of the circuit of Fig. 12*b*, which is the part of Fig. 11 to the right of the dotted line, and neglects all tube capacitances except C_0, which is included in Z_0'. From this solution e_g is found in terms of e_p. It is now *assumed* that the potential of P is not changed by reconnecting the

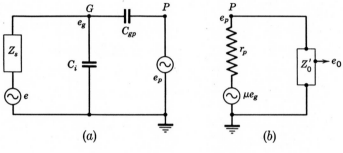

FIG. 12.　ANALYSIS OF FIG. 11.

left-hand part of Fig. 11. This is an *approximation* which is represented in Fig. 12*a* by replacing the right-hand part of Fig. 11 by the emf, e_p. In Fig. 12*a* the currents in C_i and C_{gp} may be computed directly, since the potentials at all their terminals are known. Then the current, i_s, in the input impedance, Z_s, is the sum of these condenser currents, so that the value of e may be computed by adding $i_s R_s$ and e_g.

If the output impedance, Z_0, may be considered a pure resistance the effect of C_{gp} may be represented by a "Miller" capacitance in parallel with C_i, as has been explained in Sec. 14, but this simple equivalence does not exist when Z_0 includes reactance of appreciable magnitude. Then the phase angle between e_p and e_g will not be 180 degrees, and consequently the current in C_{gp} will have a component in phase with e_g as well as one out of phase by 90 degrees. If we now wish to represent C_{gp} in an equivalent circuit by an impedance between grid and ground it must include both a capacitance and a resistance in parallel with C_i. The capacitance is a modified "Miller" capacitance and depends upon the current component which is out of phase with e_g, as explained in Sec. 13. If the reactance in the plate circuit is capacitative an ordinary positive resistance is required, but if the plate circuit is inductive the impedance corresponding to in-phase current must be a *negative* resistance, representing positive power feedback from the plate circuit to the grid circuit. When the input impedance, Z_s, is also inductive it is possible for this feedback to set up oscillation in the circuit under certain circumstances. Here again we encroach upon topics which will be considered more fully in later chapters.

16. Cascade-Amplifier Analysis.* A systematic analysis for a cascade amplifier may now be described. Let there be n stages. The

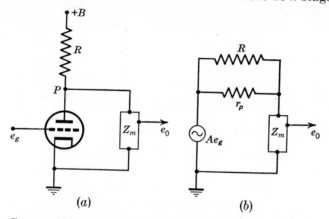

Fig. 13. Cascade Amplifier Analysis. (a) One stage. (b) A-C equivalent of (a).

analysis begins with the output and works back to the input; the advantages of this procedure have been demonstrated in several earlier examples. The nth or last stage may be analyzed by any suitable method, either one of the equivalent circuit methods of this chapter or one of the graphical methods of Chapter 4. This analysis should go from the input at the grid of this stage to the final output, and will give its gain, A_n.

Now consider the next stage back. We may represent this stage schematically as in Fig. 13a, with R the load resistance and Z_m the three-terminal impedance network between this stage and the one following. In Z_m we shall now include the output capacitance, C_0, for the tube in this stage, plus the total grid input circuit of the following tube, including the part due to C_{gp} which is described in Secs. 14 and 15. (At this point the advantage of working backward becomes apparent: the effect of C_{gp} upon Z_m cannot be computed unless the gain of the following stage is known.) To analyze this stage let us

---

* This section is more advanced than the rest of this chapter. It may be omitted, or postponed until later, without loss of context.

first disconnect Z_m, leaving only R and a tube from which all capacitance has been removed. The gain for this unit is evidently a *real* number, A, equal to $-\mu R/(R + r_p)$.

The effect of reconnecting Z_m now may be cared for with Thévenin's theorem. According to this theorem we may replace the tube part of the circuit by an a-c source having an emf equal to Ae_g, the a-c potential at P before Z_m is reconnected, and having an internal resistance equal to that of R and r_p in parallel. See Fig. 13b. The output for this circuit will be the input at the grid of the following tube. The

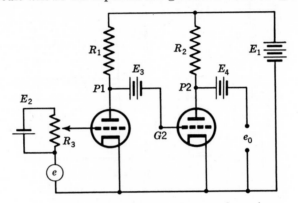

FIG. 14.   D-C AMPLIFIER.   Separate batteries.

ratio between output and input for the circuit of Fig. 13b may be represented by D. In general D is a complex number.

For each intermediate stage, including the first stage, a similar analysis may be made. For the complete amplifier there will thus be $(n - 1)$ values for A plus the value A_n for the last stage, and $(n - 1)$ values for D. In addition there will be similar quantity, D_i, for the input circuit to the first stage. The product of all these A's and D's gives the overall gain of the amplifier.

17. Direct-Coupled Amplifiers. For even the best amplifier which utilizes condensers or transformers for coupling between stages the gain must decrease to zero as the frequency goes toward zero. Cheap audio amplifiers usually "cut off" somewhere above 60 cps, to avoid the difficulty of otherwise eliminating 60-cycle pick-up from the power supply. Such degradation or even elimination of the very low-frequency components in an audio amplifier has little audible effect, since the ear is not very sensitive in this frequency range. There are times, however, when it is desired to amplify signals down to and including zero frequency: that is, to include d-c changes of input as well as a-c signals. Then it is necessary to eliminate all condensers

and transformers, and couple one stage directly to the next.   This is
not easy.   Figure 14 shows a circuit which is simple in principle, but
which in practice is hopelessly difficult to maintain in operation.
Batteries E_1 and E_2 serve the usual functions of plate-power supply
and grid bias.   Battery E_3 is required to couple plate $P1$, which is at a
comparatively high positive potential, V_1, to grid $G2$, which must
have a small negative bias; the emf of E_3 must be just enough bigger
than V_1 to supply this bias.   Likewise battery E_4 serves to make the
d-c output zero when the signal is zero.   The circuit is balanced by

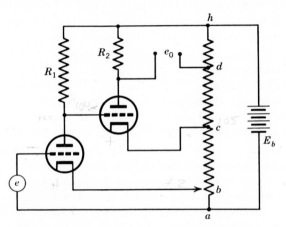

Fig. 15.   D-C Amplifier.   Common battery.

means of the tapped resistor, R_3, to make the d-c output zero.   Balance is very difficult to establish in the first place, and the smallest
changes in the emf's of any of the batteries may be sufficient to throw
it off balance, or at least to introduce false signals.   Slight changes in
cathode temperature may change the internal bias of a tube enough to
unbalance the circuit.   Thus the heater current must be carefully
regulated.

Some of these difficulties are removed in the circuit of Fig. 15,
in which all fixed potentials are derived from a single d-c source, E_b.
A regulated power supply may take the place of a battery for this
purpose.   The voltage-divider, a-b-c-d-h, must have low resistance so
that the current in it is many times larger than the plate current in
either tube.   The contacts at c and d are set by trial or by computation
and left fixed.   The circuit is then balanced by the movable contact at
b.   It is still difficult to maintain a good balance, owing to variable
tube characteristics.   The heater current must be very carefully regulated to a constant value, and it is sometimes necessary to control the

ambient temperature for the amplifier. Various other improvements have been made, but the direct-coupled amplifier still remains the last resort when all other possibilities fail.*

Quite a different means for "amplifying" a d-c or very low-frequency a-c signal has been employed with considerable success. First the signal is made to produce an a-c voltage whose amplitude is proportional to the magnitude of the signal. This a-c voltage is then amplified with an ordinary a-c amplifier, and finally the a-c output is rectified with a diode to give a d-c output which reproduces the characteristics of the original signal in amplified form. This process, which is called *modulation*, may be accomplished by various means, such as electronic tubes, saturable-core reactors ("magnetic amplifiers"), and vibrating contacts or "choppers." Modulation processes are considered in Chapter 12.

18. Current Amplifiers. A triode circuit may serve also to "amplify" very small direct currents, and enormous gain may be achieved with a single tube when the current to be amplified is from a source having sufficient emf. Such currents are encountered in phototube circuits, and in ionization chambers for measuring the intensity of X-rays or of the radiations from radioactive substances. The current to be amplified is sent through a very high resistance connected between the grid and cathode, and the impedance of the plate circuit is kept low. The resultant change in grid potential produces a corresponding change in plate current which is measured by a suitable meter. Figure 16 shows a circuit of this kind. The current i_s produces a change in grid potential equal to $i_s R_g$, causing the plate current to change from its steady value, I_0, to $I_0 + i$. If the impedance of the plate circuit is very small the change in plate potential may be considered zero, and the value of i is then, according to the small-variations equation, Eq. 28, Chapter 2,

$$i = g_m R_g i_s \tag{20}$$

The *current gain* is

$$i/i_s = g_m R_g \tag{21}$$

Some commercial receiving tubes may be found by trial which have very low grid current when operated at a relatively low plate potential and somewhat below normal heater voltage. With such a tube the value of R_g may be made 10 megohms or even higher before the grid

* For further details consult L. B. Arguimbau, *Vacuum-Tube Circuits*, pp. 115–122, and F. E. Terman, *Radio Engineers' Handbook*, p. 375. An excellent survey of direct-coupled amplifier circuits is given by M. Artzt, in *Electronics*, August 1945, p. 112.

potential becomes unstable.   If the value of g_m is 800 micromhos, as it
may well be, the current gain with a 10-megohm grid resistor would be
8000 times.   Tubes designed especially for current amplification make
possible very much larger current gain and the measurement of very

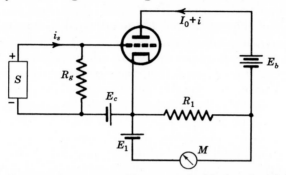

FIG. 16.   CURRENT AMPLIFIER.   No current in M when i_s and i are zero.

small current.   These tubes are sometimes called *electrometer tubes*,
since they replace electrometers in the measurement of ionization current.   The first tube of this kind, the FP-54 electrometer tube, was
developed by the General Electric Co.   Various others are now made.
The steps taken to reduce grid current in these tubes are (1) very high
insulation of the gird, with fused quartz wherever possible; (2) very
thorough evacuation and out-gassing of all parts of the tube; (3)
operation of the cathode at as low a temperature as possible; (4)
operation of the plate at a potential below the ionization potential of
what little residual gas there may be; and (5) insertion of a second grid,
between the cathode and the control grid.   This second grid is held at a
small positive potential to prevent any positive ions from leaving the
cathode, in case any are emitted thermionically from it.   Positive
potential on this grid tends also to compensate for the very low anode
potential.   The value of g_m for the FP-54 tube is only 25 micromhos,
but R_g may be made as high as 10^6 megohms.   With this value for R_g
the current gain is 25×10^6 times.   Even higher current gains are
possible with the grid free or "floating."   With this arrangement
current is measured by the rate at which the grid capacitance charges,
and determined from the rate at which the plate current changes.
Balancing difficulties plague these electrometer tube circuits also,
and set a lower limit to the current measured with them.   With circuits designed to minimize these difficulties current measurements may
be made down to 10^{-17} ampere (less than 100 electrons per second).
   Measurement of the *change* of plate current, i, involves separation
of i from I_0.   Although i might be measured with a meter in series with

the battery E_b, by reading this meter both with and without i_s in R_g, a meter which is not deflected off-scale by I_0 would be relatively insensitive and could not measure i very precisely. A much more sensitive meter may be employed if only i need be measured by it, and the potentiometer circuit formed by R_1 and E_1 in Fig. 16 makes this possible. The values of R_1 and I_0 are adjusted so that the potential difference, I_0R_1, just equals the emf of E_1. Under these conditions there will be no current in the meter, M, when i_s is zero. If the plate current changes from I_0 to $I_0 + i$, the superposition principle shows us that i will divide between the two branches in proportion to their conductances, or that the fraction of i which appears in M equals $R_1/(R_1 + R_m)$, and the fraction in R_1 is $R_m/(R_1 + R_m)$. If R_1 is much larger than R_m, the resistance of M, almost all of i will be measured by M. The initial balancing of the potentiometer may be accomplished by making R_1 variable, or by adjusting the value of I_0 with a variable grid bias, as in Fig. 17.

19. Experiment 10. Current Amplifier. The performance of a current amplifier such as described in Sec. 18 is to be studied in this experiment. The small current is conveniently furnished by a phototube in series with the battery E_2, as shown in Fig. 17. (Although the physics of the phototube has not yet been considered here, this need not trouble the student. He should regard the phototube as a convenient device for producing very small currents, whose performance he is to study empirically.) Carefully compare the rest of this circuit with that of Fig. 16. Note that the 6-volt battery, E_3, serves as the potentiometer battery, E_1, of Fig. 16 and also provides a variable bias for the grid of the amplifier tube, by means of the voltage-divider, R_2. In addition, it provides the power for heating the cathode. A low-μ triode, such as the type 37 tube specified in Fig. 17, is best for this amplifier. The phototube should be a high-vacuum type. The type 922 "cartridge" tube serves excellently. Tube sockets for the phototube and amplifier tube should be mounted on a small board which may be supported on one end of a photometer bench with the phototube in the correct position. Resistors R_1 and R_g should also be mounted on this circuit board. Long wires connect the circuit parts on this board with the batteries, the meter, and the voltage-divider, R_2. A good range for the meter is 500 microamperes. If this experiment cannot be performed in a darkroom satisfactory results may be obtained in a lighted room when the phototube circuit and the light source are properly inclosed. At George Washington University the inclosure for the phototube is a cardboard tube 30 inches long and 8 inches in diameter. The phototube circuit board is placed at one end, as shown in Fig. 18, and this end is covered over with black cloth. The other end is open, with a set of three circular light-baffles inserted as shown in the figure. These baffles and the interior of the tube are painted a dull black.

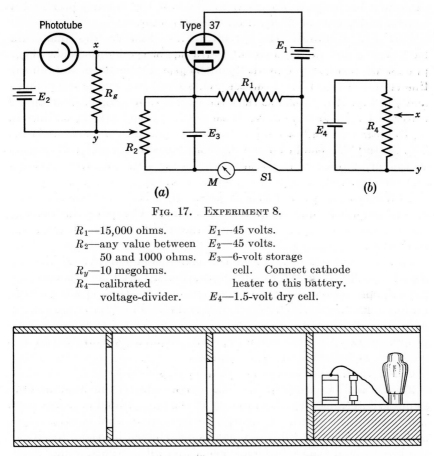

FIG. 17. EXPERIMENT 8.

R_1—15,000 ohms. E_1—45 volts.
R_2—any value between E_2—45 volts.
     50 and 1000 ohms. E_3—6-volt storage
R_y—10 megohms.   cell. Connect cathode
R_4—calibrated   heater to this battery.
     voltage-divider. E_4—1.5-volt dry cell.

FIG. 18. LIGHT SHIELD FOR PHOTOTUBE, EXP. 8.

Part I. With the light source off, adjust the grid bias by means of R_2 so that M reads zero. Check this balance frequently during the course of the experiment, since it may drift off. Then take readings for illumination ranging from the maximum, which is limited by the range of M, to the minimum obtainable. A good set of observations may be obtained if M reads full scale when the light source is 40 to 60 cm away from the phototube, on a 2-meter photometer bench.

The power of the light source should be chosen to meet this requirement. Take 8 or 10 observations, evenly spaced on the scale of M. Record the position of the lamp on the photometer bar. If the phototube is not exactly at the zero of this scale, make the measurements necessary to compute its position. Obtain the candlepower of the source, and the value of R_g, from the instructor.

Part II. Calibrate the circuit. First remove the phototube battery, E_2, and take the circuit board out of the light shield. Then put known positive potentials upon the grid, by means of the calibration circuit of Fig. 17b. Connect points x and y of Fig. 17b to points x and y in Fig. 17a. Balance the circuit for zero reading of M when the calibrated voltage-divider, R_4, is set to zero, then vary the settings of R_4 to obtain 10 calibration points evenly spaced over the scale of M. The battery E_4 should be one dry cell; measure its emf with a good voltmeter, and compute potential values for your data from this emf and the observed settings of R_4. Plot a calibration curve with potential values as y and readings of M as x. How is the transconductance of the amplifier tube related to this plot? Compute the average transconductance from it. Obtain the resistance of M from the instructor.

Part I Computations. From the calibration curve read the d-c signal input to the grid for each observation of Part I, and thence compute the phototube current (the current in R_g). Compute the illumination in meter-candles for each observation. Plot phototube current as y and illumination as x. According to theory these should be proportional. Do your results agree? Explain your answer to this question, and discuss any discrepancies.

Compute the average current gain for this circuit.

20. "Noise" in Amplifiers. The magnitude of the least audible sound is determined by the intensity of the background of noise above which it must be heard. Similarly, the least signal that may be amplified with an electron tube amplifier is determined by the intensity of the background "noise" which is generated within the amplifier itself. In an amplifier the word "noise" does not mean audible sound, but the sum-total of undesirable and meaningless a-c voltages which tend to mask the desired signal voltages. If the amplifier is operating in the audiofrequency range and driving a loud-speaker this background is actually heard as noise. By analogy, the same word is employed to designate this background even when no sound is produced.

This noise may have many causes. First of all there are hum and microphonic noise. Hum is caused by either electrostatic or electromagnetic pick-up from the cathode-heater or plate-power transformers within the amplifier, or sometimes from similar sources outside. Careful shielding will eliminate most of this pick-up, even when audio transformers are employed in the amplifier. The problem of shielding is much simplified if care is taken to arrange the parts of the amplifier, including the wiring, so as to keep sources of hum well away from the grid circuits, particularly that of the first stage. Audio transformers should be kept as far as possible from power transformers, and turned to positions in which pick-up is a minimum. The tube designer's instructions for the grounding of heater circuits should be followed carefully. Even when all these precautions have been taken there may be a very small amount of hum left. If this is steady it may be balanced out by introducing into the circuit a voltage of the same magnitude and frequency, but exactly opposite in phase. This is usually called a "hum-bucking" voltage. See Chapter 24 of *The Radiotron Designer's Handbook*, 3rd Ed., for further details concerning hum.

Microphonic noise is caused by mechanical vibrations in the tube electrodes. Such vibrations produce variations in the tube factors and thereby change the plate current in the tube. The frequency of the change will be that of the mechanical vibrations, or multiples of them. Tapping the tube will set up these mechanical vibrations, and the resultant high-pitched sounds which may be heard in a loud-speaker attached to the amplifier resemble somewhat those produced by tapping a microphone; this accounts for the name "microphonic noise." Special "shock-proof" mounting for both tube and amplifier will greatly reduce the effects of outside shock and vibration, and a special "low-microphonic" tube may be put in the first stage to further minimize this trouble. In these tubes the electrodes are supported more rigidly than in ordinary tubes.

21. Electronic Noise. After all noise from hum and microphonics has been eliminated there remains noise resulting from irregular electronic motions in electron tubes and in resistors. Electrons are not emitted from a hot cathode at a uniform rate but at random, according to the statistical laws of chance. We may compare these conditions with the steady fall of rain on a still day. The rainfall appears to be uniform, but the patter of raindrops on a roof is heard as a noise without definite pitch, whereas a tone of definite pitch should be heard if raindrops fell at an exactly uniform rate. Schottky, who first studied these fluctuations in electron current from a hot cathode, named them the *Schroteffekt* (small shot or hail effect), which may be translated as *shot-effect*. If a diode is operated in the saturation region this random emission produces random fluctuations of current. When this current is amplified sufficiently the sound from a loud-speaker resembles quite closely the sound of rainfall. For tubes operated within the space-charge region this shot-effect is very small, since mutual repulsions among electrons tend to smooth out the fluctuations; it is almost negligible in comparison with thermal noise in resistors, which also was discovered by Schottky.

Thermal noise is a very similar type of current fluctuation which occurs in resistors, as a result of thermal agitation of the atoms in the resistor material. These atomic motions produce random fluctuations of current by disturbing the flow of electrons among the atoms. Thermal noise, like the shot-effect noise, must be averaged over the entire frequency range of the amplifier. In a non-inductive resistor the effect of thermal noise is equivalent to generation within the resistor of an emf whose mean-square value is proportional to the product of the resistance, R, of the resistor, its absolute temperature, T, and $f_2 - f_1$, the frequency range of the amplifier. The proportionality factor is 4 times the Boltzmann constant, k, which equals 1.37×10^{-16} erg per degree C. The rms value of this emf is then

$$E = \sqrt{4kTR(f_2 - f_1)} \tag{22}$$

Reduced to commercial units,

$$E = 7.4 \times 10^{-12} \sqrt{TR(f_2 - f_1)} \tag{23}$$

For example, the thermal-noise emf in a *good* 0.10-megohm resistor in the input of an audio amplifier having a frequency range of 10,000 cps is about 4 microvolts. In most ordinary "radio" resistors thermal noise is much greater. Good discussions of electronic noise are found in L. B. Arguimbau, *Vacuum-Tube Circuits*, pp. 98–110, and K. R. Spangenberg, *Vacuum Tubes*, Chapter 12.

PROBLEMS

1. An amplifier circuit is made as in Fig. 2. $R_1 = 70$ K. $R_2 = 110$ K. $C = 0.025$ μf. Tube: $μ = 18.0$, $g_m = 1300$ μ-mhos. (a) Show that, at 5000 cps, the blocking condenser may be neglected in the equivalent circuit. (b) Compute the signal required to give an output of 12.0 volts at 5000 cps.

2.* Compute the signal required to produce 12.0 volts output at 100 cps in the circuit of Prob. 1.

3. *Circuit of Fig. 2.* $R_1 = 17.5$ K. $R_2 = 80$ K. $C = 0.042$ μf. Tube: $μ = 12.0$, $g_m = 1600$ μ-mhos. $I_0 = 8.0$ ma. V_0 (plate potential with zero signal) $= 114$ volts. $E_c = -2.10$ volts. (a) Diagram the circuit and compute E_b. (b)

---

* These problems (or parts of problems) require more knowledge of a-c circuit theory than do the others. They may be omitted where students do not have this preparation.

Diagram the equivalent a-c circuit and compute the output voltage for 0.65 volt input at 1500 cps. Show that the reactance of C may be neglected in this computation.

4. *Circuit of Fig. 1.* $R = 35.0$ K. In addition, a 0.00032-μf condenser is connected between plate and ground. Tube: $\mu = 20.2$, $g_m = 1270$ μ-mhos. Output is 25.0 volts at 10,000 cps. (a) Diagram this circuit. (b) Diagram the equivalent a-c circuit. (c) Compute the current in R and in the condenser. (d)* Compute the alternating plate current, the equivalent emf, μe, and the signal, e.

5. *Circuit of Fig. 3.* $R_1 = 0.90$ K. $R_2 = 1.20$ K. $R_s = 20$ ohms, in secondary winding. Tube: $\mu = 14.8$, $r_p = 13.1$ K. Transformer: $N_1/N_2 = 4.00$, $L_m = 40$ henries. Input $= 0.87$ volt at 800 cps. (a) Compute the output, neglecting the current in L_m. (b) Compute the current in L_m and show whether or not it is negligible.

Solution: (a) Total secondary resistance $= 1.20 + 0.02 = 1.22$ K. $R_2' = (4.00)^2 \times 1.22 = 19.5$ K. Total series resistance in Fig. 3b $= 19.5 + 0.9 + 13.1 = 33.5$ K. Emf $= \mu e = 14.8 \times 0.87 = 12.9$ volts. $i_p = i_2' = 12.9/33.5 = 0.377$ ma. $i_2 = 4.00 i_2' = 1.51$ ma. $e_0 = i_2 R_2 = 1.81$ volts. (b) $X_m = 2\pi f L_m = 201$ K. $e_0' = i_2' R_2' = 7.24$ volts. $i_m = e_0'/X_m = 0.036$ ma.

$$i_p{}^2 = \sqrt{(i_m{}^2 + i_2'^2)} = 0.379 \text{ ma}$$

Difference in magnitude is negligible. Difference in phase is $\theta = \tan^{-1}\left(\frac{36}{377}\right) = 5.5°$.

6. *Circuit of Fig. 3.* $R_1 = 3.9$ K. $R_2 = 250$ K. $R_s = 5.0$ K. Tube: $\mu = 12.2$, $g_m = 1450$ μ-mhos. Transformer: $N_1/N_2 = 1/3.00$, L_m very large. (a) Diagram the equivalent a-c circuit and label this diagram with numerical values for emf and resistors. (b) Compute the signal voltage for 45 volts output. (c) Compute the gain for this circuit.

7. *Circuit of Fig. 3.* $R_1 = 1.25$ K. $R_2 = 70$ ohms, including the resistance of the secondary winding. Tube: $\mu = 11.8$, $g_m = 1750$ μ-mhos. $I_0 = 8.5$ ma. $V_0 = 200$ volts. $E_c = -10.0$ volts. Transformer: $N_1/N_2 = 20.0$, L_m very large. Signal is 1.05 volts. (a) Compute E_b. (b) Compute the current in the secondary winding.

8. *Circuit of Fig. 3.* $R_1 = 700$ ohms. $R_2 = 35$ K. R_s negligible. Tube: $\mu = 11.7$, $g_m = 1340$ μ-mhos. Transformer: $N_1/N_2 = 1/1.50$. $L_m = 16.0$ henries. The output, e_0, is 12.0 volts at 500 cps. (a) Compute the current in X_m and in R_2'. (b)* Compute the signal, e.

9. An amplifier is made with self-bias, but otherwise the same as in Fig. 1. $R = 43.0$ K. Tube: $\mu = 14.5$, $r_p = 12.7$ K. $I_0 = 3.60$ ma. $V_0 = 115$ volts. $E_c = -3.20$ volts. (a) Compute R_k and E_b. (b) Compute C_k if the potential drop across C_k (assuming all alternating current in C_k) is less than $\frac{1}{50}$ of e at 300 cps.

Solution: (a) $R_k = 3.20$ volts/3.60 ma $= 0.89$ K. $E_b = -E_c + V_0 + I_0 R = 3.2 + 115 + 3.60 \times 43.0 = 273$ volts. (b) $i_p = \mu e/(R + r_p) = 14.5e/55.7 = 0.260e$ ma. $i_p X_k = e/50$. $X_k = e/(50 \times 0.260e) = 0.077$ K $= 77$ ohms. But $X_k = 1/2\pi f C_k$. Hence $C_k = 6.9 \times 10^{-6}$ farad $= 6.9$ μf.

10. An amplifier is made with self-bias. Tube: $\mu = 21.0$, $g_m = 850$ μ-mhos.

---

* These problems (or parts of problems) require more knowledge of a-c circuit theory than do the others. They may be omitted where students do not have this preparation.

$I_0 = 1.40$ ma. $V_0 = 92$ volts. $E_c = -2.50$ volts. $R = 65$ K load. $C_k = 12$ μf.   (a) Diagram the complete circuit.   (b) Compute R_k and E_b.   (c) Compute the alternating potential drop across C_k (assuming all alternating current in C_k) when the signal, e, is 150 millivolts at 200 cps.

11. The gains for the several stages of a cascade amplifier are $15.8\underline{/+18°}$, $44.2\underline{/+16°}$, and $8.3\underline{/+4°}$.   (a) Compute the overall gain and total phase shift. (b) Compute the db gain for each stage, and the total db gain.

12. The gains for the several stages of a cascade amplifier are 28.2, 35.8, and 17.7 db.   Compute the voltage-ratio gain for each stage, and for the amplifier.

13. *Circuit of Fig. 1.* $R = 500$ K.   Tube: $\mu = 100$, $g_m = 1060$ μ-mhos.   (a) Compute the output voltage for 0.250 volt at the grid, neglecting tube capacitances. (b) Diagram this circuit, including tube capacitances having values of 2.4 μμf for C_i, 3.6 μμf for C_0, and 2.4 μμf for C_{gp}.   (c) Compute the current in each tube capacitance at 5000 cps.   (d)* If the internal resistance of the signal source is 80 K, compute the signal, e.

14. *Circuit of Fig. 1.* $R = 280$ K.   Tube: $\mu = 70$, $g_m = 850$ K, $C_i = 4.0$ μμf, $C_0 = 3.0$ μμf, $C_{gp} = 3.3$ μμf.   (a) Compute the gain for the circuit, neglecting tube capacitances.   (b) Compute the "Miller" capacitance and explain very carefully what it means.   (c) Compute the grid input reactance at 15,000 cps.

15. *Circuit of Fig. 16.* $R_g = 15.0$ megohms. $R_1 = 850$ ohms. $R_m = 45$ ohms.   Tube: $\mu = 9.2$, $g_m = 960$ μ-mhos. $E_1 = 1.54$ volts. $E_b = 45$ volts. (a) Compute I_0 to give zero current in M.   (b) Compute the change in plate current for $i_s = 5.0 \times 10^{-9}$ amp.   (c) Compute the corresponding current in M.

16. *Circuit of Fig. 16.* $R_g = 25.0$ megohms. $R_1 = 1200$ ohms, $R_m = 92$ ohms. Tube: $\mu = 12.8$, $g_m = 880$ μ-mhos.   Compute the signal current, i_s, to give a meter reading of 3.0 microamperes.

17.* *Circuit of Fig. 7.* $R_1 = 400$ K. $R_2 = 1000$ K. $R_3 = 25.0$ K. $C = 0.0040$ μf.   The source of e has an internal resistance of 50 K.   First tube: $\mu = 98$, $g_m = 800$ μ-mhos, $C_i = 4.0$ μμf, $C_0 = 3.6$ μμf, $C_{gp} = 2.4$ μμf.   Second tube: $\mu = 13.5$, $g_m = 1120$ μ-mhos, $C_i = 5.5$ μμf, $C_0 = 3.4$ μμf, $C_{gp} = 2.2$ μμf. Compute the gain of this amplifier at 20, 50, 5000, and 20,000 cps.

    * These problems (or parts of problems) require more knowledge of a-c circuit theory than do the others.   They may be omitted where students do not have this preparation.

CHAPTER 4

High-Output Amplifiers

1. Graphical Analysis. Whenever the a-c output from an amplifier is small the amplifier may be analyzed by setting up and solving its equivalent a-c circuit, as has been explained in Chapter 3. The first stages of a cascade amplifier may always be analyzed in this manner. This method, however, gives relatively poor results when the output is high. Better results then may be obtained by the method illustrated in Fig. 2, which shows a graphical analysis for the circuit of Fig. 1.

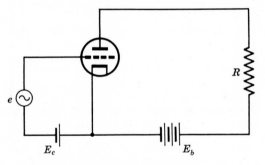

Fig. 1.   Amplifier.

We start this analysis with a set of characteristic curves for the triode in the circuit, and locate on the x-axis the point which represents E_b, the emf of the plate-supply battery. Through this point we then draw the *load-line*, $E_b I_b$, a straight line having a slope equal to $-1/R$, where R is the resistance of the load resistor. Compare this load-line with the load-line for a diode, as described in Sec. 16 of Chapter 1. Note that this load-line crosses the y-axis at the point which represents the current value, I_b, which would exist in the circuit if the tube were short-circuited; often this is a convenient way to locate the load-line.

All values of plate potential, V_p, and plate current, I_p, which are possible for this circuit are now represented by points along this line. Consider, for example, any plate potential, V_1. The potential drop across R is then $E_b - V_1$, and the corresponding value of plate current, I_1, is given by Ohm's law as

$$I_1 = \frac{E_b - V_1}{R} = (E_b - V_1)\frac{1}{R}$$

$$= (V_1 - E_b) \times \text{slope of load-line} \tag{1}$$

Hence the point, P, which represents I_1 and V_1, lies on the load-line. The point, Q, where the load-line intersects the grid-potential line (line of constant grid potential) corresponding to the grid bias, E_c, represents the values of plate current and potential when the a-c input is

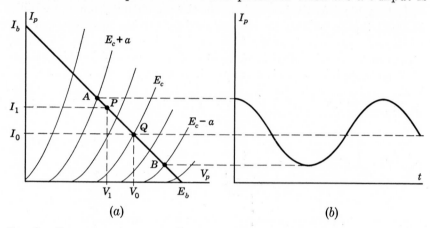

(a)　　　　　　　　　　　　　　　　(b)

Fɪɢ. 2.　Gʀᴀᴘʜɪᴄᴀʟ Aɴᴀʟʏsɪs: Cɪʀᴄᴜɪᴛ ᴏғ Fɪɢ. 1.　(a) Q-point and load-line. (b) Time plot for plate current.

zero. Hereafter this point will be called the *Q-point* ("quiescent" point).

Let us now consider what happens when the input is a sinusoidal voltage, e. Let

$$e = a \cos \omega t \tag{2}$$

The instantaneous grid potential then becomes

$$V_g = E_c + e = E_c + a \cos \omega t \tag{3}$$

The *operating point*, or the point which *at any instant* represents corresponding values of I_p, V_p, and V_g, now moves up and down along the load-line so as to follow the intersection of the load-line with the grid-potential line which represents the value of V_g at that instant. Thus, when e equals $+a$, the operating point is at A; a half-cycle later e equals $-a$ and the operating point is down at B. If the values for I_p which may be obtained in this manner are plotted as a function of time we obtain Fig. 2b. (A more complete family of grid-potential lines than shown in Fig. 2a is needed for a good time plot.)

2. Transfer Characteristic. Values of I_p for such a time plot may be obtained more easily from a *transfer characteristic*, which is a plot of I_p as a function of V_g for successive positions of the operating point. The manner in which this plot is made is shown in Fig. 3. Figure 3*a* is a repetition of Fig. 2*a*, and Fig. 3*b* is the transfer characteristic. Corresponding points are indicated by dotted lines crossing the two diagrams, and by corresponding numbers. Once the transfer characteristic is plotted the Q-point may be located upon it and values of I_p corresponding to *any* values of V_g read directly from it.

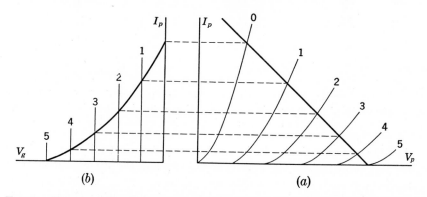

FIG. 3.   TRANSFER CHARACTERISTIC.   (*a*) Load-line.   (*b*) Transfer characteristic, derived from load-line. Note that grid-potential lines are curved in (*a*), vertical straight lines in (*b*).

3. Demonstration Experiment 1. The transfer characteristic for the amplifier of Fig. 1 may be traced on the screen of an oscilloscope with the aid of the circuit of Fig. 4. The vertical deflection is caused by the potential drop across the small resistance, r, and is proportional to the plate current in r. The horizontal deflection is produced by the a-c grid potential. At 60 cps there may be slight phase shifts in the oscilloscope amplifiers, causing the characteristic line to appear as a narrow loop. It is better to supply the a-c signal at a higher frequency if a suitable source, such as an audiofrequency signal generator, is available.

Note that the transfer characteristic obtained with this apparatus is an almost straight line for small a-c input, but shows increasing curvature as the input is raised. Note also that the curvature depends upon the position of the Q-point, which may be shifted by means of the voltage-divider, R_2. If the input impedance is low, as represented in Fig. 4, the a-c signal may drive the grid potential positive without any noticeable change in the transfer characteristic until the plate potential approaches zero.   But if the input impedance is made high, by inserting a high resistance (about $\frac{1}{2}$ megohm) at x, grid current in this resistor will cause a drop in the grid potential and the transfer characteristic then will flatten off at the upper end.

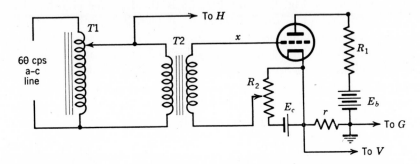

Fɪɢ. 4.   Dᴇᴍᴏɴsᴛʀᴀᴛɪᴏɴ Exᴘᴇʀɪᴍᴇɴᴛ 1.   *G*—ground terminal of oscilloscope. *H*—horizontal-deflection terminal. *V*—vertical-deflection terminal. (Connect the a-c line so that the lower end of *T*1 is the grounded terminal.)

4. Linear Operation.   It is rarely necessary actually to make a time plot for I_p, since we may determine when the operation may be considered linear, and when distorted, directly from the transfer characteristic itself.   Furthermore, when there is distortion the harmonic components which measure it may be determined directly from the transfer characteristic.   Consider linear operation first.   If the Q-point is located on a part of the transfer characteristic which is fairly straight, then the extent over which the operation may be considered linear, or free from distortion, is determined by the range of values for V_g (i.e., the amplitude of the signal, e, Eq. 2) for which it is allowable to call the transfer characteristic a straight line.   This gives a practical answer to the question as to how far the approximate methods of Chapter 3 may be considered valid: they are valid as long as the part of the transfer characteristic involved is essentially straight. Distortion begins when curvature appears within the range of operation, since then the output current is no longer directly proportional to the signal.

5. Distortion.   When the output of an amplifier is large it will always be distorted to some degree.   This may be demonstrated by examining the time plot of I_p, noting to what extent its a-c component departs from being a true sinusoid.   In Fig. 2*b*, for example, the a-c component has a greater amplitude for positive than for negative values of the signal.   Distortion is revealed even more simply by the curvature appearing in the transfer characteristic, as has been suggested in Sec. 3. It then becomes important to have a method for measuring and describing distortion in some more specific way, and the key to the method ordinarily employed is provided by many of the applications for amplifiers. In an audio amplifier, for example, distortion causes a pure tone to be heard as a complex tone, a mixture of the original tone and a series of tones of higher frequencies. In a radiofrequency amplifier, distorted output will produce resonance in circuits tuned to a whole series of frequencies, in addition to the original frequency. For each of these examples, and for many others, it is possible and advantageous to describe the distortion by giving the amplitudes and frequencies of these additional components which have been created by the distortion.

6. Harmonic Analysis. The determination of these amplitudes and frequencies is called *harmonic analysis*, because the new frequencies are all exact multiples of the original frequency and form what is known in acoustics as an harmonic sequence of frequencies. The original or fundamental frequency is designated as the first harmonic, twice the fundamental frequency is the second harmonic, etc. Many years ago Fourier proved mathematically that *any* periodic function, no matter how complex, may be represented by an infinite series of simply periodic (sinusoidal) terms, the frequencies of these terms forming an harmonic sequence. This series is called a *Fourier series.* Theoretically, an infinite number of terms is required, but a finite number will suffice for most practical applications. For most physical applications also it is sufficient to determine the amplitudes only, and often as few as two or three terms are enough.

Fourier's series may be written as a double series of cosine and sine terms. Let y be any complex periodic function of time, with a repetition frequency f, and let $2\pi ft$ be represented by θ. The Fourier series is written

$$y = A_0 + A_1 \cos \theta + A_2 \cos 2\theta + A_3 \cos 3\theta + \text{etc.}$$
$$+ B_1 \sin \theta + B_2 \sin 2\theta + B_3 \sin 3\theta + \text{etc.} \quad (4)$$

Many methods have been devised for evaluating the amplitude coefficients for the terms in this series, both by mathematical computation and by mechanical or electrical devices.* The same principle underlies all these methods. To evaluate A_0, for example, we would integrate both sides of Eq. 4 over a complete cycle. All terms in the series

---

* See Chapter 14, Sec. 30. For mechanical harmonic analyzers see D. C. Miller, *Science of Musical Sounds,* Lecture IV.

which form the left-hand side of Eq. 4 integrate to zero, except the first one. This one integrates to $2\pi A_0$. Hence

$$\int_0^{2\pi} y \, d\theta = 2\pi A_0 \qquad \text{or} \qquad A_0 = \frac{1}{2\pi} \int_0^{2\pi} y \, d\theta \qquad (5)$$

Note that this result is obvious, since A_0 is the average value of y. If y can be represented by an equation it can be integrated mathematically. If instead y is represented only by a plotted curve the integration must be made by some graphical method, such as the trapezoidal rule, Simpson's rule, or a planimeter.

To obtain the coefficient A_n for the cos $n\theta$ term we first multiply Eq. 4 by cos $n\theta$ and then integrate over a complete cycle:

$$\int_0^{2\pi} y \cos n\theta \, d\theta$$

$$= \int_0^{2\pi} [(A_0 \cos n\theta + A_1 \cos \theta \cos n\theta + \cdots + A_n \cos^2 n\theta + \cdots)$$
$$+ (B_1 \sin \theta \cos n\theta + \cdots + B_n \sin n\theta \cos n\theta + \cdots)] \, d\theta \qquad (6)$$

Now it can be shown* that the right-hand side of Eq. 6 reduces to one term, the one containing $\cos^2 n\theta$; all the rest integrate to zero. Hence

$$\int_0^{2\pi} y \cos n\theta \, d\theta = \int_0^{2\pi} A_n \cos^2 n\theta \, d\theta = \pi A_n$$

or

$$A_n = \frac{1}{\pi} \int_0^{2\pi} y \cos n\theta \, d\theta \qquad (7)$$

When y is represented graphically it is necessary to compute the product, $y \cos n\theta$, plot it, and then integrate it graphically. Figure 5b illustrates this procedure for the first-harmonic term ($n = 1$). The B-coefficients may be evaluated in like manner.

$$B_n = \frac{1}{\pi} \int_0^{2\pi} y \sin n\theta \, d\theta \qquad (10)$$

The graphical procedure for B_1 is shown in Fig. 5c.

Although this straightforward procedure is exact it is very tedious. The mechanical and electrical analyzers are far more rapid, but very expensive. When some approximations may be made several simplified methods are possible. One ingenious method has been devised

---

* The reader may take the mathematicians' word for this, or he may prove it for himself, by means of the following identities:

$$2 \cos m\theta \cos n\theta = \cos (m + n)\theta + \cos (m - n)\theta \qquad (8)$$

$$2 \sin m\theta \cos n\theta = \sin (m + n)\theta + \sin (m - n)\theta \qquad (9)$$

by G. L. Collins. Collins points out that a single plot, the original plot of y, will serve for all harmonics if the values of y are measured at a series of non-uniformly spaced values of x, and added together in the proper manner. He manufactures a set of transparent grids which

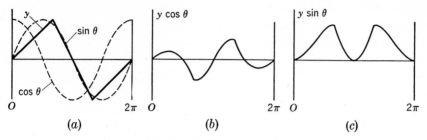

(a)   (b)   (c)

FIG. 5.   HARMONIC ANALYSIS.   See Sec. 6.

$$A_0 = \frac{1}{2\pi} \int_0^{2\pi} y \, d\theta = 0; \quad A_1 = \frac{1}{\pi} \int_0^{2\pi} y \cos \theta \, d\theta = 0; \quad B_1 = \frac{1}{\pi} \int_0^{2\pi} y \sin \theta \, d\theta = 0.79$$

serve to locate these points automatically, when they are laid over the time plot of y.

The theory for this method may be indicated as follows. Consider the $\cos \theta$ term. We may write

$$A = \frac{1}{\pi} \int y \cos \theta \, d\theta = \frac{1}{\pi} \int y \, d(\sin \theta) \cong \frac{1}{\pi} \sum y(\Delta \sin \theta) \tag{11}$$

If now the ordinates are taken so that the distance from one to the next represents the same constant value of $\Delta \sin \theta$, the summation may be made by merely adding these ordinates, reversing their signs when $\cos \theta$ is negative, and omitting the ordinates when $\cos \theta$ is zero.

7. Harmonic Analysis from the Transfer Characteristic. Let us now consider the output current in an amplifier circuit having a pure resistive load. This current may be represented by a transfer characteristic, as in Fig. 6. In this figure the signal, e, is measured from the Q-point value of V_g, as indicated; let its value be

$$e = a \cos \omega t = a \cos \theta \tag{12}$$

The Fourier series for I_p now may be written as a sum of cosine terms only.*

$$I = A_0 + A_1 \cos \theta + A_2 \cos 2\theta + A_3 \cos 3\theta + \cdots \tag{13}$$

* During one cycle the operating point moves from T to S, Fig. 6, and back again. It is now easily seen that, since the operating point traces the same path in going up as in going down, the plot of I_p as a function of θ is symmetrical about the value for θ equal to zero, or that I_p has the same value for $-\theta$ as for $+\theta$. Since this is true for cosine terms only there can be no sine terms in Eq. 13.

It is now possible to evaluate the coefficients A_0, A_1, etc., directly from this transfer characteristic, by means which are quite as general as those mentioned above for the time plot. There are, however, several approximate methods which are much shorter but generally yield quite satisfactory results. One of the best is the power-series

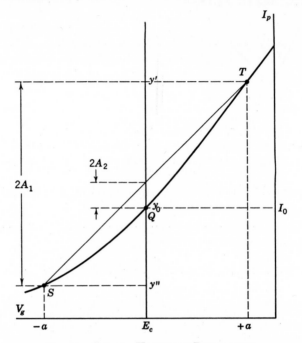

Fig. 6. Second-Harmonic Distortion.

method. To apply this method, first draw on the transfer characteristic a new y-axis which passes through the Q-point, as in Fig. 6. The new x-coordinate is then

$$x = e = a \cos \omega t = a \cos \theta \qquad (14)$$

Now represent I_p by a power series:

$$y = I_p = b_0 + b_1 x + b_2 x^2 + b_3 x^3 + \cdots \qquad (15)$$

For exact fit this must be an infinite series, but it is generally possible to fit the curve sufficiently well with only a few terms. If the curvature of the characteristic is not very great and is in one direction only, as in Fig. 6, the first three terms may suffice. The simplest procedure is to make a guess, based on the appearance of the curve, solve for the coefficients in the manner now to be described, and then check back by plotting the resulting equation on top of the experimental plot. If the fit is too poor, start again with more terms. With experience it is not difficult to guess right the first time.

From this power series we may then derive the amplitudes for the harmonic components. If we let x equal $a \cos \theta$ in Eq. 15, we obtain

$$y = b_0 + b_1 a \cos \theta + b_2 a^2 \cos^2 \theta + b_3 a^3 \cos^3 \theta + \cdots \quad (16)$$

Equation 16 now may be converted into an harmonic series by means of the standard trigonometric relationships among cosines of multiple angles and powers of $\cos \theta$. The first four of these are:

$$\cos^2 \theta = (\cos 2\theta + 1)/2 \qquad (17)$$

$$\cos^3 \theta = (\cos 3\theta + 3 \cos \theta)/4 \qquad (18)$$

$$\cos^4 \theta = (\cos 4\theta + 4 \cos 2\theta + 3)/8 \qquad (19)$$

$$\cos^5 \theta = (\cos 5\theta + 5 \cos 3\theta + 10 \cos \theta)/16 \qquad (20)$$

Detailed examples are worked out in Secs. 8 and 9. Here it is important to note two general relationships:

(a) If the nth power term is the highest one needed, the highest harmonic of any significance is the nth one.

(b) Odd harmonics are determined by odd powers only, and even harmonics by even powers. For example, if all even-power terms are missing, all even-harmonic components will be absent.

8. Second-Harmonic Distortion. Let us assume that the transfer characteristic to be analyzed is the one represented in Fig. 6, and we guess that only three terms of Eq. 15 are needed to represent it. That is,

$$I_0 = y = b_0 + b_1 x + b_2 x^2 \qquad (21)$$

We then choose three points on this curve and substitute their x- and y-coordinates into Eq. 21; this gives us three equations which may be solved simultaneously for values of b_0, b_1, and b_2. The best points are given by x equal to 0, $+a$, and $-a$, for which

$$\left.\begin{aligned} y' &= b_0 + b_1 a + b_2 a^2 \\ y_0 &= b_0 \\ y'' &= b_0 - b_1 a + b_2 a^2 \end{aligned}\right\} \qquad (22)$$

These equations are particularly easy to solve. They give

$$b_0 = y_0 \qquad b_1 = (y' - y'')/2a \qquad b_2 = (y' + y'' - 2y_0)/2a^2 \quad (23)$$

The correctness of our guess may now be checked by putting these numerical values for b_0, b_1, and b_2 into Eq. 21 and computing values of y for several intermediate values of x. If these computed values fit the experimental curve reasonably well our guess is acceptable.

If the equation is acceptable we may then interpret this result in terms of harmonic components. Put $x = e = a \cos \theta$ into Eq. 21. The result is

$$y = b_0 + b_1 a \cos \theta + b_2 a^2 \cos^2 \theta \tag{24}$$

Then, when we replace $\cos^2 \theta$ in Eq. 24 with its equivalent from Eq. 17, we obtain

$$I_p = y = (b_0 + \tfrac{1}{2}b_2 a^2) + b_1 a \cos \theta + \tfrac{1}{2}b_2 a^2 \cos 2\theta \tag{25}$$

Thus, if the transfer characteristic may be represented by Eq. 21, the alternating current has two harmonic components: the first-harmonic or fundamental component, which is the one desired, and the second-harmonic, which represents distortion. If we compare Eq. 25 with the first three terms of Eq. 13 we see that

$$\left.\begin{aligned}
A_1 &= b_1 a &&= \tfrac{1}{2}(y' - y'') \\
A_2 &= \tfrac{1}{2}b_2 a^2 &&= \tfrac{1}{4}(y' + y'' - 2y_0) \\
A_0 &= b_0 + \tfrac{1}{2}b_2 a^2 = I_0 + A_2
\end{aligned}\right\} \tag{26}$$

These relationships are represented graphically in Fig. 6. Since they depend upon only the Q-value and the end values, it is possible to apply these equations to values read directly from the load-line. The rules found in handbooks for computing the first- and second-harmonic amplitudes are equivalent to these equations.

As an example of this method, consider the following data taken for a 6J5 tube in the circuit of Fig. 1. $R = 25$ K, $E_b = 260$ volts, $E_c = -10$ volts.

V (volts)	x (volts)	y = I (ma)	y computed
0	10	11.7 (y')	
−6	4	7.9	7.8
−10	0	5.5 (y_0)	
−14	−4	3.4	3.5
−20	−10	1.0 (y'')	

From Eqs. 23 we have:

$$b_0 = 5.5 \qquad b_1 = \frac{11.7 - 1.0}{2 \times 10} = 0.535$$

$$b_2 = \frac{11.7 + 1.0 - (2 \times 5.5)}{2 \times 10^2} = 0.0085$$

or

$$y = 5.5 + 0.535x + 0.0085x^2$$

This equation is then checked by computing y for x-values of $+4$ and -4; these computed values are tabulated in the last column. The agreement with the experimental values is not exact, but close enough. From Eqs. 26 we now find: $A_1 = 5.3$ ma, $A_2 = 0.4$ ma (7.5 percent of A_1), and $A_0 = 5.9$ ma. The rms values for the first- and second-harmonic components are $A_1 \sqrt{\tfrac{1}{2}}$ and $A_2 \sqrt{\tfrac{1}{2}}$, or 3.8 ma and 0.3 ma respectively.

9. Third-Harmonic Distortion. When the curvature of the transfer characteristic reverses, as in Fig. 7, there must be at least one more

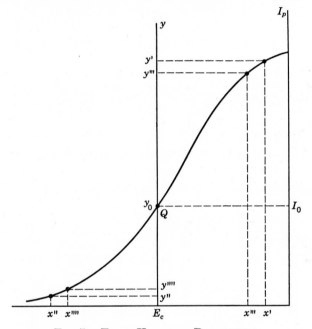

FIG. 7.   THIRD-HARMONIC DISTORTION.

term in the power series. For Fig. 7 let us try

$$y = b_0 + b_1 x + b_2 x^2 + b_3 x^3 \tag{27}$$

Putting x equal to $a \cos \theta$ converts Eq. 27 into

$$y = b_0 + b_1 a \cos \theta + b_2 a^2 \cos^2 \theta + b_3 a^3 \cos^3 \theta \tag{28}$$

This series may now be converted into an harmonic series by means of Eqs. 17 and 18.

$$y = (b_0 + \tfrac{1}{2} b_2 a^2) + (b_1 a + \tfrac{3}{4} b_3 a^3) \cos \theta$$
$$+ \tfrac{1}{2} b_2 a^2 \cos 2\theta + \tfrac{1}{4} b_3 a^3 \cos 3\theta \tag{29}$$

or

$$y = A_0 + A_1 \cos \theta + A_2 \cos 2\theta + A_3 \cos 3\theta \tag{30}$$

Evaluation of these coefficients is carried out as in Sec. 8 for the second-harmonic equations. The best values for x are $+a$, $+a \cos 30°$, 0, $-a \cos 30°$, and $-a$. (Note that these correspond to *equal* increments of $a \sin \theta$.) The corresponding ordinates are represented in Fig. 7 by y', y''', y_0, y'''', and y''. The amplitudes A_0, A_1, A_2, and A_3 are then given by

$$A_1 = \frac{y''' - y''''}{2 \cos 30°} \qquad A_2 = \frac{y' + y'' - 2y_0}{4}$$

$$A_3 = \frac{y' - y''}{2} - A_1 \qquad A_0 = y_0 + A_2$$

$$\left.\right\} \tag{31}$$

One significant point appears here. The equations for A_0 and A_2 depend upon y', y'', and y_0 only, and are the same as the corresponding ones in Eq. 26. Thus the presence of a third harmonic does not change the rules for finding A_0 and A_2.

This method of analysis may be extended to higher harmonics, although it increases in difficulty as the terms increase in number. It is not often that harmonic components above the third have appreciable amplitudes in any but the poorest amplifiers.

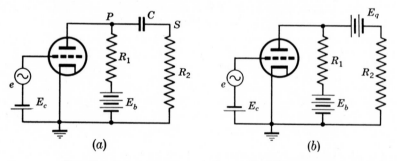

Fig. 8.   Amplifier with A-C and D-C Branches.

10. A-C Load-Lines. For circuits other than the simple one shown in Fig. 2 the load-line may have to be determined somewhat differently. For the circuit of Fig. 8a, in which the a-c output is isolated by means of the condenser, C, the load-lines would be drawn as in Fig. 9. First a line is drawn through the point on the x-axis which represents E_b, with a slope equal to $-1/R_1$. This is the *d-c load-line*. The Q-point is located at the intersection of this line with the grid-potential line representing the grid bias, E_c. Since the alternating current divides between R_0 and R_2 the a-c load-line is not the same as the d-c load-line. If we assume that the impedance of C is negligible, the *a-c* *load-line* may be drawn as a straight line with a negative slope equal to the sum of $1/R_1$ and $1/R_2$, or the conductance of R_1 and R_2 in parallel. In Fig. 9 this a-c load-line is drawn through the Q-point. The true a-c load-line runs parallel to this one, but is displaced some-

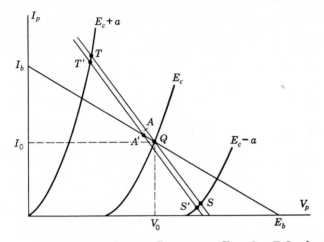

Fig. 9.   A-C and D-C Load-Lines: Circuit of Fig. 8. E_bQ—d-c load-line. $T'S'$—a-c load-line. TS—approximate a-c load-line.

what from this position whenever the average plate-current value is changed by curvature of the transfer characteristic.

To account for this displacement let us consider a second circuit, Fig. 8b, identical with the first except that the condenser, C, in Fig. 8a is replaced by a battery whose emf, E_q, just equals the potential of the plate when the circuit is quiescent (no signal). The current in R_2 will then be zero, and the currents and potentials for both circuits exactly the same. In particular, the potential drop across C will be exactly equal to the emf, E_q. Differences appear, however, when each circuit is operated with output large enough to produce considerable curvature in the transfer characteristic. Whenever this curvature produces second-harmonic (or other even-harmonic) distortion there occurs also a change in the average value of the plate current, equal to the d-c component of the output as discussed in Sec. 8. In the circuit of Fig. 8b this current change divides between R_1 and R_2 in proportion to the conductance of each branch, and the line TS in Fig. 9 is the correct a-c load-line for this circuit. The average current is represented by the point A. In the circuit of Fig. 8a, on the contrary, there can be no direct current in R_2 because of C, and all change in direct current must now occur in R_1, or along the d-c load-line. Hence the a-c load-line must shift to the left, as indicated by the broken line $T'S'$, until A', the point which represents the average value of plate current, lies on the d-c load-line. If the tube is self-biased the change in average current produces a change in bias which further complicates the problem of exactly locating the a-c load-line. For further details concerning this problem see H. J. Reich, *Theory and Applications of Electron Tubes*, pp. 102–106.

Generally the displacement of the a-c load-line is slight and does not greatly affect the values for the a-c components. Hence the load-line TS in Fig. 9 will give a very good approximation to the actual a-c performance of the amplifier unless the even-harmonic distortion is very large. Once the a-c load-line has been drawn the transfer characteristic may be derived from it and the output computed exactly as for the simple case of Fig. 1.

It is important to note that the a-c load-line, since it is steeper than the d-c load-line, cuts the x-axis (I_p becomes zero) at a potential considerably below E_b. Consequently the amplitude of the output voltage is limited to a considerably lower value than is possible with

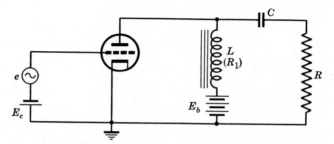

Fig. 10.   Amplifier with Choke-Coil for D-C Current.

the circuit of Fig. 1.   It is interesting to note also that, when I_p is zero in either of the circuits of Fig. 8, the current in R_2 is equal and opposite to the current in R_1.

11. Demonstration Experiment 2.   The method described in Sec. 3 for showing transfer characteristics on an oscilloscope screen is applicable to the circuit of Fig. 8a.   For this circuit, however, the transfer characteristic will probably be a loop instead of a curved line.   Unless C, Fig. 8a, has a very large capacitance its reactance will cause the phase of the output to shift, so that the operating point does not follow the same path for increasing current as for decreasing current.   If the capacitance of C is large the two sides of this loop will not be far apart.   It may be interesting to observe that this loop may be closed up by connecting a condenser C' of the right capacitance in parallel with R_2.   The value needed for C' depends upon frequency; this is a type of resonant circuit.

12. Load-Lines for Choke-Coil Output.   The same principles apply when a-c isolation is accomplished with the choke-coil and condenser combination shown in Fig. 10, but the result is different in several respects.   The slope of the d-c load-line is determined by R_1, the d-c resistance of the choke-coil; see Fig. 11.   For an ideal choke-coil this load-line would be vertical.   If we now assume that X_L, the reactance of this coil, is practically infinite, and that the reactance of the condenser is zero, the alternating current is confined to R and the a-c load-line has a slope equal to $-1/R$.   The Q-point is located by the intersection of the d-c load-line with the grid-potential line representing the grid bias, and the a-c load-line is drawn through this Q-point, as shown in Fig. 11.   The true a-c load-line, represented by

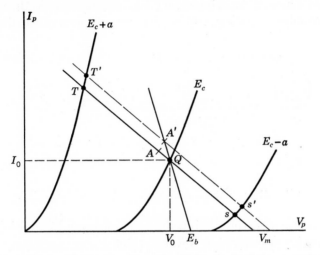

FIG. 11.   LOAD-LINES: CIRCUIT OF FIG. 10. E_bQ—d-c load-line. $T'S'$—a-c load-line. TS—approximate a-c load-line.

$T'S'$, is displaced away from Q when the output current has a d-c component, for reasons explained in Sec. 10; generally this displacement may be neglected.   Once the a-c load-line has been located the transfer characteristic may be plotted and the a-c output computed as for the simple example of Fig. 1.

An interesting and important feature of this circuit should now be observed.   When the d-c power is supplied through a large choke-coil of low resistance the d-c load-line is very steep, so that the potential, V_0, at the Q-point is nearly equal to E_b.   The a-c load-line, on the other hand, is far less steep and crosses the x-axis well beyond the point representing E_b in Fig. 11.   In explaining this we may regard the emf, E_b, in series with X_L as generating a constant current, I_0.   Then when the instantaneous value of I_p is zero, at the point V_m in Fig. 11, the current in X_L is still I_0 and the instantaneous current in R is I_0, in the *opposite* direction.   This raises the potential of the plate above V_0 by the amount I_0R, to the point V_m.   Thus the amplitude of the output voltage may approach E_b in this circuit, whereas the possible amplitude for the circuit of Fig. 1 is only half as great, and even less for the circuit of Fig. 8.

13. Transformer Output. When the output is through a transformer, as shown in Fig. 12a, graphical analysis may be made for the equivalent circuit of Fig. 12b. (Cf. Sec. 4 and Fig. 3 of Chapter 3.) In Fig. 12b, R_1 is the resistance of the primary winding, X_L the open-circuit reactance of the primary, R_2' the *reduced* value of the resistance of the secondary winding, and R' the *reduced* value of the load. The

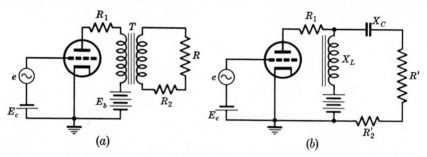

Fig. 12. (a) Amplifier with transformer. (b) Equivalent choke-coil circuit.

reduced values are computed in the usual manner, by multiplying the real values by the square of the turn ratio:

$$R' = (N_1/N_2)^2 R \qquad (32)$$

The assumptions are made that X_L is so very large that the alternating current in it is negligible, and that X_C is zero. Then the load-lines may be drawn as for the circuit of Fig. 10. The slope for the d-c load-line is $-1/R_1$, and for the a-c load-line, $-1/(R_1 + R_2' + R')$. After the amplitudes for the harmonic a-c components of the plate current have been determined from the transfer characteristic the a-c output from the secondary of the transformer may be computed by multiplying these values by the turn ratio, N_1/N_2. The output voltage and power from the transformer then are computed from these current values and the load, R. The several assumptions which have been made in this analysis will not greatly affect the results if the transformer is reasonably good, with small leakage flux and a high value for X_L.

14. Path of Operation for Reactive Output. In all graphical analyses hitherto considered it has been assumed that the output impedance has no reactive component. Fortunately, this assumption is tenable for the main part of the frequency range of many amplifiers.

Unhappily, the reactive component cannot be ignored for poorer amplifiers, or even for a good amplifier when it is operated at frequencies near the upper or lower limits of its range; and when the reactive component must be considered the load-line method of analysis is not applicable. Consider, for example, the circuit of Fig. 13, in which the load is a coil having an inductance, L, and resistance, R.

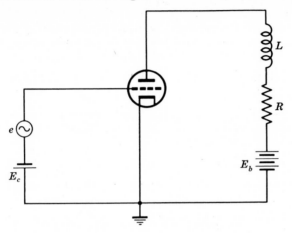

FIG. 13.   AMPLIFIER WITH INDUCTIVE LOAD.

Let us assume that the plate current, I_p, has a d-c component I_0 and a *sinusoidal* a-c component $b \cos \omega t$. That is,

$$I_p = I_0 + i = I_0 + b \cos \omega t \qquad (33)$$

Then

$$V_p = E_b - \left(I_p R + L \frac{dI_p}{dt} \right)$$

$$= E_b - I_0 R - b(R \cos \omega t - L\omega \sin \omega t)$$

or

$$V_p = V_0 - b(R \cos \omega t - L\omega \sin \omega t) \qquad (34)$$

If we plot corresponding values of I_p and V_p, computed from Eqs. 33 and 34, on top of the characteristic curves for the tube, as in Fig. 14a, this plot gives the *path of operation* for this output current. It is an ellipse which is traced in a clockwise direction. The points labelled h, k, m, and n correspond to values of 0, $\pi/2$, π, and $3\pi/2$ for the angle ωt. Note that the diagonal line, TS, which is drawn through the Q-point with a slope equal to $-1/R$, cuts this ellipse at the top and bottom points, h and m. This line would be the load-line if L were zero.

If the amplitude of this current is small, so that the grid-potential lines within this operating path may be considered straight, parallel, and equidistant, the grid signal corresponding to it is also sinusoidal. That is,

$$e = a \cos (\omega t + \alpha) \qquad (35)$$

The phase angle, α, may be obtained by solving the equivalent a-c circuit for i.

$$\tan \alpha = L\omega/(R + r_p) \qquad (36)$$

In general, when the grid-potential lines have appreciable curvature within the ellipse, as represented in Fig. 14a, a sinusoidal signal will not

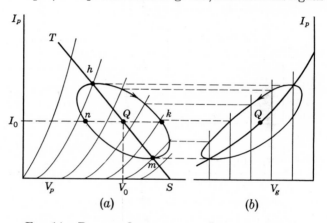

Fɪɢ. 14.   Pᴀᴛʜ ᴏғ Oᴘᴇʀᴀᴛɪᴏɴ ғᴏʀ Iɴᴅᴜᴄᴛɪᴠᴇ Lᴏᴀᴅ.

produce sinusoidal variations in the plate current. The operating path then will not be an ellipse but some more complex closed figure. If the distortion is not too great this figure will resemble an ellipse which is somewhat warped out of shape. It is quite difficult to determine graphically the operating path corresponding to these conditions. Preisman* has devised an excellent method for plotting such an operating path stepwise, but it is tedious for general use.

An indication of the amount of distortion to be expected may be obtained by working *backwards*, starting with the sinusoidal output represented in Fig. 14a, and deriving from it the grid-potential variations which would produce such a sinusoidal output. These values may be plotted as a transfer characteristic, as shown in Fig. 14b. The manner in which this plot is derived from the operating path in Fig. 14a is self-evident from the figures. If this transfer characteristic

* A. Preisman, *Graphical Constructions for Vacuum Tube Circuits.*

is a nearly perfect ellipse we are safe in assuming that distortion in the amplifier is negligible.   If, on the contrary, this transfer characteristic deviates noticeably from elliptical form, as it does in Fig. 14b, the signal required to make the output sinusoidal is not itself sinusoidal. From this result we may deduce that normal operation of the amplifier, with sinusoidal input, will produce distortion in the output.   Unfortunately, we cannot measure the degree of distortion with sinusoidal input by analyzing the amplifier in this backward fashion.   The results of such analysis indicate the nature of the distortion, but do not give its magnitude.

15. Demonstration Experiment 3.   The operating characteristics for an amplifier circuit having reactive output may be exhibited on the

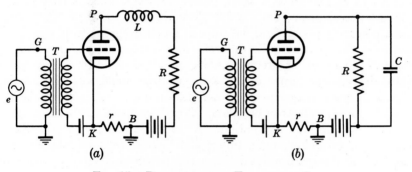

Fig. 15.   Demonstration Experiment 3.

screen of an oscilloscope with the circuits of Fig. 15.   To show the transfer characteristic (Fig. 14b) connect the ground terminal of the oscilloscope to B, the vertical-deflection terminal to K, and the horizontal-deflection terminal to G.   The operating path (Fig. 14a) is obtained by shifting the vertical-deflection connection from G to P. Since for this demonstration it is the signal, e, which is sinusoidal, distortion will appear in both the transfer characteristic and the operating path loops.   The signal, e, should be supplied by a signal generator, at a frequency between 1000 and 5000 cps.   The transformer, T, allows the cathode to be operated above ground potential. The resistance, r, should be only large enough to provide a good vertical deflection.

In Fig. 15a the inductance, L, should be large enough to provide a reactance of several thousand ohms.   A large air-core coil is best. A dust-core reactor also is good, but an iron-core reactor introduces distortion of its own.   A possible compromise is a coil having a straight, fairly short core of iron laminations, such as the secondary of a "spark" coil. The resistive part of the load may be changed by means of the variable resistance, R. It is easier to produce a reactive load capacitatively, as represented in Fig. 15b. The transfer characteristic and operating path for this circuit are similar to those for the inductive load. An analysis such as that given in Sec. 14 shows that the operating path is traced counter-clockwise for this circuit.

16. Power Amplifiers. In an amplifier which serves to deflect the electron beam in a cathode-ray oscilloscope all stages, including the last one, operate as voltage amplifiers. Amplifiers designed to produce large *voltage* output only have a few other applications, but generally the output desired from the last stage is a-c power, and that stage is then called a *power amplifier*. In many ways it is more nearly correct to call this last stage a power *converter*, since it functions to convert power drawn from a d-c source into a-c power. The circuit for a power amplifier does not appear much different from any other amplifier circuit, but quite different magnitudes are required for the resistances and other circuit elements, and "power" tubes are designed quite differently. First of all, a power tube must possess relatively high transconductance and low a-c plate resistance, while its cathode must have high electron emission. Next the plate must be designed to have large power dissipation. Since the efficiency of power conversion is quite low, even under the best conditions, the plate is required to dissipate several times the power delivered to the load. These requirements are not compatible with high voltage gain; hence the amplification factor is relatively small. Most of the required voltage amplification is accomplished in the preceeding stages of the amplifier.

17. Class A Power Amplifiers. If a single-tube power amplifier, such as might be found in the audio output of a radio receiver, is to be reasonably free from distortion its operating range must fall on a fairly straight portion of the transfer characteristic for the circuit. This type of operation is designated as class A operation.* The circuit for a typical class A power amplifier is given in Fig. 16. The plate power generally is supplied through a transformer, as in Fig. 16, or through a choke-coil, as in Fig. 17. Small power amplifiers are usually self-biased, as shown in Fig. 16, but for larger class A power amplifiers the bias is provided by a separate d-c generator or power pack rather than by self-bias, since a cathode resistor wastes considerable power.

---

* Class A is *defined* as operation such that the plate current is not zero at any time. If, in addition, the grid potential is always negative, the designation is class A1.

The analysis of this type of amplifier circuit has already been considered, in Secs. 12 and 13.

18. Power Output and Efficiency. The average power input to a class A amplifier equals the product of the plate supply voltage, E_b, and the d-c component of I_p. When the amplifier operates with little

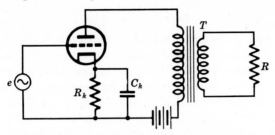

FIG. 16.   CLASS A POWER AMPLIFIER.

distortion this d-c component is practically constant and equal to I_0. The power input then equals

$$P_{\text{in}} = I_0 E_b \tag{37}$$

The average a-c power output equals

$$P_0 = \frac{1}{2\pi} \int_0^{2\pi} i^2 R' \, d\theta \tag{38}$$

The resistance R' is the reduced value of the load; see Sec. 13 and Eq. 32.   The current i is the a-c component of I_p, and may be represented by the power series

$$i = A_1 \cos \theta + A_2 \cos 2\theta + A_3 \cos 3\theta + \cdots \tag{39}$$

If this expression is inserted in Eq. 38, the product terms vanish in the integration, as explained in Sec. 6, and the cosine-squared terms give

$$P_0 = \tfrac{1}{2}(A_1{}^2 + A_2{}^2 + A_3{}^2 + \cdots)R' \tag{40}$$

When distortion is small only the first term is of any importance* and we may take

$$P_0 = \tfrac{1}{2}A_1{}^2 R' \tag{41}$$

The plate-circuit efficiency is then

$$\eta = \frac{P_0}{P_{\text{in}}} = \frac{A_1{}^2 R'}{2 I_0 E_b} \tag{42}$$

* Assume that distortion is great enough to make A_2 as much as 10 percent of A_1: then $A_2{}^2$ is only 1 percent of $A_1{}^2$.

Let us now consider how great the output can become. If we have an ideal transformer, having no d-c resistance and no other losses, together with a tube free from distortion, I_p may be allowed to swing down to zero and up to $2I_0$. The alternating current amplitude, A_1, is then equal to I_0, and the maximum efficiency, *for this ideal case*, is

$$\eta_{\max} = \tfrac{1}{2}\, I_0 R'/E_b \tag{43}$$

The product $I_0 R'$ is the amplitude of the output voltage, at the primary of the transformer, and it is obvious that this amplitude cannot exceed E_b. Indeed, if the grid potential is not allowed to swing positive, the amplitude of the a-c output is approximately equal to the difference between E_b and the value of V_p which is represented by the point T, Fig. 11, and is considerably less than E_b. It follows that the maximum efficiency can never reach 50 percent, even under ideal conditions, and is usually far below this figure.

The difference between the d-c power input and the a-c power output equals the power which must be dissipated by the plate. The average value of this power, P_p, is then

$$P_p = P_{\text{in}} - P_0 \tag{44}$$

Since P_{in} is practically constant the plate power dissipation in a class A amplifier is greatest, and the plate the hottest, when the output is zero. The plate is actually cooler when the circuit is developing a-c power.

19. Demonstration Experiment 4. This cooling may be demonstrated for a small class A amplifier by attaching a small thermometer bulb to the outside of the tube, opposite the plate, with adhesive tape. Read the thermometer with d-c power on, but no signal, and then again after the amplifier has been operating at maximum output for a minute or so. A thermocouple connected to the lecture-room galvanometer serves better for demonstrating this cooling to a large class.

20. Experiment 11. Class A Power Amplifier. The performance of a small class A amplifier may be studied with the circuit of Fig. 17. A choke-coil output type is employed to simplify the measurements. A type 45, 2A3, or 6A3 tube is suitable. (Types 2A3 and 6A3 are the same except for filament voltage.) Circuit constants specified below are for the 2A3 or 6A3 type.* Bias is produced by R_k, 800 ohms when the plate potential is between 200 and 250 volts, and C_k, at least 20 mf, with very low a-c resistance. Cheap condensers are use-

---

* For type 45 tubes the following specifications are suitable: $R_k = 1400$ ohms, $I_0 = 35$ ma, approximately. *Part I:* $R = 4000$ ohms. *Part II:* R varied by 1000-ohm steps from 1000 ohms to 8000 ohms.

less here. If the filament transformer is not center-tapped a low-value, center-tapped resistance, R_s, must be connected between the filament terminals. The connection from R_k and C_k is made to the center tap, as indicated in Fig. 17. For 1000-cps operation the inductance L should be from 10 to 20 henries with a direct current of 60 ma. The primary of a large output transformer (with the secondary open) will serve. The capacitance, C, should be about 10 mf, with 600-volt insulation. The load, R, must be capable of dissipating the power

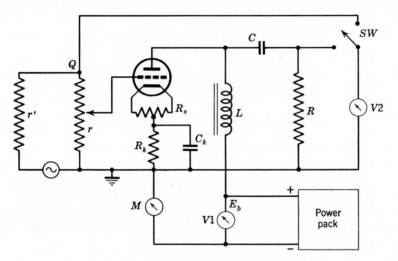

Fig. 17. Experiment 11.   Power amplifier.

without appreciable heating, so that its resistance will not change. A 100-watt, 5000-ohm, wire-wound resistor, with taps every 500 ohms, is excellent. Its resistance values should be checked with a Wheatstone bridge. (Ohmite Mfg. Co. makes a heavy-duty "Determohm" resistance box which is fine for this purpose.) The a-c voltmeter, $V2$, should be of the oxide-rectifier type; its resistance must be included in computing the load resistance.

The a-c input to the grid is determined from the reading of a calibrated voltage-divider, r, and the a-c potential at the point Q. This potential and the output are measured with the same a-c voltmeter, by means of the switch SW. Resistor r' has whatever value is needed to give the alternating potential at Q the desired value. (See Appendix 2 for details concerning a-c sources.)

Part I. Set the d-c supply voltage at the assigned value (between 250 and 300 volts) and measure the d-c potential at the cathode with the d-c voltmeter. Measure also the d-c potential drop across L

under these same conditions. From the cathode potential compute the rms value of the a-c signal which will just swing the grid potential to the cathode potential. This is the maximum usable signal. Make the load resistance about 2500 ohms and take readings for 8 or 10 equally spaced values of signal from zero up to this maximum value. *Hold the d-c supply constant at the assigned value.* If the a-c voltmeter needs calibration, compare it with a regular a-c voltmeter at 60 cps.

Represent your results by a curve plotted with output voltage as *y*, input signal as *x*. For the *maximum* output compute the a-c power output, the d-c power input, and the efficiency.

Part II. With the a-c signal set at about half maximum value, take observations for a series of values of R from 500 ohms to 4000 ohms, by 500-ohm steps. Compute the a-c power output for each value of R and plot these power values as *y*, with the corresponding R values as *x*. Compare the value of R at maximum power output with the tube handbook value for r_p, and explain why these values might be expected to be the same. Explain why the power is less at lower load resistance, and also at higher resistance.

Part III. Check your experimental results for Part I against the characteristic curves of the tube by means of a graphical analysis, from the curves given in Appendix 5. Locate the Q-point and draw the d-c and a-c load-lines as explained in Sec. 12*. Next plot the transfer characteristic from the a-c load-line, as explained in Sec. 2. Then from this plot obtain rms values for the first-harmonic output voltage, e_0, as follows: (a) compute the peak value for each signal, and the corresponding maximum and minimum values for V_g; (b) read from the transfer characteristic the corresponding values of I_p; (c) from these I_p values compute the amplitude and the rms value of the first-harmonic component of the current (see Sec. 8) and then the rms value for e_0.

Plot these values of e_0 along with the experimental ones, for comparison. The two plots should be in fair agreement. If there is any discrepancy discuss carefully the factors which might reasonably account for it. Compute from the transfer characteristic the amplitude of the second-harmonic component of the output current, and the percent distortion which it represents, at maximum output.

21. Push-Pull Amplifiers. Quite early in the development of electronic amplifiers it was discovered that a two-tube "push-pull" circuit of the type shown in Fig. 18 could be designed to give high output with very little distortion. If the two tubes are well matched the second- and other *even*-harmonic components balance out, leaving only

---

* To avoid marking the book do this work on a piece of tracing paper laid over the curve page. Attach this tracing to your report.

the odd harmonics, principally the first and the third. Let us consider how this is possible. Note first that the circuit of Fig. 18 is really two independent circuits which are as nearly identical as possible, with matched tubes and resistors ($R_1' = R_1''$ and $R_2' = R_2''$). Equal and opposite signals go to the two grids, as indicated.* Since the two

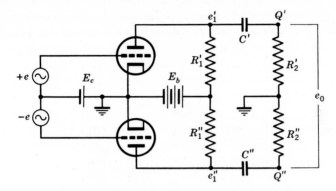

FIG. 18.   PUSH-PULL AMPLIFIER.

circuits are identical the two outputs, V_q' and V_q'', at Q' and Q'' respectively, are also identical in kind, but differ in *phase* by π radians. Thus, if we represent these potentials by harmonic series,

$$V_q' = A_1 \cos \theta + A_2 \cos 2\theta + A_3 \cos 3\theta + \cdots \qquad (45)$$

$$V_q'' = A_1 \cos (\theta + \pi) + A_2 \cos 2(\theta + \pi) + A_3 \cos 3(\theta + \pi) + \cdots$$

$$= -A_1 \cos \theta + A_2 \cos 2\theta - A_3 \cos 3\theta + \cdots \qquad (46)$$

The output, e_0, is the difference in potential between points Q' and Q'', or

$$e_0 = V_q' - V_q'' = 2A_1 \cos \theta + 2A_3 \cos 3\theta + \cdots \qquad (47)$$

Thus the even-harmonic components cancel out and distortion begins with the third-harmonic component. By proper choice of the Q-point it is often possible to make the third-harmonic component also very small and the output remarkably linear.

A push-pull amplifier of the type shown in Fig. 18 has one serious defect: although the output, e_0, is free from even-harmonic distortion it is not symmetrically balanced to ground. Indeed, the output to ground for each amplifier is exactly the same as it would be if the other

* Various "phase-splitters" are employed to produce these two signals. A center-tapped transformer secondary is the simplest. One of the best electronic phase-splitters is described in Sec. 21, Chapter 6.

amplifier were not there.   For this reason it is not profitable to connect several push-pull stages of this type in cascade.

22. Balanced Push-Pull Amplifiers.   The objectionable unbalance to ground, noted above for the output of the push-pull circuit in Fig. 18, may be eliminated by replacing resistors R_1' and R_1'' with a center-tapped choke-coil, as in Fig. 19.   If this choke-coil is well made, so that the *same* magnetic flux links with each half of its winding, then any change in flux will induce the *same emf* in each half, and in the

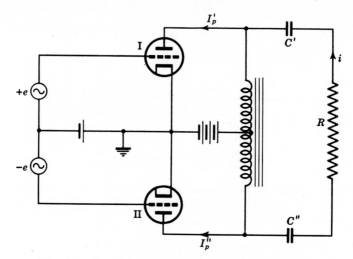

Fig. 19.   Balanced Amplifier.   Choke-coil output.

same direction.   Thus *the alternating potential at the plate of tube I is always equal and opposite to that at the plate of tube II*.   If this potential is e_1 for tube I it is $-e_1$ for tube II, and the output, e_0, is the difference, or $2e_1$, less the potential drops in condensers C' and C''.   The similarity of this circuit to that in Fig. 18 shows fairly well that its output possesses the same freedom from even-harmonic components, plus the additional advantage of balance to ground.   A more rigorous proof is given in Sec. 23.   Usually a-c isolation is accomplished with a transformer, as shown in Fig. 20.   The equivalent circuit corresponds to Fig. 19, as explained in Sec. 13 for a single-tube circuit.   The center-tapped primary of the transformer functions exactly like the choke-coil in Fig. 19 to make the alternating potentials equal and opposite at the plates of tubes I and II.

23. Theory of Operation.   The theoretical considerations below apply specifically to the circuit of Fig. 19.   They apply equally well to the circuit of Fig. 20, because of the correspondence between these circuits which is stored above. We shall now proceed to show that the output current contains no even-harmonic components. Let the currents in tube I, tube II, and the load, R, be represented by I_p', I_p'', and i respectively, and have the directions indicated in Fig. 19. The current upward in the upper half of the choke-coil is then $(I_p' - i)$, and the current upward in the lower half is $-(I_p'' + i)$. If there are

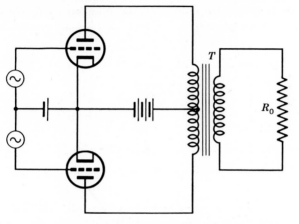

FIG. 20. BALANCED AMPLIFIER. Transformer output.

N turns in each half of the coil the magnetomotive force acting in it is then (in ampere-turns)

$$M = N(I_p' - i) - N(I_p'' + i) \tag{48}$$

If the choke-coil has a very high reactance it may be assumed that the total magnetic flux in it is constant, except for negligibly small changes needed to produce the induced emf's; hence the magnetomotive force must also remain constant. Furthermore, the value of this constant must be zero, since when there is no signal i is zero, and I_p' and I_p'' both are equal to I_0. It follows that

$$I_p' - I_p'' - 2i = 0$$

or

$$i = \tfrac{1}{2}(I_p' - I_p'') \tag{49}$$

The current I_p' may now be represented by a harmonic series

$$I_p' = A_0 + A_1 \cos \theta + A_2 \cos 2\theta + A_3 \cos 3\theta + \cdots \tag{50}$$

The current I_p'' may be represented by the same series with a phase change of π radians, since the grid and plate potentials for tube II are the same as for tube I except for this difference in phase. When θ in Eq. 50 is replaced by $(\theta + \pi)$ the series reduces to

$$I_p'' = A_0 - A_1 \cos \theta + A_2 \cos 2\theta - A_3 \cos 3\theta + \cdots \quad (51)$$

If now we substitute these values for I_p' and I_p'' into Eq. 49 we obtain

$$i = A_1 \cos \theta + A_3 \cos 3\theta + \text{other } odd \text{ harmonics} \quad (52)$$

The output from this amplifier thus has no even-harmonic components and is balanced to ground.

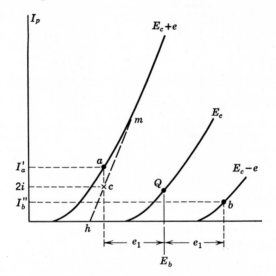

Fig. 21.　Graphical Analysis for the Amplifier of Fig. 19.

The current I_b in the plate-supply battery is the sum of I_p' and I_p'', or

$$I_b = 2(A_0 + A_2 \cos 2\theta + \text{other even harmonics}) \quad (53)$$

Thus all the even-harmonic components of current appear in the plate supply. The average value, $2A_0$, varies with the amplitude of the input and often may become several times larger than the quiescent value, $2I_0$. If the B-battery or other d-c source does not have a very low d-c resistance these changes in direct current produce a kind of secondary distortion which results from shifting the position of the Q-points of the tubes. For the same reason self-biasing is not practical for such balanced circuits.

24. Graphical Analysis for Balanced Amplifiers. Some graphical method must be employed to evaluate the coefficients A_1, A_3, A_5, etc.,

and graphical analysis is not as simple for this circuit as for the one
in Fig. 18, since the load-line for each tube is not straight but curved.
Common procedure is to combine two sets of characteristic curves, one
set for each tube, so as to obtain a set of composite lines representing
the current in the load, R. For this composite set the load-line is
straight. This method is described in many books, including L. B.
Arguimbau, *Vacuum-Tube Circuits;* H. J. Reich, *Theory and Applications of Electron Tubes;* and F. E. Terman, *Radio Engineers' Handbook.*

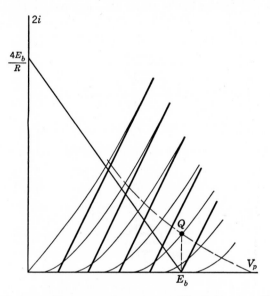

FIG. 22.　LOAD-LINE FOR BALANCED AMPLIFIER.　The light, curved lines represent
grid-potential lines for a single tube.　The heavy, nearly straight lines represent
them for the combination.

Since these composite grid-potential lines are symmetrical we need
plot only the positive half, and this may be done on a single set of tube
characteristics as shown in Figs. 21 and 22. The assumption is made
that the d-c resistance of the choke-coil and battery is zero, so that the
point representing E_b on the x-axis lies directly below the Q-point.
The composite grid-potential lines must now meet the following conditions. (*a*) If the signal is $+e$ for tube I it is $-e$ for tube II. (*b*) If
the plate potential is $(E_b - e_1)$ for tube I it is $(E_b + e_1)$ for tube II,
as demonstrated in Sec. 22. The current, i, for these composite plots
is given by Eq. 49. These conditions are met at points a and b,
Fig. 21, if a represents conditions in tube I and b conditions in tube II.
Hence $2i$ represented by c equals $(I_a' - I_b'')$. The rest of the line

hm for the signal *e* is plotted by choosing other pairs of points (other values of e_1) along the two grid-potential lines for $(E_c + e)$ and $(E_c - e)$. Above *m* the current in tube II is zero and $2i$ equals I_p'. In Fig. 22 is plotted a set of composite lines obtained in this manner. Since e_0 equals iR and also $2e_1$, the load-line is drawn with a slope equal to $-4/R$. From this load-line may be read values of *i* and of *e* with which a transfer characteristic may be plotted, and from this line the values of A_1 and A_3 may be obtained in the usual manner. In Fig. 22 the broken line is the load-line for the current in either tube. Note

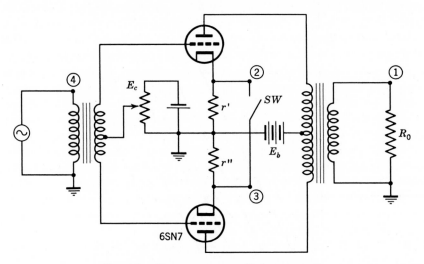

FIG. 23.   DEMONSTRATION EXPERIMENT 5.

that it is a curved line. An ingenious method for obtaining this load-line directly from the tube characteristics is described in A. Preisman, *Graphical Constructions for Vacuum Tube Circuits.*

25. Demonstration Experiment 5.   The performance of a balanced push-pull amplifier may be demonstrated with an oscilloscope and the circuit of Fig. 23. The output current may be represented on the oscilloscope by connecting point 1 to the vertical-deflection terminal of the oscilloscope. The transfer characteristic for the circuit as a whole may be produced on the screen if the horizontal deflection is then produced by the signal, by connection to point 4. Vary the grid bias, E_c, until the value is found which makes this characteristic most linear. Then observe the nature of the distortion which develops when E_c is increased or decreased from this optimum value. Note particularly that distortion is greater for small signals than for larger ones. When the horizontal deflection is produced by the sweep circuit the corresponding time plots are exhibited.

The only way to observe the current in either tube is by means of the potential drop across a very small resistor in series with its cathode. Resistors r' and r'' are inserted for this purpose, and current in either tube may be observed by connecting the oscilloscope to point 2 or point 3. It is best to do this with E_c set at its optimum value, so as to show how the current in either tube may be badly distorted even though the output is quite linear. If an electronic switch is available currents for both tubes may be viewed simultaneously; it is then possible to show graphically how even-harmonic distortion cancels out in the difference between I_p' and I_p''. This may be done with the time plots, or with the horizontal deflection produced by the signal.

If switch SW is closed, so as to connect the two cathodes together, connection of the oscilloscope to point 2 or point 3 plots the battery current, I_b, on the screen. Note that its frequency is twice that of the fundamental. The typical U-shaped pattern of a 2:1 Lissajou figure is seen when the horizontal deflection represents the signal.

The amplifier may be built up with standard push-pull transformers, following the specifications given in the tube handbook for the 6SN7 tube. This tube is employed because it has a separate connection for each cathode. Resistors r' and r'' must have as small values as possible with the oscilloscope available, since they produce some degenerative feedback, as explained in Chapter 6.

26. Class B Amplifiers. The circuits of Figs. 19 and 20 are especially well suited for power amplifiers. The first push-pull circuits were made with each tube operating class A, with the Q-point for each chosen so that the output from each side was as linear as possible. Soon, however, it was discovered that the output from the circuit as a whole could be made quite linear over a wide range by locating the Q-points so that distortion in one tube cancels distortion in the other, even though this condition produces bad distortion in the plate current for each tube. The demonstration experiment of Sec. 25 illustrates this condition. Furthermore, good linear operation is possible when the quiescent value of plate current is so low that the current in either tube may become zero when the signal is negative, and rises to relatively high value when the signal is most positive. As a result, one tube carries most of the current during one half-cycle, the other tube carries it during the other half-cycle. A power amplifier operating under these conditions requires only a small amount of d-c power input when there is no signal (stand-by conditions) and has a relatively high efficiency. This class of amplifier may be designated as class B, or class AB, depending upon how long the current is zero during any one cycle.*

Greater power may be developed with the same type of tube, and the efficiency of the circuit may be much increased, by allowing the signal to drive the grid potential positive.   Special class B tubes are designed just for this service.   Commonly two tubes are inclosed in the same bulb or "envelop," and their amplification factor is high, so that they may be operated with zero bias.   The type 6N7 tube is a typical class B twin amplifier tube.   Each unit has a plate current of only 18 ma at zero grid potential, with a plate potential of 300 volts, but may reach a peak of 95 ma at only 50 volts plate potential when the grid potential is raised to $+35$ volts.   The chief drawback to such operation is grid current.   When the grid potential is positive, current is set up in the grid circuit and power must be supplied to the grid by the source which produces the signal.   For the 6N7 tube the grid current is 28 ma when the grid potential is $+35$ volts and the plate potential is 50 volts. The instantaneous power to the grid is then almost 1 watt.

When there is grid current it will cause distortion at the grid unless the input source has a very low internal impedance, so as to be able to supply the grid input power without noticeable drop in the a-c potential at the grid.   When the signal is supplied from a cascade amplifier the last stage must be a power stage, operated with negative grid.   Either a class A1 single-tube stage or a class AB push-pull stage is suitable.   If the latter, it is well to develop higher voltage than needed and step it down in the transformer, since that lowers the source impedance.

27. Experiment 12.   Class B Amplifier.   Figure 24 shows a typical class B power amplifier circuit, equipped with meters to measure its performance: a d-c voltmeter, $V1$, for the plate supply, a d-c milliammeter, A, for the battery current, and an a-c voltmeter, $V2$, of the oxide-rectifier type for measuring the signal, e, and the output voltages, e_1 and e_0.   The a-c voltmeter includes a condenser, C, to block d-c potentials.   Transformers $T1$ and $T2$ are standard "push-pull" or class B power transformers; they must have heavy windings, with low d-c resistance.   The B-supply should preferably have good d-c regulation, but the effect of perfect d-c regulation may be attained for these tests by holding the reading of $V1$ constant for all readings.   Dry cells

---

* Amplifiers are classified as A, AB, B, or C, according to whether the plate current is never zero (class A), zero for less than a half-cycle (class AB), zero for a half-cycle (class B), or zero for more than a half-cycle (class C).   If the grid potential is always negative number 1 is suffixed.   If the grid potential goes positive at any time, number 2 is suffixed.

serve best for the grid bias, E_c.   If there is available an a-c generator of
100 watts or more at 500 to 1000 cps, it may be connected directly to
the primary of $T1$, through an auto-transformer to vary the signal.
If the a-c source is a weak one, such as an audiofrequency signal generator, it will be necessary to introduce the class A1 driver circuit shown
in Fig. 24.   The circuit of Exp. 11 will serve this need.   Transformer
$T1$ should then be a step-down transformer, and the resistance, R_1, in
parallel with its primary, should be about 1500 ohms for a 2A3 tube.

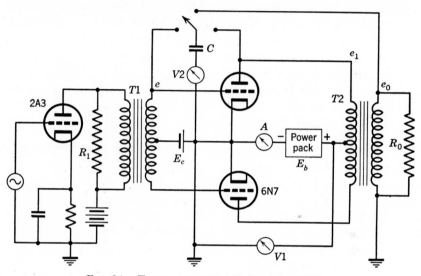

FIG. 24.   EXPERIMENT 12.   Balanced amplifier.

Part I.   Adjust e to a value of 10 or 15 volts rms, and set the reading
of $V1$ to some fixed value (250 or 300 volts).   Make R_0 about 10,000
ohms and read e_1 and e_0.   The ratio of $2e_1$ to e_0 is approximately the
turn ratio, N_1/N_2, for $T2$.   From this ratio compute the value for R_0
to make the reduced value, R (see Sec. 24), about 8000 ohms.   Now
set the grid bias equal to zero and take a set of 8 or 10 readings for e,
e_1, e_0, and I_b, holding E_b constant at some value between 250 volts and
300 volts.   Vary the signal, e, from 0 to 25 volts rms.   Represent these
results by plotting a curve having e_0 as ordinates and e as abscissae.
If this plot is a straight line the amplifier is linear, and deviations from
a straight line may be interpreted as distortion.   The slope of a
straight line drawn *through the origin* to fit the points as closely as
possible will equal the average voltage gain for the circuit.

Part II.   Repeat measurements with a bias of -4.5 volts (3 dry
cells) and also with a bias of -12 volts.   For each set of data plot

curves for e_0 and e, and obtain from them the average gain, as in Part I. From a comparison of the three plots decide which bias value gives the most linear operation.

For the conditions of one set of data make the graphical analysis described in Sec. 24, choosing the set which gives the most linear operation. Compare the gain and linearity obtained in this manner with the experimental results. Discuss any discrepancies, suggesting any possible causes for them.

For an a-c input of 20 volts rms compute the d-c input power, the a-c output power, and the efficiency, for all three sets of data. If time

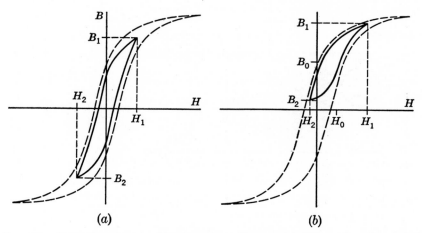

(a)   (b)

Fig. 25. B-H Curves for Transformer Core.   (a) With only alternating current.   (b) With both direct and alternating current.

permits these computations may be extended over the full range of input and efficiency curves plotted, with efficiency as y and e as x.

28. Transformers for Power Amplifiers.   One important advantage is enjoyed by all push-pull amplifiers: the transformer (or choke-coil) may be made considerably smaller than for comparable single-tube amplifiers, since the direct current is in one direction in one half of the winding, in the opposite direction in the other half, and hence the average magnetic flux in the core is zero. This statement may be explained by means of the B-H plots of Fig. 25. If the average flux is zero the alternating current in the windings of a reactor carries the iron of the core through a symmetrical magnetic cycle as indicated in Fig. 25a. Let the cross-section area of the core be S, the mean length of the flux path, s, and the number of primary turns, N_1. The average value of the induced emf is then

$$e_{av} = 2fN_1S(B_1 - B_2) \tag{54}$$

If we assume that this emf is sinusoidal its peak value, e_{pk}, is

$$e_{pk} = \pi f N_1 S(B_1 - B_2) \tag{55}$$

The magnetic field intensity is

$$H = 4\pi N_1 i/s \tag{56}$$

or the instantaneous value of the magnetizing current, i, is

$$i = Hs/4\pi N_1 \tag{57}$$

The peak value for the a-c magnetizing current, i_{pk}, is then

$$i_{pk} = (H_1 - H_2)s/8\pi N_1 \tag{58}$$

The reactance, X, of the reactor is then approximately the ratio of e_{pk} to i_{pk}, or from Eqs. 54 and 58,

$$X = \frac{8\pi^2 f N_1{}^2 (B_1 - B_2)S}{s(H_1 - H_2)} \tag{59}$$

The allowable values for $(B_1 - B_2)$ and $(H_1 - H_2)$ are determined by the kind of iron in the core. If the reactor is a good one, with both e and i approximately sinusoidal, B must remain below saturation, and $(H_1 - H_2)$ is small, as represented in Fig. 25a. For a high reactance value both N_1 and S must be made large.

Consider now a reactor in which there is a d-c component, I_0. The average flux density is now not zero but B_0, and the magnetic cycle is unsymmetrical, as shown in Fig. 25b. The allowable value for $(H_1 - H_2)$ is about the same, but $(B_1 - B_2)$ is much smaller. Hence, to have the same reactance, the cross-section area, S, must be increased. Offhand, it might seem possible to compensate for the decreased change in B by increasing N_1; this, however, would increase B_0 and make the trouble worse. Indeed, the number of turns may have to be decreased instead, so that the direct current will not saturate the core.

PROBLEMS

NOTE: Characteristic curves needed to solve problems are found in Appendix 5. To avoid marking the book, work each problem on a sheet of tracing paper laid over the characteristic curve plate.

1. In the circuit of Fig. 1, with a 6J5 triode and a load of 15,000 ohms, E_b is 240 volts and E_c is -6.0 volts. (a) Draw the load-line and find the values of

plate current and plate potential with no signal.   (b) Plot the transfer character-istic.   (c) Plot plate current vs. angle (electrical degrees) for one cycle, for a signal of 5.8 volts amplitude.

2. Find the amplitudes for the 1st- and 2nd-harmonic components of the plate current in Prob. 1, from the transfer characteristic.

3. The transfer characteristic for an amplifier is found to be

$$I_p = (6.5 + 1.40x + 0.040x^2) \text{ ma.} \qquad x = (V_g - E_c) \text{ volts.}$$

(a) Plot this curve for x between 5.0 and -5.0 volts.   (b) Obtain from this plot the harmonic components for a signal of 5.0 volts peak value.   (c) Check these values by substituting $x = 5.0 \cos \theta$ into the equation and expanding as is done in Sec. 7.

4. The transfer characteristic for an amplifier is found to be

$$I_p = (5.5 + 0.80x + 0.020x^2 - 0.0010x^3) \text{ ma.} \qquad x = V_g - E_c.$$

(a) Plot this equation for x between 10 and -10 volts.   (b) Obtain from this plot the amplitudes of the harmonic components of plate current, for a signal of 10.0 volts amplitude.   (c) Check these values by substituting $x = 10.0 \cos \theta$ into the equation and then expanding as outlined in Sec. 8.

5. The transfer characteristic for an amplifier is given by the following data.

x	-8.0	-6.0	-4.0	-2.0	0	2.0	4.0	6.0	8.0 volts
I_p	0.36	2.34	4.44	7.66	9.00	11.40	13.80	16.20	18.60 ma

(a) Plot these data.   (b) Obtain from this plot the 1st- and 2nd-harmonic com-ponents for a signal of 8.0 volts amplitude, assuming that no others exist.   Show that this is a wrong assumption by computing from these values I_p for $x = +6.0$ and $x = -6.0$ volts.   (c) Obtain the 1st-, 2nd-, and 3rd-harmonic components from this plot, assuming none higher than the 3rd, and compare these values with those of (b).

6. A current pulse has a constant value of 100 ma during one-eighth of each cycle, and is zero during the rest of the cycle.   Compute the amplitudes for the sine terms and cosine terms up to the 8th harmonic, by the theory of Sec. 6.   Take the pulse at the *middle* of the cycle.

7. In the circuit of Fig. 8a, with a 6J5 triode, $V_0 = 200$ volts, $E_c = -8.0$ volts, $R_1 = 30$ K, and $R_2 = 40$ K.   (a) Locate the Q-point and draw the d-c and a-c load-lines.   (b) Find E_b.   (c) Find the cut-off voltage for the a-c output.

8. From the results of Prob. 7, (a) find graphically the 1st-harmonic output for a signal having an amplitude of 6.0 volts (assume no harmonics above the 2nd); (b) compute the gain; (c) find the 2nd-harmonic component of the current and the percent 2nd-harmonic distortion.

9. In the circuit of Fig. 8a, with a 6J5 triode, $E_b = 300$ volts, $E_c = -4.0$ volts, $R_1 = 16.0$ K, and $R_2 = 40$ K.   (a) Draw the d-c and a-c load-lines and locate the Q-point.   (b) Find the maximum amplitude possible without current cut-off or positive grid potential, and (c) find the gain for this output.

10. The a-c load-line for a 6J5 triode amplifier passes through 225 volts on the x-axis and 100 volts for 16.0-ma plate current.   (a) Compute R_2, if R_1 is 11.5 K. (b) Draw the d-c load-line, for grid bias of -5.0 volts, and find E_b.

11. (a) Plot the transfer characteristic for the amplifier of Prob. 10.   (b) Find the 1st- and 2nd-harmonic components for a signal input of 5.0 volts amplitude.

(c) Compute the gain for this signal.   (d) Compute the percent 2nd-harmonic distortion.

12. In the circuit of Fig. 10, with a 6J5 triode, $V_0 = 245$ volts, $E_c = -10$ volts, $R = 40$ K, and the d-c resistance is 1650 ohms. Assume that X_L is infinite, and X_C zero.   (a) Draw d-c and a-c load-lines and find E_b.   (b) Find the cut-off voltage for the a-c output.   (c) Plot the transfer characteristic.

13. From the transfer characteristic plotted for Prob. 12 obtain the 1st- and 2nd-harmonic components of current, for a 7.0-volt rms input.   (b) Compute the percent distortion.   (c) Compute the voltage gain.

14. The output circuit for an amplifier is a resistance of 10.0 K in parallel with a 0.060-mf condenser. Assume that the output potential is $V = 100 \cos 2\pi ft$, at a frequency of 500 cps, and take the Q-point at 180 volts, 25 ma.   (a) Compute the current in the resistor, the current in the condenser, and the plate current.   (b) Plot the path of operation for this circuit (see Sec. 14 and Fig. 14).   (c) Show that a line through the Q-point with a slope equal to $-1/R$ cuts this path of operation at the extreme left and right sides of the ellipse.

15. In the circuit of Fig. 10, with a 2A3 triode, $V_0 = 280$ volts, $E_c = -50$ volts, $R = 2000$ ohms, and the d-c resistance is 700 ohms. Assume X_L infinite, X_C zero.   (a) Draw the a-c and d-c load-lines.   (b) Find E_b.   (c) Plot the transfer characteristic.

16. From the results of Prob. 15 obtain (a) the 1st- and 2nd-harmonic components of the voltage output, for 35 volts rms signal, (b) percent distortion, and (c) voltage gain.

17. (a) Compute the power output for Prob. 16.   (b) Compute the plate-power input. Note that the direct current is now A_0, the d-c component from the harmonic analysis.   (c) Compute the efficiency of the amplifier.

18. In the circuit of Fig. 16, with a 2A3 triode, the Q-point is at 275 volts, with a bias of -50 volts. The d-c resistance of the transformer is 650 ohms, and the reduced value of the load is 3.75 K. The transformer ratio is 6.00, and the magnetizing current may be neglected.   (a) Draw the d-c and a-c load-lines.   (b) Find E_b.   (c) Compute the value of the resistance in the secondary.

19. (a) From the load-line for Prob. 18 plot the transfer characteristic.   (b) Obtain from it the 1st- and 2nd-harmonic components of the plate current, for a signal input of 32.0 volts rms.   (c) Compute the corresponding currents in the secondary.   (d) Compute the output power.

20. A power amplifier (Fig. 16) with a 2A3 triode is operated with an effective load of 1810 ohms and an a-c input of 40 volts peak value. The d-c resistance is 220 ohms. The maximum grid potential is zero and the minimum plate current is 25 ma.   (a) Draw the a-c load-line and find the Q-point.   (b) Draw the d-c load-line and find E_b.   (c) Find the gain.   (d) Find the power output.   (e) Find the 2nd-harmonic distortion.

21. For the circuit of Fig. 18, with a 6SN7 twin triode (equivalent to a pair of 6J5 triodes), the load-line for each tube passes from 250 volts on the x-axis to 12.0 ma on the zero grid-potential line.   (a) Plot the transfer characteristics for both tubes, with a grid bias of -6.0 volts. Note that $x = e$ for one tube, $x = -e$ for the other, so that these plots appear as in Fig. 26, crossing at the grid-bias point.   (b) Compute and plot $(I_p' - I_p'')$ as indicated in Fig. 26. Since $e = e_1' - e_2'' = (I_p' - I_p'')R_{ac}$, this plot is a transfer characteristic for the push-pull amplifier. Observe its freedom from distortion. It is interesting to repeat the computations

with other grid-bias values, to discover how linearity depends upon having the right bias.

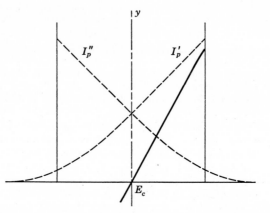

Fig. 26.   Problem 21.   Solid line represents positive end of plot for $(I_p' - I_p'')$.

22. Replot the transfer characteristics from Prob. 21 to correspond to a grid bias of -11.0 volts, and repeat the computations of Prob. 21. The result should be almost as straight a line as for Prob. 21, although each triode is now operating class AB.

23. A balanced amplifier (Fig. 19) with a 6N7 twin triode and 8000 ohms load (R) is operated with 200 volts plate supply and zero grid bias. (a) Plot the composite grid-potential line for 5.0 volts grid potential. The current in one triode may be considered zero for higher signals. (b) Draw the load-line as directed in Sec. 24, and plot the transfer characteristic for the amplifier from this load-line. (c) Compute the voltage output for a signal input of 23 volts rms.

24. A balanced amplifier (Fig. 19) with a 6SN7 twin triode and 3000 ohms load is operated at 200 volts plate supply and zero bias. (a) Plot the composite grid-potential lines. (b) Draw the load-line as directed in Sec. 24, and plot the transfer characteristic for the amplifier from this load-line.

25. Repeat Prob. 24 with a grid bias of -8.0 volts. Note the improved linearity over the result of Prob. 24.

CHAPTER 5

Tetrodes and Pentodes

1. Tetrodes and Pentodes. Many types of electron tubes have two or three grids in place of one. Sectional diagrams for a few of these types are shown in Fig. 1. Those having two grids are called tetrodes, and those with three grids, pentodes. The first grid, in both tetrode and pentode, is next to the cathode and functions quite like the grid of a

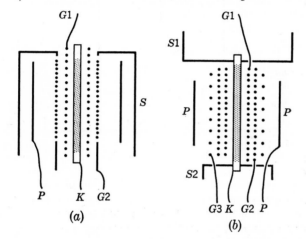

(a)

(b)

Fig. 1. Vertical Cross-sections for (a) A Tetrode (Type 24-A), (b) A Pentode (Type 6J7). Electrodes are concentric cylinders. K —cathode. P—anode. G1, G2, G3—grids. S—internal shield, connected to G2. S1, S2— internal shields, connected to K.

triode. It is the input electrode and is called the *control* grid. Almost always it operates with a negative bias. In the tetrode a second grid, called the *screen* grid, is added, between the first grid and the plate; it has a fairly fine mesh and provides an almost complete electrostatic screen between the plate and the other electrodes. It is always operated at a positive potential, and in all but a very few applications this potential is held at a constant value. The pentode structure is almost the same as for the tetrode, except for the third grid, or *suppressor* grid, located between the screen grid and the plate. This third grid is a rather coarse one which serves to correct certain physical

137

defects of the tetrode, as will be explained later. With few exceptions it is operated at a fixed potential, usually zero. Throughout most of this chapter we shall be concerned with the performance of tetrodes and pentodes when the additional grids are maintained at fixed d-c potentials; this method of operation includes the great majority of applications for these tubes. At the end of the chapter we shall develop briefly the theory which applies when a-c potentials appear on more than one grid.

2. The Screen Grid. The screen grid was added originally to improve the performance of electron tubes in radiofrequency circuits.

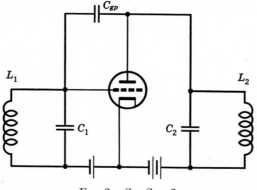

FIG. 2. See Sec. 2.

Difficulties are encountered when a triode is employed as a radiofrequency amplifier, as shown in Fig. 2, because of the electrostatic coupling between the input and output circuits which is provided by C_{gp}, the grid-to-plate capacitance within the tube. (See Sec. 14, Chapter 3.) The resonant circuits, L_1C_1 and L_2C_2, at the input and output of the tube, are coupled together by C_{gp}, as indicated by the heavy lines in Fig. 2, so that independent tuning of the input and output circuits is impossible. Furthermore, under certain conditions this coupled circuit is capable of resonant oscillations which are maintained by the amplifying action of the tube, as will be explained in Chapter 10. The circuit then becomes an oscillator, and can no longer serve as an amplifier. The simplest means for circumventing these difficulties is the screen grid. The screen grid, at ground potential as far as a-c potentials are concerned, prevents this coupling by standing as a grounded electrostatic screen between control grid and plate. Capacitance from control grid or plate to this screen is capacitance to ground, and the direct capacitance between control grid and plate is reduced almost to zero. The mesh of the screen grid is still

open enough, however, to allow a major fraction of the electron stream
to pass through to the plate.

3. Demonstration Experiment 1. The electrostatic shielding produced by the screen grid may be studied and demonstrated with the
field tank. (See Sec. 2, Chapter 2.) Plane-parallel electrodes, as
represented in Fig. 3, are best for this purpose, as we have found earlier.
The screen grid is represented by $G2$, while K, P, and $G1$ represent the
cathode, plate, and control grid respectively. The mesh is finer (rods
closer together) for $G2$ than for $G1$, to provide more effective screening.

Set the field-tank apparatus up
as in Fig. 1, Chapter 2, add the
screen-grid assembly according to
Fig. 3, and connect both $G1$ and $G2$
to K. The field probe (double
probe) will show a strong field between P and $G2$, but a very weak
field between $G2$ and $G1$. This
great reduction in field strength
demonstrates the shielding by $G2$
which is discussed above. Change
the connections, so that $G2$ is connected to P instead of to K; then
the probe will show the field between $G2$ and P to be weakened

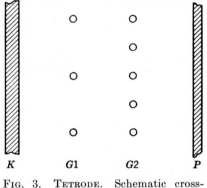

K $G1$ $G2$ P

Fig. 3. Tetrode. Schematic cross-
section for plane electrodes. K—
cathode. P—plate. $G1$, $G2$—grids.

fully as much as was the field between $G1$ and $G2$ for the first connection. *Grid $G2$ serves to screen $G1$ from the field of P, and P from
the field of $G1$.* Change connections back to the first arrangement,
with both $G1$ and $G2$ connected to K, and probe the field between
K and $G1$. This field will be found very small indeed, perhaps difficult
to detect. The cathode, K, is now *doubly* shielded, by $G1$ and by $G2$.

4. Shielding by Two Grids. The last operation of Demonstration
Experiment 1 demonstrates the double shielding of the cathode by two
grids. The field to the left of $G2$ is greatly weakened by the shielding
effect of $G2$, and to the left of $G1$ the already very weak field between
$G2$ and $G1$ is again much reduced by the shielding effect of $G1$. The
geometric amplification factor, μ_0 (see Sec. 4, Chapter 2), is therefore
very large. A rough value of μ_0 for the tetrode structure in Fig. 3 may
be measured in the field tank, with $G2$ connected to K; the procedure is
the same as outlined for a triode structure in Sec. 4, Chapter 2. When
the field near K is zero the ratio of magnitudes for the a-c potentials on
P and on $G1$ equals μ_0. Values for μ_0 of several thousand are not
unusual in commercial tetrodes and pentodes. Here again it must be

emphasized that high values for μ_0 come about by *weakening* the influence of the anode upon the field at the cathode, and *not* by increasing the influence of the control grid.

5. The Tetrode. A thermionic tube with electrodes constructed according to Fig. 3 would be a tetrode, as stated in Sec. 1. In most commercial tetrodes the grids and plate are cylindrical in form and surround the cathode, but they function in the same manner as in the structure of Fig. 3. If both grids in a tetrode are connected to the cathode, not even a very high plate potential will set up much current in it, because the region between the cathode and the first (control)

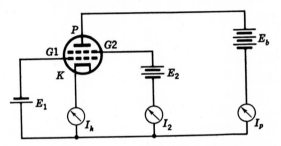

Fig. 4. Currents in a Tetrode.

grid is so effectively shielded by the two grounded grids. With these connections the tube has a very high amplification factor, but uselessly small current.

The solution to this difficulty is to put a positive potential on the second (screen) grid, as in the circuit of Fig. 4. If this potential is held fixed (e.g., by a battery having negligible resistance) this grid will serve as well as before to shield the cathode from the field of the plate, but at the same time it acts like an anode to set up cathode current. *The magnitude of this cathode current depends almost entirely upon the potentials of the two grids.* If both these potentials are held constant the cathode current will remain practically constant, regardless of the potential of the plate. The relationship between these potentials and the cathode current, I_k, is shown in Fig. 5a. (Current I_k is read by a meter placed next the cathode, as shown in Fig. 4.) For each curve plotted in Fig. 5a both V_1, the potential of the first grid, and V_2, the potential of the second grid, are held constant, at the values indicated by the adjacent numbers. The potential V_2 is held at +80 volts for all six plots, whereas V_1 changes from 0, for the uppermost plot, to −4 volts for the lowest. Each plot is practically a straight line, parallel to the axis; the very slight increase in current with plate potential is too small to show here.   (The break in these plots when V_p is zero is interesting, but will be disregarded now.)

In Fig. 5b current I_k is represented as a function of V_1 and V_2. Potential V_1 is plotted as abscissae, and each line represents a fixed value of V_2 (indicated by the adjacent number) and *any value of* V_p.* Compare Fig. 5b with Fig. 4b in Chapter 2; it is quite evident that grid 2 functions like the anode in a triode, in so far as I_k is concerned. This resemblance is further demonstrated by the plots of Fig. 5c, in which V_2 is plotted as abscissae: this figure is identical in appearance

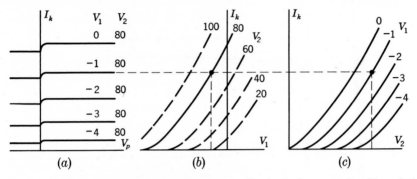

FIG. 5.   CATHODE CURRENT IN A TETRODE. I_k—cathode current. V_p—plate potential. V_1, V_2—potentials of 1st (control) grid and 2nd (screen) grid.

with Fig. 4a, Chapter 2, in which the abscissae are plate potential for a triode.

6. Plate Current in an "Ideal" Tetrode.   The electron current, I_k, divides between the screen grid and the plate.   When V_p is higher than V_2 the ratio of this current division is nearly constant, and roughly equal to the ratio of the projected areas of the grid wires and the spaces between them.   We may think of the electron stream as flowing up to the screen grid with uniform density; one part is intercepted by the grid wires, the other part goes to the plate, through the openings between grid wires.   In commercial tetrodes and pentodes between 15 and 20 percent of the electrons is stopped by the screen grid.

At lower values of V_p the fraction which reaches the plate decreases toward zero, as indicated in Fig. 6.   It will now pay us to inquire carefully into the reasons for this decrease.   We might account for it by

* More correctly, each line in Fig. 5a slopes slightly upward, and each line in Figs. 5b and 5c should be drawn as a closely bunched family of lines, one for each of a series of values for V_p.   These small differences will not show in a plot of this scale, unless the screen grid is quite coarse.

saying glibly that, when V_p is less than V_2, more electrons are intercepted by the screen grid, and some of those which do pass through this grid are turned back by the retarding potential, $V_2 - V_p$, between $G2$ and P. This statement is correct as far as it goes, but it needs explanation. Why, for example, should any electron which passes through the grid turn away from the plate when its kinetic energy, V_2e, is then enough to override the retarding potential? To answer this question let us consider the electric fields around the grid wires of $G2$, when V_p is less than V_2. The corresponding lines of force are

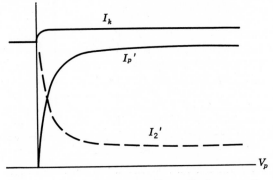

FIG. 6.   CURRENT IN AN IDEAL TETRODE. I_k—cathode current. I_p'—current *to* plate. I_2'—current *to* screen grid.

represented in Fig. 7, with arrowheads indicating the direction of the electric force on *electrons*. Between $G2$ and $G1$ these lines of force are directed toward the *right*, whereas those between $G2$ and P are directed toward the *left*. All lines of force must now bend toward the grid wires as they approach $G2$, so as to terminate on these wires, as shown; and electrons which pass through each gap between two grid wires must leave this gap as a spreading or divergent beam. (Each gap is, in fact, a cylindrical, diverging electron-lens.) The divergence is caused as the electrons cross the lines of force which converge upon each grid wire, as indicated by the dotted line in Fig. 7. The nearer an electron comes to a grid wire the more it is deflected.

The size of its angle of deflection, θ, determines whether or not an electron may reach the plate. Unless V_p is zero any electron which passes through $G2$ has enough kinetic energy to reach the plate, if it approaches the plate head-on, but an electron which is deflected may be kept from reaching the plate by reducing only the x-component of its velocity to zero. Let the mass of an electron be m, its electric charge be e, and its velocity be u. The x-component of u is then

$u \cos \theta$. The electron represented in Fig. 7 will not be able to reach P if the work done on it by the field, E, is greater than the kinetic energy represented by $u \cos \theta$; that is, if*

$$(V_2 - V_p)e > \tfrac{1}{2}mu^2 \cos^2 \theta \qquad (1)$$

Since the initial kinetic energy of the electron (as it passes through $G2$) is given by

$$V_2 e = \tfrac{1}{2}mu^2 \qquad (2)$$

it follows that the condition for failing to reach P is given by

$$V_2 - V_p > V_2 \cos^2 \theta \qquad \text{or} \qquad \sin^2 \theta > V_p/V_2 \qquad (3)$$

The critical angle is given by $\sin^2 \theta_1$ equal to V_p/V_2. When V_p is fairly large, even though it is less than V_2, relatively few electrons are

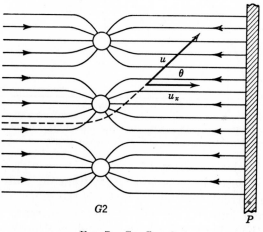

FIG. 7.   See Sec. 6.

deflected through large angles and the critical angle is large. As V_p is made smaller the critical angle decreases and the amount of scattering increases; the current then drops toward zero, as indicated in Fig. 6. This same explanation accounts for the decrease to zero with plate

---

* The electric force, Ee, acts in the x-direction, to decelerate the electron in that direction. For an electron leaving $G2$ at the critical angle, θ_1,

$$-Ee = m\frac{du_x}{dt} \qquad (4)$$

Integration gives

$$-\int_{(2)}^{(p)} Ee\, dx = (V_2 - V_p)e = \int_{u \cos \theta_1}^{0} mu_x\, du_x = \tfrac{1}{2}mu^2 \cos^2 \theta_1 \qquad (5)$$

potential of plate current in a triode, when the control grid is operated at a positive potential.

7. Secondary Emission.   At this point it is necessary to distinguish between electron current to the plate (represented by I_p' in Fig. 6) and the plate current, I_p, measured by the plate-current meter in Fig. 4.   In an ideal tetrode these are the same, but in any actual tetrode they differ because of secondary emission of electrons.   Thus for an actual tetrode the broken-line plot in Fig. 8 (reproduced from Fig. 6) might represent I_p', whereas the solid line represents I_p.   When V_p is

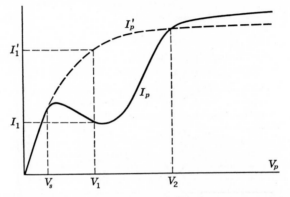

Fig. 8.   Plate Current in a Tetrode. I_p'—primary current *to* plate. I_p— plate current as measured.   Difference is due to secondary emission.

less than V_2 the electron current *to* the plate is accompanied by a simultaneous flow of secondary electrons *away* from the plate to the screen grid, and the current read by the meter is the difference between the *primary* current and this secondary electron current.   For example, when V_p has the value V_1, Fig. 8, the secondary electron current equals $(I_1' - I_1)$.   When V_p is greater than V_2 some secondary electrons leave the screen grid for the plate and I_p is somewhat higher than I_p', as shown in Fig. 8.

Secondary electrons are "knocked out" of the plate by the primary electrons.   Their existence may be proved by providing some means for, controlling their flow, such as the suppressor grid described in Sec. 9.   More elaborate means have been employed to make very careful studies of this phenomenon, from which the following conclusions have been drawn.   (1) A very few of the electrons leaving the bombarded surface, not over 2 or 3 percent, are primary electrons which bounce off the surface with little or no loss of energy.   These *elastically reflected* electrons are too few to concern us here.   (2) Most secondary electrons leave the bombarded surface with very low energies; almost all these are turned back to the surface by an opposing potential of only a few volts.   (3) The ratio of secondary electrons to primary electrons depends upon the nature of the surface and the energy of the primary electrons.   For any one surface the ratio increases from zero to a rather broad maximum as the electron-accelerating potential increases, then falls slowly as the potential is increased further.   The maximum occurs generally at an accelerating potential of a few hundred volts.   The maximum ratio may exceed unity, and may be increased to 5 or 10 by special preparation of the surface.   Surfaces

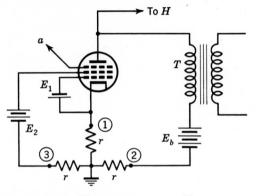

FIG. 9.   DEMONSTRATION EXPERIMENT FOR A TETRODE AND PENTODE.

may also be specially treated to reduce secondary emission, when this is desired, although it cannot be reduced to zero.

8. Demonstration Experiment 2.   The method described in Sec. 10, Chapter 2, for displaying triode characteristics upon the screen of an oscilloscope may be applied to tetrode characteristics.   The circuit is given in Fig. 9.   The tube should be a pentode having the suppressor grid brought out to an independent terminal, such as a type 6SJ7 tube. The fixed voltages, E_1, E_2, and E_b, should be supplied by batteries, and E_1 should be connected from grid 1 directly to the cathode, *not* to ground.   The a-c voltage should be supplied through an isolation transformer, T, with a peak value slightly higher than E_b.   For example, if the a-c supply is 115 volts rms, 160 volts peak, suitable values are: $E_b = 135$ volts, $E_2 = 67$ volts, and $E_1 = -1.5$ volts, for a 6SJ7 pentode.   Current is represented on the oscilloscope screen by the potential drop across resistors r, as in previous experiments.   The value of r should be only large enough to give a good deflection.

Connect grid 3 (terminal a, Fig. 9) to the plate: the tube is then a tetrode, and the curves of Figs. 5a and 8 may be shown.   When the V (vertical-deflection) terminal of the oscilloscope is connected to point

1, current I_k is shown; when the connection is to point 2, I_p is represented. The screen-grid current, I_2, may be shown by making the V connection to point 3. Adjust the oscilloscope amplifiers to make the pattern for I_p of suitable size, and leave them set the same for I_k and I_2. Curves representing currents in an *ideal* tetrode may be produced by connecting grid 3 to the cathode instead of to the plate. (The tube is then a pentode, as explained in Sec. 9.)

9. The Suppressor Grid. A tetrode will serve satisfactorily in an amplifier circuit only if the plate potential, V_p, is kept above the

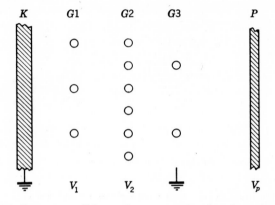

FIG. 10. PENTODE. Schematic cross-section for plane electrodes.

screen-grid potential, V_2, since the plate current varies so irregularly in the region below V_2. Thus tetrodes may be employed in the early stages of a cascade amplifier, where the output is small and high d-c plate supply is available, but never in the last stage, where power losses must be considered. An ideal tetrode, if it could be had, would not be subject to this limitation, and its equivalent may be closely realized if some means can be found to drive the secondary electrons back to the plate. One quite satisfactory means is a third grid which is placed between the screen grid and the plate and held at a low potential, usually zero (cathode) potential. Often it is connected directly to the cathode inside the tube, with no external terminal. For obvious reasons this electrode is called the *suppressor* grid. It is represented in Fig. 10 by $G3$, for the plane-parallel type of electrode structure with which we are now so familiar.

The functioning of this suppressor grid may now be analyzed by considering the plate and the two grids next to it as forming a *secondary triode*. The plate, P, serves as the cathode of this secondary triode, since it is the source of secondary electrons. Grid $G2$ serves as anode, or receiver of these electrons, and $G3$ is the control grid. *Relative to the electron source, P, the potential of the "grid," $G3$, is* $-V_p$, and of the "anode," $+(V_2 - V_p)$. If the amplification factor for this secondary triode is μ', then the equivalent diode potential (see Sec. 6, Chapter 2) is

$$V' = -V_p + \frac{V_2 - V_p}{\mu'} \tag{6}$$

Referring back to Fig. 8, we find that secondary emission is troublesome only after V_p becomes greater than the value indicated by V_s. The suppressor grid will then serve its purpose if the equivalent diode potential is zero for V_p equal to V_s, and negative for higher values of V_p; that is, if

$$0 = -V_s + \frac{V_2 - V_s}{\mu'} \qquad \text{or} \qquad \mu' = \frac{V_2 - V_s}{V_s} \tag{7}$$

The value of μ' required is never large, rarely more than 4, so that the suppressor grid is quite coarse, much coarser than the other two grids.

It is fortunate that μ' need not be large, since the presence of the suppressor grid in front of the plate, and at zero potential, reduces the field in the region between the plate and the screen grid, so that the plate current begins to decrease toward zero at a higher value of V_p than in the absence of the suppressor grid. If μ' is small the suppressor grid is too coarse to make this effect troublesome, but if μ' is larger the plate current may be reduced considerably for quite high plate potentials, and the shape of the grid-potential lines may be seriously distorted.

10. Demonstration Experiment 3. This effect of the suppressor grid upon the potential distribution may be demonstrated with the apparatus of Fig. 9, by putting a negative bias upon grid 3 (between point a and the cathode). This negative bias has much the same effect as a higher value of μ'. Only a few volts negative bias is needed to make a noticeable change in the grid-potential lines, and 9 or 10 volts will change almost completely the characteristics for a 6SJ7 pentode.

11. Pentode Characteristics. With the suppressor grid added a tetrode becomes a pentode. A typical set of plate-current characteristic curves for a pentode is shown in Fig. 12. (See also pentode data in Appendix 5.) The circuit with which they are taken is given in Fig. 11. A comparison of Fig. 12 with Fig. 6 reveals that I_p does not rise quite as quickly with plate potential in a pentode as in an ideal tetrode, for reasons that have been discussed in Sec. 9. Except for this difference the I_p, V_p characteristics for a pentode are identical with those for an ideal tetrode, and either tube, as long as its screen grid is held at a fixed potential (and the suppressor grid of the pentode held at zero potential), serves as a triode having a very high amplification factor and a variational (a-c) resistance which is likewise very high.

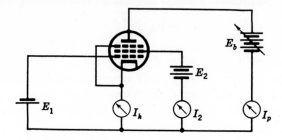

FIG. 11.   CURRENTS IN A PENTODE.   (Voltmeters not shown.)

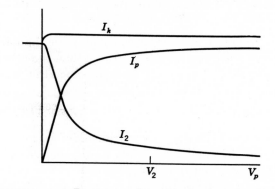

FIG. 12.   CURRENTS IN A PENTODE. I_k—cathode current. I_p—plate current.
I_2—screen-grid current.

Amplification factor, transconductance, and variational plate resistance are defined for tetrodes and pentodes just as for triodes, once it has been specified that all grids but the control grid are to be held at fixed potentials.   They may be represented by the partial derivatives

$$\mu = -\frac{\partial V_p}{\partial V_g} \qquad (I_p, \ V_2, \text{ and } V_3 \text{ held constant}) \qquad (8)$$

$$g_m = \frac{\partial I_p}{\partial V_1} \qquad (V_2, \ V_p, \text{ and } V_3 \text{ held constant}) \qquad (9)$$

$$\frac{1}{r_p} = \frac{\partial I_p}{\partial V_p} \qquad (V_1, \ V_2, \text{ and } V_3 \text{ held constant}) \qquad (10)$$

The values for these tube factors may be estimated by taking slopes of tangent lines to the characteristic curves, as explained in Sec. 21, Chapter 2, for a triode, or they may be measured experimentally by the methods described in Secs. 22 to 24, Chapter 2. It is evident, from the almost horizontal position of the upper portions of the grid-potential lines in Fig. 6, that r_p has an exceedingly high value for an ideal tetrode. For a pentode the value of r_p is considerably less than for an ideal tetrode, largely because secondary emission from the screen grid causes a small increase of plate current with plate potential, as mentioned in Sec. 7. Even so, r_p for commercial pentodes varies from about 100,000 ohms to above a megohm. Real tetrodes have similar values for r_p when the plate potential is above the screen-grid potential.

The transconductance of either a tetrode or pentode depends primarily upon the physical dimensions of the first grid and the cathode, and to a much smaller extent upon the dimensions of the screen grid. It will be recalled that this is true also for a triode, except that the screen grid in a tetrode or pentode takes the place of the plate in a triode. If comparison is made between a triode and a pentode having cathodes and control grids of identical dimensions, the *triode* will be found to have the larger transconductance. The reason is that the plate current in the triode is the total cathode current, whereas a fraction of the total cathode current is stopped by the screen grid in a pentode. For example, g_m for a 6SJ7 pentode is about 1800 micromhos with a cathode current of 6.0 ma, of which 4.6 ma reaches the plate. Now, by connecting grids 2 and 3 to the plate we have a triode with the *same* cathode and control grid, and a plate which practically coincides with the screen grid. For this triode connection, and a cathode current of 6.0 ma, g_m is 2300 micromhos. The ratio of plate current to cathode current for the pentode is 4.6/6.0 or 0.76, and the ratio of the two g_m values is 1800/2300 or 0.78, as might be expected from the discussion above. The value for μ is not often listed among the data given for a pentode; it may be computed as the product of g_m and r_p. It is a much more variable quantity than for triodes.

12. Experiment 13. Measurement of g_m for a Pentode. Transconductance may be measured for a pentode with the apparatus described in Sec. 24, Chapter 2, for a triode. The circuit is exactly the same except for the addition of a screen-grid supply battery, E_2, as shown in Fig. 13. This must be a fresh battery, of low impedance. Also, since E_2 is held fixed, the bias for grid 1 must be variable, as shown. Follow the instructions given under Part II, Exp. 5. The following procedure is recommended for a 6SJ7 or 6J7 pentode.

Part I. Pentode Connection. For the connections of Fig. 13, E_c should be 4 dry cells and R_1 a low-resistance voltage-divider (50 to 200 ohms). Two 45-volt B-batteries will provide E_2, and E_b may have any convenient value, from 135 to 250 volts. Read currents I_p and I_2, and measure g_m, for values of V_g from -1 to -5 volts, by 1-volt steps. Plot your results as curves having V_g as abscissae and g_m, I_p, I_2, and I_k as ordinates.

Part II. Triode Connection. Remove E_2, connect both screen and suppressor grids to the plate to make a triode, and reduce E_b to the

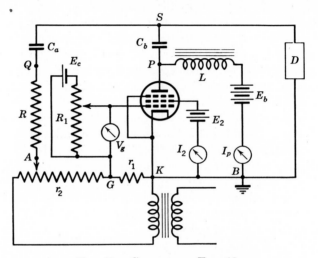

FIG. 13.　CIRCUIT FOR EXP. 13.

value used for E_2 in Part I. Read I_p and measure g_m for the same grid-bias values as in Part I. Plot these values for g_m on the same sheet with the values of g_m for Part I, for comparison. Explain the differences. Plot I_p on the same sheet with the current plots for Part I, and to the same axes. Explain carefully why these values for I_p are so close to those for I_k in Part I.

The amplification factor, μ, may also be measured as in Exp. 5, with suitable modified apparatus. This might be assigned to the student as a project, leaving him to work out the details.

13. Pentode Circuits. In all its normal applications, in which the screen and suppressor grids are maintained at fixed potentials, a pentode functions as a triode with somewhat unusual characteristics. Thus a pentode may replace a triode in any type of amplifier circuit, with no other changes than provision of a power supply for the screen grid and a suitable change in bias potential. This is illustrated by the

circuits of Figs. 14, 15, 16, and 17, which are the pentode counterparts
of the triode circuits of Figs. 1, 2, and 3 of Chapter 3, and Fig. 10
of Chapter 4, respectively.   The screen-grid potential may be equal to
the quiescent (no-signal) plate potential, or lower.   Almost never is it
higher.   It may be supplied by a separate battery, as in Fig. 14, or
from a portion of the plate-supply battery, as in Fig. 15.   When the

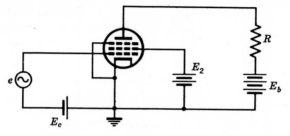

FIG. 14.   SIMPLE PENTODE AMPLIFIER.

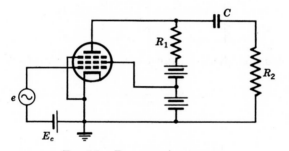

FIG. 15.   PENTODE AMPLIFIER.

d-c power is supplied to the plate through a transformer or choke-coil
the screen grid and the plate may be supplied from the same d-c
source, as in Figs. 16 and 17.   Bias for the control grid may be obtained
from a cathode resistor, as in Fig. 16, providing this resistor is by-passed
by a very large condenser; this condenser must be much larger for a
pentode than for a triode, since the gain in the pentode is higher.   The
reason is given in Sec. 8 of Chapter 3.

Figure 18 illustrates another way to supply power to the screen grid
when its potential is lower than the emf of the d-c source.   The screen-
grid potential, V_2, here equals E_b minus the product of the *average* screen-
grid current and the resistance of R_2, the so-called "dropping resistor."
Condenser C_2 serves to maintain this potential at constant value.   The
current in R_2 is only the d-c part of the current to the screen grid; the
a-c part is supplied from the charge stored in C_2, and C_2 must be large

enough to supply this current without appreciable change in the potential difference between its terminals.   This is the physical picture of what happens.   From the point of view of a-c circuit theory we may regard C_2 as a short circuit between the screen grid and the cathode,

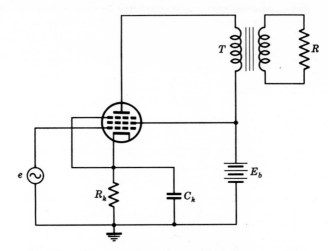

FIG. 16.   PENTODE AMPLIFIER.   Transformer output.

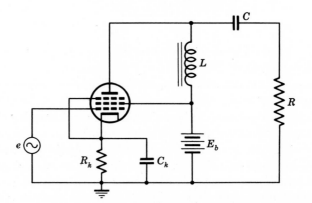

FIG. 17.   PENTODE AMPLIFIER.   D-C supply through choke-coil.

so that the a-c potential of the screen grid is always zero, relative to the cathode.   In this respect R_2 and C_2 function in much the same manner as do R_k and C_k, which provide the bias for grid 1.

14. Stability in Pentode Circuits.   Satisfactory operation of a pentode circuit requires rather close control of E_c and E_2, the d-c potentials on the first two grids.   When these potentials are supplied from separate sources, as in Fig. 14, a small change in either one may either reduce the quiescent plate current, I_0, so close to zero that the quiescent plate potential, V_0, is nearly equal to E_b, or increase I_0 until the potential drop in R_1 lowers V_0 almost to zero. The circuit of Fig. 18, on the contrary, is quite free from this difficulty, once suitable magnitudes have been found for R_1, R_2, and R_k. Both E_c and E_2 are then determined by I_0 and I_0', the d-c components of plate current and screen-grid current respectively, and remain at values which give

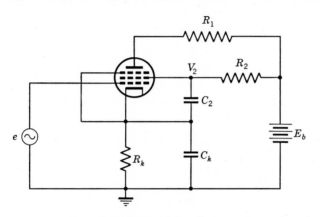

FIG. 18.   PENTODE AMPLIFIER.   Common B-supply.

satisfactory performance even when E_b is varied over a considerable range. Any increase or decrease in I_0 will change E_c in such a direction as to oppose the change in I_0, and in like manner any change in I_0' is opposed by the changes which it produces in both E_c and E_2. This aspect of the performance of this circuit is an example of negative feedback at zero frequency, a topic which is discussed in Chapter 6.

Tetrodes are not commonly employed in amplifier circuits of the kinds here considered. Their chief usefulness is in radiofrequency circuits, where they serve somewhat specialized functions.

15. Equivalent-Circuit Analysis for a Pentode Circuit. When the output from a pentode circuit is low this circuit may be represented by an equivalent a-c circuit (see Sec. 20, Chapter 2) just as for any triode circuit. For example, if such an equivalent circuit is made for the circuit of Fig. 14, the alternating current, i_p, is found to be

$$i_p = \mu e/(r_p + R) \tag{11}$$

The output voltage is then

$$e_0 = -\mu eR/(r_p + R) \tag{12}$$

and the gain of the circuit is

$$A = - \mu R/(r_p + R) \tag{13}$$

In triode circuits, r_p is generally smaller than R, so that the gain is somewhat comparable with μ in magnitude. In pentode circuits, however, r_p is almost always so very much larger than R that only a small error is made by dropping R from the denominators of the right-hand terms in Eqs. 11, 12, and 13. That is,

$$i_p \cong \mu/r_p = g_m e \tag{14}$$

$$e_0 \cong -g_m R e \tag{15}$$

and

$$A \cong -g_m R \tag{16}$$

When this approximation is admissible the pentode performs almost like a constant-current generator, delivering a nearly constant current whose value is given by Eq. 14. This is a convenient approximation, but we should never forget that it is only an approximation.

From these considerations it is evident why the gain of a pentode amplifier, although it may be high as compared with that of a triode amplifier, never approaches the expectations aroused by the fantastically high values of μ for a pentode. Except in rare instances it is impossible to employ a load impedance which is comparable with the likewise fantastically high plate resistance. For a pentode, indeed, g_m is a much more important factor than either μ or r_p.

16. Equivalent Circuit with Constant-Current Source. It is often advantageous to compare a pentode circuit with one in which a source of constant alternating current is shunted by a resistance equal to r_p. This circuit is diagrammed in Fig. 19, for the pentode circuit of Fig. 14. The magnitude of the constant current is taken as

$$i_0 = g_m e \tag{17}$$

This current divides between r_p and the part of the circuit which is external to the tube, the load R in this case. The output voltage, e_0, is then equal to i_0 times the parallel impedance of r_p and R, with a negative sign, or

$$e_0 = -i_0 \frac{r_p R}{r_p + R} = - \frac{g_m e \, r_p R}{r_p + R}$$

$$= - \frac{\mu e R}{r_p + R} \tag{18}$$

Equation 18 is the same as Eq. 13, and we may take this as proof* that the circuit of Fig. 19 does correctly represent the part of the circuit *which is external to the tube* in Fig. 14. To that extent Fig. 19 is an *equivalent circuit* for Fig. 14, but the equivalence ends at the terminals of the tube. The alternating current in the tube is neither i_0 nor the current in r_p in Fig. 19. On the contrary, the equivalent circuit of Fig. 10, Chapter 2, does represent correctly the alternating currents and potentials for the entire circuit, providing only that these are small enough for the usual approximations to hold.

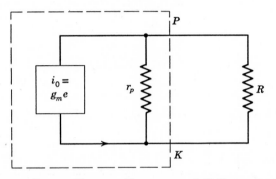

FIG. 19. CURRENT-SOURCE TYPE OF EQUIVALENT A-C CIRCUIT. This circuit is equivalent *only* for the part *outside* the broken-line outline.

17. Experiment 14. Pentode Amplifier. The operation of a pentode amplifier, for small output, may be studied as in Exp. 6 for the triode amplifier. A suitable test circuit is given in Fig. 20; it differs only in minor detail from the triode test circuit of Fig. 4, Chapter 3. The circuit constants specified under this figure are for a 6J7 pentode. Whenever screen-grid and plate power are supplied from separate d-c sources, as in Fig. 20, it is *very important that the screen-grid power be turned on last.* If the screen-grid power is turned on before the plate power has been connected, and the control grid biased negatively,

---

* This substitution is one familiar to general circuit theory and may be made in *any* circuit. For example, let us suppose we have a box with two exposed terminals, but know nothing about what is in the box. If we can (1) measure the impedance, Z_i, between these terminals, and (2) measure the current i_0 when we short the terminals through an ammeter of zero impedance, we may then *imagine* that the box contains a source of constant current i_0, and that, inside the box, the terminals are shunted by an impedance Z_i. From this assumption we can compute correctly the current and potential values for any circuit which we may connect to these terminals. The only proviso is that the circuit elements within the box are linear.

excessive current to the screen grid may damage the tube. For the
same reason the screen-grid power must be turned *off first*.

Part I.   Plate-Current Characteristics.   Leave the a-c power to T,
and the vacuum-tube voltmeter, turned off for this part of the experiment, and also for Part II.   Short out R by closing switch $S3$; voltmeter $V2$ now reads plate potential, V_p.   Also, since there is no a-c
signal, $V1$ reads V_g.

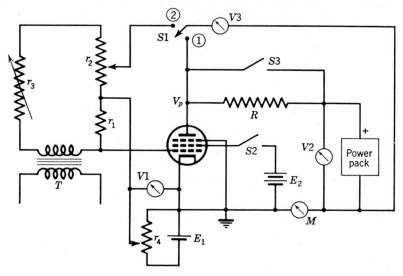

FIG. 20.   CIRCUIT FOR EXP. 14.

E_1—6 volts (4 dry cells). R—50 K, non-inductive, 5 watt.
E_2—90 volts (B-batteries). r_1—fixed "precision" resistor, equal
 T—transformer to supply 5–10 volts   to about $\frac{1}{100}$ of the maximum
     at 400–1000 cps.   value of r_2.
   The other details are described under Exp. 7, in Sec. 5, Chapter 3.

(*a*) Set V_g at -2.0 volts and V_p at 200 volts, then close $S2$.   Note
that there is no plate current until $S2$ has been closed.   Read I_p
(milliammeter M) as V_p is varied from 250 volts down to zero.   Take
8 or 10 points, closer together where the current changes most rapidly.
Plot a curve with I_p as y, V_p as x.

(*b*) Starting with the same initial conditions, hold V_p constant
at 200 volts and vary V_g from 0 to -5 volts, by 0.5-volt steps.   Plot
these data as a curve with I_p as y, V_g as x.

Part II.   Transfer Characteristic.   Start with conditions the same
as in Part I, but open $S3$, so as to include R between the plate of the
tube and the power supply.   Voltmeter $V2$ now reads E_b.   Hold

E_b constant and vary V_g as in Part Ib, reading I_p. Plot I_p as y, V_g as x, on the same sheet and to the same axes as the plot for Part Ib. Explain why these two plots almost coincide over much of their range. Near zero value for V_g the plot for Part II bends toward the horizontal and falls away from the plot for Part Ib. Why should this be?

Part III. Amplifier Gain. Measure the gain in the manner described in Exp. 6, for a series of values for grid bias from -1 to -5 volts, with E_b held fixed at 200 volts. Each time turn $S1$ to point 1 and adjust r_3 to given nearly full-scale deflection of $V3$; then turn $S1$

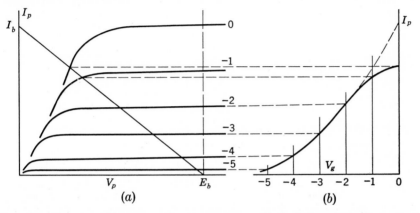

FIG. 21. PENTODE TRANSFER CHARACTERISTIC. Dotted lines indicate method of construction. Broken line in (*b*) shows corresponding I_p, V_1 characteristic.

to point 2 and adjust r_2 to give the same reading of $V3$. (Check back to point 1 to make sure.) Compute the gain from r_1 and r_2, and plot gain as y, grid bias as x.

Compute the gain from the transfer characteristic of Part II, by measuring its slope at the point representing the grid bias for each case: $-R$ times this slope equals the gain. Explain why. Compare these computed values with the directly measured ones by plotting them on the same sheet and to the same axes.

18. Graphical Analysis for Pentode Circuits. When the output in a pentode circuit is large it must be found graphically, just as for a triode. The Q-point is located, the load-line drawn, and the transfer characteristic plotted, all as described in Secs. 1 and 2 of Chapter 4. This procedure is illustrated in Fig. 21, for the circuit of Fig. 14. The figure is self-explanatory. The S-shape of this transfer characteristic is typical for pentodes. The curvature at the lower end corresponds to the curvature in a triode transfer characteristic and has the same origin, namely the space-charge law. The reverse curvature at the top has a different origin: as may be seen from Fig. 21, it is produced when the load-line crosses the region where the grid-potential lines turn down toward zero, and are thus crowded together. This curvature has its counterpart in triode transfer characteristics, but only when the grid potential swings positive, for example in class B2 operation. Because of its S-shape a pentode transfer characteristic has only a short portion which may be considered straight, and the Q-point must be located at the center of this portion for best operation. When the amplitude of the output exceeds this straight portion the

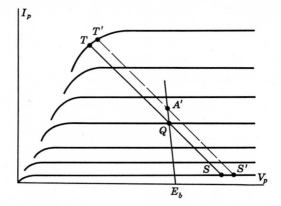

Fig. 22.   A-C and D-C Load-Lines for Pentode Circuit of Fig. 17. $T'A'S'$— a-c load-line.   Line TQS is *not* a-c load-line because average point, A', must lie on d-c load-line, QE_b.

distortion will include odd- as well as even-harmonic components; indeed, if the Q-point is properly located the even harmonics may be negligible, leaving the third harmonic as the chief component of distortion.

For a circuit having both d-c and a-c branches, for example that of Fig. 17, the a-c and d-c load-lines are drawn as explained in Secs. 10 to 12 of Chapter 4. For the circuit of Fig. 17 they are represented in Fig. 22. As explained in Sec. 10, Chapter 4, the a-c load-line may shift in position when the output is large, owing to a change in direct current under these conditions. This shift may generally be neglected for triodes, but not for pentodes; the reasons are obvious from a comparison of Fig. 22 with Fig. 11, Chapter 4. Fortunately, when the Q-point is well located, so that the second-harmonic content is small, the change in direct current is likewise small.

19. Demonstration Experiment 4. The transfer characteristic for a pentode amplifier may be shown on the screen of an oscilloscope with

the aid of the apparatus of Fig. 20.   The simplest way to do this is to
connect the plate of the pentode to the V terminal of the oscilloscope,
and put the signal on the H terminal.   Since I_p is proportional to
$-V_p$, this arrangement shows the transfer characteristic upside down.
With $S3$ closed the pattern will be the broken line in Fig. 21; with $S3$
open, the solid line.

20. Power Pentodes.   A pentode may be designed to serve as a
power tube by giving it the characteristics described for a power triode
in Sec. 16, Chapter 4.   These changes lower both the amplification
factor and the a-c plate resistance, but the tube still performs as a
pentode: the voltage gain is still much higher than for a triode of
comparable output, and the a-c plate resistance is still so high that
the a-c plate current is largely independent of the load impedance.
Greater voltage gain is the chief advantage of the power pentode over a
power triode, whereas high plate resistance is its chief disadvantage
in most applications.   With few exceptions, principally in radiofrequency circuits, a power source having low internal impedance is
far better than one having high internal impedance.

This is especially true when the load is a loud-speaker.   When the
source impedance is high the diaphragm of the speaker is damped only
by air resistance.   It follows poorly the changes in amplitude of the
driving current, and "blasts" at resonant frequencies.   Its behavior is
quite different when the source impedance is low.   Then the emf which
is generated in the voice coil by its motion in the magnetic field sets up
in the circuit a current (superimposed upon the driving current) which,
according to Lenz's law, reacts with the magnetic field to strongly
damp the motion of the diaphragm.

The inherently poor characteristics of a pentode may be largely
compensated by inverse feedback, as explained in Chapter 6.   It is
possible also to employ inverse feedback to give a pentode circuit a
low output impedance.   Characteristic curves for a typical power
pentode (type 6F6) are given in Appendix 5.

21. The Beam Tube.   For the type of screen-grid tube called the
beam tube it is possible to obtain characteristics which are better than
for any power pentode because, in this tube, secondary emission is controlled by the space-charge of the electron beam itself, and no suppressor grid is required.   In any screen-grid tube, when the plate
potential is lower than the screen-grid potential so that there is secondary current, the primary electrons slow down as they approach the
plate and the space-charge density therefore increases toward the
plate.   The beam tube is designed to keep the primary electron stream

together into a narrow beam, so that the space-charge concentration is sufficient to serve in place of a suppressor whenever it is needed.

The electrode structure in a beam tube is shown in horizontal cross-section in Fig. 23; it is close to the plane-parallel structure which we

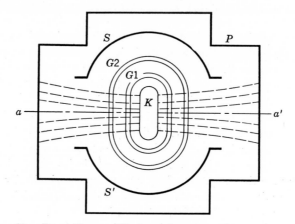

Fig. 23.   Beam Tube.   Horizontal cross-section (schematic).

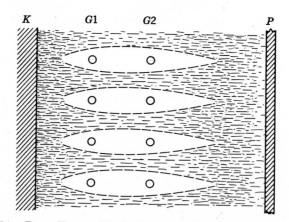

Fig. 24.   Beam Tube.   Vertical cross-section along a-a' in Fig. 23.

have found so convenient for demonstration and theory. The cathode, K, is surrounded by the two grids, and the plate is some distance away on either side. The electron stream is confined to two beams, one from each face of K, by the "beam-forming" electrodes, S and S', which are connected internally to K. By proper design of these electrodes each electron beam is made to travel straight toward the plate, without spreading out. The control and screen grids, $G1$ and $G2$, have the same spacing, with the grid wires of one exactly in line with those of the other, so that almost all the electrons pass through both grids without coming near the screen-grid wires. This essential detail is shown in Fig. 24, which is a vertical cross-section through one side of the tube (along a-a', Fig. 23). If the grid were constructed otherwise, so that any considerable portion of the electron beam passed close to the screen-grid wires, the beam would not be uniform when V_p is low. Instead it would spread out as explained in Sec. 6. A

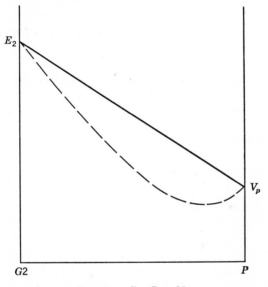

FIG. 25. See Sec. 23.

second advantage of this grid structure is that it keeps the screen-grid current to less than 5 percent of the total current.

The manner in which this beam tube functions to control secondary emission now may be explained by reference to Fig. 25. The solid line in Fig. 25 represents the potential distribution along the path of the electron beam from the screen grid, $G2$, to the plate, P (along the line a-a', Fig. 23), *with no current in the tube*. (Between the screen-grid wires this plot should be slightly lower than E_2, the fixed potential of $G2$, but this difference is unimportant here and may be neglected.) When there is current in the tube this potential distribution is altered by space-charge, the charge carried by the electrons in transit from $G2$ to P. Then, as explained in Sec. 6, Chapter 1, this space-charge causes the line representing the potential distribution to *sag* between $G2$ and P, as represented by the broken line in Fig. 25.

22. Demonstration Experiment 5. The potential distribution between $G2$ and P, with no space-charge present, may be represented by a cord stretched tight between E_2 and V_p in Fig. 25. For this demonstration, Fig. 25 should be reproduced on the blackboard. The effect of space-charge then may be represented by loosening the cord so that it sags under the force of gravity. This represents a uniform distribution of space-charge; to represent the potential distribution in the beam tube more closely, we may string beads along the cord, some distance apart. The beads then may be put closer together or farther apart to represent variations in space-charge density. The cord should fit the holes in the beads so that they will stay where put. Several strands of small cord are preferable to a single larger cord. Large wood beads from the toy store are suitable.

23. Beam-Tube Characteristics. When V_p is equal to or greater than E_2 the space-charge is small and the sag is of no importance, but when V_p is low the electrons slow down as they approach P and the space-charge density near P increases in inverse proportion to the electron speed. (See Eq. 8, Chapter 1.) The potential distribution may then be as represented in Fig. 25 by the broken line. When the potential at the bottom of the sag is lower than V_p, as it is in Fig. 25, the potential rises from this potential minimum toward the plate, so that any electrons between this point and the plate are pushed toward the plate. This potential minimum thus bars the escape of secondary electrons from the plate. The distance from $G2$ to P is determined so that this potential sag drops below V_p before secondary emission becomes large enough to be troublesome. Unlike the suppressor grid, however, this space-charge potential barrier does not drop far below V_p, and hence does not seriously disturb the flow of primary electrons toward the plate until V_p is almost zero. For this reason the beam tube makes a better power tube than the suppressor-grid pentode.

A set of plate-current characteristics for a 6L6 beam tube is given in Appendix 5. At very low plate-current values the space-charge density is insufficient to suppress secondary emission, as shown by the plots for grid potentials below -15 volts. Note that these plots resemble those given for a tetrode in Fig. 8. Observe also that the plots for positive grid potential do not bend smoothly downward as the plate potential approaches zero but break suddenly, passing through a region of instability* which is represented by the hook at this break point. Fortunately, normal operation for a beam tube lies outside this region of instability, as well as outside the region of low

* A detailed explanation for this instability is given in K. R. Spangenberg, *Vacuum Tubes*, p. 263.

plate current where secondary emission current is appreciable.   Within its region of normal operation a beam tube has transfer characteristics very similar to those for a triode, together with the advantages of a pentode, such as high gain and full electrostatic screening between control grid and plate.

24. Multigrid Tubes.   Up to this point we have considered both tetrodes and pentodes as modified triodes, with the additional grids operated at fixed d-c potentials.   Such considerations cover the vast majority of electron-tube applications.   There are times, however, when a-c potentials appear on more than one grid.   Sometimes this is incidental; for example, when the dropping resistor to the screen grid (see Fig. 18) is insufficiently by-passed.   At other times it is intentional, and tubes are designed with as many as five grids, two or more of these grids being planned for operation at a-c potentials.

Whenever two or more grids are operated at a-c potentials the methods which are developed in Chapter 2 for representing tube characteristics are no longer sufficient.   First of all, there are more potentials and more currents than can be represented by any single *family* of characteristic curves.   Thus for a pentode there are two currents: I_p, to the plate, and I_2, to the screen grid.   To these may be added I_1, to the control grid, and I_3, to the suppressor grid, when these grids have positive potentials.   And each current is a function of V_1, V_2, and V_3, the potentials of the three grids, and of V_p, the potential of the plate.   Even if only the total (cathode) current is considered it must be represented as a function of all four potentials, whereas only two potentials may be included in a single family of curves.   For this reason curves representing all the characteristics for a tetrode or pentode are rarely if ever available.   When more data are needed the user of a tube must measure them himself, or make a guess at them from such data as are given.

25. Tube Factors for N Grids.   For small variations in the electrode potentials we may represent the corresponding variations in current by the mathematical equation for infinitesimal changes, as is done for a triode in Sec. 15, Chapter 2.   Consider, for example, a tetrode (or a pentode with the suppressor grid tied to the cathode).   For the total or cathode current we may write

$$\Delta I_k = \frac{\partial I_k}{\partial V_1} \Delta V_1 + \frac{\partial I_k}{\partial V_2} \Delta V_2 + \frac{\partial I_k}{\partial V_p} \Delta V_p \tag{19}$$

Similar equations may be written for I_2 and I_p, and also for I_1 when V_1 is positive.   For the present we shall consider that I_1 is zero. These equations are

$$\Delta I_p = \frac{\partial I_p}{\partial V_1} \Delta V_1 + \frac{\partial I_p}{\partial V_2} \Delta V_2 + \frac{\partial I_p}{\partial V_p} \Delta V_p \tag{20}$$

$$\Delta I_2 = \frac{\partial I_2}{\partial V_1} \Delta V_1 + \frac{\partial I_2}{\partial V_2} \Delta V_2 + \frac{\partial I_2}{\partial V_p} \Delta V_p \tag{21}$$

The partial derivatives appearing in Eqs. 19, 20, and 21 have the *dimensions of conductance;* compare with Sec. 15, Chapter 2. Since the letter g, the usual symbol for conductance, is pretty well overworked in electron-tube notation, we shall now use s in its place. (This notation was first introduced by Chaffee.) Superscripts and subscripts serve to designate the currents and potentials involved. Thus we may write

$$\frac{\partial I_p}{\partial V_2} = s_2{}^p \tag{22}$$

In this notation, Eqs. 20 and 21 become

$$\Delta I_p = s_1{}^p \Delta V_1 + s_2{}^p \Delta V_2 + s_p{}^p \Delta V_p \tag{23}$$

$$\Delta I_2 = s_1{}^2 \Delta V_1 + s_2{}^2 \Delta V_2 + s_p{}^2 \Delta V_p \tag{24}$$

For the total current we shall omit the superscript, writing Eq. 19 as

$$\Delta I_k = s_1 \Delta V_1 + s_2 \Delta V_2 + s_p \Delta V_p \tag{25}$$

It is evident that $s_1{}^p$ is the same as g_m for a tetrode as defined in Sec. 11. Likewise, $s_p{}^p$ is the same as $1/r_p$. The seven remaining s's are tube factors not hitherto considered.

26. Relationships and Magnitudes. It is obvious that all these conductances are not independent. Since the total current, I_k, equals the sum of I_p and I_2,

$$s_1 = s_1{}^p + s_1{}^2 \qquad s_2 = s_2{}^p + s_2{}^2 \qquad s_p = s_p{}^p + s_p{}^2 \tag{26, 27, 28}$$

For almost all tetrodes and pentodes the value of s_p may be taken equal to zero, as explained in Sec. 5. Equation 28 then may be written

$$s_p{}^2 = -s_p{}^p = -1/r_p \tag{29}$$

This equation may be interpreted as saying that the increase in I_p is at the expense of I_2, the total current remaining unchanged.

Other relationships may be obtained by considering the triode connection (plate and screen grid tied together). For this connection the triode current, $I_p{}'$, equals I_p plus I_2, and the triode plate potential, $V_p{}'$, equals both V_p and V_2. Equation 25 then gives

$$\Delta I_p{}' = s_1 \Delta V_1 + (s_2 + s_p) \Delta V_p{}' \tag{30}$$

If the transconductance and the a-c plate resistance for this *triode* connection are represented by g_m' and r_p' respectively, then

$$g_m' = s_1 \quad \text{and} \quad 1/r_p = s_2 + s_p \cong s_2 \qquad (31, 32)$$

Consider a typical example. For a 6J7 pentode, operated with both plate and screen grid at 100 volts, and the control grid at -3 volts, the plate and screen-grid currents are 2.0 ma and 0.5 ma respectively. For these conditions the conductances have the following approximate values, in micromhos.

$$s_1{}^2 = 260 \qquad s_1{}^p = 1160 \qquad s_1 = 1420$$
$$s_2{}^2 = 15 \qquad s_2{}^p = 60 \qquad s_2 = 75$$
$$s_p{}^2 = -1 \qquad s_p{}^p = +1 \qquad s_p = 0$$

For most tubes the only available data are $s_1{}^p = g_m$, $s_p{}^p = 1/r_p$, $s_1 = g_m'$, and $s_2 = 1/r_p'$. However, if these factors are known for the same operating potentials it is possible to compute $s_1{}^2$ and $s_p{}^2$ from Eqs. 26 and 27. Values for the remaining factors may now be estimated by assuming that $s_2{}^2$ and $s_2{}^p$ are proportional to the corresponding currents, I_2 and I_p. It may be seen that this ratio is checked by the values given in the table above. It is interesting to note also that this proportion holds roughly for $s_1{}^2$ and $s_1{}^p$: the ratio of $s_1{}^2$ to $s_1{}^p$ is 0.23, whereas the current ratio is 0.25. When comparable triode data are not available, this proportion is useful in estimating values for the s's from the pentode data and the amplification factor, μ', for the triode connection.

Let us apply this method of estimation to data for a type 6F6 pentode, under the following operating conditions: $V_1 = -16.5$ volts, $V_p = V_2 = 250$ volts, $I_p = 34$ ma, and $I_2 = 6.5$ ma. For the pentode connection, g_m is 2500 micromhos and r_p is 80,000 ohms. For the triode connection, μ' is 6.8. The s-values in the table below *which are not in parentheses* are obtained *directly* from these data.

$$s_1{}^2 = (480) \qquad s_1{}^p = 2500 \qquad s_1 = (2980)$$
$$s_2{}^2 = (70) \qquad s_2{}^p = (370) \qquad s_2 = (440)$$
$$s_p{}^2 = (-12) \qquad s_p{}^p = +12 \qquad s_p = (0)$$

The estimated values are enclosed in parentheses. They are computed as follows. First $s_1{}^2$ is computed from the current ratio:

$$s_1{}^2/s_1{}^p = 6.5/34 \quad \text{or} \quad s_1{}^2 = 480 \text{ micromhos}$$

Then each figure in the second row is obtained by dividing the figure just above it by μ':

$$s_2{}^2 = s_1{}^2/\mu' = 480/6.8 = 70 \text{ micromhos}$$

Such estimated values are quite rough, but are very serviceable for preliminary computations.

27. Amplification Factors. We may define a whole set of amplification factors for a tube having N grids. Thus, for the tetrode considered in Sec. 26 we may define three amplification factors for changes in V_1, V_2, and V_p which, taken alone, produce the same change in I_k; three more for I_p; and three more for I_2. These nine factors will now be represented by the letter u, with one superscript and *two* subscripts. The second subscript designates the *current* concerned. For example, the u-factor which represents changes of V_1 and V_p, each of which, by itself, will produce the same change in I_p, is represented by $u^p{}_{1,p}$. The definition given in Sec. 13, Chapter 2, may be modified to fit each of these u-factors, but it is more convenient here to define them in terms of partial derivatives. Thus we may define $u^p{}_{1,p}$ by

$$u^p{}_{1,p} = -\frac{\partial V_p}{\partial V_1} \ (I_p, \ V_2 \text{ constant}) \tag{33}$$

It is now possible, following the method laid out in Sec. 16, Chapter 2, to show that

$$u^p{}_{1,p} = \frac{s_1{}^p}{s_p{}^p} \tag{34}$$

or, in general,

$$u^i{}_{j,k} = \frac{s_j{}^k}{s_i{}^k} \tag{35}$$

where i, j, and k represent any desired combinations of electrodes. Equation 35 is a generalization of the tube-factor equation of Sec. 16, Chapter 2. When dealing with a tube having more than one grid, one finds the u-factors of much less importance than the s-factors.

28. Experiment 15.   Characteristics for a Two-Grid Tube. A type 49 tetrode is chosen for this experiment because it has a rather coarse second grid. Most tetrodes and pentodes have screen grids of so fine mesh that the effect of plate potential upon the current is hard to measure. This tube has a filamentary cathode, and heater power should be supplied from a 2-volt storage cell, with the negative terminal connected to the common ground point as shown in Fig. 26. The characteristics for this tube are to be obtained in the neighborhood of a Q-point specified by -3.0 volts for V_1, 67 volts for V_2, and 90 volts for V_p. (These are nominal values. The exact values will be determined by the B-batteries and should be read with a voltmeter.) A voltage-divider of several thousand ohms, across a battery of 10 dry cells, provides V_1. If the voltage-divider has a scale of equal parts, more precise values for V_1 may be obtained from this scale reading and the emf of the battery, than may be read by a voltmeter between grid 1 and the cathode.   In several parts of this experiment one of the two potentials, V_2 and V_p, is held constant, the other varied.   In the test circuit of Fig. 25 provision is made to supply the fixed potential from B-batteries, the variable one from a power pack.   Switch S enables these to be interchanged when necessary.   In the George Washington University laboratory all three currents are measured with the same milliammeter: the three meter positions indicated in Fig. 26 are

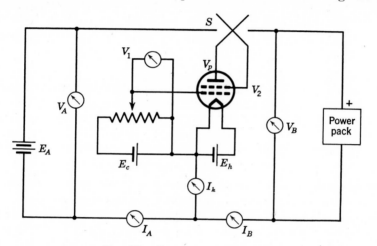

FIG. 26.   CIRCUIT FOR EXP. 15.

occupied by three closed-circuit phone jacks, and a phone plug is connected to the milliammeter.

Part I.   Characteristic Curves.   Obtain the following three sets of characteristic curves intersecting at the Q-point.

(*a*) With S thrown so as to use B-batteries for V_2, vary V_p from 0 to 150 volts, holding V_1 and V_2 fixed at the Q-point values.   Read all currents each time, and take observations close enough near the foot of the curve to follow the variations caused by secondary emission.   Plot characteristic curves for each current, on the same sheet and to the same axes.

(*b*) Holding V_2 and V_p fixed at the Q-point values, vary V_1 from 0 to -15 volts.   Plot a curve for each current, on the same sheet and to the same axes.

(*c*) Reverse S so as to use the B-batteries for V_p, hold V_p and V_1 fixed at the Q-point values, and vary V_2 from 0 to 100 volts.   Plot corresponding curves.

Part II. Conductance Factors.   Draw tangent lines to each of these nine curves, at the Q-point, and obtain from the slopes of these lines values for the nine s-factors defined in Sec. 25.

Part III. Amplification Factors.   Proceed as follows to obtain values for the three u-factors for constant total current, I_k, by the method of small increments.

(a) Obtain $u^p{}_{1,k}$ by varying V_1 and V_p simultaneously from the Q-point so as to keep I_k constant.   Increase V_1 by about 1 volt and vary V_p to bring I_k back to its Q-point value.   Repeat for V_1 decreased by the same amount.

(b) Obtain $u^p{}_{2,k}$ in similar manner.   Vary V_2 by adding several dry cells in series with the 67-volt B-battery.   Repeat with the added dry cells in series-opposition.

(c) Likewise obtain $u^2{}_{1,k}$ with the power pack in the grid 2 circuit.

As a check on your experimental values, compute these u-factors from the s-factors of Part II.

Multiply $u^2{}_{1,k}$ by $u^p{}_{2,k}$ and compare the product with $u^p{}_{1,k}$.   Prove that these values should be equal.

29. Remote Cut-Off (Variable-Gain) Pentode.   Unless the plate potential is quite low the plate current in a pentode is determined almost entirely by V_1 and V_2, the potentials of the control and screen grids respectively.   If the pentode is symmetrical* this dependence is determined by the *combination* of V_1 and V_2 given by

$$V = V_1 + V_2/\mu'' \tag{36}$$

The amplification factor μ'' is a constant, and would be represented by $u^2{}_{1,p}$ in the notation of Sec. 27.   It is practically equal to the amplification factor for the triode connection.   It follows that I_p falls to zero at a "cut-off" grid potential V_c such that V equals zero, or

$$V_c = -V_2/\mu'' \tag{37}$$

Such a symmetrical pentode has I_p, V_1 characteristics as shown in Fig. 5b, and is generally called a *sharp cut-off* pentode.

An unsymmetrical pentode may be constructed by dividing the control grid into two or more sections, making the grid-wire spacing different for each section.   The result is a *remote cut-off* pentode with I_p, V_1 characteristics of the kind shown in Fig. 27.   See also the data for a 6SK7 pentode in Appendix 5.   In analyzing the performance of this type of tube we may regard it as practically equivalent to several

---

* See Sec. 6, Chapter 2.   The structure of a symmetrical pentode is such that the electron stream from its cathode is uniformly distributed over its surface.

symmetrical tubes in parallel, one for each grid section, all having the same grid potentials.   Figure 27 is drawn to represent current for a tube having a small section of quite coarse grid, the remainder of the grid being much closer spaced.   The current through the coarse section is represented by plot A.   For this section μ'' is small, since the grid is coarse, and cut-off occurs at a, a fairly large negative value of V_1.   Plot B represents current through the finer grid section, with a

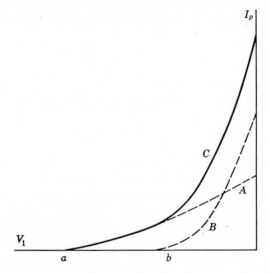

Fig. 27.   Current in Remote Cut-Off Pentode.   See Sec. 29.

cut-off potential at b; and plot C, which represents current for the entire tube, is obtained by adding the currents for plots A and B.

The important property of this type of tube is its variable gain, which may be controlled over a wide range by changing its grid bias. This property makes it serviceable in certain types of electronic instruments, such as DB meters, where non-linear operation is desired.* Its principal use, however, is in the RF stages of AM radio receivers, in connection with AVC (automatic volume control).   In AVC circuits the variable bias is produced by a rectifier-filter unit at the output of the IF amplifier (see Sec. 18,   Chapter 12) and is proportional to the average value of the IF output.   This rectifier unit is in parallel with the detector which produces the audiofrequency output, and differs from it chiefly in the output filter.   The filter for the detector must pass the entire audiofrequency range; for AVC the output is a slowly

* A DB meter of this kind is described by F. V. Hunt in *Review of Scientific Instruments*, Vol. 4 (1933), p. 672.

varying d-c voltage. For circuits and other details see F. E. Terman, *Radio Engineers' Handbook*, Sec. 9, Par. 5.

PROBLEMS

NOTE: Characteristic curves needed to solve problems are found in Appendix 5. To avoid marking the book, work each problem on a sheet of tracing paper laid over the characteristic curve plate.

1. (a) Plot a curve with plate current as y, grid potential as x, for a 6SJ7 tube, with its screen-grid potential and its plate potential each at 100 volts. (b) Obtain g_m from this plot by measuring slopes of tangent lines. Obtain enough values for a good plot of g_m as y, cube-root of plate current as x.

2. (a) Plot a curve with plate current as y, grid potential as x, for a 6F6 pentode, with 250 volts screen-grid potential, 150 volts plate potential. (b) Obtain g_m from this plot by measuring slopes of tangent lines, and plot g_m as y, cube-root of plate current as x.

3. (a) Plot plate current as y, grid potential as x, for a 6L6 beam tube, with 250 volts screen-grid potential, 150 volts plate potential. (b) From this plot obtain g_m graphically and plot g_m as y, cube-root of plate current as x. Compare this plot with the corresponding ones for Probs. 1 and 2.

4. Secondary emission becomes troublesome in a certain pentode above 40 volts plate potential, with a screen-grid potential of 200 volts. Compute the value of μ' required for the suppressor grid (see Sec. 9) and explain your answer carefully.

5. The value of μ' (see Sec. 9) for the suppressor grid in a pentode is 4.0. At what plate potential does this grid begin to be effective, if the screen-grid potential is 100 volts? Explain your answer.

6. In the circuit of Fig. 15, R_1 is 80 K, R_2 is 150 K, and C is 0.020 μf. For the tube, g_m is 1120 μ-mhos, r_p is 950 K. (a) Diagram the equivalent a-c circuit of the voltage-source type. (b) Solve this circuit for the output voltage, for a signal of 125 mv at 1500 cps. (c) Find the percent error introduced by the approximate solution of Eq. 16.

7. (a) Diagram the equivalent a-c circuit of the current-source type for the data given in Prob. 6. (b) Solve this circuit for the output voltage, for the signal specified in Prob. 6.

8. In the circuit of Fig. 17, R is 55 K, C is 0.50 μf, and L is 10.0 henries. For the tube, g_m is 2500 μ-mhos and r_p is 750 K. (a) Diagram the equivalent a-c circuit of the current-source type. (b) Solve this circuit for the signal, if the output is 6.5 volts at 5000 cps. Neglect the current in L. (c) Solve the circuit, including the current in L.

9. In the circuit of Fig. 16, R is 600 ohms, the primary resistance in the transformer is 500 ohms, the secondary resistance is 80 ohms, N_1/N_2 is 2.80, and the inductance is very high. For the tube, g_m is 1800 μ-mhos and r_p is 970 K. (a) Diagram the equivalent a-c circuits of *both* types. (b) Solve one for the current in the secondary, for a signal of 340 mv.

10. In the circuit of Fig. 18, with no signal, V_p is 120 volts, V_2 is 100 volts, V_1 is -3.0 volts, I_p is 5.0 ma, I_2 is 0.60 ma, R_1 is 30.0 K, g_m is 2700 μ-mhos, and r_p is 1100 K. (a) Compute E_b, R_2, and R_k. (b) Diagram the equivalent a-c circuit of the current-source type. (c) Compute the signal for 8.5 volts output.

11. A power amplifier (Fig. 17) with a 6F6 pentode is operated at a Q-point for which V_1 is -5.0 volts and both V_2 and V_p are 250 volts. The load is 2500 ohms.

(a) Draw the load-line.   (b) Plot the transfer characteristic.   (c) Obtain from this transfer characteristic the amplitudes of the first three harmonic components, for a signal of 25.0 volts amplitude.

12. (a) Plot the transfer characteristic for a 6SJ7 pentode, if the load-line passes through 6.0 ma on the y-axis and 500 volts on the x-axis.   (b) Locate the Q-point on this plot so that the second-harmonic content will be a minimum for a signal of 4.0 volts amplitude.   (c) Compute values for R_2, E_b, and R_k, assuming the circuit to be that of Fig. 18.   Take the screen-grid current to be 24 percent of the plate current.

13. (a) Plot the transfer characteristic for a 6L6 beam tube, from a load-line passing through 325 ma on the y-axis and 500 volts on the x-axis.   (b) Take the Q-point at -5.0 volts grid bias, and find the harmonic content (up to the third harmonic) of the output for a signal of 10.0 volts rms value.   (c) Locate the point on the load-line representing the *average* value of I_p.   This point lies also on the d-c load-line (see Sec. 10, Chapter 4).   Take the d-c resistance of the choke-coil to be 200 ohms and draw the d-c load-line through this point to find E_b.

14. From the data given for a 6J7 pentode in Sec. 26 find numerical values for the nine u-factors which are defined in Sec. 27 for a tetrode: $u^p{}_{1,p}$, $u^p{}_{1,2}$, $u^p{}_{1,k}$, $u^2{}_{1,p}$, $u^2{}_{1,2}$, $u^2{}_{1,k}$, $u^p{}_{2,p}$, $u^p{}_{2,2}$, and $u^p{}_{2,k}$.   (b) Show that these nine u-factors are not all independent, and that $u^p{}_{1,p}$, $u^p{}_{1,2}$, and $u^p{}_{1,k}$ may be derived from the others.

15. The following data are given for a pentode: $g_m = 4750$ μ-mhos, $r_p = 300$ K, $I_p = 5.5$ ma, $I_2 = 1.6$ ma, and μ for triode operation is 45.   Compute approximate values for the nine s-factors.

16. In the circuit of Fig. 14, with a 6J7 tube, R is 55 K.   A second generator, having an emf e_1 and negligible resistance, is inserted in series with the screen grid and E_2.   Find the a-c plate current and the output voltage when e is 40 mv, and e_1 is 180 mv, with e_1 180 degrees out of phase with e and both of the same frequency.   Use the small-variations equation and the s-factors given in Sec. 26.

17. In the circuit of Fig. 18, with a 6J7 pentode, R_1 is 72 K, R_2 is 300 K, and the signal, e, is 50 mv.   Assume that the reactances of C_2 and C_k are zero, and compute i_p and i_2, the a-c components of the plate and screen-grid currents, from the small-variations equations 20 and 21, and the s-factors given in Sec. 26.

18. Compute the smallest value for C_2 in the circuit of Prob. 17 to make the change in V_2 at 60 cps no greater than e.   NOTE: Use the value of i_2 computed in Prob. 17, and remember that i_2 is the current in C_2.

19. In the circuit of Fig. 18, with a 6F6 pentode, R_1 is 6.0 K, R_2 is 30.0 K, R_k is fully by-passed, but C_2 is left out.   Compute the gain.   SUGGESTION: In Eqs. 20 and 21, $\Delta I_p = i_p$, the alternating current in R_1; $\Delta I_2 = i_2$, the alternating current in R_2; $\Delta V_1 = e$; $\Delta V_2 = -R_2 i_2$; and $\Delta V_p = -R_1 i_p$.   Substitute these values in Eqs. 20 and 21, and solve the two numerical equations simultaneously for i_2 and i_p.   Then $e_0 = -i_p R_1$.

CHAPTER 6

Feedback Circuits

1. Feedback. In many electron-tube circuits the a-c potential at the grid (always specified relative to the cathode) is made up partly of the signal, which is supplied from some outside source of emf, and partly of a voltage derived in some manner from the output side of the circuit itself. The latter component is called a *feedback voltage*. Its magnitude may be large or small relative to the signal, and it may add to the signal in any phase. The first applications of feedback, in early radio circuits, utilized *positive* feedback, in which the feedback voltage aids the signal. In the regenerative receiver, for example, positive feedback is employed to increase greatly the sensitivity, and positive feedback makes possible the operation of electron-tube oscillators. On the other hand, positive feedback is often a great nuisance, and the screen-grid tube was invented as a means for controlling it. At the present time positive feedback is limited largely to the maintenance of electrical oscillations, and to a few other special applications.

The advantages of *negative* feedback, in which the feedback voltage opposes the signal, are less apparent and were not so early recognized. At the present time, however, voltage gain is so easily obtainable that we can afford to expend some of it for the advantages offered by negative feedback, such as increased linearity and circuit stability. It is possible to approach this subject of feedback in a perfectly general manner, as is done in many textbooks, but it is more instructive to examine first several simple but important special examples of negative feedback.

2. Cathode-Resistor Feedback. In Fig. 1a is seen a simple amplifier circuit having a resistance R_k between the cathode and ground. If R_k is by-passed by an adequate condenser, as in Fig. 6, Chapter 3, it may be disregarded entirely in solving for the alternating currents and potentials in the circuit, since it is then short-circuited by the condenser. In the circuit of Fig. 1a, however, it is necessary not only to include R_k as a part of the impedance in the plate circuit, as shown in the equivalent a-c circuit of Fig. 1b, but also to recognize that *the potential-drop across R_k is a part of the grid potential*. Remembering

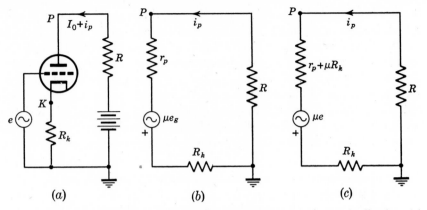

FIG. 1. CATHODE-RESISTOR FEEDBACK. Also called "current" feedback. (a) Circuit. (b) Equivalent a-c circuit. (c) Another equivalent a-c circuit.

now that the grid potential, V_g, is always referred to the cathode, we may write its value in Fig. 1a as

$$V_g = e - (I_0 + i_p)R_k \tag{1}$$

Then e_g, the a-c component of V_g, is

$$e_g = e - i_p R_k \tag{2}$$

The equivalent a-c circuit may now be represented as in Fig. 1b, with an emf equal to μe_g. For this circuit Ohm's law then gives

$$\mu e_g = \mu(e - i_p R_k) = i_p(R + R_k + r_p) \tag{3}$$

or

$$\mu e = i_p(R + R_k + \mu R_k + r_p) \tag{4}$$

The output voltage is then

$$e_0 = -i_p R = -\frac{\mu R e}{R + R_k(1 + \mu) + r_p} \tag{5}$$

The gain of the circuit is

$$A' = \frac{e_0}{e} = -\frac{\mu R}{R + R_k(1 + \mu) + r_p} \tag{6}$$

Without feedback (i.e., with R_k properly by-passed) the gain is

$$A = -\frac{\mu R}{R + r_p} \tag{7}$$

Another effect of this feedback may be found by examination of Eq. 4, which is seen to represent also the circuit of Fig. 1c, in which the current and load are the same as in the original circuit (Fig. 1a) but the source has an emf μe and an internal resistance $r_p + \mu R_k$. Thus Fig. 1c is another equivalent a-c circuit for the amplifier circuit of Fig. 1a, although not an obvious one.

Two significant results are thus produced by this cathode-resistor feedback.   (1) The gain of the circuit is reduced, it may be by a large amount.   (2) The effective internal impedance of the equivalent

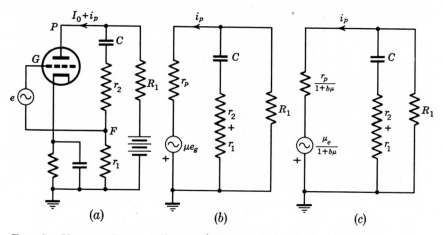

Fig. 2.   Voltage-Type Feedback.   (a) Circuit.   (b) Equivalent a-c circuit. (c) Another equivalent circuit.

source (Fig. 1c) is increased by the amount μR_k, which may be quite large.   These results are not necessarily undesirable.   Indeed, they may often prove quite advantageous, as will be explained later on.

3. Voltage Feedback.   Another type of feedback circuit is represented in Fig. 2a.   In this circuit the feedback voltage, e_f, at the point F, is derived from the output voltage, e_0, by means of the resistors r_1 and r_2, connected between the plate, P, and the ground.   The blocking condenser, C, which keeps direct current out of these resistors, will now be assumed so large as to have zero a-c impedance.   It is then evident that

$$e_f = +\frac{r_1}{r_1 + r_2}\, e_0 \tag{8}$$

If we represent the *feedback ratio*, $r_1/(r_1 + r_2)$, by b

$$e_f = be_0 \tag{9}$$

The signal, e, is inserted between F and the grid, G, so that the a-c grid potential is

$$e_g = e + e_f = e + be_0 \tag{10}$$

The equivalent a-c circuit is shown in Fig. 2b. Let us write R' for the resistance of R and $(r_1 + r_2)$ in parallel:

$$R' = \frac{R(r_1 + r_2)}{R + r_1 + r_2} \tag{11}$$

Then, for the circuit of Fig. 2b, Ohm's law gives

$$\mu e_g = \mu(e + be_0) = i_p(R' + r_p) \tag{12}$$

and

$$e_0 = -i_p R' \tag{13}$$

Insertion in Eq. 12 of the value of e_0 from Eq. 13, and rearrangement of terms, yield

$$\mu e = i_p(R' + \mu b R' + r_p) \tag{14}$$

From Eqs. 13 and 14 the output voltage for this circuit is found to be

$$e_0 = -\frac{\mu R' e}{R' + \mu b R' + r_p} \tag{15}$$

and the gain of the circuit with feedback is

$$A' = \frac{e_0}{e} = -\frac{\mu R'}{R' + \mu b R' + r_p} \tag{16}$$

Without feedback the gain is, of course,

$$A = -\frac{\mu R'}{R' + r_p} \tag{17}$$

The advantages of this circuit may be discovered by dividing Eq. 14 by $1 + \mu b$. Then

$$\frac{\mu e}{1 + \mu b} = i_p\left(R' + \frac{r_p}{1 + \mu b}\right) \tag{18}$$

Thus the circuit of Fig. 2c, in which the emf is $\mu e/(1 + \mu b)$, and the internal resistance $r_p/(1 + \mu b)$, is an a-c equivalent to the original circuit and displays the important features of this type of feedback. With voltage feedback, (1) the gain is reduced, as for negative feedback generally, and (2) the impedance of the equivalent source is also reduced, by the factor $1/(1 + \mu b)$. Contrast result (2) with the change in internal impedance produced by current feedback.

4. The Feedback Equation. In any type of feedback the a-c grid potential, e_g, is the sum of the signal, e, and the feedback voltage, e_f; and the latter is always some fraction, b, of the output voltage, e_0. This relation has been expressed already in Eq. 10. If the gain of the circuit *without feedback* is A, equal to e_0/e_g, then e_0 may be replaced by Ae_g in Eq. 10, giving

$$e_g = e + bAe_g \qquad (19)$$

In the most general applications of feedback both A, the gain without feedback, and b, the feedback ratio, represent changes in phase as well as amplitude, and hence these quantities must be represented in general by complex numbers. The general case will be considered in Sec. 12. For the present we shall limit our attention to circuits in which the only phase shift is 180 degrees, which may be represented by a change of sign. Then it may be seen from Eq. 19 that the kind of feedback is determined by the sign of the product, bA, and not by the sign of either b or A alone. If this product is *positive* (but less than unity)* the feedback voltage, bAe_g, aids the signal and the feedback is *positive* or *regenerative*. If, on the other hand, bA is *negative*, the feedback voltage opposes the signal and we have *negative* or *degenerative* feedback. The examples of Secs. 2 and 3 both represent negative feedback since, in both, A is negative, b is positive, and hence bA is negative.

Equation 10 is the most fundamental form for the feedback equation. If we divide it through by e_0 and remember that A', the gain with feedback, equals e_0/e, we obtain

$$e_g/e_0 = (e/e_0) + b \qquad \text{or} \qquad 1/A = (1/A') + b \qquad (20)$$

Equation 20 may be written also as

$$A' = A/(1 - bA) \qquad (21)$$

Equation 21 shows that A' is greater than A when the product, bA, is positive (but less than $+1$), but that A' is less than A when bA is negative. For any particular circuit it is safer to set up the equivalent a-c circuit and solve it as we have in the examples of Secs. 2 and 3, rather than to depend upon a general formula. Equations 20 and 21 become meaningless when bA is equal to or greater than $+1$, and other methods of analysis then become necessary.

5. Feedback in Cascade Amplifiers. Next consider voltage feedback in a two-stage amplifier, as diagrammed in Fig. 3. Here, as in

---

* The performance of circuits when bA equals or exceeds $+1$ will be considered in Sec. 23 and in Chapters 10 and 11.

Fig. 2a, the feedback voltage, ef, is a positive fraction, b, of the voltage output, in this case the output from the second stage. The a-c potential at the grid of stage 1 is then

$$e_g = e + e_f = e + be_0 \qquad (22)$$

For a two-stage amplifier, however, e_0 and e_g have the same sign, as has been explained in Sec. 10, Chapter 3. Hence be_0 aids e and the feedback is positive or regenerative. This result agrees with the criterion stated in Sec. 4: the feedback product, bA, is positive since

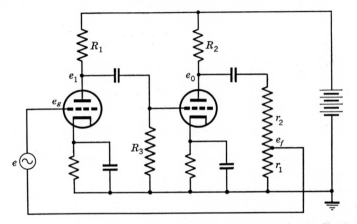

FIG. 3.   TWO-STAGE FEEDBACK.   Positive or regenerative feedback.

b is positive and A, which is the product of A_1, the gain of the first stage, and A_2, the gain of the second, is also positive, although both A_1 and A_2 are intrinsically negative.

When this voltage-type feedback is extended over three stages it is again degenerative, since A is again negative. In general, this type of feedback is degenerative for an odd number of stages, regenerative for an even number. It is now possible to explain why cascade amplifiers almost never include more than three stages. Voltage-type feedback from a fourth stage is regenerative and may be effected by a very small feedback voltage, since the gain over four stages is so very large (between 10,000 and 1,000,000 times, generally). Unless extreme care is taken in the construction and operation of a four-stage amplifier sufficient feedback may occur unintentionally to make the product, bA, equal to or greater than $+1$, and then, as explained in Sec. 23, the circuit no longer operates as an amplifier. Feedback may occur in many ways, by means of electric fields, magnetic fields, leakage currents, or any combination of these modes. Indeed, feedback of some sort will be present always unless the utmost care is taken to isolate and shield all circuit elements, and its effects become increasingly troublesome as the frequency rises.

Negative feedback may be achieved for two stages with the circuit of Fig. 4a. Here it is seen that the feedback voltage is supplied to the *cathode* of the first stage and thus, since it has the same sign as the signal, serves to reduce the potential of the grid with respect to the cathode. The feedback resistor, r_1, serves also to bias tube 1; since

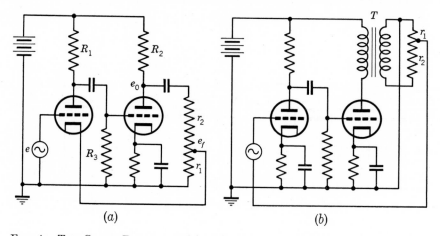

Fig. 4. Two-Stage Degenerative Feedback. (a) Through cathode of first tube. (b) Phase reversal with a transformer.

it is not by-passed by a condenser, this resistor causes additional feedback in the first stage. Negative feedback in a two-stage amplifier may also be produced with a transformer, as shown in Fig. 4b.

6. Distortion Reduction with Negative Feedback. Although negative feedback reduces the gain in an amplifier, this apparent objection is compensated by many advantages. Chief among these is inherent reduction of distortion, which may be explained physically as follows. Without feedback the a-c potential at the input grid of the amplifier is undistorted, and the output contains the full distortion developed in the amplifier. If now we could *distort the input* in just the right way we might compensate for distortion in the amplifier so as to obtain an undistorted output. Negative feedback does just this in part; if the feedback product, bA, is large enough it does so in very large part.

Let us figure out how big we may expect this distortion to be. For the fundamental component (the only one present in the signal) we may write, from Eq. 22,

$$e_g = e + bAe_g \tag{23}$$

or

$$e_g = e/(1 - bA) \tag{24}$$

Since there is distortion, A is not a fixed quantity and we shall have to use an approximate value here. When bA is negative, and large, the value of e_g for this fundamental component is very much less than the signal, e. For example, if bA equals -20, e equals $21e_g$. Now consider the distortion components in the output. Let us suppose that,

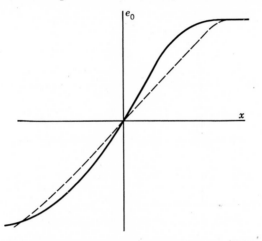

Fig. 5. Transfer Characteristics with Feedback. Solid line—without feedback: $x = e_g$. Broken line—with feedback: $x = e$, to a reduced scale to make plots comparable.

when the output for the fundamental is e_0, without feedback, it is accompanied by a distortion component e'. With negative feedback, and the signal increased until the output is again e_0 for the fundamental, the distortion component will be much less, say e_x. An estimate of the amount of reduction in distortion may be made by assuming that e_x is the resultant of e' and of e'', the output component which is produced by be_x, the feedback to the grid from e_x; that is, that

$$e_x = e' + e'' = e' + Abe_x \tag{25}$$

or

$$e_x = e'/(1 - bA) \tag{26}$$

For example, when bA equals -20 the distortion is reduced by a factor of 21, so that, if the distortion without feedback is 21 percent, with feedback it is only 1 percent. Since the superposition principle (see Sec. 19, Chapter 2) holds for linear circuits only, this estimate of the

decrease in distortion is based upon questionable assumptions.   Nevertheless it is of value in giving the order of magnitude of the reduction.

7. Graphical Analysis for Negative Feedback.   An exact representation of the gain in linearity with feedback may be obtained by
plotting the transfer characteristic with feedback, computing the
requisite values of e with Eq. 22 and values of e_g and e_0 read from the
transfer characteristic without feedback.   Such a plot is shown in
Fig. 5, for an average feedback product of 5.0.   Comparison of the
broken and solid lines, which represent the transfer characteristics

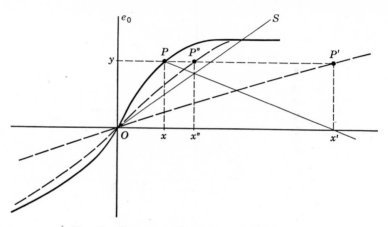

FIG. 6.   GRAPHICAL CONSTRUCTION FOR FIG. 5.

with and without feedback respectively, reveals that a remarkable gain
of linearity is possible with even this small a feedback product.

A simple graphical method for plotting the transfer characteristic
with feedback is illustrated in Fig. 6.   The solid line is the transfer
characteristic without feedback.   Through any point P on this line
draw a straight line Px' with a slope equal to $1/b$.   The corresponding
value of e is given by x', and P' is one point on the transfer characteristic with feedback.

PROOF: Since

$$(y - 0)/(x - x') = 1/b \qquad (27)$$

$$x' = x - by = e_g - be_0 = e \qquad (28)$$

Other points on this transfer characteristic are plotted in similar
manner.   The values of e may be plotted to a condensed scale, as in
Fig. 5, by taking as e the abscissae for the intersections of the slant
lines with a diagonal straight line such as OS in Fig. 6.   The point P'',
having the abscissa x'', is located in this fashion.

8. Demonstration Experiment 1. The reduction of distortion by negative feedback may be demonstrated with the single-stage pentode amplifier of Fig. 7. Except for the feedback branch (R_3, R_4, and C_1) the equipment and procedure are essentially the same as for Demonstration Experiment 4 in Chapter 5. Suitable circuit constants are specified in Fig. 7 for a frequency of 500 cps or over; if the signal is obtained from the 60-cps line the capacitances must be increased 10

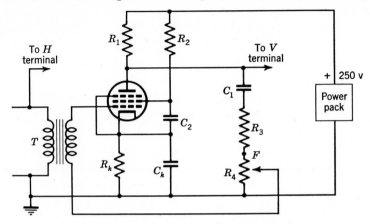

Fig. 7. Demonstration Experiment 1.

R_1—100 K.	C_1—0.05 µf.
R_2—500 K.	C_2—0.10 µf.
R_3—200 K.	C_k—12-µf.
R_k—0.5 K.	6J7 tube.
R_4—25-K potentiometer.	

times. The signal must be inserted between the feedback point, F, and the grid through a transformer, T. Variable feedback is provided by means of the voltage-divider, R_4, and b may be varied from 0 to 0.11. Distortion shows up best in the transfer characteristic, obtained (upside down) when connections to the oscilloscope are made as indicated.

Adjust the input to produce appreciable distortion in the output without feedback. Then add feedback, at the same time increasing the input to keep the output amplitude constant, and note the straightening out of the transfer characteristic. Note, however, that if the input is so great that the ends of the transfer characteristic (or the peaks of the time plot) become horizontal lines, no correction of this distortion is possible. (See also Fig. 5.) Feedback can function only when the gain from the tube is quite high, and the gain falls to zero when the capacity of the tube is exceeded.

9. Precision Amplifiers. It is possible to employ negative feedback to produce an amplifier which not only is quite precisely linear, or distortion-free, but which also has a gain that is practically constant over a wide range of frequencies, and constant with time. Furthermore, this gain will show no noticeable change if tubes are replaced by others of the same type, or if the line voltage changes by 10 or 20 percent. To understand how such performance is possible, consider Eq. 21, repeated here:

$$A' = A/(1 - bA) \qquad (21)$$

If bA is negative, with an absolute value very much greater than unity, the first term in the denominator may be neglected and, to a close approximation,

$$A' = -1/b \qquad (29)$$

In other words, A', the gain with feedback, is practically independent of A, providing only that A remains very large; its value depends almost entirely upon the feedback ratio, b, which is as invariant as the resistors which determine its value. Even a moderate value for bA will cause a great reduction in the importance of A. For example, if A is 10,000 and b is $-1/500$, bA equals -20, and A', from Eq. 21, is 10,000/21 or 476. If now A should increase by 50 percent, to 15,000, A' would change only to 484, or about 1.6 percent. (Note that the approximation of Eq. 29 gives A' equal to 500.)

Since the value of A figures so little in determining A' it is evident that distortion in the amplifier is almost entirely cancelled by feedback, as long as A remains very high. This statement might serve as a proof for the reduction of distortion by feedback, but the detailed proof in Sec. 6 has the advantage of explaining how this reduction comes about, and predicting its magnitude.

In the above discussion we have assumed that all condensers in the circuit are so large that their reactances are negligibly small. When we consider the operation of an amplifier at the high and low ends of its frequency range the reactances in the circuit cannot be neglected, even when we have negative feedback. Indeed, it is possible for the feedback to introduce added complications at the ends of the frequency range. Consider, for example, a three-stage amplifier with voltage-type feedback, as in Fig. 9. Without feedback the gain is high over a rather wide frequency band, but falls off at both ends of the frequency scale as shown by curve A, Fig. 8. With feedback the gain is much less but far more constant, over a wider range, as shown by curve B. It will be found also that the negative feedback has reduced the overall phase shift of the amplifier, or the phase difference between the input and output, for the entire frequency range over which the gain has been equalized. At the two ends of the frequency scale the gain may drop off quite abruptly, as indicated in curve B; this is the most desirable condition. On the contrary, the gain with certain degrees of feedback may show abnormal rise at the ends of the frequency scale as shown by curve C, even above the gain without feedback. It will

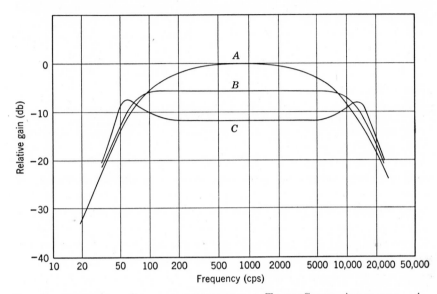

FIG. 8. FREQUENCY CHARACTERISTICS FOR A THREE-STAGE AMPLIFIER. A—Without feedback. The poor characteristics are intentional, to show attenuation within the audible range. B—With optimum negative feedback. C—With too much negative feedback.

be observed that this undesirable condition results when the feedback is quite large, considerably larger than the most favorable value represented by curve B. For even greater amounts of feedback the amplifier may become unstable, as described under positive feedback. Positive feedback is in fact the cause for this peculiar behavior of an amplifier with high feedback: at the very low and very high frequencies the phase shifts in the condensers add up to change negative feedback into positive feedback. This condition is not reached until the gain in the amplifier, without feedback, is quite low, too low to make trouble if the feedback ratio, b, is not excessive. The theory to explain these conditions is given in Secs. 12 and 13.

10. Demonstration Experiment 2. The effect of negative feedback upon the performance of an amplifier, as discussed above, may be demonstrated with the three-stage circuit of Fig. 9, which has been designed to accentuate the faults of this type of amplifier. The series condensers, C_1, C_2, and C_3, are made small, to degrade the low-frequency gain, and shunt condensers C_5, C_6, and C_7 have been added to attenuate the gain at high frequencies. The resistors R_{13} and R_{14} permit the input to have one terminal grounded, at the cost of half

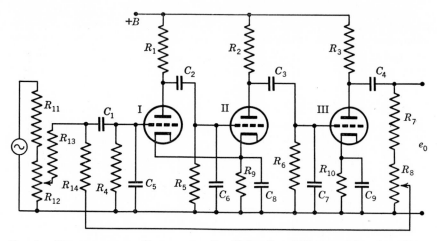

FIG. 9.   DEMONSTRATION EXPERIMENT 2.   Tubes I and II: two sides of a 6SN7. Tube III: two sides of a 6SN7 in parallel.

R_1, R_2, R_7—100 K.	C_1, C_2, C_3—0.008 μf.
R_3, R_{13}, R_{14}—50 K.	C_4—0.50 μf.
R_8—1-K potentiometer.	C_5, C_6, C_7—0.001 μf.
R_9, R_{10}—1.8 K.	C_8, C_9—10 μf.
R_{11}—50 K variable.	
R_{12}—100-ohm potentiometer.	

the input voltage. In building this circuit care must be taken to avoid feedback due to crowding of the parts.

The output is indicated best by the height of the time plot on an oscilloscope screen. Frequency changes are then also made evident by changes in the width of the cycles. With R_8 set for zero feedback, adjust the oscilloscope amplifier and the input to give nearly full-screen amplitude in the frequency range where the gain is largest. Leave these adjustments unchanged, and observe the changes in amplitude as the frequency is varied from 20 to 20,000 cps. Note the upper and lower frequencies at which the gain drops to half-value. Repeat with various amounts of feedback, obtained by changing the setting of R_8. Each time the reduction in amplifier gain which results from feedback may be compensated for by increasing the input so as to give the same amplitude in the middle-frequency range for each set. If the input is increased by means of a calibrated voltage-divider the reduction in gain caused by feedback may be found from the voltage-divider reading.   By varying the amount of feedback both types of curves shown in Fig. 8 may be studied, and it may be possible to demonstrate the self-oscillations which result from excessive feedback.

11. Pentodes in Feedback Circuits.   So far only triodes have been represented in feedback circuits, to simplify the figures.   For the most part pentodes will serve as well as triodes.   In voltage-type feedback circuits no changes are needed beyond provision for screen-grid power.   In cathode-resistor ("current") types the screen grid

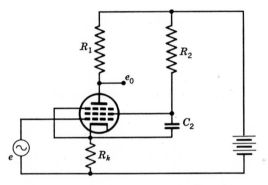

Fig. 10.   Pentode in Feedback Circuit.   Cathode-resistor type of feedback.

must be maintained at the same potential as the *cathode*, by connecting the by-pass condenser, C_2 in Fig. 10, between these two electrodes. Figure 10 is the pentode equivalent of Fig. 1a.   The screen grid then has an a-c potential, relative to the ground, the same as the cathode potential, and an alternating current is set up in the "dropping" resistor, R_2.   In effect R_2 is then in parallel with R_k (since the upper end of R_2 is at zero a-c potential) and this parallel combination serves as the feedback resistor.   Ordinarily, R_2 is so much greater than R_k that this detail may be disregarded.

Pentode circuits are subject also to a type of feedback peculiar to themselves.   This is negative feedback through the screen grid. When the condenser C_2 in Fig. 10 is too small, or when it is omitted, as in Fig. 11, alternating current in R_2 causes the potential of the screen grid to fluctuate, in such phase as to reduce the gain in the tube.   Qualitatively, we can see that, when e is positive in Fig. 11, i_2 is positive and e_2 is negative.   This negative value for e_2 then opposes e in its effect upon the a-c plate current, i_p, causing i_p and

e_0 both to be smaller. The amount of this feedback may be worked out quantitatively by means of the theory developed in Sec. 25, Chapter 5, and expressed by Eqs. 23 and 24 in Chapter 5. If we replace the incremental currents and potentials in these equations by

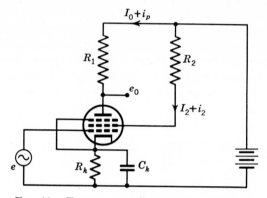

FIG. 11.   FEEDBACK IN SCREEN-GRID CIRCUIT.

the small alternating currents and voltages indicated in Fig. 11, they may be written (see Sec. 25, Chapter 5) as

$$i_p = s_1{}^p e + s_2{}^p e_2 + s_p{}^p e_0 \tag{30}$$

$$i_2 = s_1{}^2 e + s_2{}^2 e_2 + s_p{}^2 e_0 \tag{31}$$

But $e_2 = -i_2 R_2$, and $e_0 = -i_p R_1$.   Hence

$$i_p = s_1{}^p e - s_2{}^p R_2 i_2 - s_p{}^p R_1 i_p \tag{32}$$

$$i_2 = s_1{}^2 e - s_2{}^2 R_2 i_2 - s_p{}^2 R_1 i_p \tag{33}$$

Since an algebraic solution for i_p and i_2 from Eqs. 32 and 33 would be complicated, let us obtain a numerical solution for a typical example.   Take the data given in Sec. 26, Chapter 5, for a 6J7 pentode, and assume a 300-volt power supply.   The values for R_1 and R_2, Fig. 11, are then 0.100 and 0.40 megohm respectively.   (The potential drop in each is 200 volts, and the currents are 2.0 ma in R_1, 0.50 ma in R_2.) If we insert into Eqs. 32 and 33 these resistance values, in megohms, and the s-values in micromhos given in the table in Sec. 26, Chapter 2, we obtain two numerical equations for i_p and i_2, in microamperes.   Simultaneous solution of these equations gives

$$i_2 = 40e \; (\mu\text{-amp}) \qquad\qquad i_p = 186e \; (\mu\text{-amp})$$

$$e_2 = -i_2 R_2 = -16e \text{ volts} \qquad e_0 = -i_p R_2 = -18.6e \text{ volts}$$

When the screen grid is fully grounded by a large condenser,

$$e_2 = 0 \qquad \text{and} \qquad e_0 = -105e \text{ volts}$$

This type of feedback is not a desirable one, since in it the feedback ratio depends upon the screen-grid tube factors, which are uncertain and variable. However, such feedback cannot be avoided at low frequencies, so must be taken into account when pentodes are employed in wide-band amplifiers.

12. Phase Shift and Negative Feedback. In an exact analysis of negative feedback we must take account of the phase shifts produced by the reactances in an amplifier, and consider quantitatively how these phase shifts affect feedback. A qualitative discussion of the results of this theory has been given at the end of Sec. 9. Happily, the theory of Sec. 4 may be applied to this general treatment without change, if we treat the a-c voltages, e, e_g, e_0, and e_f, as *vector* quantities (rotating vectors in the complex plane) in the usual fashion of a-c circuit theory. For example, Eq. 10 must be regarded as a *vector equation*, which we may rewrite as

$$\mathbf{e} = \mathbf{e}_g - \mathbf{e}_f = \mathbf{e}_g - b\mathbf{e}_0 \qquad (34)$$

To indicate that these are now vector quantities the symbols representing them are printed here in heavy ("boldface") type. This vector equation is represented by the vector diagram of Fig. 12a, for conditions found in a three-stage amplifier. This diagram reveals (1) that $\mathbf{e}$ is longer than $\mathbf{e}_g$, but not as much longer as it would be if there were no phase angle, α, and (2) that $\mathbf{e}$ is more nearly in line with $\mathbf{e}_0$ than is $\mathbf{e}_g$. The latter observation may be interpreted by saying that the overall *phase shift has been reduced by negative feedback*. In drawing this diagram we start with $\mathbf{e}_0$. (How many times we find it advantageous to work backwards, from the output!) If we represent $\mathbf{e}_0$ by a *unit* vector (to a very large scale) then the lengths of $\mathbf{e}_g$, $\mathbf{e}$, and $\mathbf{e}_f$ are $1/A$, $1/A'$, and b respectively. Figure 12a may now be relabeled, as in Fig. 12b, to represent these quantities as vectors.

The direction and length of $1/\mathbf{A}$ depend upon frequency, so that the tips of vectors representing the entire frequency range plot a curve such as the one drawn in Fig. 12c; the frequency corresponding to each point on this curve may be indicated by a scale marked off along this curved line. If $\mathbf{b}$ is independent of frequency it may be represented by a single vector, as in Fig. 12c, and the vector $1/\mathbf{A}'$, for any frequency f, is drawn from the tip of $\mathbf{b}$ to the point that represents f on the curve for $1/\mathbf{A}$. By following this point around the curve we may see how A' changes with frequency for any amount of feedback, and find the value for $\mathbf{b}$ which produces any desired result, e.g., the most constant gain. We may see also that the length of $\mathbf{b}$ cannot equal (or exceed) OC without making the amplifier unstable. If we remember that OC represents $\mathbf{e}_g$ for some frequency f_1, we see that making $\mathbf{b}$ equal to OC supplies $\mathbf{e}_g$ by feedback alone, with no external signal needed, and oscillations at f_1 will then be self-sustaining. If the magnitude and direction of $\mathbf{b}$ depend upon frequency a curve must be plotted representing the locus of the tip of $\mathbf{b}$ as it changes with frequency. The

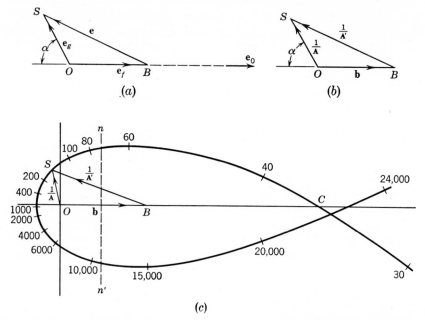

FIG. 12. PHASE SHIFT IN NEGATIVE FEEDBACK. (a) Vector diagram for Eq. 34. (b) Vector diagram of Eq. 20. (c) Phase, inverse-gain plot for a three-stage amplifier. (Cf. Figs. 8 and 9.) Note that the triangle OBS is the same as (b). Line n-n', the perpendicular bisector of OB, separates degeneration (to the left) from regeneration (to the right).

vector $1/\mathbf{A}'$ for any frequency f is then drawn between the points which represent f on the $\mathbf{b}$ plot and on the $1/\mathbf{A}$ plot.

13. The Nyquist Diagram. Another diagram to represent the amplitude and phase relationships for feedback in an amplifier is shown in Fig. 13. It is called a Nyquist diagram from its inventor, and is found in most treatises on this topic. In the Nyquist diagram we start with $\mathbf{e}_g$, which is represented by a unit vector, OD. The feedback voltage, $\mathbf{e}_f$, then has the magnitude bA, and may be plotted as a vector OS whose tip delineates a curve in Fig. 13 as the frequency is varied. From Eq. 34 we see that the vector joining point D with the point on the curve corresponding to any frequency f represents the signal, $\mathbf{e}$, and has a length equal to A/A'. When this length is greater than unity the circuit is degenerative. The circle of unit radius drawn about D marks the boundary between degeneration and regeneration.

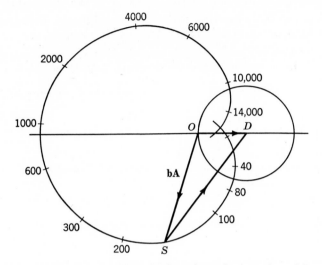

FIG. 13. NYQUIST DIAGRAM. Plot of bA against phase angle. $OD = 1$, $OS = bA$, and $DS = A/A'$.

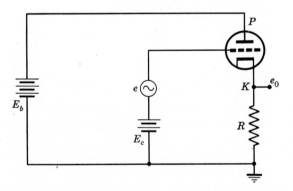

FIG. 14. CATHODE-FOLLOWER CIRCUIT. Positive bias to ground.

If the curve passes through D, or crosses the line through CD to the right of D, the circuit will become unstable, as explained in Sec. 9.

14. The Cathode-Follower Circuit. Figure 14 shows a circuit of very unusual appearance. The plate of the tube is connected directly to the positive terminal of the B-battery, and the load, R, is connected between the cathode and the ground. Since this raises the cathode to a relatively high d-c potential, the d-c grid potential also must be raised above ground potential. For example, if E_b in Fig. 14 is 250 volts, R is 25,000 ohms, and the direct current is 3.6 ma, with a type 76 triode, the d-c potential of the cathode is 90 volts and the grid potential is $+82$ volts above ground. In Fig. 14 this potential is supplied by a battery, E_c. More frequently the grid bias is supplied by other means, as shown in Fig. 15. In Fig. 14 the source of a-c signal is connected in series with the biasing battery, E_c, but in Fig. 15

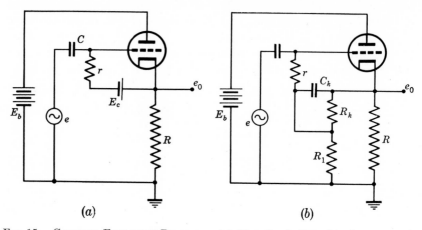

(a) (b)

FIG. 15. CATHODE-FOLLOWER BIASING. (a) Negative battery bias from cathode. (b) Cathode-resistor bias. R_1 and R_k are quite large, C_k relatively small. The load current *by-passes* C_k.

this source is connected between the grid and the ground, through a blocking condenser, C. In any case the a-c signal, e, is measured from grid to ground, whereas the alternating grid potential e_g, is measured from grid to cathode, *as always*. The output voltage, e_0, is observed at the cathode, between cathode and ground. It follows that

$$e = e_g + e_0 \qquad \text{or} \qquad e_g = e - e_0 \qquad (35)$$

One striking and important characteristic of this circuit now should be observed. Because of the location of the load between cathode and ground, e_0 is *in phase* with e_g and e. If we define A (for the tube) in the customary way, as

$$A = e_0/e_g \qquad (36)$$

then A is positive, not negative as it is always when the load is next the plate. The value of A may be obtained by solving the equivalent a-c circuit in Fig. 16. Except for the location of the ground-point this circuit is the same as for any tube circuit having a load R in its cathode-to-plate branch. From it we may obtain for A, as defined in Eq. 36,

$$A = + \mu R/(r_p + R) \tag{37}$$

Next we observe that this is a negative feedback circuit in which the whole output, e_0, with the sign reversed, is the feedback voltage; the feedback ratio, b, equals -1 and the feedback product is negative and equal to $-A$. This feedback relationship is expressed by Eq. 35. The output voltage, e_0, is now *less* than the signal, e, by the amount of the alternating grid potential, e_g. However, e_g is generally very small as compared with e or e_0, so that e and e_0 are almost equal in magnitude as well as of the same sign. In other words, the output voltage "follows" the signal very closely. For this reason the name "cathode-follower" has been given to this circuit.

As usual, the gain, A', for this circuit may be defined as

$$A' = e_0/e \tag{38}$$

From Eq. 35,

$$e = e_0 + e_g = e_0 \left(1 + \frac{1}{A}\right) \tag{39}$$

Hence

$$A' = A/(1 + A) \tag{40}$$

15. Cathode-Follower Output Impedance. From Eq. 40 we see that the "gain" of the cathode-follower circuit is less than unity! The advantages possessed by this circuit must therefore be sought elsewhere, and one of the most important is the very low output impedance possible with this circuit. Let us now derive the equation for this impedance. For the equivalent circuit of Fig. 16 we may write

$$\mu e_g = i_p(R + r_p) \tag{41}$$

and from Eq. 35

$$e_g = e - e_0 = e - i_p R \tag{42}$$

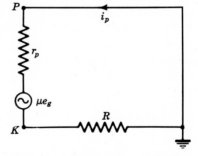

FIG. 16. EQUIVALENT A-C CIRCUIT FOR CATHODE-FOLLOWER.

Elimination of e_g from Eqs. 41 and 42 gives

$$\mu e = i_p(R + \mu R + r_p) \tag{43}$$

If we now divide Eq. 43 by $(1 + \mu)$ we obtain

$$\frac{\mu}{1 + \mu} e = i_p \left(R + \frac{r_p}{1 + \mu}\right) \tag{44}$$

Equation 44 now fits the circuit of Fig. 17, which represents the load R in series with an a-c source having an emf slightly less than e, and a very low internal impedance, $r_p/(1 + \mu)$. For example, if r_p is 5000 ohms and μ is 10, this internal resistance is only 455 ohms. The equation for this internal resistance may be written as

$$r_0 = \frac{r_p}{1 + \mu} = \frac{r_p}{\mu}\frac{\mu}{1 + \mu} = \frac{1}{g_m}\frac{\mu}{1 + \mu} \quad (45)$$

From Eq. 45 we see that the important factor, when low output impedance is concerned, is g_m and not μ. This very low output impedance is one of the outstanding features of the cathode-follower circuit; whenever a very low output impedance is required a cathode-follower output stage serves better than any other. Any number of tubes (of the same type) may be connected in parallel to make the output impedance still lower.

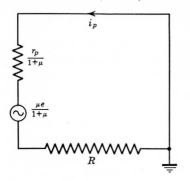

FIG. 17. MOST USEFUL EQUIVA-LENT CIRCUIT FOR CATHODE-FOLLOWER.

16. Experiment 16. Cathode-Follower Circuit. This experiment is a study of the performance of the cathode-follower circuit in Fig. 18, with particular reference to its output impedance. The tube may be any power amplifier tube; a 6L6 beam tube, triode connected, is recommended. For any tube the conditions for maximum output may be found as follows: (1) observe the d-c potential at the cathode with the circuit as shown, and a trial value for E_b; (2) then connect the grid directly to the cathode and observe the d-c potential at the cathode for the same value of E_b. For best operation this second d-c potential should be twice the first one. Change E_b (or E_c) until values are found which approximate this condition. For a 6L6 tube, with a load of 5000 ohms, E_b should be about 250 volts with E_c 67 volts, or 300 volts with E_c 90 volts.

The a-c output and input are measured with a rectifier-bridge type a-c voltmeter; this may be a commercial meter, or it may be built up of parts, as indicated, and calibrated by comparison with an ordinary a-c voltmeter. The a-c output is limited by zero plate current at one end of its swing, and by zero value for V_g (relative to the cathode) at the other. If the Q-point is chosen halfway between these points, in accordance with the directions given above, the peak value of the maximum a-c output voltage may equal the d-c potential at the cathode.

Part I. *"Gain" and Linearity.* Having established E_b and E_c at suitable values for a load of 5000 ohms, hold these values constant and take 10 observations of e and e_0, the input and output voltages, from zero to about 10 volts above the maximum output specified by the theory. Each time observe the direct current. Plot your data as a

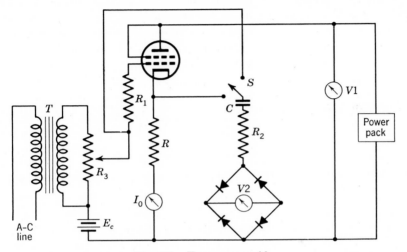

FIG. 18.   EXPERIMENT 16.

R—load. 10,000 ohms, 100 watt; tapped at 1000-ohm steps.

R_1—0.25-megohm protective resistor.

R_3—25-watt, 1000-ohm (or higher) potentiometer.

T—isolation transformer.

V_1—0- to 300-volt d-c meter.

V_2—0- to 100-volt rectifier-type a-c meter. A 1-ma d-c meter, meter rectifier, and $R_2 = 150$ K will serve.

I_0—0- to 50-ma d-c meter.

E_c—90-volt B-battery (measure emf).

C—0.5 mf.

curve having e_0 as y and e as x. Does this plot verify the predictions of theory for cathode-follower circuits? Discuss this point carefully. The slope of this line should equal the gain A' predicted by Eq. 40. Carry through the computations necessary to check this point. Obtain the necessary data from Appendix 5.

Part II. *Output Impedance.* Starting with the same initial conditions as in Part I, hold e constant at about 35 volts rms and vary R from 10,000 ohms down to 2000 ohms, by 1000-ohm steps. For each observation compute the alternating current, i_p, from e_0 and the corresponding value of the load (R and the meter $V2$ in parallel). Plot a curve having e_0 as y and i_p as x. The equation for this plot may be obtained by replacing $i_p R$ in Eq. 44 with e_0 and rewriting this equation as

$$e_0 = \frac{\mu}{1 + \mu} e - \frac{r_p}{1 + \mu} i_p \qquad (46)$$

If r_p could be considered constant this would be the equation of a straight line having the effective emf, $\mu e/(1 + \mu)$, as its y-intercept, and a negative slope equal to $r_p/(1 + \mu)$, the equivalent internal resistance of the circuit (see Fig. 17). Since r_p increases as i_p decreases the plot is not necessarily a straight line, and has less slope; for some tubes it may be nearly straight and horizontal.

Part III. Influence of the Supply Voltage. Turn off the a-c power, set R at 5000 ohms, and observe I_0 as a function of E_b, as E_b is varied by 20-volt steps from 300 volts down to where I_0 breaks sharply downward. Compute V_0, the potential at the cathode, from I_0 and R, and plot a curve having V_0 as y, E_b as x. Note that the break in I_0 comes at the point where V_0 equals E_c, and explain why. Above this break the plot should be straight, with a slight negative slope. The value of this slope is obtained from Eq. 50 and is

$$\text{slope} = -\frac{1}{1 + \mu + r_p/R} \qquad (46a)$$

Measure this slope and compare it with the value computed from Eq. 46a.

17. Graphical Analysis for Cathode-Follower Circuits. The performance of a cathode-follower circuit may be analyzed graphically in the manner described in Chapter 4. Thus, for the circuit of Fig. 14 (or Fig. 18) the load-line might be drawn as in Fig. 19a, passing through E_b and having a slope equal to $-1/R$, just as for all previous examples. The transfer characteristic for the tube, shown by Fig. 19b, then is derived from this load-line in the usual fashion. The output potential is now the cathode potential, V_k, which equals the product of I_p and R. The total input potential, V_i, is the potential of the grid with respect to the ground, or the algebraic sum of V_k and V_g. The transfer characteristic for the circuit is obtained by plotting V_k as y, V_i as x, as in Fig. 19c. Since V_g is quite small, this plot almost coincides with the straight line in this figure, which is a plot of V_i against itself. Except at the very foot, the plot of V_k is as straight a line as may be desired. The upper terminus of this line corresponds to zero for V_g; if the output goes beyond this point there will be grid current in the input circuit. The largest output (without grid current) may be obtained by locating the Q-point halfway down this line toward the x-axis, as explained in Sec. 16.   If, however, the Q-point is a little higher up the slight curvature at the foot of this plot may be avoided.

18. Cathode-Follower Input Impedance.   Another very important property of the cathode-follower circuit is its very high input impedance.   In the circuit of Fig. 14 this impedance is chiefly capacitative, and due to the grid-to-plate and grid-to-cathode capacitances, C_{gp} and

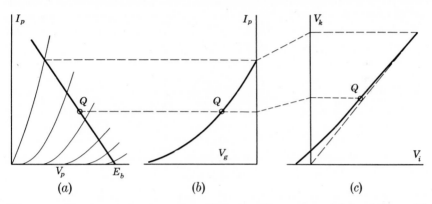

Fig. 19.   Graphical Analysis for Cathode-Follower.   (a) Load-line.   (b) I_p-V_g transfer characteristic.   (c) V_k-V_i characteristic.

C_i.   Since the alternating potential of the plate is zero, C_{gp} is in effect directly across the input terminals.   The potential difference across the terminals of C_i, on the contrary, is only e_g, or $e/(1 + A)$, and an equivalent condenser across the input terminals would have a capacitance of only $C_i/(1 + A)$.   Thus the effective input capacitance* is

$$C' = C_{gp} + \frac{C_i}{1 + A} \qquad (47)$$

For example, C_{gp} and C_i for a 6J7 tube, triode connected, are 2 and 5 micro-microfarads respectively.   If A is 15, C' equals $2 + 5/16$ or 2.3 micro-microfarads.

When grid bias is obtained as in Fig. 15 the grid resistor, r, must be considered in figuring the input impedance.   Since the potential difference across r is only e_g, or $e/(1 + A)$, the equivalent resistance,†

* When the load is not a pure resistance, but has a reactive component, A must be represented by a complex quantity in Eq. 47.   The admittance, $j\omega C_i/(1 + A)$, then will have a real part which represents a very small conductance.

† When the output has a reactive component, A is complex (see previous footnote) and $r(1 + A)$ then has a *reactive* component.

or one which would have the same current if connected between the grid and the ground, would be $(1 + A)r$. For example, if r is 1 megohm and A is 15, the equivalent resistance across the input terminals would be 16 megohms. Note that the important factor in determining the input impedance is tube gain, A. The very high input impedance of a cathode-follower circuit makes it ideal for the input of an amplifier which must be supplied from a very weak (very high internal impedance) source, or from a source which must be disturbed

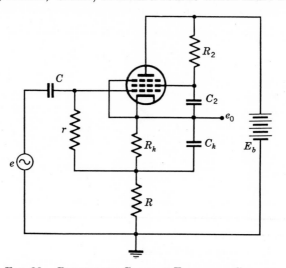

Fɪɢ. 20.   Pᴇɴᴛᴏᴅᴇ ɪɴ Cᴀᴛʜᴏᴅᴇ-Fᴏʟʟᴏᴡᴇʀ Cɪʀᴄᴜɪᴛ.

as little as possible by the amplifier connection. In cathode-follower circuits the only need for a cathode-resistor by-pass condenser, such as C_k, Fig. 15b, is to increase the input impedance, and very often it is omitted. If C_k is omitted in Fig. 15b the potential difference across r is increased to $[e_g + e_0 R_k/(R_k + R_1)]$, and the equivalent input resistance is then $r(1 + A)$ times $(R_k + R_1)/(R_k + R_1 + AR_k)$, or roughly half of $r(1 + A)$.

19. Pentodes in Cathode-Follower Circuits. Pentodes find infrequent use in cathode-follower circuits, since triodes serve satisfactorily in almost all applications, and triode circuits are easier to set up. Figure 20 illustrates the difficulties encountered with pentode circuits. In order to isolate the screen grid, so that its potential may be the same as that of the cathode and change with it, this grid must be supplied by a separate battery having a low capacitance to ground, or through a dropping resistor, R_2, as shown in Fig. 20, with a large capacitance between the screen grid and the cathode. In the latter arrangement R_2 is effectively in parallel with R, as explained in Sec. 11, and thus becomes part of the load. In addition, the d-c supply voltage must be made enough higher to supply the potential drop through R_2. Somewhat better linearity may be achieved with pentodes, but linearity is already so good with triodes that there is little need to improve it.

The chief advantage offered by pentode circuits is higher input impedance, and here also triode circuits are about as good as needed for all but a few special applications. A pentode in a cathode-follower

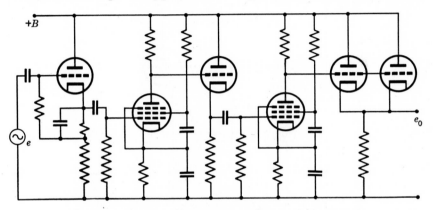

FIG. 21.   CATHODE-FOLLOWERS IN CASCADE AMPLIFIER.

circuit provides an input capacitance which is very much less than is possible in any other way, and a very high input resistance. The input capacitance to the tube is somewhat larger than for a triode, since it includes the capacitance from control grid to screen grid, but in the cathode-follower circuit this capacitance is divided by $1 + A$, which is large. The other term in the input capacitance to the circuit is the grid-to-plate capacitance, and this is negligibly small for a pentode. Consider for example, a 6J7 pentode for which C_i and C_{gp} are 7 $\mu\mu$f and 0.005 $\mu\mu$f respectively. Its effective input capacitance in a cathode-follower circuit, when A is 50, is then $C' = 0.005 + \frac{7}{51} = 0.14$ $\mu\mu$f. In this same example, if r is 0.5 megohm the effective input resistance is 25 megohms.

20. Cathode-Follower Units in a Cascade Amplifier. Many of the advantages possessed by cathode-follower circuits are illustrated in the cascade amplifier diagrammed in Fig. 21, in which cathode-follower units are placed between the amplifier stages, as well as at the input and the output. Note that the coupling from the amplifier plates to the cathode-follower grids is direct, so that the d-c plate potential supplies the required positive grid bias. Because of this mode of coupling this circuit has no more condensers than are needed without the cathode-follower units. The purpose of the input unit has already been explained in Sec. 18, and the output unit, with two tubes in parallel, provides a very low output impedance, as explained in Sec. 15. The input and interstage units serve to extend the frequency

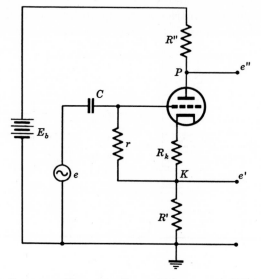

Fɪɢ. 22. Pʜᴀsᴇ-Iɴᴠᴇʀᴛᴇʀ Cɪʀᴄᴜɪᴛ. For audiofrequency, 6J5 tube, 180 to 250 volts d-c.

R', R''—50 K. r—1.0 megohm.
R_k—1.5 K*. C—0.05 μf.

range somewhat at its lower end and very much more at its upper end. The high input impedance of the amplifier accounts for the improvement at low frequency. At high frequency, the low output impedance of the cathode-follower units greatly reduces the attenuation due to the input capacitances of the amplifier tubes.

21. Phase-Inverter Circuit. The circuit in Fig. 22 represents one electronic means for providing two voltages of equal magnitude but opposite sign, such as are needed for the input to a push-pull amplifier. The lower half of this circuit is essentially a cathode-follower unit, and e' is almost equal to e, the signal. Then, if R' and R'' are equal, e'' equals $-e'$, since the same current is in R' and in R''. This circuit is only one of a considerable number of electronic "phase-inverter" or

* Adjust R_k to make the potential at K close to 100 volts d-c.

"phase-splitter" circuits, but it is the simplest and will operate over a wider frequency band than other types.

This circuit is useful also as a means for supplying an oscilloscope with alternating potentials of either sign. It is particularly useful in demonstration experiments with amplifiers, when the plate potential is proportional to the plate current but opposite in sign. The plate current may be represented on the oscilloscope screen with the proper sign by interposing this circuit between the plate terminal of the amplifier and the oscilloscope, with the oscilloscope connection to

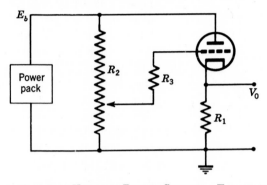

FIG. 23.   SIMPLE VARIABLE-VOLTAGE POWER SUPPLY. For up to 75 ma at 250 volts, with 6L6 tube, triode-connected:

E_b—425 volts. R_2—100 K.
R_1—30 K. R_1—0.1 megohm.

P.   Suitable values for building this circuit are given in Fig. 22. The high input impedance of this circuit is an added advantage. If it is overloaded by the plate potential of the amplifier a voltage-divider may be contrived with megohm resistors.

22. Cathode-Follower Voltage Regulation. Part III of Exp. 16 illustrates one valuable application of the cathode-follower circuit. The load represented by R in Fig. 18 may be any device requiring a-c power, for example, an amplifier circuit. If the grid of the tube is maintained at a constant d-c potential above ground then the load will be supplied power at a d-c potential which is almost unaffected by changes in either E_b or the power taken by the load. The d-c grid potential controls the value of the d-c potential at the load. It may be supplied by a battery, as in Fig. 18, or from a high-resistance voltage-divider connected between the power-supply terminals if the power-line regulation is good. The latter arrangement is shown in Fig. 23, for a simple variable-voltage power supply. A power tube must be employed in this circuit since it serves to dissipate the waste power, equal to the product of the load current and the difference between the load voltage, V_0, and the supply voltage, E_b.

The good regulation of the circuits of Figs. 18 and 23 with respect to change in the load power is accounted for by the low internal impedance of the equivalent source, as explained in Sec. 15. The regulation with regard to changes in E_b, when the grid potential with respect to the ground is furnished by a battery or other constant-potential source, must be explained otherwise. These conditions are represented in Part III of Exp. 16, and the circuit of Fig. 18 may then be represented by the variational equivalent circuit of Fig. 24, in which ΔE_b is a small change in E_b and ΔI is the resultant change in the load current, I. The change in the grid potential with respect to the cathode is then ΔV_g, equal to $-R\,\Delta I$, and the equation for the circuit is

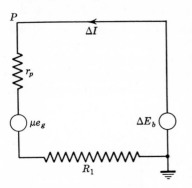

FIG. 24. EQUIVALENT CIRCUIT. To explain voltage regulation in cathode-follower circuits.

$$\Delta E_b + \mu\,\Delta V_g = \Delta E_b - \mu R\,\Delta I = \Delta I(R + r_p) \qquad (48)$$

or

$$\Delta I = \frac{\Delta E_b}{R + \mu R + r_p} \qquad (49)$$

The change in the load voltage is then

$$\Delta V_0 = R\,\Delta I = \frac{\Delta E_b}{1 + \mu + r_p/R} \qquad (50)$$

For a triode-connected 6L6 tube the regulation factor, $1 + \mu + r_p/R$, is between 9 and 10. In Chapter 14 is described a more elaborate voltage-regulator circuit in which a cathode-follower unit is combined with gaseous-discharge tubes and an amplifier to produce very fine regulation.

23. Positive Feedback. As stated in Sec. 4, when feedback is positive the feedback voltage, e_f, aids the signal, e, so that the gain is greater than without feedback. Positive feedback is represented by a positive value of the feedback product, bA, in the feedback equation (Eq. 19):

$$e_g = e + e_f = e + bAe_g \qquad (51)$$

The gain is given by Eq. 21. In the early days of radio, when tubes were expensive and inefficient, positive feedback, or regeneration as it was then more generally called, was employed extensively as a means of increasing the sensitivity of radio receivers.   Positive feedback does possess this advantage, but it has also several disadvantages. For one, it is difficult to regulate, especially when bA is close to unity, since a small change in b then makes a very large change in A'.   Little use is made of it in modern radio amplifiers, now that tubes are cheap, and high gain is possible otherwise.   Positive feedback may be made very selective with regard to frequency; indeed, this is one objection to regeneration in radio receivers.   On the other hand, when high

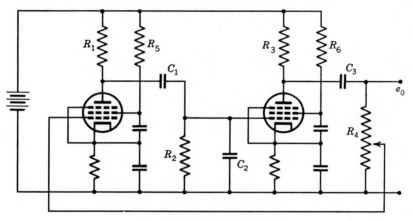

FIG. 25. R-C OSCILLATOR.

selectivity is desired in an amplifier, positive feedback is sometimes employed to obtain it.   (Usually positive feedback is combined with negative feedback at the undesired frequencies.)

When bA equals $+1$ we can see from Eq. 51 that the feedback voltage then equals e_g and no external signal is needed.   For an ideal linear amplifier having the same gain at all frequencies this condition is indeterminate.   For any real amplifier, however, this condition is first reached at some one frequency, and the amplifier then starts to oscillate at that frequency.   Under any practical conditions bA will exceed $+1$ somewhat and the oscillations will build up to an amplitude that includes all the straight portion of the transfer characteristic and a little of the curved portions.   As bA is increased above $+1$ the oscillation increases in amplitude and becomes more and more distorted. If bA is much larger than $+1$ other modes of oscillation are also possible in an ordinary amplifier (e.g., Fig. 9) and the output becomes very complex.   Sometimes it becomes intermittent, a condition variously described as "blocking" or "motorboating."   As soon as any oscillation starts, the circuit becomes useless as an amplifier.   Occasionally these oscillations are above audibility, and their presence is indicated only by the failure of the amplifier.

24. R-C Oscillators. If an amplifier is designed for maximum gain at some one frequency then, as explained in Sec. 23, it may be made to oscillate at that frequency by positive feedback such that bA just exceeds $+1$, and if the feedback is carefully adjusted the oscillations will stay within the straight portion of the transfer characteristic and be quite sinusoidal. As an example consider the circuit of Fig. 25. In this amplifier circuit the gain is a maximum at a frequency f_1 which

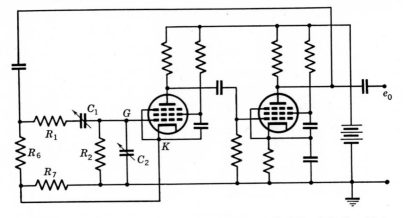

FIG. 26.   AUDIOFREQUENCY SIGNAL GENERATOR.   Stabilized R-C oscillator.

is determined by C_1, C_2, R_1, R_2, r_p (the a-c plate resistance for the first tube), and C_i, the input capacitance of the second tube. If R' is the resistance of R_1 and r_p in parallel, and C' the capacitance of C_2 and C_i in parallel,

$$f_1 = \frac{1}{2\pi \sqrt{C_1 C' R_2 R'}} \qquad (52)^*$$

When the adjustable contact on R_4 is set so that oscillations just start they will occur at the frequency f_1.

Similar circuits are employed in most commercial signal generators. Various R-C networks are utilized as tuned circuits, and provision is made for automatic amplitude control. One of the best of these circuits is shown in Fig. 26.† In it there is strong positive feedback

---

* This equation assumes that C_3 is so large that no appreciable phase shift occurs in the feedback, and that no phase shift is produced by the grid-biasing networks in the cathode leads.

† F. E. Terman, R. R. Buss, W. R. Hewlett, and F. C. Cahill, *Proceedings of the I.R.E.*, Vol. 27 (1939), p. 649.

from the output, e_0, to G, the grid of the first tube, through the $R\text{-}C$ network R_1, C_1, R_2, C_2. At the same time there is negative feedback to K, the cathode of the first tube, through R_6 and R_7. To stabilize the output, R_7 is made a small tungsten lamp whose resistance increases rapidly with current, so that the negative feedback ratio, $R_7/(R_7 + R_8)$, increases with power output. The output stabilizes at an amplitude for which the alternating potential at K is only slightly below the alternating potential at G. It may now be shown that

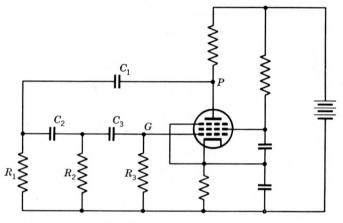

FIG. 27.   PHASE-SHIFT OSCILLATOR.

R_1, C_1, R_2, C_2, R_6, and R_7 form a Wien bridge circuit which is nearly balanced when the output is stabilized. At balance,

$$f = \frac{1}{2\pi \sqrt{R_1 C_1 R_2 C_2}} \tag{53}$$

and

$$\frac{R_6}{R_7} = \frac{R_1}{R_2} + \frac{C_2}{C_1} \tag{54}$$

By making R_1 equal to R_2, and C_1 and C_2 identical variable condensers, ganged together, $f = 1/2\pi R_1 C_1$, and the amplitude is practically independent of frequency.

A frequency-sensitive $R\text{-}C$ feedback circuit which needs but a single amplifier tube is shown in Fig. 27. At some one frequency the phase shift from P to G is just 180 degrees and the circuit will oscillate at this frequency if the feedback is sufficient. Sinusoidal oscillations require exact adjustment of the feedback, as in all $R\text{-}C$ oscillators.

25. *L-C* Oscillators.   In the circuit of Fig. 28, positive feedback is obtained electromagnetically, through interaction of the coil L_2, in the grid circuit, with the alternating magnetic field produced by current in the coil L_1 in the plate circuit.   The frequency at which the gain is greatest is approximately the resonant frequency for the mesh containing L_1 and C, which is

$$f_1 = \frac{1}{2\pi \sqrt{L_1 C}} \qquad (55)$$

Oscillations start when the mutual inductance between L_1 and L_2 is increased to just the right amount.

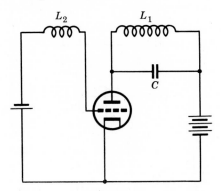

FIG. 28.   RESONANT-CIRCUIT OSCILLATOR.

All these examples of electronically maintained electrical oscillations may be called class A oscillations.   When feedback is increased beyond the point at which oscillations just start, the oscillations in any of the *R-C* coupled circuits (Figs. 25, 26, and 27) become distorted, as explained in Sec. 23.   In the circuit of Fig. 28, however, the output voltage remains nearly sinusoidal for any degree of feedback, because of the electromagnetic "inertia" of the resonant circuit, $L_1 C$.   Like the balance wheel of a watch, this circuit is capable of free oscillations which die away fairly slowly, and even a series of intermittent pulses of power, occurring at the frequency f_1, will serve to maintain these oscillations at constant amplitude.   Figure 27 illustrates but one of many possible oscillators of this resonant-circuit type.   Further consideration of such circuits is deferred to Chapter 10.

26. Decoupling.   Unwanted feedback may occur in many ways, and painstaking detective work often is required to locate it.   One troublesome source of feedback is the impedance of a common d-c source.   In a three-stage amplifier, for example (see Fig. 9), the resistance of the B-battery may bring about an alternating potential at the $+B$ terminal, due to alternating current in the battery. Although this current is the sum of the alternating currents in all three tubes, that in the last tube is so much larger than all the rest that it alone need be considered here. It follows that this alternating potential at the $+B$ terminal is in phase with the alternating plate potential for tubes 1 and 3, but out of phase for tube 2. We need to consider only the potential at the plate of tube 1. Evidently there is positive feedback from the $+B$ terminal to the plate of tube 1, and thence to the grid of tube 2; if the impedance of the d-c source is

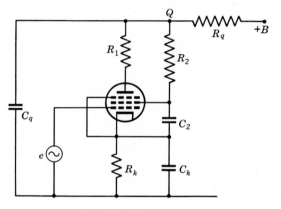

FIG. 29. DECOUPLING.

appreciable, and the gain large for stages 2 and 3 together, this feedback may be quite troublesome and even set up oscillations.

Figure 29 indicates a method to nullify this feedback, by "decoupling" the plate circuit of the first tube from the others. A resistance, R_q, is inserted between the $+B$ terminal and the point Q from which all connections are made to the first stage, and the point Q is connected to ground through a large capacitance, C_q. The alternating potential drop from $+B$ to ground is now divided between R_q and X_q (the reactance of C_q); if R_q is very much larger than X_q at the lowest frequency to be encountered the trouble is eliminated. Of course this device lowers the effective d-c potential for tube 1 to that at Q, but this is not objectionable since the a-c output from stage 1 is always very small in amplitude. Similar decoupling may be applied to attenuate unwanted feedback in other circuits.

PROBLEMS

1. The load in an amplifier circuit is 50 K between $+B$ and the plate, and 80 K in series with a large capacitance between plate and ground. Take $\mu = 24.0$

and g_m = 1600 μ-mhos.   The cathode resistor is 2.10 K.   (a) Diagram the circuit and the equivalent a-c circuit, when R_k is fully by-passed, and solve for the gain. (b) Diagram the equivalent a-c circuit (*not* Fig. 1c) when there is no by-pass condenser, and solve for the gain.   (c) Check this result against the circuit of Fig. 1c.

2.   The load in an amplifier circuit is 75 K in series with the plate and B-battery. Take μ = 18.0, g_m = 2350 μ-mhos.   It is desired to make the gain of this circuit exactly 10.0, by means of cathode-resistor type of feedback.   (a) Diagram the circuit and the equivalent a-c circuit.   (b) Solve this circuit for the value of R_k required.   (c) Compute e_g and e_f when e_0 is 10.0 volts.

3.   The grid and cathode part of an amplifier circuit is shown in Fig. 30a. Take the load = 100 K, R_a = 2.45 K, R_b = 1.20 K, μ = 30.5, g_m = 1400 μ-mhos,

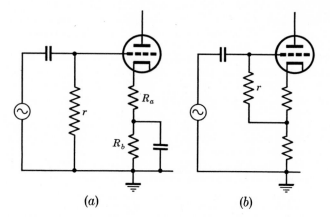

(a)   (b)

FIG. 30.   SEPARATING BIAS AND CATHODE-RESISTOR FEEDBACK.   (a) When bias resistor is greater than feedback resistor.   (b) When feedback resistor exceeds bias resistor.

and the d-c plate current = 0.90 ma.   (a) Diagram the equivalent a-c circuit and compute the gain.   (b) Compute the grid bias.   Consider the condensers of negligible reactance.

4.   In a pentode amplifier the load is 65 K, g_m = 1750 μ-mhos, r_p = 0.95 megohm, and I_0 = 3.15 ma.   (a) Diagram the equivalent a-c circuit and solve it for the gain.   (b) Compute the value for the cathode resistor needed to reduce this gain to 25.0.   (c) Compute the value of the cathode resistor needed to produce a grid bias of 2.20 volts.   (d) Diagram the grid and cathode part of this circuit and indicate the values for the resistors needed: see Fig. 30.

5.   (a) Diagram the circuit for a triode amplifier having 85 K between the plate and the +B terminal, 150 K and a 0.020-μf condenser in series between plate and ground.   (b) Diagram the equivalent a-c circuit and compute the gain at 1000 cps, if μ = 30.5 and g_m = 1540 μ-mhos.   (c) Diagram the circuit for voltage-type feedback produced by insertion of 10.0 K between the 150-K resistor and ground, and compute the gain with feedback.

6.   The load for a beam-tube amplifier is 8000 ohms in series with a large condenser.   The direct plate current is supplied through a large choke-coil.   Take g_m = 5200 μ-mhos and r_p = 33.0 K.   (a) Diagram the circuit and compute the

gain. (b) Add to this circuit voltage-type feedback to reduce the gain to 4.00, and compute the feedback ratio required. (c) Compute the equivalent source impedance.

7. For the two stages of a pentode amplifier the gains are -58.3 and -35.2. (a) Compute the alternating grid potential to produce 25 volts output without feedback. (b) Compute the feedback ratio to double the gain with voltage-type feedback. (c) Compute the feedback voltage for 25 volts output, and the signal with this feedback.

8. In the circuit of Fig. 4a the gain in each stage is -18.4 and $R_1 = R_2 = 80$ K, $R_3 = 200$ K, $r_1 = 0.50$ K, $r_2 = 200$ K. For 30 volts output compute (a) the alternating grid and plate potentials for each tube, (b) the feedback voltage, and (c) the gain with feedback.

Solution: (a) At the grid of tube 2 and plate of tube 1, $e_1 = 30/(-18.4) = -1.63$ volts. At the grid of tube 1, $e_g = -1.63/(-18.4) = 0.089$ volt. (b) Voltage feedback: $e_f = -30(0.50/200) = -0.075$ volt. Current feedback: $e_f' = -1.63(0.50/80) = -0.010$ volt. (c) $e_g = e + e_f + e_f'$, or $e = 0.174$ volt. $A' = 30/0.174 = 173$. A (without feedback) $= 338$.

9. Take the transfer characteristic for an amplifier to be given by $e_0 = 875(e_g + 4.25e_g{}^2)$. (a) Plot this curve for e_g between -0.075 and $+0.075$ volt, and find the percent second-harmonic distortion for a signal of this amplitude. (b) Obtain graphically a plot of e_0 as a function of the signal, e, when there is negative feedback equal to $\frac{1}{150}$ of the output, and obtain the percent distortion with this feedback, for the same output. (c) Compute the average gain over this interval, with feedback. Compare this result with Eq. 40.

10. (a) Draw the load-line for a 6L6 tube from 300 volts on the x-axis to 100 ma on the y-axis, and plot the transfer characteristic from it, for the grid-potential range from $+30$ to -30 volts. (b) Determine graphically the transfer characteristic with feedback equal to one-third of the output voltage. (c) Locate the grid bias for output with feedback between these limits.

11. The gains for the three stages of an amplifier are -40.7, -58.0, and -15.6. (a) Compute the feedback ratio to make the net gain just 2000. (b) Compute the gain with this feedback if the second-stage gain changes to -45.0.

12. For a two-stage amplifier the gain without feedback is 600, with the input leading the output by 40 degrees from its phase with negligible reactances. Negative feedback (Fig. 4b) equal to $\frac{1}{200}$ of the output is added. (a) Represent e_g and e_f by vectors drawn to scale, and find the vector representing the signal, e. (b) Compute the gain and the phase shift of the amplifier with feedback.

13. The gains for the three stages of an amplifier are -24.0, -68, and -19.2, with phase shifts of $+31$, $+38$, and $+53$ degrees in the input and interstage couplings. There is feedback from the output to the first grid, with a feedback ratio of 22.0×10^{-5}. (a) Compute the alternating grid potential and the feedback voltage for 1.00 volt output. (b) Represent these voltages by vectors and find the magnitude and direction of the required signal. (c) Compute the gain and compare it with the gain computed with Eq. 40, neglecting phase shifts.

14. In a single-tube amplifier having self-bias the load is 42 K, the biasing resistor is 3.0 K, and the by-pass condenser is 4.0 μf. The gain at 1000 cps is -37.0. (a) Compute the a-c grid potential for 10.0 volts output. (b) Compute the alternating potential drop across the cathode resistor and condenser with 10.0 volts output at 50 cps. (c) Compute the signal corresponding to (b) and the corresponding gain, including phase angle.

15. In a cathode-follower circuit the load is 4500 ohms, $\mu = 22.0$, and $g_m = 3200$ μ-mhos. (a) Compute the *grid* potential to give 20.0 volts output, from the equivalent circuit of Fig. 16. (b) Compute the signal required.

16. Find the alternating current and output voltage in a cathode-follower circuit if the load is 2700 ohms, $\mu = 18.0$, $r_p = 2400$ ohms, and the signal is 38.0 volts.

17. Take $g_m = 6500$ μ-mhos and $r_p = 1.80$ for the tube in a cathode-follower circuit. (a) Compute the emf and the internal resistance for the equivalent source, with a signal of 67 volts. (b) Compute the output voltage with a load of 8.0 K. (c) Find the change in output voltage if the load is changed to 4.0 K.

18. Design a cathode-follower circuit with a 6L6 tube, triode connected. (a) Take $E_b = 300$ volts and draw load-lines for 3.0 K and 6.0 K. (b) Find the best values for the Q-point data (current, grid bias, and cathode potential) for each load. (c) For each load compute R_k, Fig. 15b, when R_1 is 100 K.

19. The input to an amplifier is through a 0.20-μf condenser, and the grid resistor (grid to ground) is 0.25 megohm. The source driving the amplifier has an emf $= 35.0$ mv at 500 cps, and an internal resistance of 0.50 megohm. (a) Compute the alternating grid potential. (b) To avoid this loss of potential the amplifier is provided with a cathode-follower input unit, as in Fig. 21. For this unit $\mu = 20.0$, $r_p = 22.0$ K, the load is 100 K, and the grid resistor (r, Fig. 15) is 0.25 megohm. Compute the alternating potential at the grid of the amplifier with this addition.

20. The triode in the cathode-follower unit of Prob. 19 is replaced with a pentode, for which $g_m = 900$ μ-mhos and $r_p = 1.80$ megohms; other constants are left the same. Compute the input to the grid of the amplifier with this change.

21. The gains for a three-stage amplifier are -20.0, -26.9, and -15.8. The output load is 50 K, the impedance of the d-c source 200 ohms. (a) Compute the alternating potential at the grid of each tube, for 10.0 volts output. (b) Compute the approximate value for the alternating potential at the $+B$ terminal of the d-c source. Is it big enough to make troublesome feedback? (c) The d-c supply is 250 volts, and 150 volts d-c at 0.75 ma is sufficient for the first stage. Compute the values for the decoupling resistor, R_q, and condenser, C_q, in Fig. 29, to make the feedback voltage at Q only 10 percent of the signal input to grid 2 at 40 cps. (NOTE: The alternating potential drop, from Q to ground, is divided between R_1 and the plate resistance of tube 1. With a triode there is a big reduction at the plate of tube 1 because r_p is small; with a pentode r_p is so large that the potential at the plate may be taken equal to that at Q.) (d) Discuss corrections to be applied because of current in tube 2.

22. A transformer having a turn ratio, N_1/N_2, equal to 4.00 is put between cathode and ground in a cathode-follower circuit. A load of 300 ohms is connected to the secondary terminals. Assume that transformer losses are negligible, and take $\mu = 9.0$ and $r_p = 2.10$ K. (a) Compute the emf and internal resistance of the equivalent a-c source on the primary side of the transformer. (b) Compute the corresponding emf and resistance for the secondary side. (c) Compute the voltage and power output in the secondary for 80 volts rms input to the cathode-follower.

23. In Fig. 31 is shown a type of negative feedback (called parallel feedback) sometimes employed when the driver tube, $T1$, is a pentode. (a) Prove that

$$A/A' = 1 + (1 - A)R'/R_3$$

where R' is the parallel resistance of R_1, R_2, and r_p for $T1$, and A' and A are the

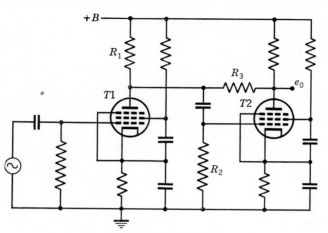

FIG. 31.   "PARALLEL" FEEDBACK.

gains (in $T2$) with and without feedback respectively.   (b) The main objection to this type of feedback is that the current in R_3 greatly increases the load for $T1$ and thereby can adversely affect the performance of $T1$.   Show that R_3 is equivalent to a resistor equal to $R_3/(1 - A)$ in parallel with R_2.

CHAPTER 7

Electron Emission

1. Introduction. In the chapters preceeding this one we have not been concerned with the nature of thermionic emission, as long as the flow of electrons from the cathodes in our electron tubes is sufficient to maintain operation within the space-charge region. Now, however, it is appropriate to inquire into the physical conditions under which electron emission may take place. First of all, it must be realized that an electric field cannot, of itself, pull electrons out of a conductor,* since the electric field cannot penetrate into the conductor. Only after electrons have been ejected through the surface, by some other means, can an electric field set up electric current in an electron tube. Thermionic emission of electrons represents only one of the several means whereby electrons may be induced to leave the interior of a solid and become free in space. Two other means of great importance are photo-emission, and secondary emission produced by electron bombardment. Methods of lesser importance are bombardment by heavier particles, such as ions or even uncharged atoms, and "field emission" (see Sec. 24). Knowledge of all these methods of electron emission is important to the practical development of electron tubes, in addition to revealing much concerning the nature of solids.

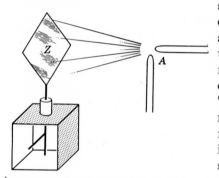

Fig. 1. Photoelectric Effect.
A—arc light. *Z*—zinc plate.

2. The Photoelectric Effect. Let us consider first the photoelectric emission of electrons from a metallic surface, a phenomenon which may be demonstrated with a clean zinc plate connected to the knob of a gold-leaf electroscope, as indicated in Fig. 1. If the plate, *Z*, is charged *negatively*, then exposed to light from a bare arc-lamp placed a foot or so away, it will lose charge at a rate which is proportional to the

---

* The only exception is field emission (Sec. 24), by *very intense* fields.

intensity of the light.   On the contrary, if the plate is charged positively, no such loss of charge takes place.   Only ultraviolet light of
very short wavelengths will produce this effect in zinc, waves so short
that a sheet of clear glass placed in the path of the light will stop the
loss of charge.   For success with this experiment the zinc must be
freshly cleaned, by scrubbing with sandpaper.   By making a zinc
plate the cathode in a cathode-ray tube Lenard proved that the negative charge is carried away from the plate by electrons which are
liberated by the ultraviolet light.

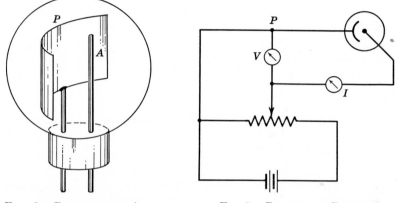

FIG. 2.   PHOTOTUBE.   A—   FIG. 3.   PHOTOTUBE CIRCUIT.
    anode.   P—cathode.

Metals which exhibit this photoelectric effect with visible light,
such as sodium, potassium, and cesium, are so active chemically that
they must be inclosed in an evacuated bulb, or in an inert gas, to keep
their surfaces clean enough.   A second electrode then must be inclosed
to serve as collector for the electrons.   Such a *phototube* is diagrammed
in Fig. 2.   The inside surface of the curved plate, P, is the photo-
sensitive surface, and the rod A is the collector, or anode.   In most
phototubes the emissive metal is cesium, the cesium surface being
formed within the tube by condensation of cesium vapor onto a
plate of copper or silver.   First the bulb is evacuated and baked until
it is free of all gases which can contaminate the sensitive surface,
then the surface of P is lightly oxidized by admitting just the right
amount of oxygen, and finally the cesium vapor is introduced, usually
by a heat-induced chemical reaction within the bulb itself.   The
cesium vapor condenses upon the oxidized surface in a layer which is
about one atom deep for best results.   Similar phototubes may be
made with sodium, potassium, or rubidium surfaces.

3. Phototubes. The physical characteristics of a phototube may be investigated with the circuit of Fig. 3. Under constant illumination the phototube current reaches saturation at quite low potential, as shown in Fig. 4, since the current is quite small and the cathode area relatively large. The saturation current is found experimentally to be directly proportional to the intensity of the light, as long as the spectral quality (relative intensity at different wavelengths) remains the same. The spectral sensitivity for several kinds of photoelectric surfaces is represented in Fig. 5. For each plot the ordinates represent

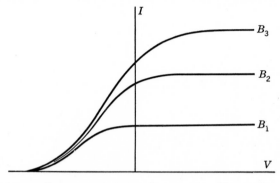

FIG. 4. PHOTOTUBE CHARACTERISTICS. *I*—current. *V*—anode potential. B_1, B_2, B_3—brightness of illumination.

current for equal values of monochromatic radiant energy, throughout the spectrum, and the scale is adjusted to give equal peak values for all three plots. The sensitivity curves for a complete phototube must include also the transmission of the bulb. Since glass absorbs most of the ultraviolet, quartz windows must be inserted in ultraviolet tubes, or the bulb must be made of a special glass which is transparent to the near ultraviolet. Since phototube currents are always small it is generally advantageous to provide a d-c amplifier, as illustrated and explained in Chapter 3, Fig. 17 and Sec. 18.

4. Experiment 17. Phototube Characteristics. *Part I. Light Intensity.* The linear dependence of phototube current upon light intensity may be demonstrated with Exp. 10. This experiment may be postponed to this point, or it may be performed earlier and the results reviewed here.

Part II. Anode Potential. The dependence of photocurrent upon anode potential may be investigated with the apparatus of Exp. 10. Set the lamp (source of light) at a fixed distance from the phototube, so as to provide constant illumination. Choose this distance so that the saturation current causes nearly full-scale deflection of the meter. Vary V from 10 volts down to zero, then in the negative direction until the phototube current falls to zero or starts to reverse.   Take readings close together where the current changes rapidly.   Since the phototube current causes a potential drop in the resistor R_g the anode

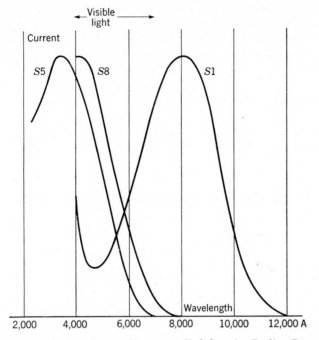

FIG. 5.   SPECTRAL SENSITIVITY.   Data supplied by the Radio Corporation of America.

potential is lower than E_2.   Correct the anode potential for this potential drop, and represent your results by a curve plotted with phototube current as y, anode potential as x.

Repeat this procedure with a red-glass filter between the lamp and the phototube.   (Move the lamp closer, to make the saturation current the same as before.)   Repeat again with a blue-glass filter.   The fact that the anode potential must be made negative by several volts before the current falls to zero indicates that electrons leave the cathode with an appreciable amount of initial energy, and the measurements made with the colored filters show that this energy is greater for blue light than for red.   The source of this initial energy, and the reason for the difference observed with light of different wavelengths, are explained in the next section.

5. Photoelectric Theory.   For each type of surface represented in Fig. 5 it will be noted that the photocurrent falls to zero at some definite wavelength, λ_0, which is called the long-wavelength limit or threshold for that surface.   Light of wavelength longer than this limit will not liberate electrons from that surface, no matter how intense it may be.*   It will be noted also, in Fig. 4, that the photocurrent does not become zero until the anode potential reaches an appreciable negative value.*   If monochromatic light (light of a single wavelength, or more exactly, a very narrow wavelength band) is employed, the potential, $-V_f$, at which the current just reaches zero is found to be the same for any intensity of light, at that wavelength, but increases (in the negative direction) as the frequency of the light is increased. Experiments which were first performed by Millikan† show that V_f is directly proportional to the excess of this frequency over the frequency, f_0, which corresponds to λ_0.   That is,

$$V_f \propto f - f_0 \tag{1}$$

This relationship may be written also as

$$V_f e = h(f - f_0) \tag{2}$$

or

$$hf = V_f e + hf_0 \tag{3}$$

According to Einstein's theory for this photoelectric effect, hf represents the energy of the *photons*, or light particles, in light of frequency f; hf_0 represents the work required to just liberate an electron from the surface, or the potential energy gained by the electron in escaping; and $V_f e$ is the work to stop the most energetic electron, and equals its kinetic energy of escape.   Equation 3 then represents the energy exchange between a photon and an electron, when *all* the energy of the photon, or hf, is given to a *single* electron.   More often the energy of the photon is shared by other particles and the escaping electrons have less kinetic energy; thus most photo-electrons are stopped by lower potentials.   According to this theory, also, the

---

* These statements are exactly true only if the metal is at absolute zero of temperature.   The differences are not appreciable at room temperature.   A more exact yet very readable discussion of this theory is given by L. A. DuBridge, in the *American Journal of Physics*, Vol. 16 (1948), p. 191.

† These experiments are very difficult.   The light must be very pure, the cathode surface must be perfectly clean, and the anode must not emit any electrons.   In commercial cesium phototubes some cesium vapor always condenses upon the anode, so that the phototube current reverses when the anode potential becomes sufficiently negative.   Experiment 16 demonstrates these phenomena qualitatively but does not serve to measure h.

number of electrons freed will be proportional directly to the number of photons striking the photosensitive surface, or the photoelectric current is directly proportional to light intensity, as has been observed experimentally.

The factor h is Planck's *quantum* constant, and this experiment provides one of the cornerstones upon which the whole quantum theory of physics is built. The quantity hf_0 may also be written w_0 and called the *work-function* of the emitting surface. It may be represented also by the potential difference, ϕ_0, through which an electron must be moved to give it energy equal to w_0:

$$w_0 = \phi_0 e \tag{4}$$

Another name for this work-function is electron affinity.

6. The Electron-Volt. Many times it is convenient to use ϕ_0 as a measure of *energy*, and this we may do if we define a new *unit* of energy, called the *electron-volt* and abbreviated *ev*. One electron-volt measures the work done in moving an electron (or any other particle carrying one fundamental unit of electric charge, e) through a potential difference of 1 volt. The conversion factor is thus

$$1 \text{ ev} = 1.60 \times 10^{-12} \text{ erg} \tag{5}$$

The work-function may be expressed as ϕ ev.

7. Phototube Applications. Applications for phototubes are almost innumerable. Any device which may be made to occult a light may thereby operate a phototube so as to detect intruders, open doors, stop a machine before the operator is injured, time horse races, or perform a multitude of other special functions. In the laboratory, phototubes replace the human eye in many types of photometric devices, either for direct measurement of light intensity or as a means for indicating an intensity balance. Another big field of application is typified by the reproduction of sound from the sound-track of a moving-picture film.

The basic circuits for all these applications are relatively simple. For steady (or slowly changing) illumination the current amplifier of Fig. 17, Chapter 3, is the basic circuit. For certain applications the d-c meter may be replaced by a sensitive relay. When greater sensitivity is needed a d-c amplifier may be employed, or the light may be interrupted or modulated at a suitable frequency so that an a-c amplifier may be used. The reproduction of sound from a moving-picture film illustrates the latter method. Still a third class of circuits utilizes a phototube to trigger a thyratron tube (see Chapter 9). For many applications also it is possible to employ the gas-type phototube, which is described in Chapter 8. In this phototube the current is amplified many times by ionization of gas atoms. Another method for amplification of phototube currents is the electron-multiplier tube described in Sec. 20, in which amplification is accomplished by secondary-electron emission.

8. Thermionic Emission. Thermionic emission of electrons from a hot cathode may be accurately described as an *evaporation* process. It should not be confused with boiling; the correct analog is instead the escape of water molecules from the surface of water liquid which is at a temperature far below the boiling point. In this analog, water molecules are moving about within the liquid with speeds for which the root mean square value, $\bar{u}$, is determined by the temperature of the liquid, in accord with the kinetic-theory equation* for the average kinetic energy of a molecule. If T is the absolute temperature of the liquid, m the mass of each molecule, and k the Boltzmann constant (the gas constant per molecule), then

$$\tfrac{1}{2}m\bar{u}^2 = \tfrac{3}{2}kT \tag{6}$$

If all the molecules had the same speed, $\bar{u}$, none would be able to escape through the surface of the liquid until the boiling point was reached, and the fact that evaporation does occur proves the true motion to be quite different. The speed for individual molecules may range from very high to very low values, although those having speeds near $\bar{u}$ outnumber greatly those whose speeds depart far from this value. Thus there are always a few molecules moving toward the surface with enough speed to escape into the space above the liquid, and the number of these increases rapidly as T increases.

Richardson explained thermionic emission of electrons in like manner. As he pictured it, the *conduction* electrons in a metal (one, or sometimes two, for each atom) move freely about among the atoms with an average kinetic energy determined by the temperature of the metal, in accord with Eq. 6. The electron current in a thermionic tube then is maintained by the very small fraction of the electrons which are able to escape from the metal, against the forces binding them to it, because they possess in the metal kinetic energies far above the average and are moving toward the surface.

9. Richardson's Equation. From these assumptions Richardson derived the following equation for the number of electrons emitted per unit area of a metal surface, per unit time.

$$n = a \sqrt{T} \epsilon^{-w'/kT} \tag{7}$$

* For this and other references to the kinetic theory of matter, see Chapters XI and XII in T. B. Brown, *Foundations of Modern Physics*.

Since the saturation current is obtained when these electrons are carried to the anode as fast as they are emitted, so that none return to the cathode, the saturation current density (current per unit area of cathode) corresponding to Eq. 7 is

$$J = ne = ae \sqrt{T} \epsilon^{-w'/kT} \tag{8}$$

In Eqs. 7 and 8, a is an integration factor, ϵ is the Naperian constant, 2.72, and the quantity w' is the *work-function* of the surface and represents the work done in removing one electron from it. In the evaporation analog w' corresponds to the heat of vaporization *per molecule*.

We now know that certain of Richardson's assumptions are wrong; this will be explained in Sec. 18. When the correct assumptions are made the equation for the saturation current density becomes

$$J_0 = AT^2\epsilon^{-w_0/kT} \tag{9}$$

Equation 9 may be called Richardson's corrected equation, or Dushman's equation. In it w_0 is the true work-function for the surface, and A is another constant determined by the nature of the surface. Theory indicates that A should be 120 amp/cm^2, but experimental values do not agree with this figure, and are different for each type of surface. It is possible to account for these differences in several ways, although the experiments do not show which is the correct explanation.

Experiments to verify this equation encounter several difficulties. First of all, the thermionic current does not reach a constant value as the anode potential is raised but continues to rise slowly, even when the potential is so large that all electrons are drawn away from the cathode to the anode as fast as they are emitted. Evidently the rate of emission is being increased by the anode potential, or rather, by the electric field produced at the cathode by that potential.

10. The Schottky Effect. Schottky showed that the effect of an external field, E, is to reduce the work-function of the surface by an amount equal to $\sqrt{Ee^3}$,* so that the work-function under these conditions is

$$w = w_0 - \sqrt{Ee^3} \tag{10}$$

When there is an external field, w must replace w_0 in Eq. 9, and the saturation current density is J instead of J_0:

$$J = AT^2\epsilon^{-w/kT}$$

$$= AT^2\epsilon^{-w_0/kT}\epsilon^{\sqrt{Ee^3}/kT} \tag{11}$$

* See Appendix 4 for this proof.

or, from Eq. 9,

$$J = J_0\epsilon^{\sqrt{Ee^3}/kT} \tag{12}$$

From Eq. 12 we may obtain directly

$$\log_e J = \log_e J_0 + \frac{\sqrt{e^3}}{kT}\sqrt{E} \tag{13}$$

Since E is proportional to V, the anode potential, we may write also

$$\log_{10} J = \log_{10} J_0 + C\sqrt{V} \tag{14}$$

The constant C includes the factor for conversion from natural to base-10 logarithms, as well as the other constants in Eq. 13 and the proportionality factor between E and V.

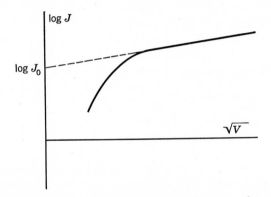

Fig. 6. Schottky Plot. V—anode potential. J—saturation current density at cathode. J_0—saturation current density for zero field.

Equation 14 provides a means for obtaining values of J_0 with which to verify Richardson's equation and obtain values for A and w_0. At each temperature, observations of J are made for a series of values for V; these values then are plotted as shown in Fig. 6, with $\log J$ as ordinates and $\sqrt{V}$ as abscissae. For smooth metal cathodes the upper (saturation) part of this plot is a straight line, thus verifying Schottky's theory. The y-intercept of its projection (broken line in Fig. 6) gives the value of $\log J_0$, as shown by Eq. 14.

11. Verification of Richardson's Equation. The values of J_0 obtained in the manner described above may be checked against Richardson's corrected equation by substitution in Eq. 9. It is easier, however, first to convert Eq. 9 into the equation of a straight line by dividing through by T^2, then taking logarithms of both sides, so as to give

$$\log_e \frac{J_0}{T^2} = \log_e A - \frac{w_0}{k} \frac{1}{T}$$ (15)

Equation 15 indicates that a plot of $\log_e (J_0/T^2)$ against $1/T$, as represented in Fig. 7, should be a straight line, and experimental data do give a straight line over values of J_0 ranging from the smallest measurable current up to that corresponding to the highest workable temperature for each metal being studied. It is customary to express the work-function in electron-volts, and then to represent it by ϕ_0. (See Sec. 6.) The exponent, w_0/kT, in Eqs. 9 and 15 then becomes

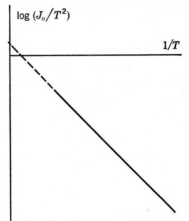

$$w_0/kT = 11{,}600\phi_0/T$$ (16)

The value of w_0 (or ϕ_0) for the metal studied is obtained from the plot of Fig. 7; its slope equals w_0/k, or $11{,}600\phi_0$.

Fig. 7. Richardson's Equation Plot. J_0—saturation current density (zero field). T—absolute temperature of cathode.

It would seem that this straight-line plot would be excellent proof for the correctness of Eq. 9 instead of Eq. 8, but this does not follow. Unfortunately, an almost equally straight line may be obtained for Eq. 8, by plotting $\log_e (J_0/\sqrt{T})$ against $1/T$. The slope of this line is somewhat greater than for the one plotted in Fig. 7, and represents w'/k. The effect of T^2, or of $\sqrt{T}$, is so small in comparison with that of $1/T$ in the exponent of ϵ that the experimental data do not decide between these two equations. Experimental evidence in favor of Eq. 9 is found, however, by comparing these values of the work-function with the photoelectric work-function given by Eq. 3. When photoelectric and thermionic currents are measured for the same surface the photoelectric work-function is found to agree better with the w_0 of Richardson's corrected equation than with the w' of his original equation. The best validation for Eq. 9, however, is given by evidence to be considered later on.

12. Experiment 18. Thermionic Emission. To verify Richardson's equation for thermionic emission we must have a straight filamentary cathode of pure metal, and we must be able to measure its temperature. Furthermore, since the temperature of any filament falls off toward its ends, because of thermal conduction to its supports, accurate values for A and ϕ_0 cannot be obtained unless we are able to measure the electron current from only the central portion of the filament, where the temperature is uniform. Fortunately, a good

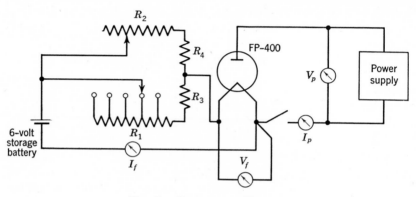

FIG. 8.   CIRCUIT FOR EXP. 18.

R_1—2.5 ohms, tapped at 0.1, 0.2, 0.4, R_3—1 ohm, 10 watts.
    0.6, 1.0, 1.5, and 2.0 ohms. R_4—5 ohms, 10 watts.
R_2—25 ohms, 50 watts.

check of Richardson's equation, and a fair value for ϕ_0, may be obtained with a simple diode having a filament which is very long as compared with its diameter, and these requirements are met by the FP-400 Kenetron,* which has a pure tungsten filament, 1.25 inches long by 0.005 inch diameter, along the axis of a cylindrical anode about ½ inch in diameter.

The circuit is diagrammed in Fig. 8.   Most trouble with this experiment arises from poor contacts in the heating circuit, at junction points, switch points, and rheostat sliders.   All connections should be made with screw-clamps and binding-posts, not spring connectors. In place of the ordinary socket use screw-clamps for the tube terminals, or better still solder these connections.   Storage-battery connections likewise should be screw-clamped, not made with battery clips.   The main rheostat, R_1, should be of the heavy-duty, step-resistance type, with brass blocks for switch-points.   Fine adjustment may be made

* Made by the General Electric Co.

with a tubular rheostat, R_2, in parallel with R_1. Keep a thin film of petroleum jelly over all surfaces of contact, especially on sliding surfaces of switches and rheostats.

Filament current and voltage, I_f and V_f, must be read very closely, since they change by small amounts. Both meters should have large scales, finely graduated. The cathode temperature is determined from I_f, in the manner described in Part I.   Do not exceed 4.25 volts for V_f, and do not hold it above 4.0 volts longer than needed to take observations.   Correct I_f for the voltmeter current, computed from V_f and the resistance of this meter. A sequence of milliammeters is required to cover the range of values for I_p, the electron current, with enough overlap to keep all readings at least one-tenth of full-scale.   Take 9 or 10 sets of observations, each set for a different value of I_f.   Choose I_f so that the resultant values of I_p are spaced uniformly along a logarithmic scale.   A suggested sequence of values for I_p is 40, 20, 8, 4, 2, 0.8, 0.4, 0.2, 0.08, and 0.04 ma, measured at 100 volts anode potential.   For each set take readings of I_p for anode potentials of 300, 250, 200, 150, and 100 volts.   Check I_f and V_f frequently to make sure they stay fixed throughout each set.

Part I.   Temperature. The absolute temperature, T, may be determined from I_f and the diameter, d, of the filament. According to work of Jones and Langmuir,* T is a function of $I_f/d^{3/2}$, values of which are tabulated in their paper. Since d must be taken from the tube maker's data and may be several percent in error, T may be determined sufficiently well for this experiment from the following *empirical* equation.

$$T = 60.2 \sqrt{\frac{I_f}{d^{3/2}}\left(1 + 0.083 \times 10^{-3}\frac{I_f}{d^{3/2}}\right)} \qquad (17)$$

Compute $I_f/d^{3/2}$ (amp/cm$^{3/2}$) from your data; then compute T for each set.

Part II.   Schottky Effect. Make a Schottky plot (Fig. 6) for each set of data and obtain I_0 from it. Semi-log plotting paper is very useful for these plots.

Part III.   Richardson's Equation. (a) From the values of T and I_0 obtained in Parts I and II make the plot of Fig. 7, with $1/T$ as x, $\log I_0/T^2$ as y. Draw the straight line which fits the plot best, and find ϕ_0 from its slope. A value for A may be computed from the

---

* H. A. Jones and I. Langmuir, *General Electric Review*, Vol. 30 (1927), pp. 310, 354. The tables are reproduced in E. L. Chaffee, *Theory of Thermionic Vacuum Tubes*, p. 100.

y-intercept, but this value will be poor, since the effective area of the cathode is uncertain.

(b) A shorter procedure, and one which has to be followed if the filament diameter is unknown, is to assume that T is proportional to $I_f^{1/2}$ (see Eq. 17) and plot $1/I_f^{1/2}$ as x, log I_0/I_f as y. Over the range of temperature involved this assumption is reasonably good, and the plot should be a fairly straight line, in accord with Richardson's equation.

13. Work-Function Values. Values of ϕ_0 for most metals lie between 5.0 ev, for platinum, and 1.8 ev, for cesium. The usefulness of a metal as a thermionic cathode, however, depends not only upon the value of ϕ_0, but also upon the temperature at which the metal may be operated safely. In this respect tungsten is one of the best. Although its work-function is 4.52 ev, it may be operated without excessive evaporation above 2500 degrees K. Tungsten filaments are found in X-ray tubes, and in radio power tubes which are operated at high voltages.

For most purposes, various composite surfaces serve better than pure metals as thermionic cathodes. For example, thoriated tungsten, or tungsten covered with a monatomic layer of thorium, has a work-function much less than that for pure tungsten, less indeed than that for pure thorium, and operates best at a temperature for which its emission exceeds by one or two hundredfold that of pure tungsten at 2500 degrees K. Thoriated tungsten filaments are made from tungsten in which has been dissolved, in the molten state, 1 to 1.5 percent of thoria (thorium oxide). This filament is "activated" by heating it for a short time at about 2800 degrees K, then for 15 to 30 minutes at about 2100 degrees K. At the higher temperature thorium atoms are formed by reduction of some of the thoria; at the lower, these atoms diffuse to the surface, there to form an emissive layer. Thorium tends to evaporate from the surface, and must be replenished by diffusion of new atoms from the interior. At about 1900 degrees K these processes balance and a monatomic layer may be maintained. Above this temperature the evaporation is too rapid, and the diffusion is too slow if the temperature is much below this value.

The profound influence of a monatomic layer of thorium upon the emission from a tungsten cathode emphasizes the fact that thermionic emission is a *surface* phenomenon. Surface layers of other substances may produce comparable changes in the emission characteristics of cathodes, and many substances, for example oxygen, tend to lower or "poison" the emission. To avoid such poisoning, great care is taken to clean thoroughly all materials entering into the structure of an electron tube, and to evacuate it as thoroughly as possible. Gases and vapors which are adsorbed or absorbed in the glass and metal parts are driven off by baking the tube at as high a temperature as the glass will stand, sometimes for many hours, and by heating the metal parts to incandescence, either by electron bombardment or by high-frequency induction.

14. Oxide Cathodes. Receiving tubes and similar low-power tubes generally have "oxide" cathodes, in which the emitter is a layer of mixed barium and strontium oxides, coated on a metal (usually nickel) support. Such cathodes produce copious emission of electrons at temperatures lower than 1000 degrees K. The barium oxide appears to be primarily responsible for the electron emission, but the mixture is more efficient and stable than barium oxide alone. Even the type of metal which supports the oxide coating is important to the successful operation of an oxide cathode, certain nickel alloys being much better than pure nickel. The first step in making an oxide cathode is to coat the metal support with a paint-like mixture of barium and strontium carbonates, held together with some adhesive. After thorough drying this cathode is mounted in the tube, which is then well exhausted. Pumping is continued while the cathode is heated to a temperature at which the adhesive burns off and the carbonates decompose, leaving the oxides. This oxide coating then must be "activated" by suitable heat and electrical treatment, to make it a good emitter of electrons. Although the thickness of this oxide layer is only a small fraction of a millimeter it is very large in terms of atoms, and the phenomena which take place in it are quite complex. The electron emission from an oxide cathode does not saturate as it does from a metal one, and attempt to reach saturation current produces an electric field at the cathode surface which damages it. For this reason the operation of oxide cathodes is restricted to the space-charge region.

The oxide cathode possesses many advantages over other types. First of all, the heating power expended per unit of electron current is very much lower than for any other type. Then, because of the low operating temperature, it is possible to make an oxide cathode in the form of a cylinder or box of metal, coated on the outside with the oxide layer and heated from the inside, by radiation or conduction from a suitable electric heater. This method of construction is illustrated in Fig. 9. Almost always the metal is nickel, with the heater made of tungsten wire, insulated by a coating of aluminum oxide. The heater wires are looped or coiled in such a manner as to make a non-inductive resistor, so that a-c heating is possible and a common a-c source may serve any number of cathodes. Another great advantage is that the entire cathode surface is at the same potential, whereas the potential of a filamentary cathode varies from one end to the other. These advantages are limited, however, to tubes operated within the space-charge region, as stated above.

The work-function for an oxide cathode appears to be in the neighborhood of 1 ev, and may be even less for well-activated surfaces. It cannot be determined very satisfactorily, owing to difficulties in

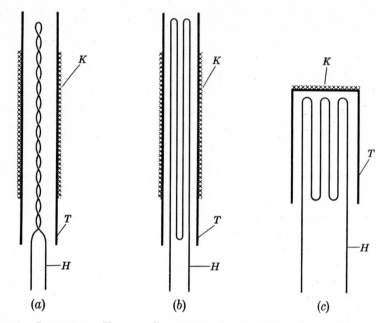

FIG. 9. INDIRECTLY HEATED CATHODES. (a, b) For receiver tubes. (c) For cathode-ray tube. K—oxide coating. T—nickel tube. H—heater.

obtaining saturation-current values for such cathodes. As has been mentioned above, when the anode potential goes beyond the space-charge range the electric field then appearing at the cathode surface may damage an oxide cathode if maintained for more than a very brief time. This difficulty may be circumvented by *pulsing* the anode potential, that is, by periodically raising it from zero to the desired value for a very brief time, then dropping it back again to zero, the current being measured during the pulse. Even when this method is employed the current from an oxide cathode does not approach saturation in the manner observed for a smooth, metal surface. The rough, porous nature of the oxide surface may account in large part for this difference. An additional cause may be non-uniform emission; it has been shown that the surface of an oxide cathode consists of small areas or "patches" having interspersed strong and weak emission.

Many of the difficulties encountered with oxide cathodes in tubes of high power are eliminated in a new type called the Philips L-cathode, a development of the Philips Research Laboratories in Holland. In it the barium-strontium oxide layer, which is quite thick, is covered over by a porous plate of sintered tungsten powder, which holds it in place and protects it from disintegrating factors such as positive-ion bombardment and high electric fields. Emission is from a monatomic layer of barium atoms, cemented to the outer surface of the tungsten plate by an intervening mona-tomic layer of oxygen atoms. The tungsten plate also plays an active part in the liberation of barium from the oxide. High emission with long life, and the possibility of operation at current values close to saturation, are among the advantages claimed for this cathode.*

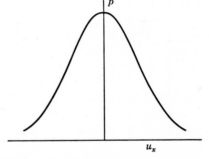

FIG. 10. DISTRIBUTION IN VELOCITY FOR MOLECULES. u_x—x-velocity. p—probability function; see Sec. 15.

15. Maxwellian Distribution. In the evaporation analog for thermionic emission the average kinetic energy of molecules in the vapor state is the same as in the liquid state, and is determined by the temperature, according to Eq. 6. Although the molecules which escape the liquid state do so because they are far more active than the average, they lose kinetic energy (and gain an equal amount of potential energy) in escaping. In either state the molecular motions are randomly distributed, in both speed and direction. The distribution in speed has already been mentioned. For the present we are more interested in the distribution in velocity, which is represented in Fig. 10 for the x-component. The same plot represents also the y- and z-components. This distribution is determined by the law of chance, and has the equation

$$p = \sqrt{\frac{m}{2\pi kT}} \, \epsilon^{-mu_x^2/2kT} \tag{18}$$

The ordinates, p, of this plot may be interpreted as follows. The probability that any molecule has its x-velocity in the range between u_x and $u_x + \Delta u_x$ is $p \, \Delta u_x$, and out of a total of N molecules, $Np \, \Delta u_x$

* Further details are given in *Electronics* for August 1951, p. 104.

have velocities within this range at any instant.   For low temperatures the plot is narrow and high; as T increases it widens and becomes lower, so that the area under the plot is always unity.

Equation 18 was derived by Maxwell from the laws of chance or probability.   It is checked for molecules by many experiments, although almost none of these experiments demonstrates molecular motion directly.   For electrons, on the contrary, the distribution in velocity may be determined directly from the data taken for a diode with negative anode potential.   For simplicity, let us consider that the electrodes are plane and parallel.   Then, when the anode potential, V, is negative, the current to the anode is carried by electrons which leave the cathode with x-velocity components, u_x, sufficient to carry them to the anode against the opposing field.   An equivalent statement is that an electron can reach the anode only if the part of its kinetic energy which may be computed from u_x is greater than $-Ve$, the energy required to take it from cathode to anode; that is, if

$$\tfrac{1}{2}mu_x{}^2 \geqq -Ve \tag{19}$$

The minus sign is necessary since V itself is negative, and the energy is positive.   If the distribution in velocity among these electrons is the same as that given in Eq. 18, for molecules, we may obtain, by integration,* an equation for the anode current which is

$$I = I_0 \epsilon^{Ve/kT} \tag{20}$$

If there is no space-charge, I_0 in Eq. 20 is the saturation current, or the anode current when V is zero.

A straight-line equation may be obtained from Eq. 20 by taking logarithms of both sides.

$$\log_e I = \log_e I_0 + \frac{e}{kT}\,V = \log_e I_0 + \frac{11{,}600}{T}\,V \text{ (volts)} \tag{23}$$

* Proof for this equation is as follows.   Let the limiting value for u_x in Eq. 19 be u_1.   That is,

$$\tfrac{1}{2}m_1 u^2 = -Ve \tag{21}$$

From the definition of p the number of electrons having x-velocity in any interval du_x is $Np\,du_x$, and their contribution to the anode current is dI equal to $eu_x Np\,du_x$. The anode current is then

$$I = Ne \int_{u_1}^{\infty} pu_x\,du_x = Ne\sqrt{\frac{kT}{2\pi m}}\,\epsilon^{-mu_x{}^2/2kT}$$

$$= Ne\sqrt{\frac{kT}{2\pi m}}\,\epsilon^{Ve/kT} \tag{22}$$

Experimental data taken with a diode having plane electrodes, and a smooth metal cathode, yield a plot of log I as y, V as x, which is quite straight, in accord with Eq. 23, until V approaches zero.   Then the space-charge effect causes it to curve as shown in Fig. 11.   The slope of the straight portion should be equal to $11,600/T$, and the value of T obtained in this manner is in good agreement with the cathode temperature as measured in other ways, when the cathode is smooth metal. Thus these data verify closely the assumption that thermionically emitted electrons, outside the cath-ode, have a Maxwellian distribution in velocity corresponding to the cathode temperature.   Indeed, this experimental verification is better than can be made experimentally for molecules.   For smooth metal cathodes this plot provides a very reliable method for measuring cath-ode temperature.   When the elec-trodes are not plane-parallel Eq. 23 does not apply exactly and this method of interpreting the data is only approximate.   Chaffee*

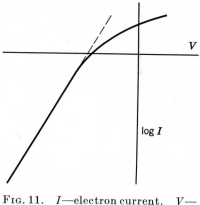

FIG. 11. I—electron current. V—anode potential.

describes a method which is more precise when the electrodes are cylindrical.

For thoriated tungsten and oxide cathodes the plots obtained in this manner are good straight lines over the more important part of the current range, but the temperature determined in this manner does not always agree with the temperature values measured otherwise. Such disagreement is not unexpected in view of the composite nature of these emitting surfaces.   Nevertheless, even for oxide cathodes this method is valuable for comparative temperature measurements, such as comparisons of several tubes of the same type, or the same tube with different heater currents.

16. Experiment 19.   Cathode Temperature.   In this experiment the theory given in Sec. 15 is to be checked for a commercial diode, and the apparent temperature of the cathode measured.   The poten-tial drop along a filamentary cathode invalidates results in an experi-ment such as this one, unless elaborate circuits are employed.   (These circuits provide for intermittent heating of the cathode, and for taking electron-current measurements only while the heater current is zero.) Hence this experiment is performed with a tube having an equi-

* E. L. Chaffee, *Theory of Thermionic Electron Tubes*, pp. 80–81.

potential, oxide cathode, indirectly heated. Good data may be taken with a 6H6 diode, or even for a triode with the grid and plate tied together.

Current measurements cover a wide range of values. It is best to use a sensitive wall galvanometer with telescope and scale, provided with an Ayerton-Perry shunt whereby exact sensitivity reductions may be made. The galvanometer sensitivity without shunt should be at least 10^{-8} amp/mm at a scale distance of 50 cm, and the shunt should have ratios of 1, 10, 100, 1000, and 10,000. Since we shall use only the logarithms of I, it is unnecessary to reduce galvanometer

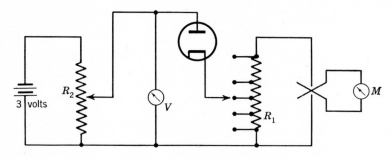

FIG. 12.   CIRCUIT FOR EXP. 19.

readings to standard current values. It is sufficient to reduce all readings to equivalent scale-readings at the 1:1 ratio. For example, a reading of 13.26 cm with a shunt ratio of 1:100 is equivalent to 1326 cm at the 1:1 ratio. Potential measurements are best made with a potentiometer. Next best is a good voltmeter with a long scale and fine graduations, as represented in Fig. 12. The heater current is best supplied from a storage battery, with a good voltmeter or ammeter to hold it to exact value.

Set up the apparatus as shown in Fig. 12. Find by trial the voltmeter reading when the galvanometer reads 1 or 2 cm with the 1:1 ratio, and again when the reading is nearly full-scale with the least sensitive ratio. These voltmeter readings define the range of observations. Take readings of I and V over this range, for equal increments of V, taking 10 or 15 readings in all. For each value of V take direct and reversed readings of the galvanometer, and average. (Do not fail to record the shunt setting.) If the shunt and galvanometer together have high resistance it may happen that the potential drop through them will make the anode potential different from the voltmeter value. Make check computations to ascertain this, and if the drop is not negligible compute it and correct V for it.

Plot log I as y and V as x, as shown in Fig. 11. It will be more convenient to plot base-10 logarithms and to correct Eq. 23 accordingly than to reduce all values to base-e logarithms. Semi-log plotting paper is very convenient for this plot. From the slope of the straight portion of this plot compute the apparent cathode temperature. If time permits repeat the experiment with lower heater current.

17. Electron Refraction. Further information concerning the emission of electrons from metals is given by the phenomenon of electron

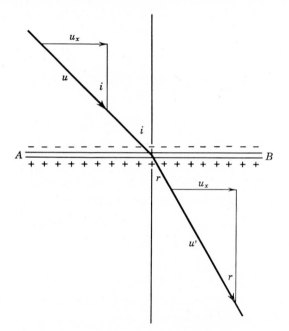

FIG. 13. REFRACTION OF ELECTRON BEAM.

refraction. As explained in Sec. 5, an electron which escapes from the interior of a metal must traverse a potential difference ϕ_0, equal to w_0/e. Furthermore, this change in potential must take place over a very short distance right at the surface of the metal, since the force on an electron inside the metal is zero until it is close under the surface, and becomes zero again a short distance above the surface. Let us now inquire how this sharp potential drop affects the trajectory of an electron as it passes through the surface. We might produce such an abrupt potential change with a thin dielectric sheet, A-B, Fig. 13, having its upper surface negatively charged and its lower surface charged positively. There is then a potential difference, V_1, between the regions above the sheet and below it, whose value is given by the condenser equation

$$V_1 = 4\pi Q_1 a/K \tag{24}$$

in which a is the thickness of the sheet, K its dielectric constant, and Q_1 the charge per unit area on either side. Let us assume for this discussion that the sheet offers no mechanical resistance to penetration by cathode-ray electrons. Then if an electron having kinetic energy equal to $V_0 e$ shoots through this sheet from above its kinetic energy will increase to $(V_0 + V_1)e$, and its speed will increase from u to u', these values being given by the energy equations

$$\tfrac{1}{2}mu^2 = V_0 e \quad \text{and} \quad \tfrac{1}{2}mu'^2 = (V_0 + V_1)e \tag{25}$$

From these equations we find that the ratio of u' to u is a *constant*, n, whose value is

$$n = \frac{u'}{u} = \sqrt{\frac{V_0 + V_1}{V_0}} \tag{26}$$

If the electron crosses A-B obliquely, as indicated in Fig. 13, the component u_x of its velocity which is *parallel* to the surface will not change, because the force acting on the electron is normal to the surface. It follows that

$$\frac{\sin i}{\sin r} = \frac{u_x/u}{u_x/u'} = n \tag{27}$$

Since n is a constant Eq. 27 is Snell's law, the same as for the refraction of light. The value of n given by Eq. 26 may therefore be called the *index of refraction* for electrons.

In 1926 C. J. Davisson and L. H. Germer* discovered that electrons are refracted in this manner when they pass through the surface of a metal, and thus showed that the potential at the interior of a metal is higher than at its surface by an amount V_i, called the *inner potential* of the metal. For nickel their measurements gave approximately 17 volts as the value of V_i. Since the work-function for nickel is only about 5 ev, corresponding to an inner potential of only 5 volts, there appears to be here a very serious discrepancy.

18. Quantum Mechanics. Davisson and Germer contributed also to clearing up this discrepancy. In 1924 L. deBroglie predicted that any particle of matter might manifest itself as a *wave*, the wavelength

---

* See F. K. Richtmyer and E. H. Kennard, *Introduction to Modern Physics*, Chapter VII, for a discussion of this work.

being inversely proportional to the momentum of the particle.   The proportionality factor is Planck's constant, h.

$$\text{momentum} = mu = h/\lambda \quad \text{or} \quad \lambda = h/mu \qquad (28)$$

The existence of these waves has been proved for electrons by the interference patterns produced by electron beams which have been diffracted in a crystal.   These experiments were carried out by Davisson and Germer, as well as by G. P. Thomson, and it was in the course of these experiments that they discovered the refraction of electron beams.   Equation 28 states one of the most fundamental relationships in the modern physical theory concerning the nature of matter and energy which is called *quantum mechanics* or *wave mechanics*.*

Let us now consider how this theory accounts for the emission of electrons from a metal.   According to it we may regard the conduction electrons as essentially free particles, each of which must be represented by a separate *standing-wave* pattern in a box the size and shape of the metal block.   The distribution in energy of the electrons is now subject to a very fundamental rule: *no two wave patterns may be alike*.   When the concentration of electrons is low, as for the free-space electrons discussed in Sec. 15, this restriction is of little significance, and the distribution in energy follows the laws of chance, as explained in that section.   Inside a metal the situation is quite different.   Here the electron concentration is so high that the wavelengths for some electrons must be very short to meet this condition, even at absolute zero of temperature, and the corresponding kinetic energy for these electrons must be quite high.   For nickel (assuming two conduction electrons per atom) this theory indicates that the maximum kinetic energy at absolute zero is 11.7 ev.   In general we shall represent this maximum kinetic energy by V_q.

It is customary to represent these conditions with an energy-level diagram, as in Fig. 14.   The vertical line is the boundary between the metal, to the left, and the space outside, to the right.   If the energy (per electron) outside the metal is taken as zero and represented by the zero level, the *potential energy* of an electron inside the metal is represented by a negative level at $-V_i$ (ev).   This base level represents the energy of an electron at rest.   For electrons in motion, each possible electron-wave pattern corresponds to a particular energy level at a height above the base level determined by the corresponding kinetic energy.   The number of electrons possible to each energy level is limited by the rule stated above, so that, at absolute zero, the

* See T. B. Brown, *Foundations of Modern Physics*, Chapters VII and XIII.

levels are pre-empted or "filled" up to a height V_q above the base level. For nickel V_q is 11.7 ev.

The additional energy needed to liberate an electron from the metal is now the difference between V_i and V_q, and this difference is the quantity which we have called the work-function, ϕ_0. For nickel this difference is 5.3 ev, and ϕ_0 is 5.0 ev; the discrepancy is well within the limits of experimental error for V_i. Since the only way in which electrons in a metal may gain thermal energy is for the kinetic energy of some to increase above V_q, a rise in temperature above absolute

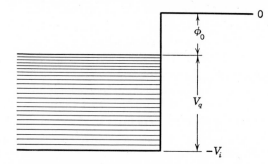

Fig. 14.   Energy-Level Diagram for a Metal. V_i—inner potential. V_q—Fermi potential. ϕ_0—work function.

zero brings about a redistribution of energy among some of the electrons in the top levels. The exact mathematical theory describes the nature of this redistribution and leads to Eq. 9, the corrected Richardson equation. Outside the metal the electrons which escape end up with a Maxwellian distribution in velocity because most of the kinetic energy which they possessed inside the metal is lost in jumping the inner-potential barrier.

19. Secondary Emission. Another means for ejecting electrons from a metal surface is to bombard it with electrons. A very few of the primary, bombarding electrons are reflected with little or no loss of energy; usually this small fraction may be disregarded. Most of the primary electrons enter the metal. In doing so, however, they cause secondary emission of other electrons from the surface. The secondary-emission ratio, which is defined as the ratio of the secondary current to the primary current, depends upon the nature of the surface and the energy of the primary electrons. It is represented in Fig. 15 for a typical metal surface. The energy of these secondary electrons is very small, so that almost all may be returned to the bombarded surface by an adverse potential of only a few volts. Secondary emission has already been discussed earlier, in Sec. 7, Chapter 5, in connection with the functioning of tetrodes.   There it is regarded as a troublesome phenomenon, and means have been invented for minimizing its effects.   However, secondary emission is not always a nuisance; it can also be very useful, as in the electron-multiplier tube.

20. Electron-Multiplier Tube.   In the electron-multiplier tube, secondary emission serves to produce enormous amplification of very

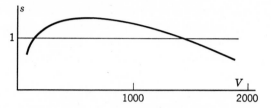

Fig. 15.   Secondary Emission. V—accelerating potential. s—ratio of secondary current to primary current.

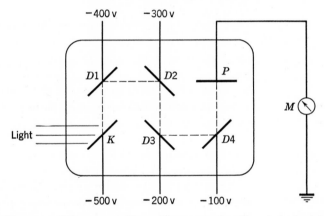

Fig. 16.   Electron Multiplier Tube (Schematic). K—photoelectric cathode. $D_1 \cdots D_4$—dynodes. P—anode.

small current, such as photoelectric current, and to do so quite linearly. The principle of operation is illustrated in Fig. 16.   The source of primary electrons is here a photoelectric cathode, K.   The electrodes $D1$, $D2$, $D3$, and $D4$ are called dynodes; they are made of a metal for which the secondary-emission ratio is high, and this ratio is further increased by special preparation of their surfaces.   Electrode P is the collector anode, here shown connected to ground through a current meter, M.   The potential differences between K and $D1$, $D1$ and $D2$, etc., are set to some value, V_s, which will give a high secondary-emission ratio.   In Fig. 16 V_s is represented as 100 volts.   If the secondary-emission ratio for each dynode is s, the secondary current from $D1$ to $D2$ is s times the photoelectric current from K to $D1$, and

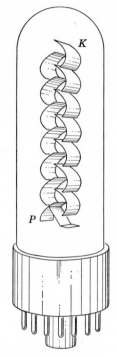

the current to P, after multiplication at each of the four dynodes, is s^4 times the primary photo-current. In practical electron-multiplier tubes the electrodes are curved in the manner shown in Fig. 17, so that the electrons do not go astray in traveling from one electrode to the next. Commercial electron-multiplier phototubes are constructed in similar manner, except that the dynodes are ranged in a circle about the axis of the tube to make the structure more compact. A typical example is the type 931-A tube, which has 9 dynodes and an overall gain, with 100 volts between electrodes, of over a million times. (This gain corresponds to a secondary-emission ratio of 4.6 for each dynode.)

21. Experiment 20. Secondary Emission. The overall gain for a 931-A phototube is difficult to measure because of its great magnitude, and also because of the high voltages required. It is simpler and more instructive to study the secondary emission from a single dynode, as in this experiment. The circuit is diagrammed in Fig. 18.

Fig. 17. Electron Multiplier Tube. Made in The George Washington University Research Laboratory, under the direction of Dr. Zoltan Bay. Primary electrons are emitted by K, as a result of X-ray or gamma-ray bombardment. The collector anode is P, and the remaining electrodes are dynodes. Supports and electrical connections not shown.

Only the photoelectric cathode and the first two dynodes are used, with the second dynode serving as anode. All the other electrodes should be connected to the second dynode. The photocurrent, I_p, from the cathode, K, and the secondary-electron current, I_s, to the anode, $D2$, are both measured with the same meter, M, by throwing the switch, S, to position A or position B. In Fig. 18, M is represented as a galvanometer with a reversing switch. It may also be a microammeter with a full-scale range as high as 50 μa. In normal operation of this tube the currents to $D1$ and $D2$ are exceedingly small, to keep the anode current down to a maximum of 1 ma, but when only the first three electrodes are employed it is safe to let the current to the third be much larger.

The light intensity may be controlled as in Exp. 10, or both the light source and the phototube may be inclosed in a light-tight box, as illustrated in Fig. 19*a*.   A partition across the middle of this box has an opening which is covered with a diffusing screen, such as a piece of ground glass, and the light intensity is varied by changing the area of this opening.   An iris diaphragm will serve.   So will the simple guillotine diaphragm sketched in Fig. 19*b*.   Means should be provided for operating this diaphragm from outside the box.

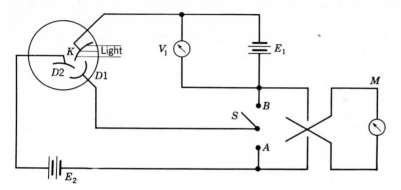

FIG. 18.   CIRCUIT FOR EXP. 19.

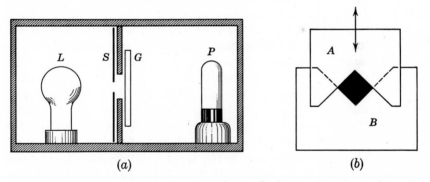

FIG. 19.   LIGHT BOX FOR EXP. 19.   (*a*) Box.   *L*—lamp.   *P*—phototube.   *G*—
ground glass.   *S*—aperture.   (*b*) Simple aperture.

Part I.   Secondary Emission.   Maintain the value of E_2, the potential difference between $D1$ and $D2$, Fig. 18, at about 12 volts. The source for E_1, the potential of $D1$, may be a power supply, or suitable combinations of B-batteries and dry cells.   Adjust the light intensity to give full-scale reading for I_s when E_1 is 125 volts, and leave it fixed at that value.   Take observations for 8 or 10 uniformly spaced values of E_1, from 0 to 125 volts.   For each value take readings of M, direct and reversed, for both positions of S, and compute the secondary-emission ratio, s. Plot a curve with s as y, E_1 as x. From your data compute the gain for all 9 dynodes, assuming that the others are identical with $D1$. Plot the logarithm of overall gain as y, log E_1 as x. Compare your result with the commercial tube data.

Although the values of s measured in this experiment are a good measure of the gain per dynode they differ somewhat from the true values of secondary emission for the dynode surface, for several reasons. First, there is some photoemission from $D1$ to $D2$, produced by light reflected from K. Second, a fraction of the primary electron current, I_p, goes directly to $D2$, by passing $D1$. Neither of these effects is very much dependent upon E_2, and I_s is far too small to show any space-charge effect. Hence, as may be demonstrated by an obvious extension of the experiment, I_s remains constant over a considerable range of E_2. Above this range I_s begins to decrease, and this decrease may be explained as due to an increase in the fraction of I_p which goes directly to $D2$. As E_1 is lowered the fraction of I_p going directly to $D2$ appears to increase, although it cannot be measured directly.

Part II. Linearity of Secondary Emission. Set both E_1 and E_2 at fixed values, of about 100 volts and 45 volts respectively. Vary the light intensity, and take readings for 8 or 10 uniformly spaced values of I_p. Plot a curve with I_s as y, I_p as x. If this plot is not entirely straight try to find an explanation for the deviations.

22. Secondary Emission from Insulators. If an electron beam bombards the surface of an insulator, the fluorescent screen of a cathode-ray tube, for example, it will cause secondary electrons to be emitted from that surface. If the secondary-emission ratio is greater than unity the secondary-electron current will at first exceed the primary current in the beam. Very shortly, however, the surface will acquire a positive charge over the area being bombarded, sufficient to cut the secondary current down to a value equal to the primary current. The beam then will continue to bombard that area, the electric charge brought to the area by the beam being carried away to neighboring conductors by the secondary emission. Since the secondary electrons have very little energy the potential of the insulator area never differs from the potential of the surrounding region by more than a few volts positive. For the fluorescent screen of a cathode-ray tube, the potential of the surrounding region is that of the last anode (the Aquadag coating, in a modern cathode-ray tube).

The secondary-emission ratio for an insulator follows a curve similar to the one shown in Fig. 15 for a metal. If the accelerating potential for the electron beam is so low that the secondary-emission ratio is less than unity, the beam current will exceed the flow of secondary electrons away from the bombarded area. This area then will charge up negatively and spread until the beam is deflected entirely away from the insulator. At the other extreme, if the accelerating potential is so high that the secondary-emission current is again less than the beam current, then the bombarded area will charge up negatively until the potential difference between it and the cathode drops to the value for which the secondary-emission ratio is unity. For example, if the ratio for a certain fluorescent screen falls below unity when the accelerating potential exceeds 8000 volts, and if the potential difference from the last anode to the cathode is 12,000 volts, then the fluorescent screen will charge up to 4000 volts negative.

23. Cold-Cathode Emission. Emission of electrons from a cold cathode may be produced by bombarding it with positive ions. This process is the primary source of electrons for the glow discharge (see Sec. 15, Chapter 8) as well as for cold-cathode type of cathode-ray tubes and X-ray tubes. It is relatively inefficient. In the glow discharge, for example, the emission ratio may be only 1 electron per 10 positive ions, for an accelerating potential of 100 to 200 volts. The other 9 electrons needed to maintain the glow discharge are produced by collisions with gas atoms.

24. "Field" Emission. It has been found experimentally that very small but measurable electron current may be obtained from a cold cathode *in a very high vacuum,* if the electric field at the surface of the cathode has a very high value. Such strong fields are obtained by making the cathode in the form of a sharp, highly polished point. This "field" emission cannot be accounted for as thermionic emission at room temperature, made possible by the action of these very strong fields in reducing the effective work-function, because field-emission current does not depend to any degree upon cathode temperature. Instead, it changes very rapidly with anode potential, V, according to the empirical equation

$$I = BV^2\epsilon^{-b/V} \tag{29}$$

The constants B and b are determined experimentally.

The true explanation for this field emission is given by the quantum theory of metals which has been discussed briefly in Sec. 18, and the principal importance of this type of emission at the present time is the support it gives to this theory. If the external electric field is very intense the potential energy of an electron outside the metal surface drops rapidly as the electron moves away from the surface, so that the electrons inside the metal are confined there by only a thin "potential wall," as represented in Fig. 20. (Cf. Fig. 14, and note that the top of this wall represents zero energy, corresponding to zero potential at the surface of the metal.) According to the older theory an electron could be removed from the metal only by increasing its energy sufficiently to carry it over the top of this wall. But according to quantum theory there exists a probability (determined by the wave characteristics of electrons and by the thickness of the wall) that an electron may "leak through" the wall, even at absolute zero of temperature. This probability accounts for field current. The explanation is the same as that developed by Gamow (and independently by Gurney and Condon) for the emission of alpha particles from radioactive substances.*

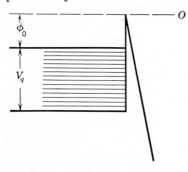

Fɪɢ. 20.   Fɪᴇʟᴅ Eᴍɪssɪᴏɴ.

25. Semi-Conductors. It is becoming more and more necessary to expand the domain of electronics to include devices whose operations depend upon the peculiar properties of a class of substances called semi-conductors. These substances include chemical elements such as silicon, germanium, and selenium, and compounds like Carborundum, galena, and copper oxide. The devices include the crystal and oxide rectifiers mentioned in Chapter 1 and elsewhere in this book, photocells of the type found in photoelectric exposure meters, and that newest arrival, the transistor. Incidentally, the invention of the transistor has contributed greatly to our understanding of the phenomena occurring in semi-conductors. It is necessary to include these devices in the realm of electronics primarily because many of their applications parallel those of electron tubes, and analysis of their circuits requires the methods developed for electron-tube circuits. Nevertheless these devices, their applications, and the phenomena upon which they depend constitute a quite separate branch of the science and should properly be so considered. A brief introduction to this field is given in Appendix 6.

PROBLEMS

See Appendix 3 for any constants needed.

1. Derive the value for 1 ev in ergs.

2. The long-wavelength limit for a certain photoelectric surface is found to be 5500 A. Compute the work-function for this surface (*a*) in ergs, (*b*) in electron-volts.

* See T. B. Brown, *Foundations of Modern Physics*, Appendix VI.

3. Light of 2357-A wavelength falls upon the surface described in Prob. 2. Compute the maximum kinetic energy for the escaping electrons, (a) in ergs, (b) in electron-volts.

4. Find the saturation current density, J_0, for a thoriated tungsten filament (a) at 1900°K, (b) at 1600°K. Assume ϕ_0 to be 2.63 ev, and A to be 3.00 amp cm^{-2} degrees.$^{-2}$

5. Make a Richardson plot (Fig. 7) for tungsten. Take A as 60 amp cm^{-2} degrees.$^{-2}$

6. A certain Phillips L-cathode has an emission of 10 amp/cm^2 at 1150°C. Assume the work-function to be 1.70 ev and compute A for this cathode.

7. A diode has plane electrodes, 2.00 mm apart. Compute the reduction in the work-function of its cathode due to the Schottky effect, when the anode potential is 300 volts, (a) in ergs, (b) in electron-volts.

8. From the result of Prob. 7 compute the percent effect of the anode potential upon the saturation current at 1600°K cathode temperature.

9. (a) Compute the peak value for the distribution curve of Fig. 10, for electrons emitted from a plane cathode at 2000°K. (b) Compute the value of u_x for which p has half the peak value. (c) Find the anode potential required to just turn electrons having this value of u_x away from the anode.

10. Compute the ratio of anode current to saturation current if the anode potential has the value computed for Prob. 9c, and the other conditions are the same.

11. The cathode temperature in a diode is 1700°K and the saturation current is 40.0 ma. Compute the current when the anode potential is negative by (a) 0.50 volt, (b) 0.75 volt.

12. The current in a diode is 270 μa at an anode potential of -0.650 volt, 8.1 μa at -0.942 volt. (a) Find the cathode temperature from these data. (b) Find the corresponding saturation current. Consider the internal bias negligible.

13. Electrons which have been accelerated through a potential difference of 450 volts pass through a plane boundary which separates a field-free region whose potential is 450 volts from another whose potential is 500 volts. (a) Compute the speed of the electrons in each region. (b) Compute the angle of refraction at this boundary for a beam of these electrons falling upon the boundary at an angle of incidence of 50.0 degrees.

14. A beam of electrons having kinetic energy of 100 ev is shot into a nickel crystal at an angle of incidence of 40.0 degrees. Compute the angle inside the crystal, if the inner potential for nickel is 17.0 volts.

15. The current gain (due to secondary emission) in a photomultiplier tube having 9 dynodes is found to be 9.7×10^5 times. Compute the secondary-emission ratio for each dynode, assuming all to have the same characteristics.

16. In a field-current apparatus one electrode is a sharp point which may be regarded as spherical, with a radius of $\frac{1}{20}$ mm. (a) Compute the electric field intensity, E, at this point for a potential difference, V, between electrodes of 90,000 volts. (b) Compute the reduction in work-function brought about by this field. NOTE: From electric theory, $E = V/R$ at a spherical surface of radius R.

CHAPTER 8

Gas in Electron Tubes

1. Gas in "Vacuum" Tubes.   Hitherto we have considered electron tubes to be quite void of gas.   Even though this is far from true, these *vacuum* tubes have actually functioned *as if* no gas were present, because of the exceedingly small size of gas molecules, as will be explained in Sec. 2.   Nevertheless, the presence of gas molecules in electron tubes cannot always be ignored, and at higher gas pressures (more exactly speaking, higher densities) they produce profound effects, some of which are considered in this chapter and the one following.   These phenomena belong to a broader field of physics called gaseous conduction of electricity, which includes many complex and perplexing phenomena.   Here we shall confine our attention to a few special examples, chosen first of all for their simplicity.   Fortunately these examples include most phenomena which are important to the operation of practical electron tubes.   Before considering these phenomena, however, we must first review some physical principles and facts concerning gas molecules and atoms.

2. Mean Free Path.   In most receiving tubes the gas pressure is down to about one-billionth of an atmosphere (10^{-9} atm), at room temperature.   (Room temperature will be assumed whenever temperature is not specifically mentioned.)   In a high-voltage tube, such as an X-ray tube or transmitting tube, the pressure may be 10 to 100 times lower, and in experimental tubes it is now possible to produce and measure pressure below 10^{-13} atm.   Although it might be imagined that molecules would be quite scarce at such low pressures, the molecular population is still dense at the lowest attainable pressure. At room temperature and atmospheric pressure this population density is 27×10^{18} molecules/cm^3, and at 10^{-13} atm it is still nearly 3 million molecules/cm^3, with the average distance between molecules about $\frac{1}{10}$ mm.   In a receiving tube the order of magnitude of the molecular population density is 10^{10} per cm^3; of the average distance apart, $\frac{1}{100}$ mm.

In an electron tube, however, the significant factor is not the average distance from a molecule to its nearest neighbor, but the *mean free path* of the electrons, or the average distance an electron may travel without

colliding with a gas atom.   At atmospheric pressure and room temperature the mean free path for a gas molecule is of the order of magnitude of 10^{-5} cm; for ordinary gases it ranges from about 0.9×10^{-5}
cm for nitrogen to 2.5×10^{-5} cm for helium, the value depending
upon the size of the molecule.   For electrons moving through a gas
the mean free path is approximately 4 times that for a molecule of the
gas.   Since the mean free path is inversely proportional to the pressure
(at constant temperature), the mean free path for electrons at 10^{-9}
atm, the pressure assumed for a receiving tube, is of the order of
magnitude of 4×10^4 cm or 400 meters.   At a pressure of 10^{-13} atm
the mean free path for electrons exceeds 1000 kilometers.

The mean free path of electrons in a vacuum tube determines the
extent to which gas molecules interfere with the motion of the electron
stream.   If the distance traveled by electrons from cathode to anode
is s, and is very much smaller than the mean free path, then the *probability* for a collision of an electron with a gas molecule before it reaches
the anode equals s divided by the mean free path, and this probability
equals the fraction of the electrons in the electron stream which will
collide with gas molecules in going the distance s.   In a receiving tube,
for example, s might be 4 mm or less, and the mean free path equal to
4×10^4 cm.   Then 10^{-5} of all the electrons in the electron stream, or
0.001 percent, will collide with gas molecules before reaching the
anode.   For most purposes this is a negligible fraction.

3. Collisions.   What happens when an electron does collide with
an atom or molecule?   From here on we shall confine our attention to
monatomic gases, or gases for which the molecule is a single atom, both
because all phenomena are simpler in monatomic gases and also
because the gas-type electron tubes almost always contain a monatomic
gas or vapor.   For a monatomic gas we may answer this question as
follows.   If a very slow electron collides with a gas atom the collision
is elastic.*   Since the atom is far more massive than the electron, the
electron bounces away with a change in direction but only a very small
loss of kinetic energy.   Collisions are always elastic unless the kinetic
energy of the electron exceeds a certain minimum called the lowest
excitation energy of the atom.   When this energy value is exceeded
the collision *may* be (but does not have to be) inelastic, with this

---

* In an elastic collision between two particles the total kinetic energy remains
unchanged.   In an inelastic collision there is generally a conversion of more or less
kinetic energy into energy of some other form, such as energy of excitation.   Sometimes, however, there may be an increase of kinetic energy, as in a collision between
a normal and an excited atom.   In *any* kind of collision the *momentum* must be
conserved.

amount of energy being given to the atom by the electron.   In order to explain further what takes place in an inelastic collision we must first consider the structure of an atom, and how it changes when energy is absorbed.

4. Atomic Structure.   It is assumed that the reader is acquainted with the fundamentals of atomic and molecular structure from earlier studies.*   For the present we need review only the following aspects of this theory.   An atom of atomic number Z has a nucleus which carries a positive charge equal to Ze.   In the *normal* state of the atom this nucleus is surrounded by Z electrons, arranged in a pattern or "configuration" for which the energy is the lowest possible for that atom. For the same atom there exist also other possible states, called *excited* states, each being represented by a different electron configuration and possessing a characteristic value of energy.   Thus it is possible to represent all these configurations or states as *energy levels* in a diagram in which energy is plotted veitically.   (The configurations are also identified by sets of numbers, called *quantum* numbers, and for many purposes it is necessary to arrange the energy levels in separate columns according to certain of these numbers.   For present purposes this is unnecessary.)   Only the outer one or two electrons are involved in the energy changes which concern us here.   The energy required to change an atom from its normal state to an excited state is called an *excitation energy*.   The energy which is just enough to *remove* an electron from the normal atom is called the *ionization energy*.   In making an energy-level diagram the ionization-energy level is taken as the zero level, so that all other levels have negative values.   Next in importance to the ionization energy is the minimum excitation energy, which changes the atom from its normal to its first excited state.

An atom may be excited in several ways, practically all of which involve a *collision*† between it and some other particle.   The other particle may be an electron, a photon, or another atom, as well as one of several other particles less commonly encountered.   A *near* collision with a very energetic particle will serve also; for example, an alpha particle passing near an atom may excite it or even ionize it by its strong electric field.   Ordinary electric fields are not sufficient in

---

* See T. B. Brown, *Foundations of Modern Physics*, Chapters VIII, IX, and X; L. B. Loeb, *Atomic Structure*, Chapter XII; G. P. Harnwell and J. J. Livingood, *Experimental Atomic Physics*, Chapter VIII; J. D. Stranathan, *The "Particles" of Modern Physics*, Chapter 6, Sec. 2.

† By collision is meant an interaction between the atom and another particle which approaches the atom to within a distance comparable with the diameter of the atom.   This is not necessarily a collision in the ordinary sense.

themselves; they may produce excitation only by setting into motion electrons or other electrically charged particles, which then collide with atoms.

5. Ionization. The potential difference through which an electron must fall to acquire energy equal to the ionization energy is called the *ionization potential*. (The ionization potential, in volts, is numerically equal to the ionization energy in electron-volts.) Ionization will not start in an electron tube until the anode potential exceeds the ionization potential. If ionization occurs with the energy of the colliding electron only slightly above the ionizing energy, the result is a positive *ion* (atom with one electron removed) and *two* free electrons having almost no kinetic energy. When ionization is produced by an electron of greater energy the excess energy is shared with the electron ejected from the atom. After ionization is started it sometimes may be maintained with an anode potential lower than the ionization potential, by multiple collisions. One electron collision may excite the atom to an intermediate excited state, the next collision supply the remaining energy needed for ionization. This process is of importance only when collisions occur very frequently, since atoms remain in an excited state for only a very brief time.

6. De-excitation. After a time an excited atom will return spontaneously to its normal state. Generally this time interval is very short. The return may be directly to the normal state, with the emission of all the lost energy as a single photon of light, or it may be by way of several intermediate states, with a separate photon emitted for each change of state or "jump." Another way in which an excited state may be changed is by collision with another atom. For example, a collision may occur between an excited atom and a normal atom, with the transfer of part or all of the excitation energy from the first to the second. If the second atom is one of lower ionization energy, it may even be ionized in such a collision. It is also highly probable that a collision between an excited atom and a normal one will leave both in their normal states, the energy of excitation appearing as additional kinetic energy of the two atoms.

7. Deionization. An atom must remain ionized until it can capture an electron. A free electron is a very poor prospect, however; it is far more likely to circle around the ion and fly away again, rather than be caught. On the other hand, if a free electron first attaches itself to a neutral atom, the negative ion thus formed may then pass the electron over to a positive ion, in a collision with it. Deionization occurs most readily, however, at the surface of an electrode, or at the walls of the tube.

8. Ion-Drift Current. We shall now consider specific examples illustrating these processes. Our first example will be the drift currents which may be set up in comparatively dense gases (e.g., air at atmospheric pressure) which have been weakly ionized by X-rays or other ionizing radiations. Ions of both signs are present in equal numbers, and recombination is very slow, except at solid surfaces, since the ions are very few in number as compared with the neutral atoms by which they are surrounded. The negative ions are principally negatively charged atoms, formed by attachment of electrons to neutra atoms. If an electric field is set up in such an ionized region, e.g.

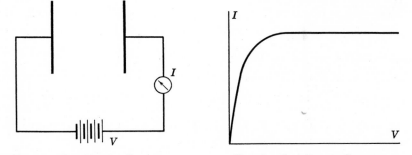

FIG. 1.   ION-DRIFT CURRENT.   FIG. 2.   ION-DRIFT CURRENT.

between plane-parallel electrodes as represented in Fig. 1, a slow drift of ions toward the electrodes will be superimposed upon their to-and-fro thermal motions, the positive ions going toward the negative electrode, the negative ions toward the other. Unless these ions are neutralized by recombination on the way, they ultimately reach the electrodes, where they give up their charges and become neutral atoms.

This ion drift constitutes an ion current in the space between the electrodes, which may be measured by a suitable meter placed as shown in Fig. 1. This current is so small that a very sensitive meter, such as an electroscope or electrometer, is required. Certain electron tubes, called electrometer tubes, also have been developed for measuring such very small currents. See Sec. 18, Chapter 3. As the potential difference between the electrodes is increased from zero the current at first rises, but above a certain value of the potential difference it attains a constant, saturation value. See Fig. 2. For low values of potential difference the drift is so slow that some ions have time to become neutralized by recombination, but above the saturation value practically all reach the electrodes first. The saturation current then measures the rate of production of ions; it equals the number of atoms ionized (number of *ion-pairs* produced) per unit time in the space between the electrodes, multiplied by the elementary electric charge, e. (This assumes that all ions are singly charged, an assumption which is nearly always true.)

9. Gas-Type Phototube. In the example of Sec. 8 the current is carried almost entirely by atomic (or molecular) ions. Frequently free electrons constitute a large part, often a predominant part, of the current carriers. Consider our next example, a phototube into which a considerable amount of some monatomic gas has been introduced.* Light falling upon the photo-sensitive cathode releases photo-electrons from it at a rate which is directly proportional to the intensity,

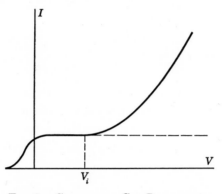

FIG. 3.   CURRENT IN GAS PHOTOTUBE.

of the light. The electron current thus produced is very small; in a vacuum phototube the saturation current is quickly reached, as represented by the broken line of Fig. 3. In a gas-type phototube the space-charge region and the first part of the saturation region are the same as for a vacuum phototube, but the current starts to increase again as soon as the anode potential exceeds the ionization potential for the gas, and rises at an ever-increasing rate as the potential goes above that value. This is shown by the solid line in Fig. 3. Since the rate of production of photo-electrons is unchanged, the increase in current must result from the production of additional free electrons (and positive ions) from the gas atoms in the tube.

* At atmospheric pressure the loss of energy in elastic collisions is sufficient to prevent electrons from acquiring enough energy to produce ions by collisions with gas atoms, unless the electric field is very high. Although the energy loss in a single collision is almost infinitesimal, there are over 10,000 collisions per centimeter. The gas density in a phototube should be high enough to permit frequent collisions, but low enough that the energy losses due to elastic collisions may be neglected.

A qualitative explanation for this rise in current may be made with reference to Fig. 4. In this figure a *primary* photo-electron leaving the cathode at *a* is represented as making an ionizing collision at *b*. A positive ion and two electrons leave this collision. The positive ion starts from rest (except for a very small amount of thermal energy) and travels toward the cathode. The two electrons share what little is left over of the energy possessed by the first electron before collision, after the ionization energy has been subtracted. Farther on, after each has gained enough energy to produce ionization, these two electrons make similar ionizing collisions at *c* and *d*. In Fig. 4 this *electron doubling* process is repeated again at *e*, *f*, *g*, and *h*, so that eight electrons arrive at the anode for one primary electron leaving the cathode. The seven positive ions which are produced travel in the opposite direction, ending their journey at the cathode.

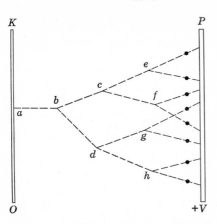

Fig. 4. Cascade Process. Dotted lines do not represent trajectories. Elastic collisions with gas atoms cause the electrons to follow erratic paths between *a* and *b*, *b* and *c*, etc.

10. Cascade Law. The number of times this electron-doubling process may be repeated depends upon the anode potential, V, and the ionization potential, V_i. Ionization cannot occur at all unless V exceeds V_i, and the average number of repetitions of the electron-doubling process is directly proportional to $(V - V_i)/V_i$. If p represents this number,

$$p = \alpha \frac{V - V_i}{V_i} \tag{1}$$

The probability factor, α, is always less than unity. If n_0 electrons leave the cathode and n' electrons arrive at the anode, it follows that

$$\frac{n'}{n_0} = 2^p = 2^{\left(\alpha \frac{V - V_i}{V_i}\right)} \tag{2}$$

The current in the phototube is increased in the same ratio. If the primary (photoelectric) current is I_0, the current in a gas-type phototube, for V greater than V_i, is

$$I = I_0 2^{\left(\alpha \frac{V - V_i}{V_i}\right)} \tag{3}$$

At this point it must be emphasized that the current has the same value throughout the tube. At the anode it is electron current, as stated above. At the cathode it is partly the primary electron current, I_0, but in greater part it is positive-ion current, $I - I_0$. At points between the cathode and the anode the current is made up by electrons moving toward the anode and positive ions moving toward the cathode.

By taking logarithms we obtain from Eq. 3

$$\log I = (\log I_0 - \alpha \log 2) + \frac{\alpha \log 2}{V_i} V \qquad (4)^*$$

Since Eq. 4 represents a straight line having $\log I$ as y, and V as x, it is easily checked against experimental data. Figure 5 shows a plot of this kind for a gas-type phototube, and the slanting portion, for V greater than V_i, is a straight line, in agreement with Eq. 4.

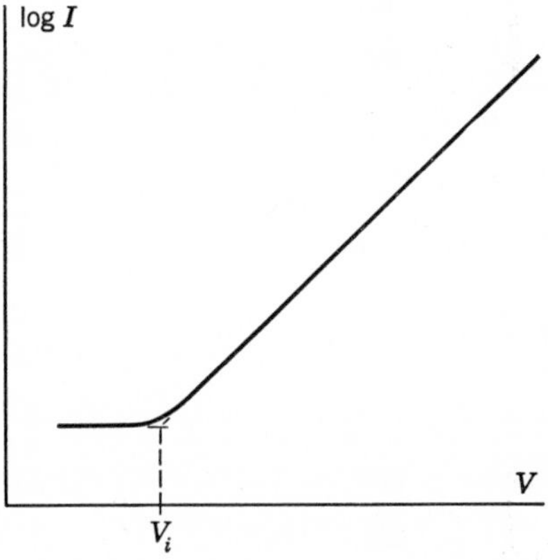

The electron-doubling process discussed above may be called a *cascade process*, and Eq. 4 (or Eq. 5) the cascade law. It is also sometimes called a Townsend process, from the physicist who first worked out the law for this kind of current increase. We have considered here a photoelectric source

FIG. 5.   LOG PLOT OF PHOTOTUBE CURRENT.

for the primary electrons, since the gas-type phototube is the best-known practical application of this process. The source of primary electrons could just as well be a thermionic cathode, operated at so low a temperature that saturation is reached at a very low anode potential, or any one of several other electron sources which saturate at low anode potentials.

11. Experiment 21. The Gas-Type Phototube. The characteristics of a gas-type phototube may be studied with the circuit shown in Fig. 6. A phototube such as type 930 (octal base) or 921 (cartridge form) is suggested. It will be convenient to employ for this experi-

* In other books this equation may be found in the form

$$\log_e I = a + bV \qquad (5)$$

It is evident that

$$b = \frac{\alpha \log_e 2}{V_i}$$

ment the same equipment (optical bench, light shield, etc.) used in Exp. 10. The current may be measured with a current amplifier as in Exp. 10, or with a galvanometer having a full-scale reading of about 5 microamperes. If the amplifier is used, the grid resistor should be reduced, so that current up to 5 microamperes may be measured. The anode potential, V, is varied by means of a voltage-divider, R, connected across a 90-volt battery and provided with a calibrated scale. Values of V are computed from the scale readings of this "potentiom-

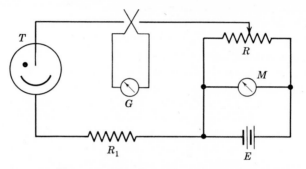

Fig. 6. Circuit for Exp. 21. T—phototube. G—galvanometer. E—90-volt B-battery. M—voltmeter. R_1—100-K protective resistor.

eter" and the reading of the voltmeter in parallel with R. Correct these values for the IR drop in the protective resistance, R_1.

Part I. Anode Potential. Adjust the light source to a position which gives nearly full-scale current reading when V is 90 volts. (The maximum allowable value for V is 90 volts for most phototubes of this type.) Then take direct and reversed readings of the galvanometer for each of a series of values for V from 90 volts down to zero, spaced about 5 volts apart. Open the galvanometer switch *immediately* if the meter suddenly jumps off-scale. (This should not happen unless the maximum anode potential is exceeded, or unless the light is too intense.) Check with your instructor before closing the switch again.

Compute the current from your readings, and plot a curve such as in Fig. 5. Observe that this plot consists of a horizontal straight line connected to a slanting, straight line by a short, curved transition section. The horizontal line represents the saturation current, the slanting line the conditions which fit Eq. 4. Extend the straight-line portions until they meet; the intersection lies close to V_i on the V-scale. (Unfortunately, the voltmeter readings are subject to a correction of possibly a volt, because of contact potential.) Measure the slope for the slanting line and determine from it the value of α.

Part II. Illumination. Measure the current with varying illumination, holding the anode potential, V, at the top value of 90 volts. Vary the illumination as explained in Exp. 10. Plot a curve with I as y and intensity of illumination as x. Consult Sec. 12 for an explanation for the curvature in this plot.

12. Limitations of Gas-Type Phototubes. Gas-type phototubes are not applicable where rapid variations of light intensity must be followed, as in the reproduction of sound from the "sound-track" on moving-picture film, because the current in these tubes depends upon positive ions as well as electrons. Since positive ions are very massive as compared with electrons, their speeds are relatively very slow, and this sluggishness prevents the current from changing fast enough to follow rapid changes in illumination. We may see how this occurs by considering the change in current when the illumination is suddenly cut off. In a vacuum phototube the current ceases almost as suddenly, since the flight time for electrons is negligibly small. In the gas-type tube, on the contrary, the current does not cease until all positive ions have reached the cathode, and the time required for this is not negligible.* This type of phototube is most useful for relay operation and other industrial switching operations.

For all gas-type phototubes there exists an upper limit to the anode potential at which the tube will operate safely. If this limit is exceeded the tube may break down and operate as a glow tube, as explained in Sec. 13. Under very strong illumination this breakdown may occur even when the normal safe limit is not exceeded. As explained in Sec. 13, break-down is caused by bombardment of the cathode by positive ions. Positive-ion bombardment accounts also in part for the changes in sensitivity which occur with time and conditions of operation. Secondary electrons produced by positive-ion bombardment augment the photoelectric current and explain the upward curve of the plot for Part II of Exp. 10. The maximum current multiplication which is possible within the safe limits of anode potential is about 10 times.

13. Glow Discharge. If the potential difference across a gas phototube exceeds a critical value the current in the tube jumps to a high

---

* It is important to note here that, although the positive ions all go to the cathode, the current at the anode does not stop until all positive ions have reached the cathode. As long as there are positive ions in the region between cathode and anode there are negative charges induced on the anode by the presence of these positive ions. As the positive ions leave the space between anode and cathode these induced negative charges leave the anode, thus setting up a current at the anode, equal to the current at the cathode.

value and is no longer dependent upon the illumination. This is the "break-down" referred to in Sec. 12. Unless this current is limited by an external resistor, as shown in Fig. 7, it will rise to a very high value and the tube will be destroyed. A similar *glow discharge* may be observed for any tube or bulb containing two cold electrodes and gas at a pressure from a few milliameters of mercury down to a few thousandths of a millimeter. Very little initial current is needed, and once the discharge is started it is self-sustaining. In the photo-tube, for example, once break-down occurs the illumination may be turned off; the current is now independent of it. Generally a discharge of this kind may be started by ionization due to natural causes, such as cosmic rays, although a speck of radioactive material is often added to a glow tube to make starting more reliable. Very weak photoelectric emission will serve also as a starting current.

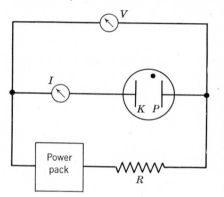

FIG. 7.   GLOW-TUBE CIRCUIT.

14. Demonstration Experiment 1. The characteristics of such a glow discharge may be studied with the circuit of Fig. 7. The tube may be a neon glow lamp, with the ballast resistor removed from its base, or a glow lamp of the type made for voltage regulation, which has no ballast. For this experiment the tube should have large electrodes reasonably close together. A suitable tube of larger size could be made in the glass shop. If the anode potential is raised slowly the discharge will start when it reaches a value called the *starting potential*. Immediately the potential drops to a lower *operating potential*, and the current jumps to a value determined by the potential drop across the ballast resistance, R, and not by the anode potential. The discharge is accompanied by a visible glow from the gas within the tube. The appearance of this glow depends upon the gas pressure and the shape and position of the electrodes. For the gas pressure found in commercial neon glow lamps the glow is brightest in a thin layer just above the surface of the cathode. The spectrum of the light emitted is characteristic of the gas. The light is a bright orange color for neon gas, paler and bluish in color for argon. The glow covers the cathode when the current is fairly large, but only partly covers it for small current.   For very small current the glowing spot flickers about over the cathode surface.

As the current is increased from a very low value, it will be observed that the anode potential remains remarkably constant from the time the flicker disappears until the glow completely covers the cathode. Over this range of current the value of the anode potential is determined principally by the nature and pressure of the gas, and the nature of the surface of the cathode.   It depends little if at all upon the size and shape of the anode, providing only that anode and cathode be reasonably close.   It changes somewhat with time and is affected slightly by other factors, such as temperature.

15. Glow Tubes.   The phenomena which occur in the glow discharge are quite complex, but the major features are the following. (1) To start the discharge, free electrons of some origin (photo-electrons, or electrons produced by radiations such as X-rays, cosmic rays, or radioactivity) produce positive ions and additional electrons by the cascade process.   This very small current is called *dark current*, because no visible glow accompanies it.   (2) The positive ions bombard the cathode and release from it electrons which increase the dark current.   The process involved is comparable with secondary emission by electron bombardment, but is less efficient.   (3) As the anode potential is raised this process becomes more efficient, and at the starting (break-down) potential, enough electrons are emitted from the cathode to maintain the discharge with no outside aid.   (4) This starting condition is unstable: the current immediately jumps to a much higher value and the potential drops to the operating value, as described in Sec. 14.   At this potential the electron yield from the cathode is just sufficient to maintain the discharge, and the discharge adjusts itself automatically to this value.   The electron emission now has several causes, including photoemission produced by the glow as well as bombardment by positive ions, and is aided by a strong electric field produced at the cathode surface by the positive ions as they approach it.   As the current is increased the area covered by the cathode glow increases proportionally, so as to keep the current density constant, until the entire cathode is covered.   It is over this range of current, for which the current density at the cathode remains constant, that, as stated in Sec. 14, the operating potential remains so nearly constant.

The glow tubes considered so far have fairly large electrodes, not far apart and not very closely hemmed in by the walls of the bulb, and the most noticeable feature of the discharge is the glow at the surface of the cathode. Several additional features may be observed in the glow tube pictured in Fig. 8, in which the electrodes are small compared with their distance apart, and the discharge is confined by a cylindrical tube. Three bright regions, *a, c,* and *e,* called respectively the cathode glow, the negative glow, and the positive column, are separated by the Crookes dark space, *b,* and the Faraday dark space, *d.* Variations of brightness, called striations, often appear in the positive column. Regions *a, b, c,* and *d* expand along the tube as the gas pressure is reduced; the positive column occupies what space is left,

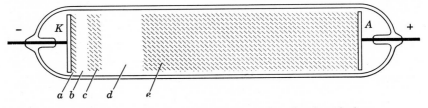

FIG. 8. LONG GLOW TUBE. *a*—cathode glow. *b*—Crookes dark space. *c*—negative glow. *d*—Faraday dark space. *e*—positive column.

and may be crowded out of existence if the tube is short and the pressure low. Indeed, regions *a, b,* and a part of *c* appear to be all that is necessary to the discharge.

The electric field is most intense near the cathode, *K,* so that much of the potential rise from *K* to the anode, *P,* occurs in regions *a* and *b.* The potential rise through these regions is commonly called the *cathode fall.* In glow lamps and other glow tubes discussed earlier the potential difference between the electrodes is nearly equal to the cathode fall and, as already stated, is almost constant over a wide range of current. In the tube represented in Fig. 8, the potential difference between terminals exceeds the cathode fall by an amount that is chiefly due to the potential drop along the positive column. This potential drop is uniform along the positive column and increases as the length of the column increases, and as its diameter decreases. In long, narrow tubes, such as "neon" sign tubes, it may be many times the cathode fall. Its most remarkable characteristic is its mode of dependence upon current: it *decreases* with increasing current. This positive column is a *plasma* region, such as is described in Sec. 22.

16. Voltage Regulation. The constant-voltage characteristic possessed by a glow tube, which is described in Sec. 14, may be utilized as a means to hold a d-c potential steady, in spite of variations in the d-c source. A simple voltage-regulator circuit of this type is diagrammed in Fig. 9a. The regulator tube, *T,* may be a simple neon glow lamp with the ballast resistor removed from its base, or it may be one of the VR tubes described in Sec. 17, which are designed especially for this purpose. The load, represented by R_0, is connected in parallel with T, and current is supplied to both from the d-c source, E_b, through a suitable "dropping" resistor, R_b. Owing to the constant-voltage characteristic of T the potential drop across R_0 stays constant at some value V_0 as long as I_T, the current in T, stays between the lower limit set by flicker of the cathode spot, and the upper limit set by complete coverage of the cathode by the cathode glow. For example, a VR-150

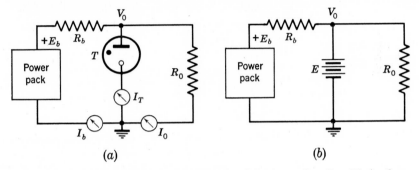

FIG. 9.   VOLTAGE REGULATION.   (a) Circuit with glow tube, T.   (b) Analogous circuit with battery.

voltage-regulator tube operates at a constant potential near 150 volts, over a current range from 5 to 40 ma. The current I_b, in R_b, is determined by the potential drop, $E_b - V_0$, across R_b.

$$I_b = (E_b - V_0)/R_b \qquad\qquad (6)$$

The current I_0, in R_0, equals V_0 divided by R_0, and the current I_T, in T, equals the difference between I_b and I_0.

$$I_0 = V_0/R_0 \qquad \text{and} \qquad I_T = I_b - I_0 \qquad\qquad (7)$$

If E_b increases, I_b increases also, but all the increase in current goes to T; the current I_0 does not change. Likewise any change in R_0 will change I_0 at the expense of current in T. Either E_b or R_0 may change up or down, independently and over a considerable range, as long as I_T remains within the limits specified, without changing V_0 by more than a very small amount.

17. VR Tubes. Although neon and argon glow lamps will serve as regulator tubes in circuits such as Fig. 9a, better performance is obtained with the VR (voltage-regulator) tubes designed especially for this service. First of all, a VR tube has a cathode of large area, specially treated to maintain constancy of operating voltage. Since the size of the anode is unimportant, the cathode is a hollow cylinder, K in Fig. 10, with a wire, A, along its axis serving as the anode. The short wire, S, attached to K and almost touching A, serves two purposes. First, it lowers the starting potential and makes starting more reliable. Second, it anchors the glow spot when the current is small. As the current builds up, the glow, which starts at the tip of S, runs along S to K, then spreads out over the inside surface of K. Commercial VR tubes are available for several operating potentials, ranging from 65 to 150 volts. Different voltages are obtained by varying the gas and the cathode surface, as mentioned in Sec. 14. Other voltages may be obtained by connecting two or more VR tubes in series, as shown in Fig. 12. Since the operating voltage, V_0, changes so little with current a VR tube is in many ways comparable to a storage battery; compare Fig. 9a with Fig. 9b.

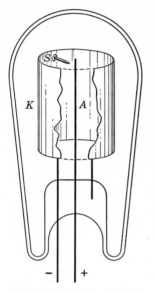

FIG. 10. VOLTAGE-REGU-LATOR TUBE. A—anode. K—cathode (front cut away to show A). S—starter rod, attached to K.

Voltage-regulator tubes cannot be operated in parallel; they will neither start together nor conduct together. When the current to be supplied is greater than the capacity of one VR tube, or when a variable potential is to be controlled, circuits of the kinds described in Sec. 19 are required.

18. Experiment 22. Voltage Regulation. In this experiment we shall study the characteristics of a VR tube and its application in a simple VR stabilizer circuit.

Part I. VR Tube Characteristics. Set up the circuit shown in Fig. 11a, with a VR-105 tube. (A VR-75 or VR-150 tube may be used, but a VR-105 tube works best with a 150-volt voltmeter.) The dropping resistor, R_b, should be about 2500 ohms, and the power supply capable of a d-c potential, V_b, 100 volts higher than the operating potential of the VR tube. Raise V_b slowly and note its value just before the VR tube starts to conduct, or "fires." This is the starting potential, or break-down potential. Observe the appearance of the glow in the tube as the current is raised from 0 to 40 ma, and back to zero. Take readings of V_0 and I_T from 0 to 40 ma and back to zero. Read the voltmeter very carefully, estimating tenths of volts. Plot these data with V_0 as y, I_T as x, and draw a straight line to closest fit to the portion of this plot which is fairly straight. Over this operating range this circuit may be compared with that for a storage battery on charge, and the emf of the equivalent battery is given by the y-intercept of this straight line. The slope of the line gives the internal resistance of this battery. Verify these statements, and obtain these quantities from your plot.

Part II. VR Regulator Circuit. Make the circuit of Fig. 11b by adding to the circuit of Part I a variable load, R_0, and an ammeter for the load current, I_0. A 10,000-ohm, 50-watt resistor, tapped every 1000 ohms, is suitable for R_0.

(a) Raise V_b until I_T is 40 ma with I_0 equal to zero. Then increase I_0 by steps of 4 or 5 ma, holding V_b constant, until I_T becomes zero.

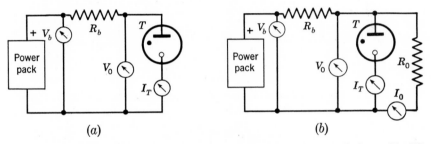

(a)   (b)

FIG. 11. CIRCUITS FOR EXP. 22. (*a*) VR tube characteristics. (*b*) VR regulator circuit.

Read both ammeters, and read V_0 very carefully, as before. Plot V_0 as y, I_0 as x. Explain the results exhibited by this plot, and show from your data that $(I_T + I_0)$ is nearly constant.

(b) Set the load for a current (I_0) of about 20 ma, and raise V_b until I_T is 20 or 30 ma. Then decrease V_b by steps of 10 volts to about 20 volts below the value at which the VR tube stops conducting. Plot V_0 as y, V_b as x. The portion of this plot which is fairly straight is the operating range. Draw a straight line to closest fit within the operating range. The reciprocal of the slope of this plot is called the *stabilizing factor*. Compute it for your data.

19. VR Power Supply. In the d-c power supply described in Sec. 22, Chapter 6, the equipment to which power is delivered serves as the load in a cathode-follower circuit. The grid of the cathode-follower tube is maintained at a constant potential above ground by a battery, so that the output potential (cathode to ground) is only little higher than the grid potential, and changes very little, even when the source voltage changes by large amounts. The circuit of Fig. 12 functions in similar manner, with the d-c battery replaced by VR tubes. The two VR tubes, $T1$ and $T2$, the dropping resistor, R_b, and the resistor R_1

function in the same manner as T, R_b, and R_0 in Fig. 9a. The grid potential for the cathode-follower tube, $T3$, is held constant at any desired value between zero and V_1 by means of the sliding contact on R_1. Thus the output potential, V_0, from the cathode of $T3$ to ground, may be controlled over a range extending from a little above zero to a little above V_1. For any setting of the slider on R_1 the output potential is changed but little by rather large changes in the supply voltage. The tube $T3$ must be a power tube, capable of dissipating power equal to the product of $(V_b - V_0)$ and the output current, I_0.

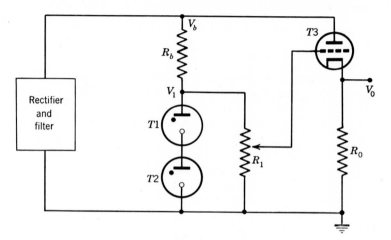

Fɪɢ. 12.   VR Pᴏᴡᴇʀ Sᴜᴘᴘʟʏ.

Far greater independence from changes in the supply voltage may be obtained with the circuit of Fig. 13. In this circuit the power tube, $T3$, is a pentode, having both the control and the screen grids held at constant potentials by means of VR tubes, as shown. It should be noted that this circuit requires a higher supply voltage than is needed for the circuit of Fig. 12, and that this increases the power dissipation at the plate, especially for lower output potentials. This circuit works best when designed to operate over a limited range of output potential.

Each of these circuits possesses the additional advantage of having low output impedance; that is, of operating as a d-c source of low internal resistance. For the triode circuit this equivalent resistance is given by Eq. 45, Chapter 6, and equals about 200 ohms for a triode-connected 6L6 tube in the circuit of Fig. 12. The equivalent internal resistance value for the pentode connection, Fig. 13, can be shown to be essentially the same. Lower values for this resistance, as well as larger current capacity, may be obtained by connecting two or more similar tubes together in parallel for *T3*, in either circuit. Even closer regulation may be obtained by adding an amplifier which causes the grid potential of the cathode-follower tube to change in a direction opposite to any change in the cathode potential, and with such a circuit the equivalent internal resistance may be reduced to a few ohms. A circuit of this kind is illustrated and described in Chapter 14, Fig. 17 and Sec. 24.

20. Experiment 23. VR Power Supply. The performance of the circuits of Figs. 12 and 13 may be studied as follows.

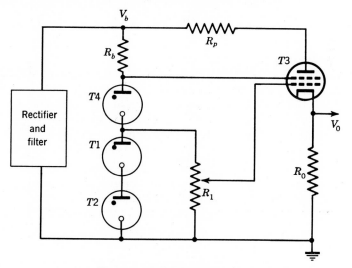

FIG. 13.   VR Power Supply.

Part I. Pentode Connection.   Make up the circuit of Fig. 13, and add voltmeters to measure V_b and V_0, and an ammeter to measure I_0, the current in R_0. Use a VR-105 tube for *T1*, a VR-150 tube for *T4*, and leave out *T2*. A 6L6 beam tube serves as *T3*. The voltage-divider, R_1, should be 50 K or higher; R_b and R_p, 1.5 K and 1 K respectively; and R_0 any variable resistance having the requisite current and power capacity.

(*a*) Set V_b to 300 volts, and make sure that the VR tubes are conducting. (A momentary higher value for V_b may be needed to start them.)   Adjust the control grid potential to make V_0 equal to 100 volts, with 50 ma for I_0. Then measure the grid potential with the same voltmeter. Decrease V_b by 5-volt steps until the VR tubes quit conducting, and for two steps further. Plot V_0 as *y*, V_b as *x*, and determine from this plot the stabilizing factor, as explained in Exp. 23.

(b) Return to the initial conditions of (a). Holding V_b fixed, vary R_0 so as to change I_0 by steps of 5 or 10 ma, from 75 ma down to zero. Plot V_0 as y, I_0 as x. This plot should be a straight line (over the operating range) having a y-intercept equal to E_0, the emf of the equivalent battery, and a slope equal to $-R_i$, the internal resistance of this battery. Verify these statements and obtain E_0 and R_i from your plot. As a check, compute the theoretical values represented in Fig. 17, Chapter 6.

Part II. Triode Connection. The triode connection of Fig. 12 may be made by connecting the screen grid to the plate, removing $T4$ and R_p, and increasing R_b to 6 K. The procedure is then the same as for Part I. Compare the results of these two parts and discuss the advantages of each circuit.

21. Gas in a Thermionic Diode. Let us consider next the effect of gas upon electronic conduction in a thermionic diode. In the gas-type phototube, and in the glow tube, the anode potential is at least several times higher than the ionization potential; the electron-multiplying, cascade process is an important factor; and electrons dislodged from gas atoms greatly exceed the primary electrons emitted from the cathode. In a thermionic diode the presence of gas in appreciable amount manifests itself in quite a different manner: the anode potential does not exceed the ionization potential and may fall considerably below it, the current is due almost entirely to electrons emitted thermionically from the cathode, and only a very small fraction of those electrons make ionizing collisions. The observable effect of gas in a thermionic diode is shown by the curves in Fig. 14. The broken line represents current in a thermionic diode which is thoroughly evacuated. In such a tube the primary obstacle to electron flow is not inadequate cathode emission, but space-charge. It is not difficult with modern methods to make thermionic emission as copious as any reasonable need may require; the problem in a vacuum diode is to get the emitted electrons across to the anode fast enough, against the mutual repulsions which oppose their travel. As the broken line shows, a high anode potential is required to approach saturation current.

The full line in Fig. 14 represents an identical thermionic diode into which is introduced gas to a pressure of a few hundredths of a millimeter of mercury. Until the anode potential, V, reaches the ionization potential, V_i, the current is almost exactly the same for both tubes. In the gas diode, the current rises sharply, however, as soon as V reaches V_i, then increases indefinitely without any further increase in V. Indeed, V generally decreases somewhat as the current increases.   At the same time a luminous glow appears in the tube, extending from the surface of the anode close up to the cathode.   The spectrum of this glow is that of the gas atoms, and gives evidence that gas ions are being produced.

The circuit for observing the data for Fig. 14 is diagrammed in Fig. 15. Note the ballast resistor, R_b, which is necessary to prevent the current from rising indefinitely.   When the tube is conducting in this manner the current is limited only by the ballast resistor.   Approximately,

$$I = (E_b - V_i)/R_b \qquad (8)$$

22. The Plasma.   Let us now seek an explanation for this extraordinary behavior of a gas-type diode.   An elementary description of the phenomena occurring within it may be given by reference to Fig. 16, in which is plotted the distribu-

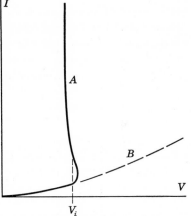

FIG. 14.   CURRENT IN GAS-TYPE DIODE.   A—in gas-type diode.   B—in vacuum diode.

tion of potential between the cathode, K, and the anode, P, for electrodes which are large, plane, and not too far apart.   (The manner in which these data are obtained is explained in Chapter 9.)   In the

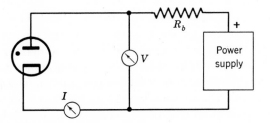

FIG. 15.   CIRCUIT FOR GAS-TYPE DIODE.

space between K and a point x_2 which is quite close to K (this distance is exaggerated in Fig. 17) the potential V rises from zero to a value approximately equal to V_i; from there on to P it remains nearly constant.   A slight drop in potential may occur close to P, but this need not be considered here.

Let us consider first the region between x_2 and P.   Within this region the electric field, which is determined by the slope of the potential plot, is constant and so small that we may regard it as zero.   It then follows (see Sec. 11, Chapter 1) that throughout this region there must be equal numbers of positively and negatively charged particles. The positively charged particles are ionized atoms, the negative particles practically all electrons. Such a region is called a *plasma*. The positive ions have random motions, with a distribution in speed corresponding to the temperature of the gas, or several hundred degrees Centigrade. The nature of the electron population of this plasma depends upon the gas density. Primary electrons enter the plasma from the cathode with speed determined by the potential rise from K

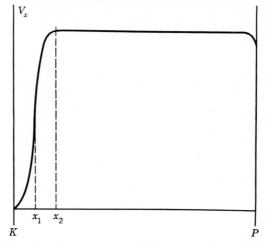

Fig. 16.   Potential Distribution in Gas Diode.

to x_2. If the gas density is quite low a considerable fraction of these primary electrons may pass straight through the plasma to the anode without collision, and may account for an appreciable part of the negative charge in the plasma. Under the conditions generally found in hot-cathode gas tubes, however, most primary electrons undergo collisions of some sort which set them wandering in random directions throughout the plasma, so that the population density for electrons in the plasma is much higher than it would be if primary electrons passed through without collision.

The motions of these plasma electrons are randomly distributed in speed as well as in direction. Under the conditions postulated above this distribution is similar to that produced by thermal agitation, at a temperature determined by the average kinetic energy of the electrons. Furthermore, since plasma electrons have kinetic energy comparable with that of the primary electrons, this electron temperature is very high. (A mean kinetic energy of only 5 ev corresponds to 39,000 degrees K.) It seems absurd even to imagine such temperatures, but they have been determined by very reliable experimental data. (See Sec. 35, Chapter 9.) The following considerations explain how they are possible. First, an electron which collides elastically with a gas atom loses very little energy to the atom; since its mass is so much less it bounces away with its speed almost unchanged. High-energy electrons would need to make innumerable collisions with gas atoms before coming to thermal equilibrium with them. Second, owing to their electrical charges, electrons interact with one another at considerable distances, and such interactions are equivalent to collisions among particles of much larger diameter and make such "collisions" relatively frequent.* Hence the plasma electrons may quickly approach a sort of thermal equilibrium among themselves, while their average kinetic energy is still comparable with that of the primary electrons. This "electron temperature" is then maintained by the continued influx of primary electrons. For gas density so low that a considerable portion of the primary electrons reaches the anode without collision the plasma electrons may not attain thermal equilibrium among themselves before leaving the plasma. Under these conditions their random distribution may suggest the existence of two or more electron temperatures.

Both positive ions and plasma electrons are continually leaving the plasma by diffusion. Positive ions may leave in all directions. Those which diffuse out through the plasma boundary at x_2 are attracted toward the cathode, and constitute a small positive-ion current to the cathode. A comparable number reaches the anode, while still others escape to the glass walls of the tube, where they are neutralized by electrons which likewise have diffused to these walls. Plasma electrons can escape the plasma by diffusing to the anode, or to the walls of the tube. Because of the potential difference between the plasma and the cathode, plasma electrons cannot reach the cathode, except for a very few which have kinetic energy far above the average. The number reaching the glass walls is also relatively small, since their rate of arrival at the walls is limited to the rate at which positive ions can reach the walls. The much higher rate of diffusion for electrons is

* A more exact statement is that the random motions of plasma electrons are brought about by small, local electric fields within the plasma. Although electrons and positive ions have equal population densities within the plasma region, in any very small volume there may be, at any instant, either an excess or a deficiency of electrons. These inequalities result from the *statistical* nature of the distribution of electrons and positive ions within the plasma. They are very small and very temporary, but the electric fields resulting from them are sufficient to account for the random motions of plasma electrons.

counteracted, in this direction, by the negative charge which is built up on the walls by the electrons which arrive there first. Most of the electrons leaving the plasma go to the anode, and this flow of electrons from the plasma to the anode is practically equal to the flow of primary electrons out of the cathode into the plasma. Positive ions account for only a negligible part of the current.

23. Plasma Maintenance. When the current is constant, the population density for both electrons and positive ions in the plasma remains constant. How are these populations maintained? Any answer to this question will depend upon many factors, including gas density. If the gas density is such that the mean free paths for both electrons and gas atoms are smaller than the linear dimensions of the plasma, the following explanation may be given. First of all, since rate of diffusion depends upon average thermal speed, the rate of diffusion out of the plasma for positive ions is very small, since their thermal energies are low and their masses relatively great. It follows that comparatively few ionizing collisions are needed to replace the positive ions leaving the plasma, and these ionizing collisions may be provided by the small fraction of the plasma electrons whose kinetic energy exceeds the ionization energy. The size of this fraction will depend upon the energy of the primary electrons, and *the potential difference across the tube will adjust itself to the value which establishes this balance.*

This very incomplete, elementary explanation overlooks many factors, including excitation energies other than the ionization energy, and the multiple-excitation processes which are mentioned in Sec. 5. A fuller explanation is far more complex, and many details are not yet completely analyzed.

24. Space-Charge Double Layer. The region between the cathode and the boundary of the plasma at x_2, Fig. 16, contains primary electrons which are being accelerated from the cathode toward the plasma, together with positive ions which have diffused out of the plasma and are being accelerated toward the cathode. Near x_2 it contains also some plasma electrons which have escaped from the plasma only to be deflected back in again. Since primary electrons are almost at rest as they leave the cathode, and gain speed as they approach the plasma, the population density of electrons is very high at the cathode and decreases rapidly toward the plasma. The reverse is true for the positive ions in this region; for these the population density is greatest at the edge of the plasma and least at the cathode, where their speed is greatest. It follows that the *net* space-charge in this region is negative next the cathode and positive next the plasma, forming a space-charge *double layer* in this region. If we now remember (see Sec. 11,

Chapter 1) that curvature of a potential plot indicates space-charge,* we can see that this double layer is indicated by the potential plot of Fig. 16. Between K and a point x_1 the curvature of this plot is upward, indicating that this is a negative space-charge region; between x_1 and x_2 its curvature is downward, corresponding to positive space-charge.

The primary electron current (which, as has been stated earlier, is practically the total current) is dependent upon the distribution of space-charge in this double layer region. Indeed, if we could neglect the positive ions here we might compare this region to a vacuum diode having plane-parallel electrodes separated by a distance x_2, with the potential difference across it equal approximately to the ionization potential V_i. Then we might apply Eqs. 4 and 5 of Chapter 1, obtaining

$$I = \frac{2.3 \times 10^{-6} A V_i^{\frac{3}{2}}}{x_2^{2}} \text{ amp} \qquad (9)$$

Since, however, the current value is controlled by the external circuit, Eq. 9 must be regarded as giving the value of x_2 corresponding to any value of I. That is,

$$x_2 = \frac{1.5 \times 10^{-3} \sqrt{A} \ V_i^{\frac{3}{4}}}{\sqrt{I}} \text{ cm} \qquad (10)$$

Because the positive ions cannot be neglected, a different space-charge equation must be used, and the distance x_2 is found to be somewhat larger than the value given by Eq. 10.

We may summarize this discussion with the rough but very useful statement that neutralization of space-charge in the plasma region brings the *effective anode* close up to the cathode, thereby squeezing the un-neutralized part of the space-charge into a region thin enough to allow the current to have the value determined by the external circuit.

25. Practical Gas-Type Diodes. Since, when a gas-type diode conducts, the effective anode lies close to the cathode, the actual anode does not need to be placed very near to the cathode, and the cathode may have any convenient shape. Thus the cathode may be made hollow, with the emitting surface on the inside, and be surrounded by a polished metal cup which serves as a heat shield. See Fig. 17. Oxide cathodes may be employed provided the potential drop across the tube

* For plane electrodes. Since x_1 and x_2 are very close to K, almost any electrode may be considered plane for this discussion.

does not exceed 20 volts. Hull* discovered that the positive-ion bombardment to which the cathode is subjected in a gas-type diode does little damage to an oxide cathode until this value is exceeded; hence oxide cathodes in argon or mercury vapor are safe as long as the current stays below saturation, because the ionization potentials of these gases

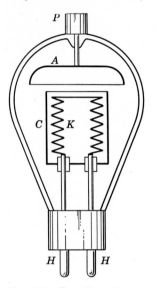

are less than 20 volts. If the current comes too near saturation, however, the potential drop across the tube may rise above 20 volts and the cathode be damaged. For this reason certain precautions must be observed with gas-type tubes. First of all, a choke or resistor must always be inserted in series with a gas-type tube to limit the peak current to a safe value, since this limitation cannot be accomplished by the tube itself. Second, the cathode must be heated to its operating temperature before any potential is put on the anode. A heating time of 5 minutes or more may be required for big tubes.

The operation of a gas-type diode is limited also by the deionization time of the gas in it. After the electron current stops, the positive ions in the plasma remain to be neutralized, chiefly by diffusion to the electrodes and walls. If the anode potential is raised to a high *negative* value before this deionization is sufficiently completed, current may be set up in the reverse direction through the tube, by positive-ion bombardment of the anode; this reverse current is called "flash-back."

Fig. 17. Gas-Type Diode Having Shielded Cathode (cross-section). *A*—anode. *C*—polished nickel cup, open at top. *K*—cathode (crimped nickel strip, oxide-coated). *P*—anode terminal. *H-H*—heater and cathode terminals.

The time required for deionization to become sufficiently complete to prevent flash-back is called the *deionization time*. Most gas-type diodes are designed to make this deionization time about 0.001 sec, a value which limits the a-c operation of such tubes to not much over 60 cps. Flash-back ruins the tube by *electron* bombardment of the oxide cathode.

26. Experiment 24. Gas-Type Diode. The ionization potential for a gas-type diode may be measured by means of an experiment due to Cuykendall.† As long as the anode potential, V, is less than V_i, the

---

* A. W. Hull, *General Electric Review*, Vol. 32 (1929), p. 213.

† T. Cuykendall, *American Physics Teacher* (now *American Journal of Physics*), Vol. 4 (1936), p. 93.

ionization potential, the current, I, in a gas-type diode is very close to being the same as that in a vacuum diode, and follows quite well the three-halves power law.   Deviation upward from this law starts at V_i, and this deviation provides a means for obtaining a fair value for V_i. If the $\frac{2}{3}$-power of I is plotted as y, with V as x, this plot is fairly straight until ionization starts; then it swings upward, as shown in Fig. 18.   The value for V_i which is indicated in this manner must be corrected for the internal bias, V_1, of the cathode, whose value is given by the x-intercept of the straight-line part of this plot, as in Exp. 1.

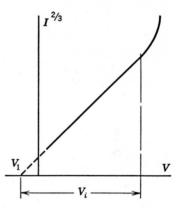

Fig. 18. Plot to Determine Ionization Potential.

The instructions given below apply to a type 82 mercury-vapor "full-wave" rectifier tube.   All commercial mercury-vapor diodes have filamentary cathodes and the potential drop along the filament distorts the three-halves power plot.   This trouble is least in the 82 tube, since its cathode requires only 2.5 volts, or 1.25 volts for each diode. Tubes containing argon gas, such as the 885 triode or the 2050 tetrode,

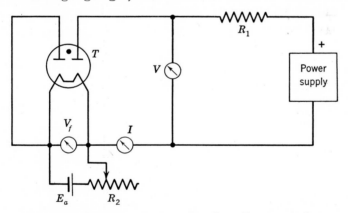

Fig. 19. Circuit for Exp. 24. T—type 82 tube. E_a—storage battery. R_1— 1000 ohms, 50 watts. R_2—rheostat to reduce voltage to 2.5 volts at filament.

have equipotential cathodes, but the gas pressure is somewhat low for this experiment.   The circuit is shown in Fig. 19.   Only one diode is used; the other plate is connected directly to the adjacent end of the filament, as indicated.

Part I.   Ionization Potential.   Heat the tube in an oil-bath to between 35 and 40 degrees C.   The exact value is not important, but it must be held constant to within a degree. Manual control of this temperature is possible, but a simple thermostat is better. Locate by trial the potential at which I breaks sharply upward, then take data from zero to a little below this potential, taking readings every $\frac{1}{10}$th volt over the last 2 or 3 volts. Plot these data as represented in Fig. 18, and read from this plot the value of V at which deviation from the three-halves power law just starts. This value equals $(V_i - V_1)$. The value of V_1 is obtained from the x-intercept of the straight line drawn to fit best the plotted points below ionization, ignoring the ones which may be out of line near the bottom (because of the potential drop along the filament).

As seen in Fig. 18, the first deviation from the three-halves power law is very slight, and V swings an appreciable fraction of a volt higher before it drops back to its operating value for higher current. The precision of this determination may be increased by making a second plot, to the same abscissae, with ordinates equal to the *difference* between the values of $I^{\frac{2}{3}}$ and corresponding values of y computed from the straight-line equation which best fits the linear portion of the first plot. Since these differences are small (nearly zero below ionization) they may be plotted to a larger scale, so that the deviation may be observed more readily. This plot will show other small deviations which are related to lower excitation potentials, but the relationship is not simple enough to identify these potentials from these deviations.

Part II. Normal Operation. Change the milliammeter to one having a larger range, and take data up to 25 or 50 ma, at room temperature. Plot V as y, I as x. For comparison, draw a horizontal line at the value of V equal to $(V_i - V_1)$. Analyze this plot in terms of the theory given above. Small fluctuations in the value of V are due, for the most part, to changes in vapor density, caused by changes in temperature.

Part III. Pressure Effect. With the tube in an oil-bath, and I held at some fixed value between 20 and 50 ma, take readings of V as the temperature is increased from room temperature up to 90 degrees C. Plot V as y, vapor pressure of mercury as x. Vapor pressure may be obtained from a plot of the following data.

Temp. (degrees C)	20	30	40	50	60	70	80	90
Pressure (10^{-3} mm Hg)	1.2	2.8	6.1	12.7	25.2	48.2	88.8	158.2

This plot shows how increased collision probability reduces the primary electron energy needed to maintain the plasma.

27. Demonstration Experiment 2. An oscilloscope will show the operation characteristics for a gas-type diode in the simple circuit of

Fig. 20.   When V_0, the peak value of the a-c voltage, is below V_i there is little or no current, but whenever V_0 is higher than V_i current will start as soon as the instantaneous a-c voltage, V, reaches V_i in the positive half of its cycle, and will continue until V drops below V_i

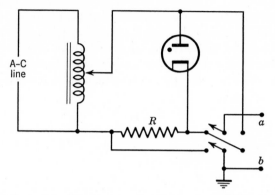

FIG. 20.   DEMONSTRATION EXPERIMENT 2.   Connect a and b to vertical-deflection terminals of the oscilloscope.

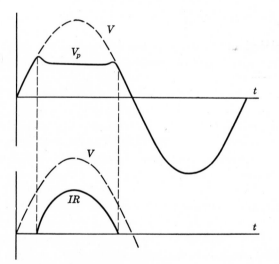

FIG. 21.   OSCILLOGRAMS FOR FIG. 20. V—a-c voltage. V_p—potential difference across tube. I—current.

again, as shown in Fig. 21.   A time plot of V_p, the anode potential, is seen with the switch (in Fig. 20) in one direction, and a time plot of the potential drop across R, which is proportional to I, with the switch reversed.   Note the slight hump in V_p at the start of current, and compare it with the observations made in Exp. 25.   This detail shows best when V_0 is not more than 2 or 3 times the ionization potential. Almost any gas-type diode will serve in this experiment; the resistor R should be chosen to limit the current to a suitable value for the tube chosen.

28. Rectifier Circuits. Gas-type diodes serve much the same as vacuum diodes in a-c to d-c power supplies, with greater efficiency because of the lower potential drop across them when they are conducting.   They are not interchangeable with vacuum diodes in all circuits, however, because of the limitations discussed in Sec. 25.

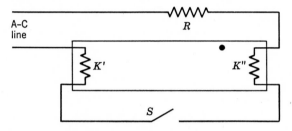

FIG. 22.   FLUORESCENT LAMP.

In circuits adaptable to gas-type diodes each diode must be in series with a suitable choke-coil or resistor, and provision must be made to heat the cathodes to operating temperature before power is turned onto the rest of the circuit.   The circuits shown in Figs. 16, 17, 24, and 26 of Chapter 1 are suitable, if a time-delay switch is inserted in the plate circuit.   This switch may be operated manually, or by a clockwork or thermal mechanism.   Gas-type diodes must not be used in "condenser-input" circuits such as those of Figs. 18, 22, and 23 of Chapter 1.

29. Fluorescent Lamps. A fluorescent lamp is essentially a gas-type diode in which the electrodes are separated by a distance of a foot or more.   Since it is designed for a-c operation it has two hot electrodes, one at either end, which serve alternately as cathodes and anodes.   A schematic diagram is shown in Fig. 22.   Since the plasma, which occupies most of the length of the tube, is long and slim, it suffers large losses of plasma electrons and positive ions by recombination at the walls of the tube; hence its maintenance requires a considerable drop in potential along the tube, in addition to the necessary sharp drop (discussed earlier) from the cathode to the edge of the plasma.   The gas is mercury vapor, and the light emitted from the plasma is the characteristic mercury line spectrum.   A small part of this light is visible but over 90 percent is of wavelength 2536 A, in the ultraviolet.* Almost all the visible light produced in this lamp is luminescence (both fluorescence and phosphorescence) excited by this ultraviolet light in the phosphor which coats the inside walls of the tube. Its color is determined by the nature of the phosphor. None of the 2536-A light appears outside the lamp, since the glass tube is opaque to it. Sterilizing lamps, on the other hand, are made in a similar manner with clear, thin-walled tubes of a glass which is quite transparent to ultraviolet light of this wavelength.

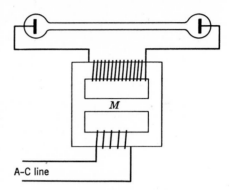

Fluorescent lamps, like all gas-discharge tubes, must be operated with an external ballast. It may be a resistor, as shown in Fig. 22, but a choke-coil is more efficient. When the lamp is started the switch, S, is closed so that the two filamentary cathodes, K' and K'', are in series with the ballast. As soon as K'

FIG. 23.   NEON-TUBE CIRCUIT.

and K'' are hot, S is opened and the full a-c line voltage appears between K' and K'' to start the discharge. The electrodes are maintained at operating temperature thereafter by electron and positive-ion bombardment. The switch is usually operated automatically, by either a thermal or magnetic mechanism.

30. Spectrum Tubes and "Neon" Sign Tubes. The luminous tubes from which "neon" signs are fabricated are glow tubes having cold electrodes, and are operated from a high-voltage a-c transformer. Like all gas tubes, they must be connected in series with a ballast resistance or choke-coil, or operated from a special transformer of the type shown in Fig. 23. This transformer has high leakage flux, through the extra core leg, M, so that it is equivalent to an ordinary transformer in series with a choke-coil. Electrical conduction in a sign tube is the same as in the one represented in Fig. 8, except that the positive column is very much longer, and accounts for almost all the potential difference between the terminals. The positive column is a plasma, as described in Sec. 22, and the potential drop along it is required to maintain plasma conditions, against the losses of positive ions and plasma electrons to the walls. In sign tubes almost all the

---

* This wavelength, 2536 A, corresponds to the return of the mercury atom from its *first* excited state (see Sec. 4) to its normal state. Excitation to this state requires a little less than 5 ev of energy and occurs frequently in the plasma.

light comes from the positive column, and is characteristic of the gas present.   The most brilliant tubes do contain neon gas, and glow a bright orange-red.   Various other gases, such as helium, argon, and mercury vapor, serve to produce other colors.   Colored glass, and coatings of phosphor on the inside walls, extend the color range further.

Small tubes of this kind are used in the laboratory to study the spectra of the inclosed gases.

31. Mercury Arc.   A most remarkable type of electronic conduction is possible when one electrode is a pool of mercury in a bulb from which

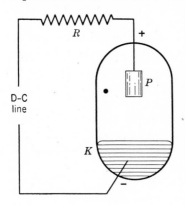

all gas but mercury vapor has been removed.   The discharge is started by tilting the bulb until the mercury bridges the gap between the two electrodes, then straightening it up again.   The potential drop across the tube is approximately the ionization potential for mercury when the electrodes are large and near together, as shown in Fig. 24. Electrons are emitted from a rather small spot on the surface of the mercury pool, which appears to be an inexhaustible source of electrons.   If the electrodes are further apart, and the tube is made narrower, the potential drop across the tube increases and the positive column

Fig. 24.   Mercury Arc.   K— mercury-pool cathode.   P— anode.

becomes quite luminous, providing a very useful source of mercury light for the laboratory.   This light source is employed to some extent also for commercial illumination.

There are several other means for starting the discharge; one of these is an *igniter* electrode, which is described in Chapter 9, Sec. 28.

32. Arcs and Sparks.   The electric arc between carbon electrodes, started by touching the electrodes together, then separating them, is one of the earliest-known types of gaseous conduction.   Its name comes from its appearance between horizontal electrodes.   The current in an arc is large; the potential difference is relatively low, and decreases as the current increases, so that a series resistance is required to limit the current.   The luminous core of the arc is a plasma region, the gas being a mixture of the surrounding atmosphere and vapors from the electrodes.   A large part of the emitted light comes from the incandescent tip of the positive electrode.   It has become customary to call any type of gaseous conduction an arc if the current is relatively large and the potential difference is comparable with the ionization potential of the gas.   Thus the type of conduction described in Sec. 31 is called a mercury arc, and a gas-type diode may be called a hot-cathode arc.

A spark occurs when a condenser, initially charged to a high potential, is discharged across a gap between cold electrodes, through a gas at approximately atmospheric pressure, or higher.   Once the spark starts the gap becomes a fairly good conductor, so that the condenser becomes almost completely discharged.   Often the spark is oscillatory, owing to the inductance of the discharge circuit.   A spark is a complex sequence of phenomena.   After the break-down which starts it, a spark may momentarily resemble a glow discharge, and may even resemble an arc if the circuit impedance is low enough.   An essential feature of a spark is its momentary character, resulting from the rapid fall of potential across the gap.   Indeed, a spark is always followed by an arc if the potential does not fall to zero and sufficient current is maintained across the gap.

Various other types of gaseous conduction, or gas discharge, are identified by special names, but careful study reveals that most aspects of these phenomena may be analyzed in terms of the fundamental phenomena considered in this chapter.

PROBLEMS

1. The pressure in a vacuum tube is 2.0×10^{-5} mm of mercury at room temperature.   (a) Compute the population density of molecules.   (b) Compute the mean free path for the molecules if the mean free path under standard temperature and pressure is 8.6×10^{-6} cm.

2. In a gas-type tube the pressure is 0.008 mm of mercury at room temperature. Compute the mean free path for electrons in this tube, assuming the same gas as in Prob. 1.

3. The mean free path for electrons in a gas at reduced pressure is 8.2 cm.   An electron beam passes through this gas.   Compute the approximate fraction of the electrons in this beam which make collisions with gas atoms in a distance of 5.0 mm.

4. The ionization potential for the gas in a gas-type phototube is 18 volts, and the anode potential is 90 volts.   (a) Compute the hypothetical maximum gain by the cascade process under these conditions.   (b) Compute the value of the probability factor, α, if the actual gain is 8.5.

5. Compute the approximate thickness of the space-charge layer next the cathode in a gas-type hot-cathode diode if the gas is mercury vapor and the current density at the cathode is 50 ma/cm^2.

6. In the voltage-regulator circuit of Fig. 11b the VR tube operates at 105 volts, between 5 and 40 ma.   The load resistor is 7.5 K and the d-c input is 225 volts.   (a) Find the resistance of the dropping resistor needed to make the VR-tube current 20 ma.   (b) Find the range of values for the d-c input within which regulation is possible.

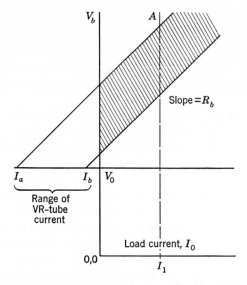

FIG. 25.   VOLTAGE-REGULATOR CIRCUIT CHART.   See Fig. 11b and Prob. 8.   If I_0
has the value I_1, then the possible range of values for V_b is given by the intersection
of the vertical line I_1A with the shaded area.

7. A voltage-regulator circuit is built with a VR-75 (75 volts) tube and a
VR-105 (105 volts) tube in series.   The current range is 5 to 35 ma.   (a) Compute
the resistance of the ballast resistor to make this circuit operate best at 375 volts
input and 50 ma load current, I_0.   (b) Compute the current range over which
regulation is possible at 375 volts input, and the range of d-c input over which
regulation is possible at 50 ma load current.

8. Prove that the operating range for the circuit of Fig. 11b is represented by
the shaded area of Fig. 25.

CHAPTER 9

Gas-Type Tubes with Grids

1. Gas in Thermionic Triodes. In Chapter 6 we have considered the effect upon thermionic conduction of an appreciable amount of gas in a diode. What influence does a grid have in such a tube? Let us explore this problem with a triode into which has been introduced a small amount of argon gas. The current in this tube will remain zero as long as the grid potential, V_g, is so negative that no electrons can leave the cathode. The requisite condition is the same as for the corresponding vacuum triode: if the initial velocities of the thermionically emitted electrons may be neglected, the current will be zero as long as $(V_g + V_p/\mu_0)$ remains less than zero.* In few other respects does the performance of this tube resemble that of a vacuum triode. Once the current has started the tube behaves exactly like a gas-type diode; the anode potential drops to a low value, approximately equal to the ionization potential, V_i, and the grid has no further control over the current, even when V_g is negative and far beyond the cut-off value.† Only if V_p is lowered below V_i will the grid regain control over the current.

2. Break-Down Characteristic. The break-down characteristic for such a gas-type triode may be investigated with the circuit of Fig. 1. First V_g is set at a fixed negative value, with V_p equal to zero. Then V_p is raised slowly until the tube "fires," or suddenly starts to conduct as a gas-type diode; when this occurs V_p drops to the neighborhood of V_i and the current jumps from zero to a value determined by the series resistor, R_1, and the potential drop across R_1. The plate-potential value, V_f, just before firing occurs, is called the *firing potential*. A plot of corresponding values of V_g and V_f, obtained in this manner, appears in Fig. 2. The upper portion of this plot is a fairly straight, diagonal line, but as V_f approaches V_i the plot bends toward the V_f-axis and crosses it horizontally at approximately V_i. According to the most elementary theory this plot should have two parts,

---

* See Sec. 6, Chapter 2.

† Extremely high negative values for V_g will cut off the current (and ruin the tube) as explained in the footnote to Sec. 4.

represented by the broken lines in Fig. 2: a horizontal part through V_i and a diagonal, straight-line part which, if extended, would pass through the origin, with a slope equal to $-\mu_0$. The horizontal part is

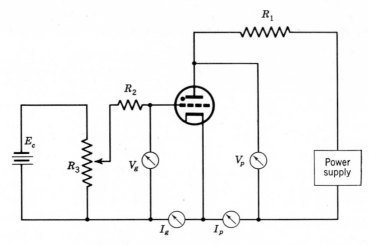

FIG. 1. CIRCUIT FOR GAS TRIODE.

accounted for by the necessity that V_p exceed V_i before ionization can occur. The diagonal part is accounted for in Sec. 1. No matter how large the value of V_p, no ionization can be produced without an initial electron current, and points below this diagonal line represent negative values for $(V_g + V_p/\mu_0)$, which prevent electrons from leaving the cathode. If the gas density is quite low the firing characteristic will come close to the hypothetical diagonal line, as indicated in Fig. 2. For higher gas densities, however, V_g must be relatively more negative and the firing characteristic shifts to the left. The most important cause for this shift is the emission velocities of the electrons, which we have so far neglected. Although the initial current must reach a finite value before ionization can become cumulative, this value is so minute, when collisions are frequent, that the relatively few electrons having initial velocities far above the average may be sufficient to start the discharge.

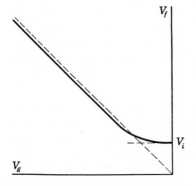

FIG. 2. THYRATRON BREAKDOWN CHARACTERISTICS. V_f—firing potential. V_g—grid potential.

3. Grid Current. After the tube fires there will be current to the grid as well as to the plate. This grid current is represented in Fig. 3 as a function of V_g, for a constant value of plate current. For zero grid potential the grid current, I_g, is large and predominantly an electron current. Its value increases very rapidly as V_g is increased in a positive direction. As V_g is made increasingly negative, however, I_g decreases to zero and then reverses.

After V_g has become several volts negative the value of I_g tends to level off, as indicated by the part of the plot to the left of a, Fig. 3. Over this range the current to the grid is carried almost entirely by positive ions. For higher values of V_g (to the right of a) both positive ions and electrons arrive together at the grid; at f the current is zero because they arrive in equal numbers.

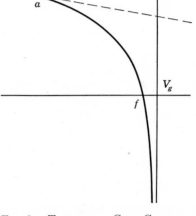

FIG. 3. THYRATRON GRID CURRENT. I_g—grid current. V_g—grid potential. I_p held constant.

4. Positive-Ion Sheath. When the tube is conducting, a plasma extends from the anode almost up to the cathode, as in a gas-type diode, and the grid finds itself imbedded in this plasma. If the grid is at a potential which is negative *with respect to the plasma* it is negatively charged; plasma electrons then are repelled by it, leaving it enveloped in a *positive-ion sheath*, a region in which positive ions exceed electrons in sufficient number to make the net positive charge in the sheath just equal to the negative charge on the grid. This positive-ion sheath then screens the rest of the plasma region from the electric field of the grid, thereby completely nullifying the efforts of the grid to control current.*

Unless the plate current is very small or the grid potential very negative, the positive-ion sheath is extremely thin.

The positive ions in the sheath are not at rest but moving toward the grid, thereby setting up the positive-ion current to the grid which is described in Sec. 3. When positive ions reach the grid their charges

---

* If the grid potential is made sufficiently negative, the positive-ion sheath may be increased sufficiently in thickness to close over the gaps between grid wires (or the opening in a box-type grid) and thereby stop the current. Unfortunately, before the current may be cut off in this manner, V_p will rise so high as to ruin an oxide cathode.

are neutralized; in the meantime other positive ions diffuse from the plasma into the sheath, and the magnitude of the positive-ion current is determined by the rate of this diffusion, and is proportional to the population density of positive ions in the plasma and to the area of the boundary between the sheath and the plasma.   The positive-ion grid current from the boundary of the plasma to the grid is controlled by positive-ion space-charge, and the sheath thickness adjusts itself according to the potential drop through it.   Thus, as the grid potential is made more negative the sheath becomes thicker, so that positive-ion current is almost independent of the grid potential as long as it is negative with respect to the plasma.   The increase in boundary area which is produced by increase in sheath thickness accounts for the small change in positive-ion current shown in Fig. 3.

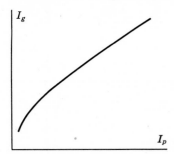

Fig. 4. Positive-Ion Current to Thyratron Grid. I_g—grid current. I_p—plate current. V_g constant.

Figure 4 shows how the positive-ion current depends upon plate current. Since the population density for positive ions in the plasma is approximately proportional to the strength of the plate current, this plot might be expected to be a straight line through the origin.   Deviations from a straight line are explained by several factors, principally the increase in thickness of the positive-ion sheath, and consequent increase in boundary area, as the plate current decreases.

5. Electron Temperature.   There is positive-ion current to the grid as long as the grid potential is below that of the plasma.   To the left of a, Fig. 3, the current is almost entirely positive ions, as has been stated earlier.   To the right of a the positive-ion current is represented by the broken line.   Usually this line is drawn straight and tangent to the plot at a point where V_g is sufficiently negative to make the plot nearly straight, as has been done here.   This line should curve slightly, but this slight curvature may be neglected.   The differences between I_g and the positive-ion current represented by this line represent *electron* current to the grid, carried by plasma electrons which have energy high enough to reach the grid against the opposing potential difference, V_n, between the grid and the plasma region.   (V_n is practically equal to $V_p - V_g$.)   The fact that many plasma electrons are able to reach the grid against an opposing potential even lower than that of the cathode is convincing evidence that the effective temperature of the plasma electrons is very high, as has been stated in

Sec. 22, Chapter 8.   Indeed, it is possible to estimate the value of the electron temperature, T_e, from the manner in which the electron current, I_n, to the grid, depends upon V_g.   If log I_n is plotted as a function of V_g, as in Fig. 5, the slope of a straight line drawn to fit the straightest part of this plot will be approximately equal to $5050/T_e$, for base-10 logarithms.   Compare this procedure with the one described in Sec. 16, Chapter 7, for determination of the effective temperature of a thermionic cathode.

6. Thyratrons.   Gas-type thermionic triodes are called *thyratrons*.   In the first thyratrons, such as the early type 885 tube, the grid was the same as for a vacuum triode.   Now, however, the grid in a thyratron is almost always a sheet-metal cup or cylinder which separates the cathode from the plate except for a comparatively small opening, as illustrated in Fig. 6. All types of thyratrons function in the manner explained above.   A thyratron will not conduct as long as the grid potential is sufficiently negative to prevent electrons from passing through the openings in the grid, even though the plate potential is many times the ionization potential.   It starts to conduct as soon as enough electrons reach the space between grid and plate to produce cumulative ionization. A plasma then extends through the grid open-

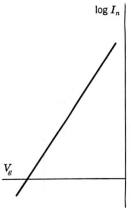

FIG. 5.   LOG PLOT FOR ELECTRON CURRENT TO THYRATRON GRID. I_n —electron current. V_g —grid potential.

ings and fills the tube from the plate to within a short distance of the cathode, and a positive-ion sheath envelops the grid so as to nullify the effect of grid potential.   Small thyratrons may contain an inert monatomic gas, such as argon, especially when constancy of firing characteristics is of importance.   Mercury vapor is almost always employed in larger thyratrons.

7. Experiment 25.   Thyratron Characteristics.   The characteristics of a thyratron may be studied with a type 884 or 885 tube.   (These are identical except for heater supply, which is 6.3 volts for the 884 tube, 2.5 volts for the 885 one.)   Obtain the following sets of data with the circuit of Fig. 1.   Make R_1 and R_2 each 10 K.   For Parts II and III it may be necessary to reduce R_1 to obtain higher current values.

Part I.   Firing Characteristic.   With V_p at zero, set V_g to a preassigned value.   Then raise V_p slowly until firing occurs.   Read V_g and V_p *just before* the tube fires.   Proceed in this manner for V_g values from zero to -15 volts, taking observations closer together around the bend of the curve (see Fig. 2).

Part II.   With V_g equal to zero, set I_p to some value such as 25 ma; then raise V_g to -15 volts.   Holding V_g at -15 volts, observe V_p and I_g for a series of values of I_p from some top value between 25 and 50 ma down to where I_p breaks suddenly down to zero, taking readings closer

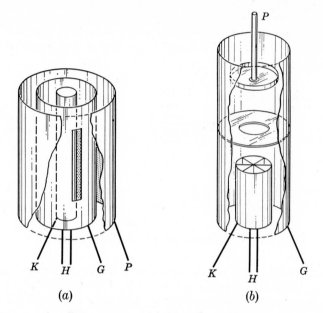

(a)   (b)

FIG. 6.   THYRATRON STRUCTURES.   (a) 884 tube.   Plate, P, cut away to show grid, G, and cathode, K.   Top and bottom are closed by mica plates.   (b) FG-27 tube.   Grid, G, cut away to show cathode, K, and plate, P. H—heater leads.

together as zero is approached.   Observe carefully the value of I_p just before the break.

Take the same sequence of observations of V_p and I_p with the grid connected to the plate, but *not* through the grid-current meter.   These data give the corresponding *diode* characteristic.

Part III.   With connections returned to the original circuit again, hold I_p constant at some convenient value and observe I_g and V_p for a series of values for V_g from -15 volts down to the point at which I_g reverses.

Plot and analyze the following curves.

(a) Plot the data of Part I as in Fig. 2, and find from this plot approximate values for V_i and μ_0.

(b) From the data of Part II, plot I_p as x, V_p as y. On the same sheet and to the same axes plot the diode characteristic. Explain why these two plots are so much alike. Note any significant differences, and try to find an explanation for them.

(c) From the data of Part III, plot V_p as a function of V_g. Does this plot show any significant change in V_p with V_g?

(d) From the data of Part II, plot I_g as a function of I_p, as shown in Fig. 4, and explain the form of this plot.

(e) From the data of Part III, plot I_g as a function of V_g, in the manner shown in Fig. 3. Draw the line representing the positive-ion current, as explained in Sec. 5.

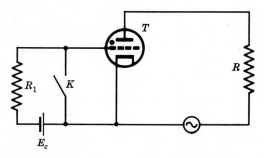

FIG. 7. THYRATRON SWITCH. Half cycle.

(f) Read from plot (e) values of the electron current, I_e, in the manner explained in Sec. 5, and plot $\log_{10} I_e$ as a function of V_g, as in Fig. 5. From this plot determine an approximate value for the electron temperature in the plasma.

8. Thyratron Circuits. Thyratrons are of greatest service as voltage-operated switches in a-c circuits. For example, there is current in the load, R, in the circuit of Fig. 7 as long as the grid of the thyratron, T, is held at zero potential by closing the key, K. The current stops the first time the plate potential reaches zero value after K is opened. The current in R is a pulsating direct current which is satisfactory for many applications. If alternating current is desired, two circuits of this kind may be combined, as in Fig. 8. In these illustrations grid potential is controlled by a manually operated key. It may be controlled otherwise, by many mechanical or electrical devices, including phototube circuits. For example, it is possible to regulate the time of operation for an a-c circuit by adjusting the electrical constants in the grid circuit of a thyratron. A very simple electronic timing circuit of this kind is diagrammed in Fig. 9. Current is started by a momentary closing of K, which charges the condenser C

to a potential equal to E_a. It is turned off again by the first reversal of the a-c plate potential which occurs after discharge of C through R_2 lowers the grid potential below cut-off value. The time required for C to discharge to this point is determined by the emf's of the batteries and the magnitudes of C and R_2. The resistor R_1 is needed to keep the grid current to a small value, and should be much larger than R_2.

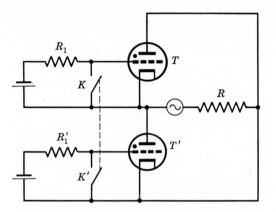

FIG. 8. THYRATRON SWITCH. Full cycle.

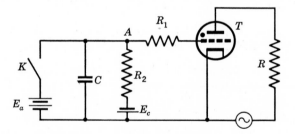

FIG. 9. ELECTRONIC TIME SWITCH.

Because of R_1 the grid potential stays at about zero value until the potential of the point A reaches zero.

9. Current Regulation. Current in a-c operated thyratron circuits may be regulated over a limited range by varying the potential of the grid in the manner represented in Fig. 10a. The thyratron will fire at some point in the first quarter-cycle, when the alternating voltage has risen to V_f, the firing potential corresponding to the bias, V_g. If the load is a pure resistance, as represented in Fig. 10a, the current then jumps to its value for zero grid potential, and from then on to the end of the positive half-cycle it is of course unaffected by grid potential.

This sequence of events is shown by the oscillograms of Fig. 10b.   It is evident that, for a pure resistive load, the lowest value of the average current, before it cuts off entirely, is at least half the value for zero grid potential.

10. Demonstration Experiment 1.   The oscillograms of Fig. 10b may be demonstrated by applying the potential drop across R, Fig. 10a, to the vertical-deflection terminals of an oscilloscope.   A type 884 thyratron serves nicely for this demonstration, although a larger one may be more spectacular and impressive.   With 115-volt, 60-cycle

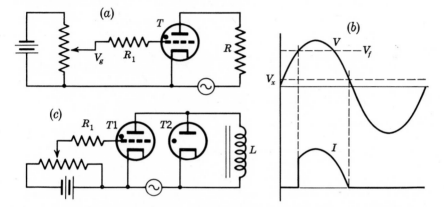

Fig. 10.   D-C Control of a Thyratron.   (a) Resistive load.   (b) Oscillograms for (a). V_f—firing potential. V_x—operating potential.   (c) Inductive load.

a-c supply and an 884 thyratron, R may be between 5000 and 10,000 ohms.   The average current may be shown with any lecture-table meter; one of the projection type is especially good.   If a suitable meter is not available a low-current lamp will serve to indicate the current.   The value of R should then be adjusted to light the lamp brightly when V_g is zero.   In a larger thyratron the glow of the discharge may be visible.

Put a choke-coil having a reactance of several thousand ohms in series with R, and reduce R to keep the average current the same as before.   With a resistive load, the current reaches zero and the thyratron stops conducting as soon as the emf of the a-c source reaches zero. With an inductive load the current lags behind the a-c emf, so that when the emf reaches zero the current is still large, and persists in the inductance and the thyratron for an appreciable fraction of a cycle longer, being maintained by the emf of self-induction in the inductance. If the inductance is large and R small this current may continue throughout the cycle and prevent the grid from regaining control.

Connect a gas-type diode of comparable current capacity across the load, as indicated in Fig. 10c. (If the thyratron is an 884 tube the diode may be another 884 tube.) This diode will not conduct as long as the emf acts in a positive direction across the load, but as soon as the self-induced emf in the inductance becomes large enough, in the reverse direction, this diode will fire and the current switch to it, allowing the grid of the thyratron to again take control. These phenomena are clearly shown by oscillograms for the potential drop across the entire load, and across R alone, the latter being proportional to the load current. It is very helpful to show the alternating

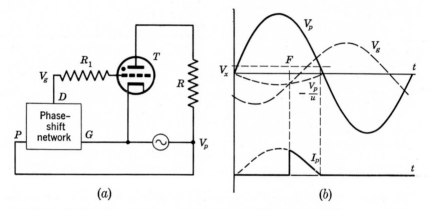

(a) (b)

FIG. 11. PHASE-SHIFT CONTROL OF A THYRATRON. (a) Circuit. (b) Oscillograms. V_p—plate potential. V_g—grid potential. I_p—plate current. F— point at which $V_g + V_p/\mu_0 = 0$, and tube fires.

emf simultaneously on the screen, by means of the electronic switching circuit described in Chapter 14.

11. Phase-Shift Control of Current. If the grid potential is obtained from the same a-c source as the plate potential, it is possible to regulate the plate current from full (half-cycle) value down to zero by changing the *phase* of the grid potential relative to the plate potential. A suitable circuit is indicated in Fig. 11a. The phase-shift circuit must be capable of shifting the grid potential continuously from in-phase with the plate potential to 180 electrical degrees behind phase, without appreciably changing its amplitude. Suitable circuits are described in Sec. 12. Figure 11b shows oscillograms when the lag of V_p behind V_p is about 135 electrical degrees ($\frac{3}{8}$ cycle). The thyratron fires when V_g is slightly negative, as indicated. During the first part of the cycle, in Fig. 11b, until V_g rises to this value, the current is zero. When firing does occur (for a resistive load) the current jumps to the line representing current for zero grid potential, and follows this line for the remainder of the positive half-cycle. When V_g lags 180 degrees behind V_p the current is zero, and as the phase lag decreases back toward zero the current increases to full half-cycle value. There is electron current to the grid during the half-cycle that the grid potential is positive, and R_1, Fig. 11a, is very necessary to keep this current to a small value. Because of R_1 the grid potential remains close to zero during this half-cycle. Many practical variants of this basic circuit have been developed.*

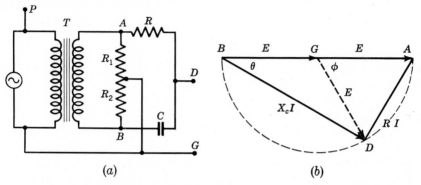

FIG. 12.   PHASE-SHIFT NETWORK.   Letters in (a) and (b) correspond.

12. Phase-Shift Circuits.   The circuit of Fig. 12a is a very convenient means for supplying the variable-phase, alternating voltage for the thyratron grid in the circuit of Fig. 11a. The phase angle is varied through 180 electrical degrees by changing R, C, or both. For operation from the 60-cycle, a-c line, T may be a unit-ratio, isolation transformer, the equal resistors, R_1 and R_2, may have any convenient value, C may be 1 mf, and R may be a 50,000-ohm variable resistor. The principle of operation for this circuit is explained by the vector diagram of Fig. 12b. Vectors BG and GA represent the two equal potential differences, from B to G and from G to A, in Fig. 12a. Likewise vectors BD and DA represent the potential differences from B to D, and from D to A. It is then evident that vector GD represents, in magnitude and phase, the potential rise from G to D, or the potential of the grid. Since the triangle ABD is a right triangle, G is the center of a circle passing through A, D, and B, or GD equals both BG and GA in magnitude. The potential represented by GD changes in direction but not in magnitude. The phase shift, ϕ, is twice θ, and $\tan \theta = R/X_c = -\omega RC$.

* See H. J. Reich, *Theory and Applications of Electron Tubes*, Chapter 12.

Another type of phase-shifter utilizes the emf induced in a coil placed in a rotating magnetic field. The phase of this emf may be altered by changing the angular position of the coil in this field. A war-surplus "synchro," having its stator supplied from a three-phase line, serves for this purpose. The rotor must be clamped tightly enough to prevent its rotation by the magnetic field, but not so tightly that its angular position may not be changed by hand.

13. Demonstration Experiment 2. Phase-shift control of current may be demonstrated in the manner described in Sec. 10 for d-c control. Show for a resistive load that control occurs for negative phase angles from zero to 180 degrees, and not for the remaining 180 degrees. This is done very easily with the synchro phase-shift device. With the circuit of Fig. 12a it is accomplished by reversing the connections from G and D to grid and ground. The demonstration should include an inductive load in addition to a resistance.

14. Gas-Type Tetrodes. For many applications of thyratrons the signal current may be very small, a phototube current, for example; and then a gas-type triode is not satisfactory. Since the grid in a gas-type triode is large in area and surrounds the cathode, the grid current may be large enough to mask so small a signal current, even when there is no plate current. An additional difficulty arises when gas-type triodes are operated with alternating plate potential. Then the alternating current in the grid circuit may be objectionably large, because of the high alternating voltage across the capacitance between the plate and the grid.

Both these difficulties are minimized in the gas-type tetrodes diagrammed in Fig. 13. In Fig. 13a the cathode, K, and the plate, P, are surrounded by the *shield grid*, $G2$, but separated from one another by a partition, S, having a small aperture, A, through which the discharge must pass. The control grid, $G1$, stands guard between this aperture and the cathode. It is small in size and some distance away from K, so that the electron current to it is quite small. Its small size serves also to minimize its capacitance to its surroundings, and it is completely shielded electrostatically from P by $G2$. In the electrode structure shown in Fig. 13b a second partition screens $G1$ from K.

In addition to meeting the needs outlined at the beginning of this section, the gas-type tetrode has other advantages over a triode for many applications. In particular, the more complete screening provided by two grids reduces the necessary bias and control potentials to quite low values, and the bias voltages may be adjusted between the

two grids.   One grid or the other may be operated at zero or even
positive bias.

15. Tetrode Thyratron Circuits.   A typical circuit for phototube
operation of a tetrode thyratron is given in Fig. 14.   The grid resistor,
R_1, may be several megohms; the upper limit is generally set at 10

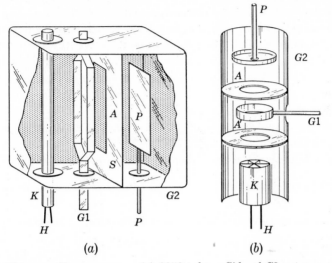

FIG. 13.   TETRODE THYRATRONS.   (a) 2050 tube.   Side of $G2$ cut away to show
interior.   (b) Large tetrode thyratron.   Front half of $G2$ cut away.

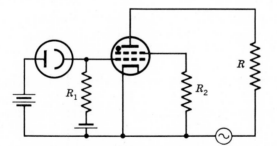

FIG. 14.   PHOTOTUBE CIRCUIT WITH TETRODE THYRATRON.

megohms.   The load, R, may be the coils of a relay, so as to control
enough power to operate lamps, open doors, or perform a multitude of
other functions.   It is possible also to operate this circuit with a-c
plate and grid-bias voltages.   The plate is connected through the
load directly to the a-c line.   For the control grid the bias is zero;

for the shield grid it is supplied through a low-voltage transformer, with the phase reversed. The shield-grid potential is negative whenever the plate potential is positive, and its peak value may be kept below the ionization potential, so as not to fire the tube.

16. Tetrode Thyratron Characteristics. Firing characteristics for a tetrode thyratron may be represented by a family of curves between V_1 and V_p, each curve for a different value of V_2. Each curve resembles in shape the curve in Fig. 2, although its slope upward is much steeper. As V_2 is made more negative the position of the firing characteristic shifts toward positive values along the axis of V_1,

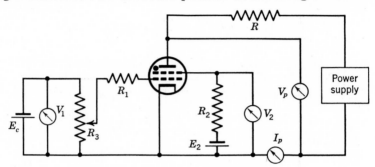

FIG. 15.   CIRCUIT FOR EXP. 26.

so that, for a fixed value of V_p, the potential V_1 increases as V_2 decreases. Thus V_1 may be adjusted to any convenient value by changing V_2, and may be negative or positive. As long as V_1 is somewhat negative the current to the control grid is exceedingly small. After the tube fires both grids are submerged in the plasma, and the current to each resembles that to the single grid of a triode thyratron.

17. Experiment 26. Tetrode Thyratron. The firing characteristics for a tetrode thyratron may be studied with a type 2050 tube. The circuit is shown in Fig. 15, and the general procedure is the same as for Exp. 26. The shield-grid potential, V_2, is best obtained with dry cells, and its value changed by units of one cell. The control-grid potential, V_1, is determined from the emf E_c and the reading of a calibrated voltage-divider, R_3. Make R_1 about 10 K, R_2 1 K or so, and R large enough to limit the plate current to within the capacity of the power pack (not over 100 ma) for the largest value of V_p.

Part I. With V_2 zero, set V_1 low (negative) enough to prevent firing. Then set V_p to its top value (250 to 350 volts) and raise V_1 until firing occurs. Repeat for enough values of V_p to make a good plot. Follow the same procedure for negative values of V_2 produced by 2, 4, and 6 dry cells, and the positive value given by 2 dry cells. From these data plot a family of curves having V_1 as x, firing potential as y.

Part II.   Change R_1 to 5 or 10 megohms and take similar observations for three values of V_2: zero, negative (6 dry cells), and positive (2 dry cells).   Plot these data alongside the plots for Part I (distinguish them by dotted lines or different-colored ink) and explain the differences observed.

18. D-C Switching Circuits.   Practical applications of thyratrons are less extensive in d-c circuits than in a-c circuits, but more varied

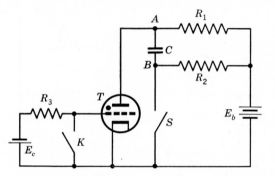

Fig. 16.   D-C Switching Circuit.   Closing K starts discharge; closing S stops it.

in kind.   In d-c switching circuits the grid functions to *start* the plate current, just as in a-c circuits, but separate means must be provided to stop it again.   The various d-c circuits differ chiefly in the means employed.   The simplest device is a switch in series with the plate, but less direct methods are usually more desirable.   The principle underlying many of these methods is illustrated in Fig. 16.   Current is started in the thyratron, T, by closing the key K momentarily. It may be stopped by closing the switch S.   Before S is closed the potential at A is the plate potential of T when it is conducting, or approximately the ionization potential, V_i, whereas the potential at B is E_b.   The condenser C is charged to a potential difference ($E_b - V_i$).   When S is closed the potential at B drops to zero, that at A becomes momentarily equal to $-(E_b - V_i)$, and this negative plate potential stops the current.   The potential at A rises again, at a rate determined by C, R_1, and E_b.   If this rise is not too rapid, deionization will be sufficiently complete before the plate potential reaches V_i again and the current will remain zero until K is again closed.

The circuit of Fig. 17 is the electronic counterpart of the one of Fig. 16.   Assume that $T1$ is conducting: the conditions in this circuit are then the same as in the one of Fig. 17 with S open. When $K2$ is closed the second thyratron, $T2$, serves as S to drop the potential at B down almost to zero, thus driving the potential at A negative, and the current switches from $T1$ to $T2$. Since the circuit is symmetrical the current may now be switched back again to $T1$ by closing $K1$.

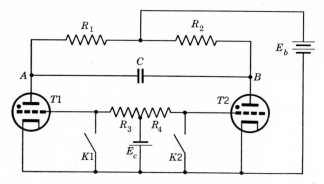

FIG. 17.   D-C SWITCHING CIRCUIT.

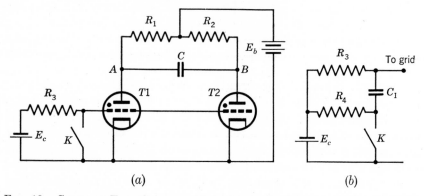

(a)   (b)

FIG. 18.   SCALE-OF-TWO CIRCUIT.   Output may be from A or B.   (b) Pulse-forming network.

19. Scaling Circuits. Figure 18a shows a simple modification of the circuit of Fig. 17, but one which has very important applications. Let us suppose that, initially, $T1$ is conducting, $T2$ is not. Closing K grounds both grids simultaneously. This does not affect $T1$ directly, since it is already conducting, but it fires $T2$. If K is held closed both thyratrons then will be conducting. If, instead, K is closed only long enough to fire $T2$, the sudden drop in the potential at B, when $T2$ fires, will drive the potential at A to a negative value, as explained in Sec. 18, and thus stop the current in $T1$. If K opens before the potential at A again rises enough to support current in $T1$, the current will have switched from $T1$ to $T2$. Successive quick taps of K will thus cause the current to alternate between $T1$ and $T2$. It may now be noted that the potential at B *rises* for every *second* tap of the key. If, for example, this point is connected to the input of a power amplifier driving an electric counter, the count recorded will be half the number of times K is tapped. Hence this circuit is called a *scale-of-two* circuit.

If two identical scale-of-two units are coupled together so that rise in potential at the output of unit 1 provides the input to unit 2, the output of unit 2 records every *fourth* input pulse to unit 1. A scale-of-four circuit is thereby produced. The input pulse to unit 2 must be no longer than is needed to switch current in unit 2, and the time constant of the resistance-capacitance coupling between units must be adjusted accordingly. This reduction in count may be extended indefinitely; the count ratio decreases according to the nth power of 2, where n is the number of units. With such scaling circuits it is possible to tally events which occur too rapidly to operate any electric counter directly; for example, the pulses produced in a G-M counter by radiations such as gamma rays and cosmic rays. A scaling unit employing vacuum tubes is described in Sec. 16, Chapter 11.

20. Demonstration Experiment 3. First set up and demonstrate the circuit of Fig. 17. Type 884 tubes will serve, although type 2050 tubes, with their shield grids grounded, are somewhat better. With 200 volts d-c supply, R_1 and R_2 may each be 20 K, R_3 and R_4 each 0.1 megohm, and C, 1 or 2 μf. Six dry cells will provide sufficient bias for type 2050 tubes, but higher bias (greater than one-tenth of the d-c supply) is needed for type 884 tubes. A tiny neon switchboard lamp, in series with 500 K, may be connected across each tube, between plate and ground, to indicate which tube is conducting.

This circuit may be converted into the one of Fig. 18 by connecting the two grids together. Either key may then be used, but should have a stiff spring so as to open quickly. If the input circuit is replaced by the one shown in Fig. 18b the length of the pulse is determined by the time constant of this input and by the grid bias, and the key need not be released so quickly. Make R_3 and R_4 each about 0.1 megohm and determine by trial the best value for C_1. It may improve the performance to raise the bias value.

21. Inverter Circuit. The *inverter* circuit of Fig. 19 is another modification of the basic circuit of Fig. 17. In this circuit the switching is initiated by alternating voltages on the grids, and the load is connected through a center-tapped transformer in the plate circuit. Condenser C serves to switch current from one tube to the other as in the basic circuit. The output is distorted alternating voltage and current, of the frequency supplied to the grids. If the coupling between primary and secondary of the plate transformer is loose (that is, if there is magnetic leakage, as in the transformer diagrammed in Fig. 24, Chapter 8) so that the load is inductive, this inductance may be tuned to resonate with C at the input frequency, and quite good waveform results. Under these conditions, the grid voltage may be derived directly from the output, and the frequency is then determined by the circuit constants, as in oscillator circuits driven by vacuum tubes.

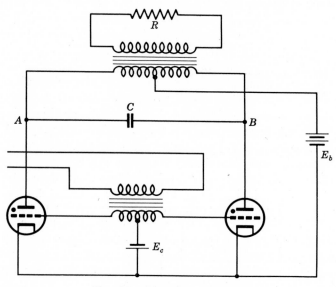

FIG. 19.   INVERTER CIRCUIT.

22. Trigger Circuits. In the trigger circuit of Fig. 20 the discharge is stopped in quite a different manner. The thyratron, T, is biased beyond cut-off by E_c, and the condenser C is initially charged to a potential equal to E_b. The thyratron is fired by a short pulse of positive potential which allows C to discharge almost instantaneously through R_1, L, and T. The discharge then stops and C recharges through R_2. Successful quenching of this discharge results from two factors. First, the high value of the discharge current, which is limited only by the low resistance, R_1, and the very small inductance, L, lowers the potential drop across T to a value appreciably below that needed for smaller current. Second, the self-induced emf in L, which slows up the rise of current to its peak value, also helps to maintain the current as it decreases, so that the potential at S falls appreciably below that at P toward the end of the discharge. For both these reasons the potential at S becomes too low to maintain the discharge and, unless R_2 is too small, it will not rise high enough to restart the discharge before deionization has permitted the grid to again take control. The process may be repeated as soon as C is recharged. The small resistor, R_1, is quite necessary to protect the tube; its value is determined by the firing potential and by the maximum current permissible.

This very short but powerful discharge may be utilized in several ways. For example, it may operate an electric count-recorder,

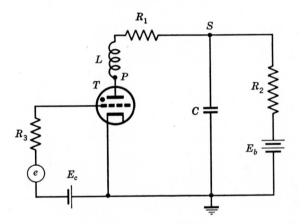

FIG. 20.   TRIGGER CIRCUIT.

inserted in the circuit in place of L and R_1. This recorder is operated by a quick-acting electromagnet which is energized by the discharge of C. In other applications, use is made of the sharp potential pulses which appear at S.

23. Sweep Circuit (Saw-Tooth Oscillator). One of the earliest applications of thyratrons is the production of a linear time axis for the cathode-ray oscilloscope. This *sweep circuit* appears the same as the one of Fig. 20, except for the omission of the input signal, e. It differs otherwise only in the magnitudes of certain of its components; R_2 is made quite large, and E_c is decreased until firing occurs at some potential V_f, which is considerably lower than E_b. See Fig. 21. When the plate power is first turned on, the potential V_s, at S, is zero, but as C charges up, V_s rises until it reaches V_f. Then the thyratron fires and V_s drops to a low value, V_x, as explained in Sec. 22. The discharge is immediately quenched and V_s starts to rise again. This operation thus repeats itself at regular intervals, as represented in Fig. 21. If E_b is several times larger than V_f the rate at which V_s rises is nearly linear in time. The potential at S is applied to the horizontal-deflection plates of the oscilloscope, so as to sweep the luminescent spot across the screen at a steady rate until the thyratron fires; then the spot jumps quickly back to the starting point and repeats the sweep periodically.

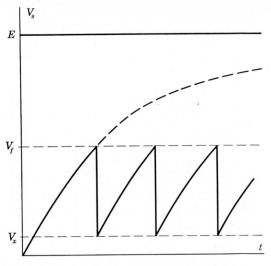

FIG. 21. SWEEP-CIRCUIT OUTPUT.

The time taken for each sweep is determined by R_2, C, and the potentials V_f, V_x, and E_b. It may be varied over a wide range of values by changing one or more of these quantities. To insure the exact repetition of any oscilloscope pattern the sweep frequency may be synchronized with the signal frequency by inserting a small a-c voltage of the signal frequency in series with the thyratron grid bias (at e, in Fig. 20). If the two frequencies are nearly commensurable, firing will occur sometime during the positive half-cycle of this synchronizing voltage, so that each repetition starts at the same phase of the signal.

In most oscilloscopes the rate of sweep is now made very linear by replacing R_2 with a pentode tube which maintains the charging current at an almost constant value over the full extent of the sweep. This arrangement is shown in Fig. 22. Note that the pentode is placed between the cathode and the ground, so that all d-c potentials may be supplied from a common source. In this circuit the frequency range is changed by switching in different values of C_1, and intermediate values of frequency are obtained by varying the bias on the control grid of the pentode.

24. Demonstration Experiment 4. The sweep circuit of Fig. 20 makes an excellent demonstration. The type 884 thyratron is designed specifically for this service. Inexpensive decade condensers provide for C, and R_2 may be any non-inductive resistance box, or even a linear volume-control resistor having a range of 100 K. The

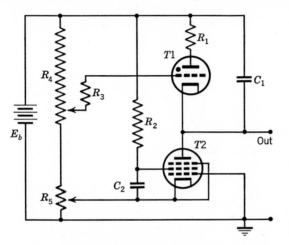

FIG. 22.   SWEEP CIRCUIT WITH PENTODE CONTROL.

choke-coil, L, may be any radiofrequency coil having an inductance of a few microhenries. The protective resistances, R_1 and R_3, should be not less than 1 K and 5 K respectively. To fix a suitable value for V_f, set the plate supply to the desired value for V_f, then decrease E_c until the tube fires. Oscillations will commence when the plate supply is raised to 250 or 300 volts. The point S should be connected to the vertical-deflection terminal of the oscilloscope (and the ground terminal to that of the oscilloscope). The output of this sweep circuit then may be compared with that of the sweep circuit in the oscilloscope. With V_f set at 50 volts the sweep is nearly linear; increase to 150 volts shows clearly the characteristic, non-linear charging curve represented in Fig. 21. Synchronizing voltage may be introduced by means of a small transformer at e, in series with E_c. It is interesting to experiment with different values for L: with no inductance the circuit may fail to quench; with too high an inductance, transient effects appear at the ends of the sweep.

The trigger circuit described in Sec. 20 may also be demonstrated with this set-up. To do this, increase the value of E_c until firing does not occur unless a positive pulse is introduced into the grid circuit. This pulse may be introduced in the manner described in Sec. 20. The oscilloscope is left connected to S, to show the shape of the output pulse. If R_2 is left as large as for the sweep circuit, the effect of tapping the key appears on the screen as one cycle of the saw-tooth oscillation. The value of R_2 should be reduced to a few thousand ohms, or as low as possible and yet have the discharge quench, so

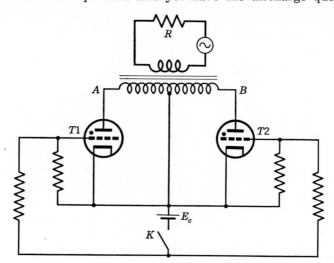

FIG. 23. THYRATRON WELDER CONTROL.

that the recovery is rapid. Note that, if the pulse is produced by a simple key, and the key is held closed too long, the thyratron will remain conducting. A switch should be provided in the plate circuit to stop the current if this happens. It is interesting to explore the effect upon this circuit also of changing the value of L.

These demonstrations may be made into a laboratory experiment if so desired.

25. Indirect Control of A-C Circuits. When the alternating current to be controlled is too large to handle directly with thyratrons (or when the circuit impedance is very low) it is possible to employ a current transformer with a full-cycle thyratron switching circuit of the type illustrated in Fig. 8. The load is connected in series with the low-impedance side of the transformer, the switching circuit to the other side. The simplest form of this circuit is represented in Fig. 23. More practical circuits are all a-c operated, and include modifications to care for certain complications, such as surges. When the key, K, is closed, the thyratrons are biased below cut-off and the transformer serves as a choke-coil which reduces the load current to a very small value.   With K open, the conducting thyratrons practically short-circuit their side of the transformer, so that the impedance at the terminals on the load side falls close to zero and the load current rises to full value.   This kind of circuit has extensive application for electric spot-welders.

26. Saturable-Reactor Control of Alternating Current.   A second method for indirect control of alternating current, and one which per-

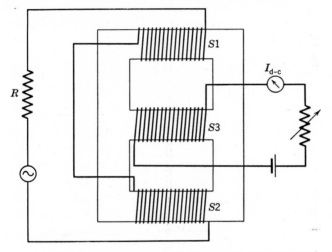

FIG. 24.   SATURABLE REACTOR FOR A-C CONTROL.   Reactance decreases as $I_{d\text{-}c}$ increases. R—load.

mits continuous variation from maximum value down almost to zero, is represented in Fig. 24.   The control element is a choke-coil having three legs, with a-c windings, $S1$ and $S2$ on the outer legs and a d-c winding, $S3$, on the middle one.   If $S1$ and $S2$ have equal numbers of turns, and are connected in the proper order, the alternating magnetic flux will be confined to the sides and ends of the core.*   Suppose now that there is direct current in S_3.   The magnetic flux produced in the center leg by this direct current must return through the outer legs, where it is superimposed upon the alternating flux.   As a result, the reactance of the choke-coil is reduced, for reasons which have been explained in Sec. 28, Chapter 4.   The presence of direct current in S_3 thus increases the alternating current.   When the d-c flux saturates the core the

* Since there is no alternating flux in the center leg of the core, no emf is induced in the d-c coil, S_3, and the impedance of the d-c circuit does not affect the impedance of the reactor.

reactance of the choke-coil becomes almost zero and the alternating current reaches full value.   The thyratron rectifier circuit represented in Fig. 10c, with its grid bias produced by the phase-shift network of Fig. 12a, will serve to supply the variable direct current.   This circuit finds extensive application to the control of theater lighting.   It is employed in the Lisner Auditorium of the George Washington University.

27. Mercury-Arc Rectifiers.   The mercury arc, mentioned briefly in Sec. 31, Chapter 8, possesses certain outstanding advantages as a high-current rectifier tube: in particular, it does not require any warm-up period, but is always ready, and the current is limited only by the power its container can dissipate. Its greatest defect is that it is difficult to start.   It may be employed as a rectifier only if the arc never goes out, and this condition is met only in multiphase operation. For example, six anodes are employed for full-cycle, three-phase operation, and the arc never breaks, just transfers itself from one anode to the next.   Single-phase, full-cycle operation is made possible by means of a second pair of anodes, called "keep-alive" anodes, supplied through choke-coils so that current to these auxiliary electrodes lags in phase behind that to the main anodes. Multiphase rectification, in huge, metal-cased mercury arcs, is employed extensively in industry.   Details concerning these installations are found in books devoted to a-c rectification.*   The single-phase rectifier mentioned above is now largely replaced by the ignitron rectifier.

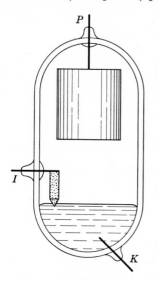

Fɪɢ. 25.   Iɢɴɪᴛʀᴏɴ. Schematic diagram.

28. The Ignitron.   The ignitron is a mercury-pool type of rectifier tube in which the arc may be started by means of a third electrode, called the *igniter*.   A schematic diagram for an ignitron is given in Fig. 25.   The anode, *P*, and the cathode pool, *K*, are the same as in any mercury arc.   The anode must be large, to be able to dissipate the power brought to it without overheating.†   The igniter rod, *I*, is

---

* For example, L. B. W. Jolley, *Alternating Current Rectification.*

† The mercury-vapor pressure depends upon the temperature of the coolest part of the mercury vapor, and must be kept below the value at which reverse current ("arc-back") will take place during the negative half-cycle.

made of silicon carbide or other suitable semi-conductor substance. The tip of this rod dips into the mercury pool as shown. The arc is started by passing a fairly large current between the igniter and the mercury, for about 1/10,000 sec; this discharge will form a small arc between I and K, close to I. If, during this time, the main anode potential is 25 volts or more, and positive, the discharge will switch from I to P and remain there until the arc is broken by reducing the current below a critical value in the neighborhood of one or two amperes. The instantaneous power required to start an ignitron is large, but the average starting power is small. It should be noted

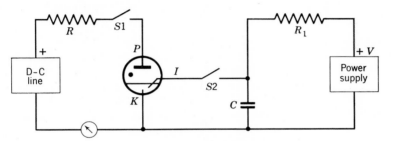

FIG. 26. D-C IGNITRON CIRCUIT FOR DEMONSTRATION. P—anode. K—mercury-pool cathode. I—igniter.

that this starting power is about the same for any size ignitron. Water-cooled, metal-cased ignitrons find extensive application to spot-welder control, as well as many other industrial applications.

29. Demonstration Experiment 5. These operating characteristics for an ignitron may be demonstrated best with d-c operation, in the circuit shown in Fig. 26. The ignitron may be one of several* glass-encased types which are available for low-power and demonstration purposes. The load, R, should limit the current to the average value specified by the maker's data. Igniter current is supplied by the discharge of C through the igniter rod, I, after C has been charged to a potential V by the power pack. The charging resistance, R_1, should be not less than 500 K.

Observe first the ignition arc with the main-circuit switch, $S1$, open. Take 4 mf for C and set V to about 200 volts. At the instant $S2$ is closed a small but bright flash should appear in the angle between I and the surface of the mercury. Opening $S2$ allows C to recharge so that the process may be repeated. It is interesting to determine by trial the least values of C and V for which an arc results. Ignition of the main arc is demonstrated by closing $S1$ before $S2$ is closed. It is

* For example, type No. GL-5779, made by the General Electric Co.

well to open $S2$ as soon as the main arc starts; a momentary switch is suggested. Note also that $S2$ must be a quick-acting, low-resistance switch, since the initial igniter current is large. The arc is stopped by opening $S1$. Do not run the tube long with direct current since it is not designed for this mode of operation.

The circuit of Fig. 27 may also be demonstrated with the glass-encased ignitron. Suitable values for the circuit elements depend

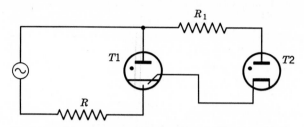

FIG. 27. IGNITRON RECTIFIER. $T1$—ignitron. $T2$—gas diode. R—load. R_1—protective resistor for $T2$.

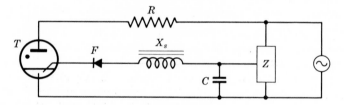

FIG. 28. CONTROL OF IGNITRON WITH SATURABLE-CORE REACTOR. X_s—saturable-core reactor.

upon the tube used, and are usually given in the instruction sheets furnished with the tubes.

30. Ignitron Rectifier Circuits. The simplest a-c circuit for starting an ignitron is represented in Fig. 27. The gas diode, $T2$, fires first, thus supplying current to the igniter rod, I, of the ignitron, $T1$. Once the ignitron has fired, the potential across $T2$ drops to the arc potential of $T1$, and the arc in $T2$ goes out. If the diode, $T2$, is replaced by a thyratron having phase control of its grid potential, the ignitron arc may be started at any point in the positive half of the a-c cycle, and the average current thereby regulated from zero to full half-cycle value. More reliable and more efficient operation results when the igniter current is a sharp, high pulse, such as produced by the condenser discharge in the circuit of Fig. 26. Circuits have been employed in which firing is produced by means of a condenser which is charged through a diode during the negative half-cycle, then discharged through a thyratron at the desired point in the positive half-cycle. A simpler means for producing the desired current peak is a saturable reactor. The principle of this method is shown in Fig. 28. The condenser, C, is charged from the a-c line through an a-c network, Z. It discharges through the saturable reactor, X_s, the heavy-duty crystal rectifier, F, and the igniter circuit. The reactance of X_s is high until its core is saturated magnetically but becomes almost zero thereafter, and the rectifier suppresses the negative pulse. A sharp, high pulse of current to the igniter results. The pulse is timed to occur at the desired point in the positive half-cycle by means of the charging network, Z, which charges the condenser in the proper phase.

31. Triode Glow Tubes. The operation of a glow tube (see Sec. 13, Chapter 8) may be controlled to a limited extent by means of a third, or *starter*, electrode. The electrode structure for such a grid-glow tube is represented schematically in Fig. 29. The cathode, K, is relatively large and has a surface specially treated to give good electron emission. The anode, A, is small and some distance away, and the starter, S, is a ring of wire supported a short distance above K and

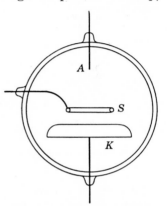

FIG. 29. TRIODE GLOW TUBE. Schematic diagram. A—anode. K—cathode. S—starter electrode, a wire ring.

between K and A. If the starter is at zero (cathode) potential the tube does not conduct until the anode potential reaches a fairly high positive value, V_1. It then operates at a lower potential, V_2, to which it drops immediately after firing occurs. If the anode potential is between V_1 and V_2 the tube may be fired by raising the potential of S to some value V_f at which a discharge is set up between S and K. This discharge then transfers from S to A if the current in it is sufficient. The starter current required to initiate the main discharge is very small and depends upon the anode potential in the manner shown in Fig. 30. If the anode potential is near V_1 the tube may be fired from a very high-impedance source, in a few microseconds of time. Grid-glow tubes may be fired by a radiofrequency signal, superimposed upon a suitable bias. The values of V_1, V_2, and V_f vary considerably from tube to tube, and through the life of a single tube. For a 0A4-G tube, V_1 is approximately 220 volts, V_2 in the neighborhood of 70 volts, and a starter potential of 70 to 90 volts is required to fire the tube, for instantaneous (or d-c) anode potentials between 150 and 185 volts.

To explain the operation of this tube we must first observe that S serves as a partial electrostatic screen between K and A. If the potential of S is zero, or any value below V_f, an anode potential equal to V_1 causes conduction to start between S and A, with S serving as

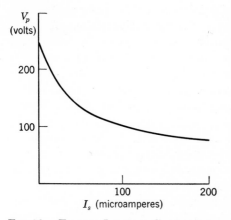

FIG. 30. TYPICAL IGNITION CHARACTER-ISTIC FOR TRIODE GLOW TUBE.

cathode. The value of V_1 is high because S is a poor cathode, on account of both its small size and its poor surface characteristics. Once the discharge is started, either in this manner or by raising the potential of S to V_f with the potential of A between V_1 and V_2, the discharge transfers to conduction between K and A. The starter electrode then is surrounded by a plasma and has no further control over the discharge. In many applications the problem of stopping the discharge is met by supplying a-c voltage to both the anode and the starter electrode.

In some cold-cathode gas triodes use is made of a characteristic of cold-cathode discharges which has not previously been mentioned here. If the current in a glow tube becomes very high the potential difference across the tube drops suddenly to a very low potential, essentially an arc potential. If the current is maintained at this high value the discharge will continue as an arc and the tube will be quickly destroyed. A condenser discharge through a glow tube may reach this state of discharge, however, without apparent damage to the tube; the condenser is almost completely discharged, and a bright flash of light is emitted from the tube, for a very brief interval of time. This phenomenon is utilized in an electric flash lamp for photographic work, or, when the flash is repeated periodically, for stroboscopic illumination of moving objects. A four-electrode cold-cathode tube, called a Strobotron, has been designed especially for such work.* The Strobotron contains neon gas, and flashes red. For photographic work a krypton-filled tube is employed, and the third electrode is placed outside the

* K. J. Germeshausen and H. E. Edgerton, *Electrical Engineering*, Vol. 55 (1936), p. 790.

glass tube, near the cathode.   Both the starting potential and the main anode potential for this flash tube are several thousand volts, and the flash is exceedingly bright.

32. Probe Measurements. It seems appropriate to close this chapter with a brief discussion of how we have learned what we know concerning plasmas in gas discharges.   In the very early work with gas discharges attempts were made to measure the potential at any point in a gas discharge, for example, the glow discharge represented in Fig. 8, Chapter 8, by inserting at that point an auxiliary electrode, called a *probe*, and measuring the potential of this probe electrostatically, with no current to or from it.   Sometimes such measurements were reasonably good, but more often they were far from satisfactory. As more was learned about the processes occurring in gas discharges it was realized that the potential of such a probe can differ greatly from that of the region in which it is inserted.   In 1923, Langmuir and Mott-Smith developed a method for making probe measurements which not only determines a satisfactory value for the potential at any point in a plasma, but in addition gives information concerning the distribution in energy of the plasma electrons.

Let us consider the application of the Langmuir-Mott-Smith method to a thermionic gas discharge, and see how it accounts for the plasma characteristics described in Secs. 22 and 23 in Chapter 8.   Let K and P, in Fig. 31a, represent the cathode and anode in such a tube, and let us consider a small probe, A, inserted at some point between K and P.   With the circuit diagrammed in Fig. 31a we may now measure the current, I_a, to this probe as its potential, V_a, is varied.   A plot of the measurements thus made appears as shown in Fig. 32.   Note that it is very similar to Fig. 3 for current to the grid in a thyratron. Indeed, the grid in a thyratron may be regarded as a type of probe.

33. Probe Current. If the probe is a thin, flat plate the current I_a, for quite negative values of V_a, will be nearly constant, as represented in Fig. 32, and is due almost entirely to positive ions collected by the plate.*   The probe is now surrounded by a positive-ion sheath (as explained in Sec. 3, for the grid of a gas triode) and this positive-ion current, which we shall represent by I_s, measures the rate at which

---

* Positive ions diffuse into the sheath across the boundary between the sheath and the plasma, and the rate at which they enter the sheath is proportional to the area of this boundary.   When the probe is flat this area is nearly equal to the area of the probe, and does not change appreciably with the thickness of the sheath. The rate at which positive ions leave the plasma is then the same for any value of V_a, and hence the positive-ion current to the probe is constant.   For a cylindrical probe, such as a grid wire, the boundary area increases with sheath thickness and the positive-ion current increases proportionally.

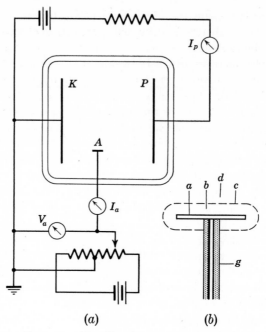

(a)   (b)

Fig. 31. Probe Circuit. (a) Circuit. K—hot cathode. P—anode. A—
probe. (b) Probe detail. a—probe. b—positive-ion sheath. c—boundary.
d—plasma.

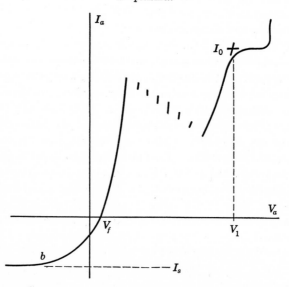

Fig. 32. Probe Current. V_1—potential in plasma at probe. The break in
the plot is caused by a reduction in the scale of I_a.

positive ions *diffuse* from the plasma into this sheath. We shall now assume that this positive-ion current does not change (except as mentioned in the footnote) as long as the positive-ion sheath surrounds the probe. This assumption is represented in Fig. 32 by the broken-line extension of the lower horizontal part of the plot. The change in I_a which begins to be apparent at b, Fig. 32, then must represent collection of electrons by the probe, along with positive ions. If I_s is subtracted (algebraically) from I_a the difference will represent the electron current, I_n, to the probe.

34. Plasma Potential. As the probe potential approaches that of the anode the probe current increases rapidly; the scale of current in the plot of Fig. 32 then must be reduced accordingly, as indicated at the right of the figure. Ultimately, however, the probe current levels off as indicated, and this horizontal portion of the plot represents electron current to the probe when it is surrounded by a negative-ion (electron) sheath. The nearly constant value of this current is explained in the same manner as for positive-ion current when

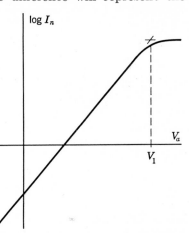

Fig. 33. Log Plot for Electron Current.

the probe is enveloped in a positive-ion sheath. The potential of the plasma at the point A, Fig. 31a, may now be found by extending the upward-rising part of this plot to meet the horizontal line, as shown in Fig. 32; it may be taken equal to the potential, V_1, represented by this intersection. Compare this value with V_f, Fig. 32, the "free probe" potential for which the probe current is zero; it is this potential, V_f, which is measured electrostatically. In this manner it may be shown by direct measurement that the plasma potential in a gas diode or triode is nearly constant from the anode close up to the cathode, and its value is almost the same as that of the anode, thus verifying what has been said in Sec. 22, Chapter 8. Similar measurements demonstrate the steady rise in potential along the plasma in a long tube such as a fluorescent lamp.

35. Electron Temperature. Figure 33 represents the electron current, I_n, by a logarithmic plot having V_a as abscissae. Below V_1 this plot is a nearly straight, upward-sloping line from which the distribution in energy for the plasma electrons may be deduced. In Chapter 7 a similar plot (Fig. 11) is obtained for electrons emitted thermionically from a hot cathode, and in Sec. 15 of that chapter it was shown that a statistical distribution in energy corresponding to a temperature T leads to such a straight-line plot, with a slope equal to $11,600/T$ when V is measured in volts, and natural logarithms are plotted. The equation for this line is (Eq. 23, Chapter 7)

$$\log_e I_n = \log_e I_0 - \frac{e}{kT} V \tag{1}$$

or

$$\log_e I_n = \log_e I_0 - \frac{11,600}{T} V \text{ (volts)} \tag{2}$$

Derivation of this equation is given in Sec. 15, Chapter 7.

When this theory is applied to the electron current to a probe, I_0 is the saturation current, as indicated in Fig. 32, and V is the potential of the probe *relative to the plasma*, or $(V_1 - V_a)$. Substitution of this value into Eq. 1 gives

$$\log_e I_n = \left(\log_e I_0 - \frac{e}{kT} V_1 \right) + \frac{e}{kT} V_a \tag{3}$$

From the slope of the plot in Fig. 33 it is then possible to compute the value of T, and verify the very high values for plasma-electron temperature assumed in Sec. 22, Chapter 8.

In applying these equations to a plasma it is assumed that interactions among plasma electrons, as discussed in Sec. 22, Chapter 8, are sufficient to establish thermal equilibrium among them. This condition exists when the tube is wide and short, the current density fairly high, and the gas density such that the mean free path for gas atoms is somewhat less than the shortest plasma dimension. A good plasma may form under much less ideal conditions, but the phenomena within it are then far more complex. When the gas density is low the population density for ions (positive ions and electrons) may vary from point to point, and primary electrons may constitute an appreciable fraction of the electron population. For such a plasma the plot of Fig. 33 will not be straight, and must be interpreted as representing incomplete thermal equilibrium. In a tube which is considerably longer than wide, one or more potential maxima or minima may exist in the plasma, and potential oscillations (*plasma oscillations*) are of frequent occurrence.*

* Consult W. G. Dow, *Fundamentals of Engineering Electronics*, 1st Ed., Chapters 19 and 20, or K. K. Darrow, *Electrical Phenomena in Gases*.

In Sec. 5 it is stated that an approximate value for the electron temperature in a thyratron may be obtained from a similar plot for the electron current to its grid. For negative grid potentials the grid does serve as a useful probe and the electron-temperature value thus found demonstrates the existence of such high-energy random motions among plasma electrons. When, however, the thyratron grid has the usual structure, and surrounds the cathode except for a small aperture, it does not serve as a satisfactory probe when its potential is above that of the cathode; then it collects many electrons directly from the cathode.

36. Positive-Ion Temperature. The distribution in energy among positive ions cannot be determined by the probe method employed for electron temperature, since the positive-ion current is negligible in comparison with the electron current in the potential region where such probe measurements must be made, namely the region where the probe is surrounded by an electron sheath and the electron current has saturation value. However, other conditions indicate that the positive-ion temperature must be comparable with that for un-ionized gas atoms. In an ideal plasma of the kind here assumed, in which the mean free path for positive ions is a fraction of the plasma dimensions and the electric field is practically zero,* it is difficult to account for a distribution in energy among positive ions which differs much from a thermal distribution corresponding to the temperature of the gas as a whole, or a few hundred degrees Centigrade. Unfortunately, direct experimental evidence in support of this conclusion is not available.†

37. References. The topic Gaseous Electronics has of necessity been treated incompletely in Chapters 8 and 9. More detailed and more advanced treatments are found in references 1, 2, and 3 below. There is also much of value in the older books (references 4 and 5). Circuits and applications are found in many electronics books and periodicals, of which references 2 and 6 to 9 are examples. Several conferences on gaseous electronics are held each year, and the proceedings of these conferences are published in various physics and engineering periodicals.

1. K. K. Darrow, *Electrical Phenomena in Gases.*
2. W. G. Dow, *Fundamentals of Engineering Electronics*, Chapters 19–20, 1st Ed.; Chapters 15–18, 2nd Ed.
3. F. A. Maxfield and R. R. Benedict, *Theory of Gaseous Conduction and Electronics.*

---

* In long plasmas, in which there is an appreciable potential gradient along the axis, the effective temperature for the positive ions may be considerably higher, owing to energy received from the axial electric field.

† See Sec. 37, reference 1.

4. J. J. Thomson and G. P. Thomson, *Conduction of Electricity through Gases*, Vols. I and II.
5. J. S. E. Townsend, *Electricity in Gases*.
6. H. J. Reich, *Theory and Applications of Electron Tubes*, Chapters 11 and 12.
7. *Electronics*.
8. *Proceedings* of the Physical Electronics Conferences at Massachusetts Institute of Technology.
9. *Advances in Electronics*, L. Marton, Editor (annual volume).

PROBLEMS

1. In the circuit of Fig. 7 the a-c emf is 75 volts rms, and the load, R, is 4000 ohms. Assume that μ_0 is 8.0 and the ionization potential is 18 volts. (*a*) Compute the least value for the grid bias, E_c. (*b*) Compute the average plate current (d-c meter reading) when K is closed.

2. In the circuit of Fig. 9 the alternating emf is 120 volts rms, E_a is 90 volts, E_c is 45 volts, and R_2 is 1.00 megohm. Assume μ_0 is 10.0 and compute the value for C to make the time of operation of the switch 5.0 sec.

Solution: The peak value for the alternating emf is 170 volts; hence the tube fires at -17 volts grid potential. The potential at A at the start is 90 volts and the current in R_2 is $[90 - (-45)]/1.00 = 135$ μa (microamperes). At the end it is -17 volts, and the current is $[-17 - (-45)]/1.00 = 28$ μa. An approximate solution may now be made by assuming that the average current is the average of these two values, or 81.5 μa. The charge lost by the condenser is C times the *change* in potential at A and is also equal to the average current times the time: $C[90 - (-17)] = 81.5 \times 5$ microcoulombs, or $C = 3.8$ μf. A more exact solution may be shown to be

$$I_t = I_0 \epsilon^{-t/R_2 C} \qquad \text{or} \qquad \log_e (I_0/I_t) = t/R_2 C$$

From this equation we find $C = 3.17$ μf. The approximation is almost good enough.

3. In the circuit of Fig. 10a the alternating emf is 115 volts rms, R is 90 ohms, and μ_0 is 12.0. Compute the average alternating current in R, (*a*) when the grid potential is zero, and (*b*) when it is -11.0 volts. Take $V_x = 10$ volts.

4. In the circuit of Fig. 12a, C is 1.00 μf. Compute the values for R needed to produce phase shifts of 30, 60, 90, 120, and 150 degrees.

5. Compute the phase-angle shift from complete cut-off required to make the current in R, Fig. 11a, equal to one-third of the full half-cycle value. Consider V_x negligible.

6. Diagram and design a timing circuit to remain closed for T seconds, using a 2050 thyratron, biased to fire at zero potential on the control grid. NOTE: The resistance from grid to ground may be as high as 10 megohms.

7. (*a*) Sketch a time plot for the potential at A, Fig. 16, after S is closed. Assume E_b is 125 volts, the tube drop when conducting is 10 volts, R_1 is 50 ohms, R_2 is 1000 ohms, and C is 30 μf. (*b*) Compute the time after closing S that the potential at A has risen to 10 volts again. This time must be greater than the deionization time for the tube.

8. Explain Fig. 17, and sketch time plots for the potentials at A and B from the instant that $K1$ is closed, with $T2$ initially conducting.

9. In the circuit of Fig. 18b, R_3 and R_4 each is 100 K, C is 300 $\mu\mu$f (micro-microfarads), and E_c is 45 volts. Sketch a time plot for the potential at the grid, and compute the time required for it to fall to -25 volts.

10. In the circuit of Fig. 22, E_b is 300 volts, the potential of the grid of $T1$ is 135 volts *above ground*, C is 0.050 μf, and the plate current in $T2$ is 0.45 ma. Take μ_0 as 10.0, and the operating potential for $T1$ as 12 volts. (*a*) Compute the maximum and minimum values for the output potential. (*b*) Compute the sweep frequency. (*c*) Make a time plot of the output potential.

11. In the circuit of Fig. 23 the transformer ratio (for the entire secondary, from A to B) is 1:80, and there is 1200 volts rms between A and B when the tubes are not conducting. When the tubes are conducting the tube drop is 8 volts and the secondary current is 5.0 amp rms. (This current is in one half of the secondary during one half-cycle, in the other half during the other half-cycle.) Compute (*a*) the primary current, (*b*) the emf of the a-c source, (*c*) the power supplied by the a-c source when the tubes are conducting, (*d*) the power taken by the thyratrons, and (*e*) the power supplied to the load and the resistance of the load, R.

12. Explain carefully why $T2$ is extinguished when $T1$ fires in the circuit of Fig. 27.

13. According to the kinetic theory the average kinetic energy of particles in thermal equilibrium at the temperature T is $3kT/2$. Compute the average kinetic energy in electron-volts for electrons at (*a*) 20°C, (*b*) 1000°C, (*c*) 2800°C.

14. Compute the electron temperature for electrons having a statistical distribution with an average kinetic energy of (*a*) 5.0 ev, (*b*) 10.4 ev. NOTE: The primary electrons from the cathode in a gas diode may have an average kinetic energy of 10.4 ev, but they cannot be said to have a corresponding temperature, since this energy does not represent random motions. The random motions among the primary electrons more nearly correspond to the cathode temperature.

CHAPTER 10

Resonant-Circuit Amplifiers and Oscillators

1. Radio Circuits. Electron tubes found their earliest applications in radio circuits, and the radiofrequency field still represents one of the major areas of electronic development. Nevertheless, there is much in this field which is not electronics, and most of the general subject of radio circuits is outside the scope of this book. We shall consider here only those topics in the radio field which are of importance to electron-tube theory and to electronic circuits.

Physically, the principal difference between electronic circuits in the radio field and most other electronic circuits is that resonant or "tuned" units are essential parts of all radio circuits. In the sections immediately following is given a summary of the chief properties of resonant circuits. It is assumed that the reader is already familiar with radio circuits in general, and for the most part this summary is intended as a review of that knowledge, not as an introduction to this topic. An introduction to this field is supplied by many good books.

2. Nomenclature. In outlining the theory for resonant circuits we shall employ *small* letters, such as i and e, to represent *instantaneous* values of current, emf, etc. The corresponding capital letters represent the amplitudes (peak values) for these quantities. This notation is illustrated in Eq. 1.

$$i = I \cos 2\pi ft = I \cos \omega t \tag{1}$$

The capital letters may also be taken to represent rms values in equations which include capital letters only. Thus Eq. 2 gives the ratio between rms values for the potential drop across a resistor and the current in it, as well as it gives the ratio of the peak values for these a-c quantities.

$$E = RI \tag{2}$$

The familiar vector diagrams are employed to represent amplitude and phase for a-c quantities. In the examples of Fig. 1 note the arrow-tips employed to differentiate between current and voltage vectors. Equation 3 illustrates the corresponding complex-number notation for representing phase and amplitude.

$$(a)\ E = RI \qquad (b)\ E = j\omega LI \qquad (c)\ E = RI + jXI \tag{3}$$

The complex-number notation is employed sparingly, in such a manner that the sections treated by this method may be passed over without loss of continuity by those not conversant with it.

In electron-tube circuits we continue to use capital letters I_p and V_p for total plate current and plate potential, and E_b, E_c, and E_2 for

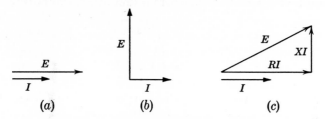

(a) (b) (c)

FIG. 1.   VECTOR DIAGRAMS. (a) For resistance, R. (b) For inductive reactance, X. (c) For R in series with X.

d-c potentials at the plate, grid, and screen grid respectively.   To avoid confusion with these symbols the a-c components of plate current and voltage in radiofrequency circuits are represented by i_a and e_a, their amplitudes by I_a and E_a.

3. Series Resonance.   The simplest resonant circuit consists of a condenser, C, and an inductance, L, connected in series to an a-c generator as shown in Fig. 2.   Let e be the emf of the generator and R be the total resistance of the circuit (chiefly the resistance of L).   The reactance, X, is

$$X = L\omega - (1/C\omega) \qquad (4)$$

This reactance is zero at the *resonant frequency*, f_0, defined by

$$2\pi f_0 = \omega_0 = 1/\sqrt{LC} \qquad (5)$$

At this frequency the current is in phase with e and has the value i_0 given by

$$i_0 = e/R \qquad (6)$$

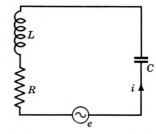

FIG. 2.   SERIES-RESONANT CIRCUIT.

For peak (or rms) values this relation may also be written

$$I = E/R \qquad (7)$$

The reactance of either L or C at the frequency f_0 has the magnitude

$$X_0 = L\omega_0 = 1/C\omega_0 = \sqrt{L/C} \qquad (8)$$

In radio circuits R is almost always very much smaller than X_0, and I

decreases rapidly as f increases or decreases from f_0, in the manner shown in Fig. 3a.   Above f_0 the reactance of L predominates and I approaches $E/L\omega$ as f increases; below f_0 the reverse is true and I approaches $C\omega E$ as f decreases toward zero.   The corresponding phase changes are shown in Fig. 3b.   The *sharpness* of resonance (measured by the width of the current plot at half-amplitude) depends

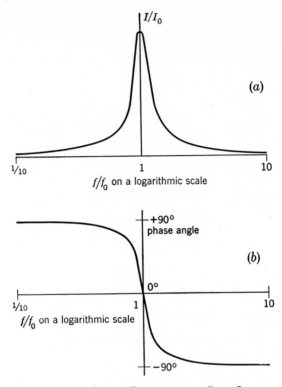

FIG. 3.   SERIES RESONANCE. $Q_0 = 5$.

upon the ratio of X_0 to R, and this ratio is called the Q, or the Q-*factor* of the circuit.   We shall represent it by Q_0.

$$Q_0 = \frac{X_0}{R} = \frac{1}{R}\sqrt{\frac{L}{C}} \tag{9}$$

4. Free Oscillations.   If the a-c source in Fig. 2 is suddenly removed from the circuit the current will continue to *oscillate*.   At each oscillation, however, its amplitude diminishes, so that ultimately it becomes zero.   The simplest way to obtain an equation for this free electrical oscillation is to start with the instantaneous potential drops around the circuit of Fig. 2.   For series resonance this sum is equated to the emf.   For free oscillations it is equated to zero:

$$L\,di/dt + Ri + q/C = 0 \tag{10}$$

To eliminate q, the charge on either plate of C, differentiate Eq. 10

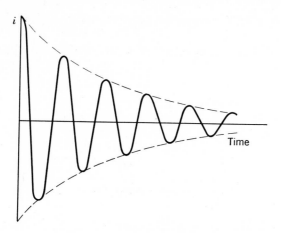

Fɪɢ. 4.   Fʀᴇᴇ Oꜱᴄɪʟʟᴀᴛɪᴏɴ.

with respect to time, and remember that dq/dt equals i.   Then

$$L\,d^2i/dt^2 + R\,di/dt + i/C = 0 \tag{11}$$

The solution to this differential equation is

$$i = I\epsilon^{bt}\cos\omega't \tag{12}$$

In Eq. 11 the constants b and ω' have the values*

$$b = -R/2L \tag{13}$$

$$\omega'^2 = \omega_0{}^2 - b^2 \tag{14}$$

A plot of Eq. 12 is shown in Fig. 4.

---

* Equations 12, 13, and 14 may be verified by differentiating Eq. 12 twice and substituting the resultant values for i, di/dt, and d^2i/dt^2 back into Eq. 11.   The result is

$$0 = [L(b^2 - \omega'^2) + 1/C + Rb]\cos\omega't - (2Lb + R)\omega'\sin\omega't \tag{15}$$

Since $\cos\omega't$ and $\sin\omega't$ pass through zero at different times, Eq. 15 requires that the coefficients of each of these quantities must equal zero separately, giving two independent equations.   Equations 13 and 14 follow from these equations, by simple algebraic manipulations.

It is often helpful to express b and ω' in terms of the Q-factor defined in Eq. 9:

$$b = -\,\omega_0/2Q_0 \tag{16}$$

$$\omega'^2 = \omega_0{}^2\left(1 - \frac{1}{4Q_0{}^2}\right) \tag{17}$$

Unless Q_0 is very small, ω' may be taken equal to ω_0 ($f' = f_0$) for almost all practical purposes.

5. Demonstration Experiment 1.   Many devices have been invented for shock-exciting a resonant circuit into free oscillations; a simple one

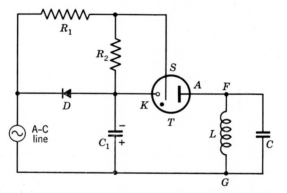

FIG. 5.   DEMONSTRATION EXPERIMENT 1. R_1, R_2—200 K each. C_1—0.02 μf. T—OA4-G tube. D—small "half-wave" rectifier for 115-volt, a-c input.

which is always ready for use is shown in Fig. 5.   Periodic excitation is made possible by a cold-cathode gas triode, of the type described in Sec. 31, Chapter 9.   The resonant circuit is connected in series with the gas triode, T, as shown, and energized once each a-c cycle by the discharge of condenser C_1.   This condenser is charged up during the negative half-cycle of the alternating emf, and is discharged through T and the resonant circuit early in the following positive half-cycle, by a positive potential difference between the starter, S, and the cathode, K. The current in T stops as soon as the condenser discharge has reduced the anode potential of T to below the operating value; the resonant circuit then oscillates free of any outside connection.   The oscillation may die away to zero before the next discharge takes place through T.

The starter potential is derived from the potential difference across D when it is not conducting.   During the quarter-cycle in which C_1 is charging the potentials of both S and K keep together up to the negative peak.   From then on until firing occurs K remains at this peak negative potential, whereas the potential of S follows the alternating emf, lagging behind it by an amount determined by R_1 and R_2. The ratio of these resistors is set so that firing occurs near the point of a-c reversal.

To represent these oscillations on the oscilloscope screen, points F and G are connected to the oscilloscope and the sweep synchronized to the a-c line frequency. The coil should have an inductance between 0.1 and 0.5 henry. The one described in Sec. 11 serves nicely. The capacitance C should not be less than C_1. It is very interesting to note that, as the frequency is changed by changing C, keeping the

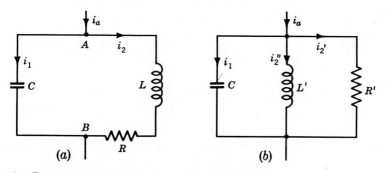

FIG. 6. PARALLEL RESONANCE. (a) Actual circuit. (b) Equivalent circuit.

initial amplitude constant by means of the gain of the oscilloscope amplifier, the envelop of the oscillation peaks remains the same. Even though the damping *per cycle* changes with frequency the damping per unit time remains the same, being determined by b, or $L/2R$. The value of b may be increased so as to change this envelop, by introducing additional resistance in series with L and C. This circuit is very convenient for demonstrating other transient phenomena. For example, the exponential discharge of a condenser through a resistor may be demonstrated by replacing L with a suitable resistor.

6. Parallel Resonance. The parallel-resonant circuit of Fig. 6 differs from a series-resonant circuit only in the way power is supplied to it. In place of a series emf (Fig. 2) it has an a-c generator connected between points A and B, supplying to it a current i_a at a potential difference e_a. Resonance occurs at a frequency very slightly lower than f_0; unless Q_0 is quite small the difference from f_0 may be neglected for all but the most precise work.* It is fortunate that this difference

---

* This treatment assumes the series resistance all in the inductance. If the series resistance is divided equally between the L and C branches the parallel-resonant frequency is exactly f_0.

is so nearly negligible, since there are several ways of defining the resonant frequency, each leading to a different value. For our purposes it is most convenient to define resonance as existing when i_a and e_a are in phase.

As a first approximation, and a very valuable one, we may describe what takes place at resonance in this circuit as oscillation of a fairly large current, i, in the closed series circuit formed by L, C, and R. In an isolated circuit this oscillation would die out, as explained in Sec. 4. In this circuit it is maintained at constant amplitude by power supplied from an a-c generator, by means of the current i_a. Since i_a must divide between the L and C branches of the resonant circuit the current i_1 in C differs from i_2, in L, and both are different from the assumed current, i. However, these differences are so small as to be negligible if Q_0 is fairly large, as we shall assume it to be, since then i_a is small as compared with i, and in quadrature with i. Let us neglect i_a in this series circuit. Then the power required to maintain oscillation is $\frac{1}{2}I^2R$, and the potential difference, e_a, between A and B, has an amplitude X_0I, just as in the series-resonant circuit. (Since e_a is in quadrature with i but, by definition, in phase with i_a, it follows that i_a and i are in quadrature, as stated above.) The power delivered to the oscillation is likewise equal to $\frac{1}{2}I_aE_a$, since i_a and e_a are in phase. Equating these two expressions for power we have (canceling the factor $\frac{1}{2}$, which is needed because all these magnitudes are peak values)

$$I^2R = I_aE_a = I_aX_0I \tag{18}$$

From Eq. 18 we then obtain

$$I_a = (R/X_0)I = I/Q_0 \tag{19}$$

and

$$E_a = (X_0^2/R)I_a \tag{20}$$

In Eq. 20 the factor X_0^2/R, which is the ratio of E_a to I_a, has the dimensions of resistance and is called the *parallel resistance* for the circuit. Let us represent it by R_0. Then

$$R_0 = X_0^2/R = L^2\omega_0^2/R = L/CR \tag{21}$$

At the resonant frequency this parallel-resonant circuit appears to the rest of the circuit to be a pure resistance of this relatively high value.

7. Parallel Resonance—Vector Method. A more exact analysis of the circuit of Fig. 6a may be made with the vector method employed in Fig. 7. The current I_1 in C equals ωCE_a, and leads E_a by 90 degrees, as shown. The current I_2 in L equals E_a/Z_2, and its in-phase and quadrature components are

$$I_2' = I_2 \cos \phi = RE_a/Z_2^2 \tag{22}$$

$$I_2'' = I_2 \sin \phi = \omega L E_a/Z_2^2 \tag{23}$$

The resultant current, I_a, has in-phase and quadrature components equal to I_2' and $(I_1 - I_2'')$ respectively.

At any one frequency it is often advantageous to consider that the actual circuit, Fig. 6a, is replaced by the equivalent circuit of Fig. 6b, in which C is the same but L' and R' have the values

$$L' = Z_2^2/\omega^2 L$$

$$R' = Z_2^2/R \qquad (24,25)$$

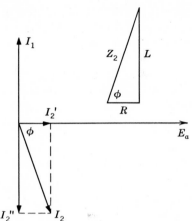

At the resonant frequency, f_1, defined in Sec. 6, the quadrature component of I_a becomes zero, or

$$I_1 - I_2'' = \omega_1 C E_a - \frac{\omega_1 L E_a}{Z_2^2} = 0 \tag{26}$$

FIG. 7.   VECTOR DIAGRAM FOR PARALLEL RESONANCE.

From Eqs. 26, 5, and 9 we may now evaluate ω_1:

$$C(R^2 + \omega_1^2 L^2) = L \tag{27}$$

or

$$\omega_1^2 = \frac{1}{LC} - \frac{R^2}{L^2} = \omega_0^2 \left(1 - \frac{1}{Q_0^2}\right) \tag{28}*$$

At resonance L' and R' become

$$L' = \frac{R^2 + \omega_1^2 L^2}{\omega_1^2 L} = \frac{L}{\omega_1^2 LC} = \left(\frac{\omega_0}{\omega_1}\right)^2 L \tag{29}$$

$$R' = \frac{R^2 + \omega_1^2 L^2}{R} = \frac{L}{CR} = R_0 \tag{30}$$

If R may be neglected in comparison with ωL in Eqs. 22, 23, 24, 25, and 28, they become

$$\omega_1^2 \cong \omega_0^2 \tag{31}$$

* See footnote under Sec. 6.

$$L' \cong L \qquad R' \cong \frac{L^2\omega^2}{R} = \left(\frac{\omega}{\omega_0}\right)^2 R_0 \qquad (32,33)$$

$$I_2' \cong \left(\frac{\omega_0}{\omega}\right)^2 \frac{E_a}{R_0} \qquad I_2'' \cong \frac{E_a}{\omega L} \qquad (34,35)$$

Often we are interested only in frequencies near f_0; then, if Q_0 is large, R' may be taken as constant, and equal to R_0.

8. Parallel Resonance—Complex-Impedance Method. The general solution for the circuit of Fig. 6a may be made also by the complex-impedance method. For the left-hand and right-hand branches of this circuit we may write

$$I_1 = j\omega C E_a \qquad \text{and} \qquad I_2 = \frac{E_a}{R + j\omega L} \qquad (36,37)$$

Then

$$I_a = I_1 + I_2 = \left(j\omega C + \frac{1}{R + j\omega L}\right) E_a \qquad (38)$$

From Eq. 38 we find that the admittance between A and B, Fig. 6a, is

$$Y_a = \frac{I_a}{E_a} = j\omega C + \frac{1}{R + j\omega L}$$

$$= j\omega C - \frac{j\omega L}{R^2 + \omega^2 L^2} + \frac{R}{R^2 + \omega^2 L^2} \qquad (39)$$

The three terms in the right-hand side of Eq. 39 are the admittances of C, L', —and R' respectively in Fig. 6b, that is,

$$Y_a = j\omega C - \frac{1}{j\omega L'} + \frac{1}{R'} \qquad (40)$$

Equations 24 to 33 now may be derived from Eqs. 36 to 40.

9. Radiofrequency Amplifiers. The load in a radiofrequency amplifier almost always may be represented as a parallel-resonant circuit, as in Fig. 8a. A pentode (or tetrode) is employed for reasons stated in Sec. 2, Chapter 5, as well as to provide an additional advantage which will appear in Sec. 10. For small output we may represent this amplifier by an equivalent circuit, as in Fig. 8b, which may be solved in the usual manner for i_a. At the resonant frequency, which we may take as f_0, this load is equivalent to a pure resistance, R_0, and the current is

$$i_a = \mu e_a / (r_p + R_0) \qquad (41)$$

If the frequency differs from f_0 the impedance of the load has a reactive

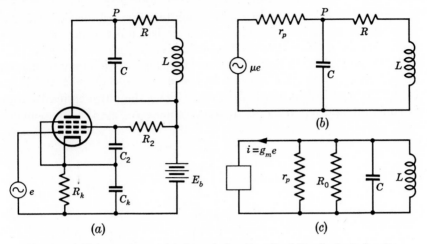

FIG. 8.   RF AMPLIFIER.   (a) Actual circuit.   (b, c) Equivalent circuits.

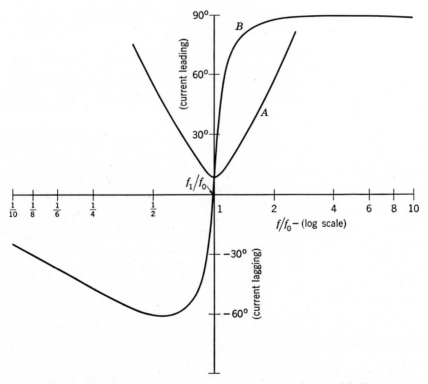

FIG. 9.   PARALLEL RESONANCE: CONSTANT VOLTAGE. A—I_a with E_a constant.
B—Phase angle between I_a and E_a.

component and is less than R_0 in absolute value.   Indeed, if the frequency difference is large this impedance is almost a pure reactance, inductive when f is less than f_0,* capacitative for f greater than f_0.

A clearer understanding of what occurs as f is varied may be had by considering two special cases.   In the first we shall take the input impedance (r_p in Fig. 8b) to be zero.   Then the output potential, e_a, is constant and equal to μe, at *any* frequency.   As the frequency is

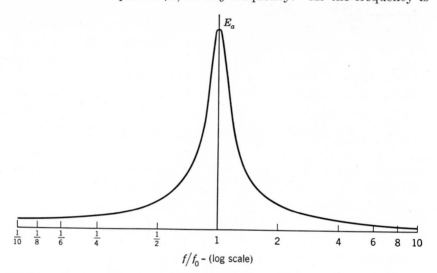

Fɪɢ. 10.   Pᴀʀᴀʟʟᴇʟ Rᴇsᴏɴᴀɴᴄᴇ: Cᴏɴsᴛᴀɴᴛ Cᴜʀʀᴇɴᴛ.   Phase angle is shown by B, Fig. 9.

varied from near zero toward infinity the current i_a passes through a minimum amplitude, $\mu e/R_0$, at f_0, as illustrated in Fig. 9, plot A, and its phase changes in the manner shown in plot B.   It is in phase with e_a at zero frequency and at f_1.   Between zero and f_1 it lags behind e_a, by a maximum of almost 90 degrees if Q_0 is high, whereas not far above f_1 it leads e_a by almost 90 degrees.

In the second case we shall assume that r_p is so very much larger than R_0 that the alternating current, i_a, is constant.   Now it is the output, e_a, which varies, in the manner shown in the frequency plot of Fig. 10.   Its amplitude reaches a peak value, R_0I_a, at f_0, and falls to very low values at frequencies much above or below f_0.†   At any one

* Unless f approaches zero.   Then the impedance approaches R.

† Maximum amplitude does not occur at f_1 but at a frequency between f_1 and f_0 which is much closer to f_0.   For all practical purposes it may be taken to be f_0.   Also, when Q_0 is small it is apparent that the peak value is slightly higher than R_0I_a.

frequency the phase angle between i_a and e_a is the same for both these cases, and is represented by plot B, Fig. 9.

10. Radiofrequency Amplifier Output.   The output from an actual amplifier may be obtained most easily from the "current-source" equivalent circuit diagrammed in Fig. 8c, in the manner explained in Sec. 16, Chapter 5.   In this circuit a constant current, $g_m e$, divides between r_p and the load, according to their respective admittances. The load is here represented as in Fig. 6b, with L' and R' replaced by their approximate equivalents, L and R_0.   As explained in Sec. 7, this approximation is good if the Q-factor is high, and f is not too far from f_0.   For other frequencies most of the current is in L or in C and the exact value of the equivalent shunt resistance is then unimportant.

In Fig. 8c we may now replace the combination of R_0 and r_p by its equivalent resistance, R_a, equal to $r_p R_0/(r_p + R_0)$.   The circuit then corresponds to the one of case two, Sec. 9, *with a lower parallel resistance*, R_a, in place of R_0.   The current I_a equals $g_m e$, and the peak output is $R_a I_a$, not $R_0 I_a$.   This effect of plate resistance upon the output of a radiofrequency amplifier may be described as a reduction of the Q-factor for the resonant circuit.   For the load itself, Q_0 is defined by Eq. 9, R_0 by Eq. 21.   Combining these equations, we obtain

$$Q_0 = \frac{X_0}{R} = \frac{R_0}{X_0} \tag{42}$$

For the amplifier

$$Q_a = \frac{R_a}{X_0} = \frac{r_p}{r_p + R_0} Q_0 \tag{43}$$

Since radiofrequency amplifiers must function in only a narrow band of frequency, and reject signals outside this band, it is necessary that Q_a be kept high in them.   It follows that in this respect a pentode, for which r_p is always very high, is much better than a triode in radiofrequency circuits.

11. Demonstration Experiment 2.   The frequency characteristics for a parallel-resonant circuit may be demonstrated with the circuit of Fig. 8a and an oscilloscope.   For this demonstration a frequency in the upper audio range, between 5000 and 15,000 cps, is better than radiofrequency, and a Q-factor between 10 and 20 better than a higher value.   A 6SJ7 tube serves very well, with the following circuit constants: $E_b = 250$ volts, $R_k = 1000$ ohms, $R_2 = 180$ K, $C_k = 0.1$ μf or higher, and $C_2 = 0.02$ μf or higher.   The coil should have an inductance between 0.1 and 0.5 henry, with an air core.   The secondary from a plate-power transformer, with the iron removed, might be found suitable.   A suitable coil may be made by winding insulated No.

24 copper wire into a circular channel of square cross-section, $\frac{3}{4}$ inch by $\frac{3}{4}$ inch, having an outside diameter of 6 inches.   Sheet plastic is a very convenient material for this coil form.   A decade condenser box is convenient for C.   The input may be supplied by a commercial audiofrequency signal generator.   Amplitude changes may be observed directly on the oscilloscope screen.   Phase angles may be demonstrated by the method described in Exp. 8, Part II.

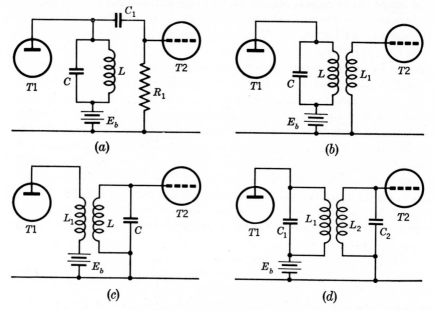

FIG. 11.   INTERSTAGE COUPLING.

A value for Q_a may be obtained by finding the frequencies, f_1 above f_0 and f_2 below, at which the output amplitude is 0.71 times that at resonance.   The difference between these frequencies measures the "width" of the resonance curve, and Q_a is given by

$$Q_a = f_0/(f_1 - f_2) \tag{44}$$

The effect of decreasing r_p may be simulated by putting resistance in *parallel* with L and C.   One-watt radio resistors are suitable.   Increase the gain in the oscilloscope so that the output at resonance is the same as before, and observe the increased width of the resonance curve.

12. Cascade Amplifier.   Greater gain at radiofrequency may be obtained by connecting two or more single-tube amplifier units in cascade, just as for audiofrequency; see Sec. 9, Chapter 3.   A condenser C_1, shown in Fig. 11a, serves to block the d-c plate potential of the first tube from the grid of the following tube, just as in an audio amplifier. In this mode of coupling, however, R_1 is a part of the load for the first tube (in parallel with R_0 and r_p in Fig. 8c) and broadens the resonance curve unless its value is much higher than R_0. A coupling device which avoids this objection is a transformer, as illustrated in Fig. 11b. The coil of the resonant circuit forms the primary of this transformer, and the secondary winding is wound close to this primary (close magnetic coupling). The secondary winding may be tuned instead of the primary, as shown in Fig. 11c. And sometimes resonant circuits are included in both the plate circuit of the first tube and the grid circuit of the following one, as in Fig. 11d. Both resonant circuits are tuned to the same frequency and loosely coupled by being placed some distance apart. When the coupling is adjusted properly the resonance curve for the combination has a narrow, almost flat top, with steep sides, so that the amplifier has a constant gain within the narrow band of frequency included by this flat top.

When cascade amplifiers must be adjustable (tunable) to a whole range of frequencies, each resonant circuit must be tuned individually; either separately, or by mechanically "ganging" the condensers together so that all are tuned by a single knob. Neither of these modes of tuning is free from objection, and the most efficient cascade radiofrequency amplifiers are designed to operate at a single frequency (or within a single narrow frequency band). An example is the intermediate-frequency amplifier of a superheterodyne radio receiver. Radio signals of many frequencies are amplified in this receiver by first "converting" them to signals of this fixed frequency. The process whereby this is accomplished is described in Chapter 12.

13. Graphical Analysis. When the output for a radiofrequency amplifier is large, graphical analysis is of course required. We shall limit our consideration of this analysis to operation at the resonant frequency, f_0, and assume that the Q-factor of the circuit is quite high. When the output is small we have seen that a resonant circuit then is equivalent to a pure resistance, R_0, but when the output is high this similarity disappears. For a resistance load the load-line is straight, the transfer characteristic curved, as shown in Fig. 3, Chapter 4, and the a-c components of both plate current and plate potential are distorted in the same manner. On the contrary, with a resonant-circuit load the alternating current, i_a, may be distorted, but the alternating voltage output, e_a, is almost exactly sinusoidal, unless Q_0 is very small. If the input is also sinusoidal the transfer characteristic between V_p and V_g is a straight line, whereas the load-line is curved, as shown in Fig. 12.

Freedom from distortion in the output may be accounted for by saying that the resonant circuit will respond only to frequencies close to f_0, and reject all higher harmonics. A clearer physical explanation, however, is the one given in Sec. 6. When Q_0 is high the resonant

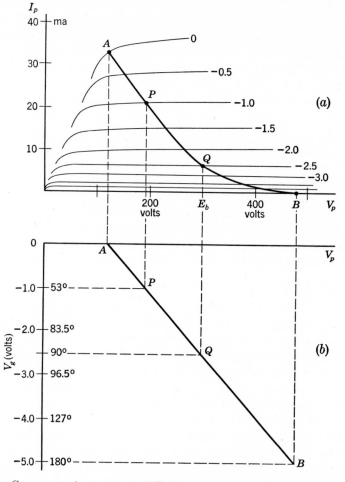

Fig. 12.   Graphical Analysis for RF Amplifier.   (a) Load-line.   (b) Transfer characteristic.

circuit may be regarded as a series-resonant circuit in which the current i oscillates, with this oscillation being maintained by the fluctuations of the plate current, I_p. Although the a-c components of I_p are now added to i, they are so much smaller in magnitude that the current in L and in C remains practically equal to i, and sinusoidal.   It follows that e_a is also sinusoidal, since E_a equals X_0I.

Once we have drawn the transfer characteristic, represented by the line AQB in Fig. 12b, we may plot the load-line, AQB in Fig. 12a. Each point on the load-line is located by the corresponding values of V_p and V_g, which may be read from the transfer characteristic.   For example, the Q-point is located where the ordinate through E_b (300 volts) crosses the -2.5-volt grid line in Fig. 12a, since these voltages

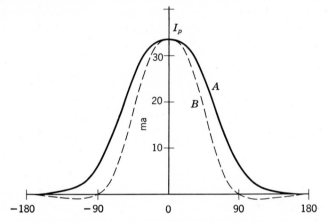

FIG. 13.   ANGLE (TIME) PLOT FOR RF AMPLIFIER CURRENT. A—I_p.
B—$I_p \cos \theta$.

are the coordinate values for the Q-point in Fig. 12b.   Dotted lines show how the point P is similarly located.

At this point let us pause to ask a question: Suppose we have a circuit such as the one in Fig. 8a, and we know the values for R, L, C, and the other circuit constants, including the input voltage, e.   How shall we draw the transfer characteristic which will predict the performance of this circuit?   Unhappily, the answer to this question is that there are no rules by which this may be done.   The best we can do is to decide upon values for E and E_a, draw the transfer characteristic accordingly, plot the load-line from this transfer characteristic, and then deduce from this load-line the kind of resonant circuit which can be made to produce the output, E_a, with which we started.   First we must make from the load-line a plot of I_p as a function of the angle θ ($\theta = \omega t$), as shown in Fig. 13.   The angle values are determined from the values of e corresponding to each current value:

$$e = E \cos \theta \qquad \text{or} \qquad \theta = \cos^{-1} e/E \qquad (45)$$

Angle values are given alongside the V_g-axis in Fig. 12b.   From the plot of Fig. 13 we may then derive the amplitude for the first-harmonic component of I_p, by any of the methods described in Sec. 6, Chapter 4. The Collins grids provide one of the quickest methods.   Let this amplitude be I_a; then the parallel resistance, R_0, is equal to E_a/I_a. For the example represented in Figs. 12 and 13, E_a is 180 volts, I_a is 17.0 ma, and hence R_0 is 10.6 K.

14. The Tank Circuit.   The resonant circuit, or tank circuit as it is often called, must now be designed to have this value for R_0.   Suppose, for example, that the a-c power output is to be delivered to a load which may be represented by R in Fig. 8a.   (R includes also the resistance of the coil.)   Then, from Eq. 42,

$$Q_0 = \sqrt{R_0/R} \qquad (46)$$

The value for Q_0 given by Eq. 46 should be reasonably high, certainly not less than 10, and R must be made low enough to meet this condition.   Assuming that this condition is met, we may then compute X_0 from Eq. 42.

$$X_0 = R_0/Q_0 \qquad (47)$$

This value of X_0 then enables us to compute L and C for operation at any frequency.

Consider again the example represented in Figs. 12 and 13, with R equal to 12.0 ohms.   From Eqs. 46 and 42,

$$Q_0 = \sqrt{10,600/12.0} = 30 \qquad \text{and} \qquad X_0 = 10.6/30 = 0.35 \text{ K}$$

For operation at 1000 Kcps (10^6 cps), $\omega_0 = 2\pi \times 10^6 \text{ sec}^{-1}$, and

$$L = \frac{X_0}{\omega_0} = \frac{350}{2\pi \times 10^6} = 56 \ \mu\text{h}$$

$$C = \frac{1}{X_0\omega_0} = \frac{1}{350 \times 2\pi \times 10^6} = 450 \ \mu\mu\text{f}$$

15. Class C Amplifiers.   As explained in Sec. 13, the output from an amplifier having a resonant-circuit load remains undistorted, or sinusoidal, regardless of the manner in which the plate current varies during the cycle.   Even if the plate current falls to zero during a large part of the cycle the current in the resonant circuit will maintain itself during that part of the cycle, as a free electrical oscillation. Thus it is possible to increase the efficiency of a radiofrequency amplifier by limiting the plate current to *pulses* which occur in only that part of the cycle in which they are most effective.   The essential

features of such a *class C amplifier** are shown in Fig. 14.   A comparison of Fig. 14 with Fig. 8a will show that the only apparent difference
is the method for biasing the control grid.   In Fig. 14 a battery
replaces the cathode-resistor bias of Fig. 8a, and E_c is so large that
I_p consists of pulses less than a half-cycle wide.   When the circuit is
tuned to the signal frequency these current pulses reach maximum
value when the signal, e, is a maximum and V_p is a minimum, as
shown by the oscillograms of Fig. 15.

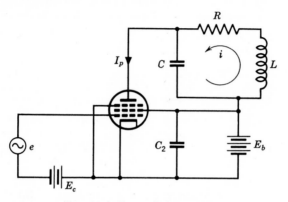

FIG. 14.   CLASS C AMPLIFIER.

Let us now consider the power relationships for this circuit.   Since
the output voltage, e_a, is the a-c part of the plate potential, V_p, and
E_b is the d-c part,

$$V_p = E_b + e_a \qquad (48)$$

or

$$E_b = V_p - e_a \qquad (49)$$

If I_p is the instantaneous value of the plate current, the instantaneous
power supplied by the d-c source is then

$$I_p E_b = I_p V_p - I_p e_a \qquad (50)$$

In Eq. 50 the product $I_p V_p$ equals the instantaneous power received
by the plate.   This power is wasted as heat at the plate, and must be
removed by thermal radiation or other means.   The remaining product, $-I_p e_a$, equals the instantaneous power delivered to the oscillating
circuit.   This power is positive and a maximum when the power lost
at the plate is least, or at the point in the cycle when e_a is a maximum
in the negative direction, and this is also the point at which the current

* See Sec. 26, Chapter 4, for definitions of the several classes of amplifiers.

pulses have their peak value, as seen in Fig. 15.   Thus the current pulses occur at just the right place in the cycle to deliver a maximum of power to the output circuit, and a minimum of power to the plate. The operation of this amplifier may be compared with that of a clock. The resonant circuit is analogous to the clock pendulum, the current pulses to the mechanical pulses with which the escapement mechanism

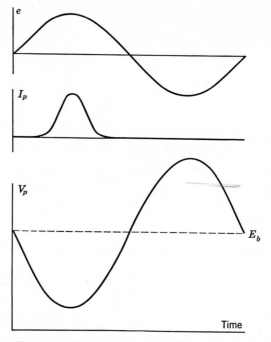

FIG. 15.   OSCILLOGRAMS FOR CLASS C AMPLIFIER.

of the clock sustains the oscillation of the pendulum.   The d-c source is analogous to the weight or spring which supplies power to the mechanism.

Class C amplifiers are power amplifiers, designed to operate with high power output and high efficiency at some one frequency (or narrow band of frequencies) and with constant output.*   Almost always the grid potential is allowed to swing to positive values, since this greatly increases the power output.

16. Demonstration Experiment 3.   The demonstration apparatus described in Sec. 11 may be modified as shown in Fig. 16 to function as a class C amplifier.   The screen grid is supplied from a separate source (a fresh 90-volt B-battery) so that I_p may be observed.   The bias for the control grid is furnished by batteries and made variable

---

* Exceptions to this are noted in Chapter 12.

from 0 to 15 volts negative (10 dry cells).   The average values of I_p
and I_g are measured by d-c meters, and a small resistance, r, provides a
means for indicating the instantaneous value of I_p on the oscilloscope
screen.

Connect point A to the vertical-deflection terminal of the oscilloscope, with the horizontal deflection produced by the sweep circuit,
and make the grid bias large enough to reduce I_p to zero.   Then turn

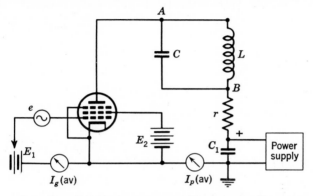

FIG. 16.   DEMONSTRATION EXPERIMENT 3.

on the signal generator and raise the input until plate current starts.
Tune the circuit (by changing either C or the signal frequency) until
the amplitude of the output is a maximum, then raise the input until
there is a small grid current.   (A slight retuning then may be necessary.)   Observe that the pattern on the oscilloscope screen is a pure
sinusoid.   Shift the oscilloscope connection from point A to point
B, to observe the (upside-down) plate-current pulses.   The angular
width of these pulses, or the *angle of operation*, may be estimated from
this oscilloscope pattern.   Increase the bias, and raise the signal to
bring the output back to its original value; then it will be observed
that the d-c values for I_p and I_g are approximately the same as before,
but the plate-current pulses are higher and narrower.

The transfer characteristic is displayed by connecting point A to
the horizontal-deflection terminal of the oscilloscope, the grid to the
vertical-deflection terminal.   If tuning is exact the pattern seen will
be a diagonal, straight line, as in Fig. 12b.   Any deviation from exact
tuning will open this line into an elliptical loop.   The load-line is seen
if the connection to the vertical-deflection terminal is shifted to point
B.   The horizontal part of this pattern shows the part of the cycle in
which I_p is zero.   Note that this line also becomes a loop unless tuning
is exact.   (A 2-megohm resistor between A and the oscilloscope will
minimize the detuning effect of this connection.)

17. Frequency Doubler. If, in the demonstration of Sec. 16, the resonant frequency of the tank circuit is made twice the signal frequency, and the bias increased until the pulse width is reduced to about 90 degrees, strong output may be produced at *double* the frequency of the input. If these conditions are included in the demonstration two interesting points are noted. First, the transfer characteristic is not a straight line but the Lissajou figure for the 2:1 ratio shown in Fig. 17. The interpretation is easily made.* Second, if

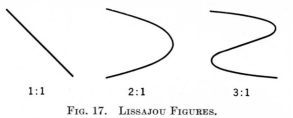

1:1   2:1   3:1

Fｉｇ. 17.   Lｉssａｊｏｕ Fｉｇｕｒｅs.

the time plot for e_a includes four output (two input) cycles, damping of the oscillation is seen in the second and fourth cycles, or the cycles in which no plate-current pulse occurs, and this damping reveals clearly the mechanism of oscillation maintenance discussed in Sec. 15. The damping may be accentuated by loading the tank circuit, either by increasing the series resistance, or by connecting a fairly high resistance in parallel with it. It should be possible also to demonstrate frequency *tripling*, by tuning the tank circuit to three times the input frequency. The transfer characteristic then corresponds to the 3:1 Lissajou figure of Fig. 17.

18. Efficiency for Class C Amplifiers. The average power input to the plate circuit of a class C amplifier equals

$$P_{\text{in}} = E_b I_p(\text{av}) \tag{51}$$

The average power output may be computed from E_a, the peak value of e_a, and I_1, the amplitude of the first-harmonic component of I_p.†

$$P_{\text{out}} = \tfrac{1}{2} E_a I_1 \tag{52}$$

* These conditions are analyzed in L. B. Arguimbau, *Vacuum-Tube Circuits*, pp. 287–289, under the title, "Frequency Multiplication." The design of such "Harmonic Generators" is treated in F. E. Terman, *Radio Engineers' Handbook*, pp. 458–462.

† The average power output equals $1/2\pi$ times the integral of $e_a I_p$ over a complete cycle. If I_p is expanded into a Fourier series, this integral becomes

$$\int_0^{2\pi} E_a \cos \theta (I_0 + I_1 \cos \theta + I_2 \cos 2\theta + \text{etc.}) \, d\theta = \pi E_a I_1$$

since all product terms except the second integrate to zero. See Sec. 6, Chapter 4.

The efficiency is then

$$\text{Efficiency} = \frac{E_a I_1}{2 \times E_b I_p(\text{av})} \tag{53}$$

For very narrow current pulses it may be shown that I_1 is approximately equal to $2I_p(\text{av})$. This approximation gives, *for very narrow current pulses,*

$$\text{Efficiency} \cong E_a / E_b \tag{54}$$

For wider pulses, I_1 is less than $2I_p(\text{av})$ and the efficiency is lower than

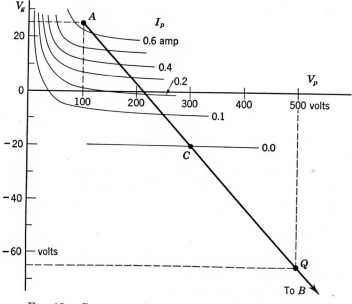

FIG. 18.   GRAPHICAL ANALYSIS FOR CLASS C AMPLIFIER.

that given by Eq. 54.   Then it is necessary to obtain values for I_1 and $I_p(\text{av})$ by the graphical method described in Sec. 13.

The following example will serve as another illustration of this method. Let $E_b = 500$ volts, $E_c = -65$ volts, $E_a = 400$ volts, and $E = 90$ volts. The swing of V_p is then from 100 to 900 volts, while V_g swings from $+25$ volts to -155 volts. These data locate the operating line AQB on the plot of Fig. 18.   The characteristics of the tube (one side of a type 829-B tube) are represented in this plot as a family of *constant-current* curves.   When these constant-current curves are available the analysis is greatly simplified, as will be seen.   If they are not available it is necessary to proceed as in the example of Sec. 13.

From the intersections of the operating line with these constant-current curves we may read directly values for V_p and I_p.   For example, for point P, $V_p = 185$

volts, $I_p = 0.30$ amp.   Then $e_a = 500 - 185 = 315$ volts, $\cos \theta = {}^{315}\!/_{400} =$ 0.785, and $\theta = 38°$.   In this manner values are obtained for plotting I_p as a function of θ, as in Fig. 19.   From this plot, $I_p(\text{av})$ may be obtained, by dividing the area between the plot and the axis by the base-line distance of 360°.   The value of I_1 also may be obtained from this plot, by means of the Collins templates, or by integrating a plot of $I_p \cos \theta$, which is represented by the broken line in Fig. 19. According to Sec. 6, Chapter 4, the area under this plot, divided by half the base-line distance (180°), will give the value of I_1.*   For this example, $I_p(\text{av}) = 0.129$ amp, and $I_1 = 0.236$ amp.   [Note that $I_p(\text{av})$ is also the value read by a d-c meter in the plate circuit.]   From these values we may compute, from Eqs. 51, 52, and 53, that $P_{\text{in}} = 64.5$ watts, $P_{\text{out}} = 47.2$ watts, and the plate efficiency is 73 percent. Note that Eq. 54 gives 80 percent as the maximum possible efficiency for these values of E_a and E_b.   The resonant circuit may now be designed as in Sec. 14, starting with R_0.   The value for R_0 is $E_a/I_1 = 400$ volts$/0.236$ amp $= 1700$ ohms.

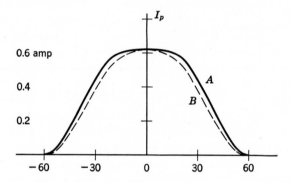

Fig. 19.   Angle (Time) Plot for Current in Class C Amplifier. $A—I_p$ $B—I_p \cos \theta$.

19. Grid-Input Power.

Since there is grid current in a class C amplifier during a part of each cycle the input source must be able to supply *power* to the grid circuit; if this source is an amplifier it must be a power amplifier.   The power delivered to the grid circuit at any instant is the product of the input voltage, e, and the grid current, I_g. The latter may be represented by an harmonic series which includes the d-c (average) value, $I_g(\text{av})$, and the first-harmonic component of amplitude $I_1(\text{grid})$.   If then e is sinusoidal, as has been assumed, with an amplitude E, the average power input to the grid circuit is

$$P_g = \tfrac{1}{2}EI_1(\text{grid}) \tag{55}$$

Since the grid pulses are quite narrow a fair approximation (on the safe side because it is too big) may be obtained by taking $I_1(\text{grid})$ equal

---

* A very useful approximate method for evaluating I_1 and $I_p(\text{av})$ is described in F. E. Terman, *Radio Engineers' Handbook*, pp. 446–448.

to twice I_g(av). A better value may be obtained by the procedures mentioned above for I_p. The grid-bias battery (or resistor) absorbs a part of this power equal to $E_c I_g$(av). The remainder is dissipated as heat by the grid. In designing the circuit care must be taken that this grid dissipation does not exceed the safe value given for the tube.

20. Class B Radiofrequency Amplifiers. In Sec. 15 it has been pointed out that class C amplifiers are intended primarily for operation at constant output, with constant input. They will not serve to amplify a signal having a variable amplitude, such as amplitude-modulated radio signals, since the output- and input-voltage amplitudes are not proportional. A class C amplifier is not a linear amplifier in this respect. This lack of linearity is illustrated by the example cited in Sec. 18. If the amplitude of the signal in that example were reduced from 90 volts to 45 volts the value of E_a would not drop from 400 volts to 200 volts, but from 400 volts to zero, since, as may be seen in Fig. 18, a signal having only 45 volts peak value is below cut-off during the entire cycle.

An amplifier which is suitable for the amplification of modulated signals is obtained by reducing the bias to just above cut-off, so that the plate-current pulses are a full half-cycle wide. The amplifier then is a class B amplifier. Although its efficiency is not much better than half that of a class C amplifier, a class B amplifier will amplify signals from zero amplitude up to the maximum, and the proportionality between input and output may be made quite good by careful design of the circuits.*

21. Electronic Oscillators. In Sec. 24, Chapter 6, it is explained how electrical oscillations may be self-excited by feeding back to the grid of an amplifier tube a sufficiently large fraction of the output potential, in the proper phase. In that section we were concerned with linear operating conditions, where the output is small and may be limited to a small, nearly straight portion of the transfer characteristic. Oscillators of this type are often useful for laboratory work, but they are too inefficient and develop too little power for most applications. Class C operation, on the contrary, is in many ways ideal for producing self-oscillation, and most electronic oscillators belong to this class. Consider, for example, the circuit of Fig. 14. If a second coil is wound with about one-quarter as many turns as in the coil L, on a coil form of somewhat smaller radius so that it may be slipped inside L, the emf induced in this coil will be approximately one-quarter of the out-

---

* The design of RF class B or "linear" amplifiers is discussed in detail in F. E. Terman, *Radio Engineers' Handbook*, pp. 452–458.

put voltage. If now this coil is connected into the input circuit in place of the signal source, with its polarity such that V_g is increased when V_p is decreased, then this circuit should be able to supply its own signal, and continue in oscillation *once it is started*. Since the grid is biased beyond cut-off this oscillation will not start of itself, but must be initiated by some external means. A momentary grounding of the grid will generally supply the impulse needed to set it into oscillation.

A more practical oscillator circuit is shown in Fig. 20. First of all, the pentode of Fig. 14 is replaced by a triode. In radiofrequency

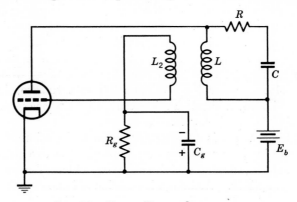

FIG. 20.   PLATE-TUNED OSCILLATOR.

circuits the chief purpose of a screen grid is to prevent feedback from the plate to the grid circuit. In an oscillator, obviously, this function is not needed, and a triode is then the more efficient tube. Second, the grid bias in Fig. 20 is produced by the charge in condenser C_g. Before the oscillation starts the charge in C_g is zero and the grid is at cathode potential. The plate current is large, and conditions are favorable for the start of oscillation by any transient disturbance. This biasing thus circumvents the difficulties mentioned above, when the bias is fixed by a battery. As the oscillation builds up, however, the pulses of grid current charge C_g, with the polarity indicated in Fig. 20, thus building up a negative grid bias which approaches the peak value of the grid-potential oscillation. In this respect the grid and cathode of the triode function as a diode rectifier, with R_g the load resistor and C_g the filter condenser, as described in Chapter 1. Almost any capacitance will serve for C_g, providing it is not too small. (The product of R_g and C_g must be large in comparison with the time of one oscillation.) The value of R_g is more critical, since it determines in large part the amount by which the grid potential swings positive each cycle.   The circuit will oscillate for a wide range of values for R_g, but oscillates best when R_g has been adjusted somewhat carefully.

22. Oscillator Circuits.   Electron-tube oscillators take many forms, but all must possess certain fundamental characteristics.   All must have a resonant circuit, or tank circuit, and the connections to the

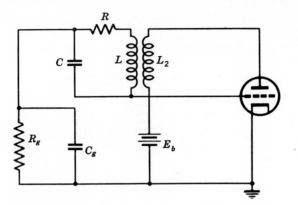

FIG. 21.   GRID-TUNED OSCILLATOR.

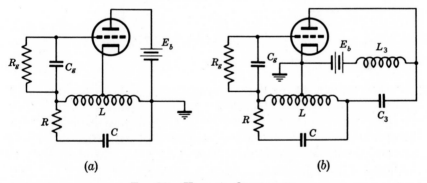

FIG. 22.   HARTLEY OSCILLATOR.

plate and grid from this tank circuit must always be such that the a-c potentials at the grid and at the plate are of opposite sign, or 180 degrees out of phase.   Figures 20, 21, 22, and 23 show several standard forms of oscillator circuits.   In Fig. 20 the tank circuit is in series with the plate, and the grid potential is derived from the tank circuit by mutual induction between the coil L and the coil L_2 in series with the grid.   In Fig. 21 these elements are interchanged, but in either figure the a-c potentials of grid and plate are of opposite sign when the coil L_2 is connected properly.   In the Hartley circuit of Fig. 22a the grid and plate potentials are given opposite signs by connecting the grid and the plate to opposite ends of the same coil.   Figure 22b shows the same a-c circuit, with the plate-supply battery, E_b, connected differently.   In Fig. 22a, E_b is in series with the plate.   Since this power supply almost always has large capacitance to ground, the ground connection must be placed as shown, and this forces the cathode potential to oscillate.   If the heater supply to the cathode also has appreciable capacitance to ground this capacitance is in parallel with the plate end (the right-hand end in Fig. 22a) of the tank coil.   The

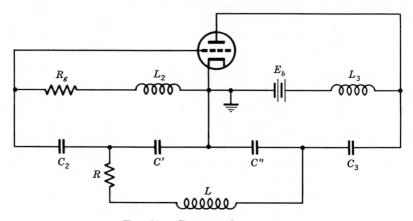

FIG. 23.   COLPITTS OSCILLATOR.

circuit of Fig. 22b allows both E_b and the cathode to be at ground potential, but puts the choke-coil, L_3, in parallel with the plate end of the tank coil.   The choke-coil, L_3, presents a low impedance to direct current, but has so high an impedance at the oscillation frequency that there is very little alternating current in it.   The condenser C_3 is practically a zero impedance for alternating current but an open circuit for direct current.   The Colpitts circuit of Fig. 23 has a divided condenser, C' and C'', in place of the divided coil of the Hartley circuit. In other respects it is very similar.   It is obvious that the parallel d-c feed is necessary for this circuit.

23. Loading Radiofrequency Amplifiers and Oscillators.   In the radiofrequency amplifier and oscillator circuits up to and including Fig. 23 the load is represented by a resistance, R, in series with L and C.   For most applications the useful load ("pay load") is not a series resistance, but is located outside the resonant circuit, in a secondary circuit which is coupled in some manner to the tank circuit.   For example, the load may be an antenna, electromagnetically coupled to the tank coil, L, as indicated in Fig. 24; or it may be a volume of conducting material, placed near or inside the tank coil so that it may be heated by eddy currents. Whatever the load may be, if it is coupled electromagnetically to the tank circuit it may. be represented as a resistance, R_2, in series with a secondary coil, L_2, as in Fig. 25. If Z_2 is the impedance of this secondary circuit, and M the mutual inductance between L and L_2, this coupled circuit of Fig. 25 is equivalent to the original tank circuit with its series resistance increased by an amount R_2' and its inductance decreased by the amount L_2'. These changes are given by*

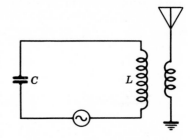

$$R_2' = (M^2\omega^2/Z_2{}^2)R_2 \qquad (56)$$

and

$$L_2' = (M^2\omega^2/Z_2{}^2)L_2 \qquad (57)$$

FIG. 24.   ANTENNA LOAD.

The effective series resistance, R, is the sum of R_1, the resistance of the coil itself, and R_2', which is proportional to M^2. Since M may be made variable, it is possible thus to adjust R to a value suited to the circuit in which it appears.

Less frequently the external load is coupled to the tank circuit electrostatically, through its oscillating electric field. For example,

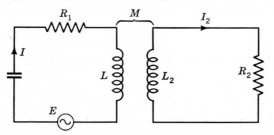

FIG. 25.   SCHEMATIC LOAD.

a body made of poorly conducting material may be heated by placing it between plates which are connected to the terminals of the condenser in the tank circuit. In some applications these plates form the tank condenser. For these conditions also the load may be represented as an effective series resistance. Thus it is possible always to regard the load in radiofrequency amplifier and oscillator circuits as a series resistance.

* Derivations for these equations are found in any book on circuit theory. For example, see F. E. Terman, *Radio Engineers' Handbook*, p. 149.

24. Tapped Coil Loading. Still another means for adjusting the load for an oscillator, a radiofrequency amplifier, or other circuit having a resonant-circuit output, is a coil which is provided with intermediate connection points, or "taps," so that the connection to the driving circuit (e.g., to the plate of an amplifier tube) may be shifted along the coil to a point at which best results are obtained. When connection is made to some intermediate point, x, Fig. 26, on a coil having a high Q-factor, the alternating potential, e_x, at that point is less than the potential, e_a, at A, the end of the coil, *but it is in phase with* e_a. Hence, if the circuit is tuned to parallel resonance with the driving connection at A, it will be still in resonance for connection at x.

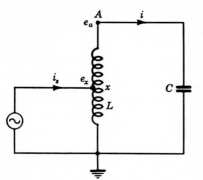

To show this, let the inductance of the whole coil be L, the inductance of from x to ground be L_x, and the mutual inductance between the parts to either side of x be M.

FIG. 26.   TAPPED-COIL LOAD.

If the Q-factor for the coil is high, the current i which circulates in the resonant circuit, at resonance, is so much larger than i_s, the current from the source, that i_s may be neglected in comparison. The potential e_a, at A, has the magnitude

$$E_a = L\omega I \tag{58}$$

and leads i in phase by 90 degrees. The magnitude of the potential e_x, at x, is

$$E_x = (L_x + M)\omega I \tag{59}$$

This potential also leads i in phase by 90 degrees, and is in phase with e_a. It follows that

$$E_x/E_a = (L_x + M)/L \tag{60}$$

For a short cylindrical coil with windings close together, the ratio E_x/E_a is approximately equal to the ratio of the number of turns from each point to the ground.

It follows that, at resonance, i_s and e_x are in phase and hence the impedance between x and ground is a pure resistance, R_x. Its value may be obtained from the equation for power input to the coil. For the same power dissipation, P, the inputs at x and at A may be expressed, in rms values, as

$$P = E_x^2/R_x = E_a^2/R_0 \tag{61}$$

Hence

$$R_x = (E_x^2/E_a^2)R_0 \tag{62}$$

25. Graphical Analysis for Oscillators. An electron-tube oscillator may be regarded as a self-driven class C amplifier, and may be analyzed graphically in almost the same fashion. Only one difference must be noted: in the oscillator the power required to drive the grid circuit is taken from the tank circuit, and must be included as a part of the total load. The procedure to follow is best explained by working through an example.

Consider the design of a Hartley oscillator, to the following specifications.

Type 800 tube. $E_b = 1000$ volts E_a (peak) $= 800$ volts

$$E_c = -140 \text{ volts} \qquad E \text{ (peak)} = 260 \text{ volts}$$

Let us suppose now that, following the procedures outlined in Secs. 13 and 18, we have obtained the following current values from the tube characteristics.

$$I_p(\text{av}) = 83 \text{ ma} \qquad I_1 \text{ (plate)} = 144 \text{ ma}$$

$$I_g(\text{av}) = 26 \text{ ma} \qquad I_1 \text{ (grid)} = 48 \text{ ma}$$

The power values then may be computed.

D-c plate input $= I_p(\text{av}) \times E_b = 0.083 \times 1000 \qquad = 83.0$ watts

Output power $= \frac{1}{2}I_1$ (plate) $\times E_a = 0.144 \times \frac{800}{2} = 57.6$

Grid circuit power $= \frac{1}{2}I_1$ (grid) $\times E = 0.048 \times \frac{260}{2} \quad = 6.2$

Grid bias power $= I_g(\text{av}) \times E_c = 0.026 \times 140 \qquad = 3.6$

Grid dissipation $= 6.2 - 3.6 \qquad\qquad\qquad 2.6$

Since the grid power must be supplied from the output, the *net* output power is $57.6 - 6.2 = 51.4$ watts.

Next we compute the potential difference from one end of the coil to the other. In the Hartley circuit the coil is partly in the plate circuit and partly in the grid circuit, so that the peak value of the alternating potential difference between its ends is $(E_a + E)$, or 1060 volts for our example. The cathode is connected to the coil at a point approximately one-fifth of the way from the grid end.

To design the tank circuit we find first its parallel resistance, R_0, from the net power and the potential difference, $E_a + E$.

$$P = (E_a + E)^2/2R_0 \qquad \text{or} \qquad R_0 = (E_a + E)^2/2P \tag{63}$$

For our example, $R_0 = (1060)^2/(2 \times 51.4) = 10,920$ ohms. Assume that Q_0 is 30. Then the series resistance, R, is R_0/Q_0^2, or 12.2 ohms. The reactance of the coil is $X_0 = R_0/Q_0 = 364$ ohms, and the peak value of the tank current, I, is $\frac{1060}{364} = 2.91$ amp, the rms value 2.06 amp.   The required values for L and C may be computed from X_0 and the frequency.   For operation at 5.00 Mcps, L should be 11.6 microhenries, and C, 87.5 mmf.

The total series resistance is 12.2 ohms.   Let us suppose that we have measured the a-c resistance of the coil by itself to be 2.0 ohms.   This leaves 10.2 ohms to represent the external load, which may be coupled to the tank circuit in one of the ways mentioned in Secs. 23 and 24.   Thus, if this load is an antenna transmission line it may be coupled to the tank coil by a small secondary coil, as in Fig. 24, or the two ends of the line may be connected to taps on the coil, near the ground point.

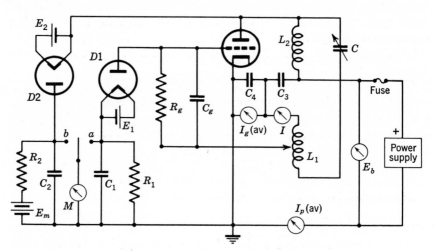

FIG. 27.   CIRCUIT FOR EXP. 27.

R_1, R_2—1 megohm.
C_1, C_2—0.05 µf.
C_3—0.01 µf, 600 volts, mica.
C_4—0.005 µf, mica.
C_g—0.0002 µf, mica.
C—0.0005 µf, 1000 volts.
E_m—45 or 90 volts, as needed.

Fuse—⅛ amp.
I_p(av)—50-ma range.
I_g(av)—10-ma range.
I—RF meter, thermocouple type
(several ranges, from 0.2 to 1.0 amp).
M—vacuum-tube voltmeter, 100 volts
d-c range.

26. Experiment 27.   Oscillator Performance.   The circuit to be studied is diagrammed in Fig. 27.   It is a Hartley circuit, modified to facilitate measurements.   Instructions are given for a type 45 tube. The tank inductance consists of two coils, L_1 and L_2, wound on a common coilform about 2.75 inches in diameter, ½ inch apart.   Each coil has 25 turns of No. 16 insulated wire, and L_1 has taps at 3, 6, 9, and 12 turns from the grid end.   The adjacent ends of L_1 and L_2 are at zero alternating potential and L_1 is at zero d-c potential, but L_2 is at the potential E_b.   The tuning condenser, C, must have plates spaced far enough apart to operate safely at 1000 volts peak value. Condensers C_3 and C_4 must be good mica condensers; C_3 must be especially good, since it is in the tank circuit and carries the tank current, I, with a voltage E_b between its terminals.

The quantities which may be measured directly are $I_p(\text{av})$ and $I_g(\text{av})$, the direct currents to plate and grid, and the RF (radiofrequency) current I in the tank circuit. We need to know also E_a and E, the amplitudes of the RF voltages in the plate and grid circuits, and these are determined indirectly, by measuring V_m, the minimum value of the plate potential (the plate-potential *trough*), and V_h, the maximum positive value of the grid potential, with the diode circuits indicated at the left in Fig. 27. Condenser C_1 is charged to the potential V_h through $D1$, and V_h is then measured with the high-resistance voltmeter, M, connected to a. To measure V_m the diode $D2$ must be reversed, and will not conduct at all unless, in the plate-potential trough, its cathode potential is less than its plate potential. This condition is produced by the battery if E_m is greater than V_m; then C_2 charges to the potential V_m, which is read by M if it is switched to b. It is obvious that

$$E_a = E_b - V_m \qquad E = -E_c + V_h \qquad (64,65)$$

The grid bias, E_c, equals the negative of the product of R_g and $I_g(\text{av})$. These diodes must be well insulated, have individual filament batteries, and be mounted so that the terminals connected to plate and grid of the oscillator tube have low capacitance to ground. Each may be a diode-connected 1H4-G or type 30 triode, with one large flashlight cell to supply filament current. Although the normal filament requirement for this tube is 2.0 volts, cathode emission sufficient for this purpose is produced at 1.5 volts. The cell for $D2$ must be supported clear of its surroundings to minimize its capacitance to ground.

Contrary to the practice in earlier experiments, it is desirable to build this circuit up in permanent form with all parts, except meters and power supply, mounted on a baseboard. It is well to cover the lower side of this baseboard with sheet copper or zinc, and make all ground connections to this metal sheet. Note that neither terminal of C is at ground potential, so that it is necessary to put an inch or so of fiber rod between the rotor shaft and the control knob. All connections in which there is RF current should be made short, but connections to d-c meters, power supplies, etc., in which there is no RF current should be long enough to keep these parts a foot or more away from the RF circuits. Be cautious in working with this circuit: keep in mind that the plate side of the tank circuit is at high d-c potential, and both sides are at high RF potentials. With this circuit it is possible to study the performance of an oscillator under a variety of conditions.

Part I.   Effect of Feedback.   The grid connection to L_1 is made with a small bronze spring-clip, clipped to one of the taps. The amount of feedback may be varied by changing this tap connection.

(a) Start with the spring-clip at the end of L_1, R_g equal to 50 K, and no load other than the RF meter. After the cathode is hot raise E_b gradually, watching the current meters. If oscillation starts properly, (with some grid current, and a moderate plate current) raise E_b to the working value of about 300 volts. Set the frequency somewhere in the AM broadcast range and read all meters. The frequency may be measured in any convenient manner. If a frequency meter is not available, place a small radio receiver several feet away from the oscillator and tune it to a radio station at the desired frequency. Then change the oscillator frequency until a beat-frequency whistle is heard. The frequency of the oscillator equals the radio-station frequency when this beat-note frequency is reduced to zero. (Caution: If the receiver is too close several sets of beat-notes are heard, as a result of harmonics. Move the receiver so far away that only one is heard.)   Read the current meters and the values of V_h and V_m.

(b) Reduce E_b to zero, move the spring-clip to the next tap, and repeat (a). Observe how much this change alters the frequency, and in which direction. In this manner take data for the remaining taps, or for as many as possible. Oscillation may not occur for the lowest taps, or may occur with excessive plate current. Do not exceed 50 ma at 300 volts d-c. Compute E_g, E, and E_a, and represent these results as plots of these quantities as y, with number of turns in L_1 as x. Plot also the RF current, I, to the same x values. For good operation V_h should be less than V_m; 0.7 to 0.9 times V_m is considered best. Note which tap on L_1 meets this condition.

Part II.   Effect of Grid-bias Resistor.   Clip the grid to the tap on L_1 found best in Part I and vary R_g, taking observations in the same manner as in Part I. The range for R_g may be determined by a preliminary trial. Observe what happens if R_g is too high, or too low. Plot curves having the same y-values as in Part I, but with $1/R_g$ as x. Explain carefully why E_g and I change in the manner shown by these data.

Part III.   Effect of D-C Supply.   Set the grid tap and R_g at the values found most satisfactory in Part I and II, and take data as before for values of E_b from 300 volts down to zero (or to where oscillation stops), by 25-volt steps. Plot curves having E_b as x and E_c, E,

E_a, and I as y. For good operating conditions these plots should be nearly straight lines.   Explain why.

Part IV.   Effect of Load.   Increase the load by putting a 10-ohm, 20-watt, non-inductive resistor in series with the RF ammeter.   Set the grid-clip at the end of L_1, with R_g equal to 50 K, and observe the currents and voltages with E_b equal to 300 volts.   Compare these results with those of Part Ia, and discuss carefully any differences.

Part V.   Angles of Operation.   The part of each cycle during which there is grid current is measured by $2\theta_g$, the angle of operation for grid current.   It is evident that θ_g is obtained from

$$E \cos \theta_g + E_c = 0 \qquad (66)$$

Likewise the duration of the plate-current pulse is measured by its angle of operation, $2\theta_a$.   Since plate current is zero when $(\mu V_g + V_p)$ is zero or negative, θ_a is given by

$$\mu(E \cos \theta_a + E_c) + (E_b - E_a \cos \theta_a) = 0 \qquad (67)$$

Compute θ_a and θ_g from the data of Parts Ia and IV.   It is interesting to compute also these angles for the other data, to show by plot how they vary with the various operating conditions.   This may be done if time permits.

Part VI.   Power.   For the data of Parts Ia and IV compute the power input, power output, and efficiency, following the example worked out in Sec. 25.   For exact computations it is necessary to know I_1 and I_1(grid), the first-harmonic components of plate current and grid current, and these quantities cannot be measured in any simple manner.   However, we may obtain fair results from the direct currents and the angles of operation, by the following approximation. For very narrow current pulses (θ_a less than 35 degrees) I_1 is approximately equal to $2I_p$(av).   For larger angles I_1 may be computed to within a few percent from the following empirical equation.*

$$I_1/I_p(\text{av}) = 2.00 - 6.6 \times 10^{-3}(\theta_a - 35°) \qquad (68)$$

Equation 68 may be used also to compute I_1(grid).   If output power is computed for data taken with the spring-clip not at the end of L_1 the a-c potential may be computed from E by means of the approximation mentioned in Sec. 24.

---

* This equation is derived from data given by F. E. Terman and W. C. Roake in "Calculation and Design of Class C Amplifiers," *Proceedings of the I.R.E.*, Vol. 24 (April 1936), p. 620.   These data are reproduced in Fig. 77, p. 447, of F. E. Terman's *Radio Engineers' Handbook*.

Finally, for the data of Parts Ia and IV compute Q_0 (from I_1 and I), R (from I and the net power output), R_0 (from Q_0 and R), and X_0 (from I and E_1).   Be careful to avoid confusion between rms and peak values.

27. Other Oscillator Circuits.   Electron-tube oscillators are considered further in Chapter 13, with particular reference to operation at very high frequency, and also in Chapter 14, where the emphasis is upon precision of operation and frequency control.   The control of oscillator frequency by the mechanical vibrations of a quartz crystal is discussed in Chapter 14.   Since changes in load may alter slightly the frequency of an oscillator it is general practice to generate oscillations with a *master oscillator* of comparatively low power and good frequency stability and obtain the desired power from a class C amplifier which is driven from the master oscillator.   Very often the master oscillator is crystal-controlled.   The circuits are designed so that the power expended in driving the amplifier is relatively only a light load on the oscillator.   Details of these and other circuits employed in radio communication are found in the many textbooks on this topic.

PROBLEMS

Abbreviations: mv = millivolt; μf = microfarad; $\mu\mu$f = micro-microfarad; mh = millihenry; μh = microhenry; μ-mho = micromho; cps = cycles per second; Kcps = kilocyles per second.   Problems marked * involve complex-impedance methods.

1. In a series-resonant circuit L is 255 μh, C 1580 $\mu\mu$f, R (total resistance) 7.0 ohms, and the emf is 2.50 volts rms.   (a) Compute the frequency at which the current is a maximum, and the value of this current.   (b) Compute the potential difference between the condenser terminals at this frequency.   (c) Compute the Q-factor.

2. (a) Compute the current in the circuit of Prob. 1 for a frequency which is 10.0 percent above the resonant frequency.   Neglect R in this computation.   (b) Show the extent to which R is negligible in (a).   (c) Compute the current in this circuit at a frequency 10.0 percent below f_0.

3.* Solve Prob. 2 without neglecting R, by means of complex impedances.

4. A series circuit is designed to resonate at 1800 Kcps, with a Q-factor at resonance of 83 and a total resistance of 12.3 ohms.   Compute the values for L and C.

5.* (a) For the circuit of Prob. 4 find the frequency at which the current has half the maximum value.   (b) Find the phase angle for this current.   Solve by the complex-impedance method or the vector method.

6. A free oscillation is set up in a series circuit made up of a 450-mh inductance, a 0.100-μf capacitance, and a 185-ohm resistance.   Compute (a) the frequency of oscillation, (b) the Q-factor of the circuit, (c) the time required for the current amplitude to fall to half its initial value.

7. A free oscillation, in a series circuit having L = 320 mh, C = 0.0470 μf, and R = 140 ohms, has an initial current amplitude of 0.500 amp.   (a) Compute

the frequency of oscillation. (b) Compute the initial amplitude of the potential difference between the condenser terminals. (c) Compute these current and voltage amplitudes at a time $\frac{1}{60}$ sec later.

8. Complete the proof begun in the footnote under Sec. 4.

9. In the circuit of Fig. 6a take $C = 195 \ \mu\mu f$, $L = 168 \ \mu h$, $R = 42.0$ ohms, and assume that a current oscillates in this circuit with a constant amplitude of 0.75 amp. Compute (a) the series-resonant frequency, (b) the Q-factor, (c) the potential difference between A and B which is produced by this oscillation, and (d) the power required to keep this current constant. (e) From this power compute the current I_a. Check your value by Eq. 19.

10. Circuit of Fig. 6a. $f_0 = 450$ Kcps, $X_0 = 195$ ohms, $Q_0 = 65.0$, and E_a = 125 volts rms. (a) Compute the value of I_a and of the oscillatory current I. (b) Compute L, R, and C.

11. Represent the circuit of Prob. 10 by the equivalent circuit of Fig. 6b, making the approximations noted in Sec. 7. From this circuit find the amplitude and phase of the current I_a at 490 Kcps.

Solution: At 490 Kcps the reactance of C is $-(^{450}\!\!/_{490})195 = -179$ ohms, and the magnitude of $I_1 = 0.698$ amp. L' is put equal to L and the reactance at 490 Kcps is $(^{490}\!\!/_{450})195 = 212$ ohms; the magnitude of $I_2'' = 0.589$ amp. Since $R_0 =$ 12,700 ohms, $I_2' = 0.0098$ amp. Hence I_a has a component 0.0098 amp in phase with E_a, a component 0.109 amp in quadrature. The resultant is 0.1095 amp and leads E_a by 84.9°.

12. Circuit of Fig. 6a. $L = 285 \ \mu h$, $C = 450 \ \mu\mu f$, $R = 4.60$ ohms, and $E_a = 85$ volts rms. Represent this circuit by the equivalent circuit of Fig. 6b, making approximations as in Prob. 11. (a) Compute I_a at the resonant frequency, and at 1.300 times the resonant frequency. (b) From these results, by proportion, compute E_a at each frequency for a constant value of 2.10 ma for I_a.

13. Circuit of Fig. 6a. $L = 88.0 \ \mu h$, $R = 5.90$ ohms, $f_0 = 1400$ Kcps. Represent this circuit by the equivalent circuit, making approximations as in Prob. 11, and assume a constant driving current, I_a, of 0.58 ma. (a) Compute the value of E_a at 1400 Kcps. (b) Compute E_a at 1600 Kcps.

14. Circuit of Fig. 6a. $X_0 = 1000$ ohms, $Q_0 = 5.00$, $f_0 = 100$ Kcps. (a) Compute L, R, and C. (b) Draw to scale the vector diagram (Fig. 7) for this circuit, for $E_a = 100$ volts and $f = 50.0$ Kcps. (b) From this diagram find the phase angle between I_a and E_a. Check your value against the one given in plot B, Fig. 9.

15.* Solve Prob. 14 by the complex-impedance method.

16. Solve Prob. 14 by the equivalent-circuit method employed in Prob. 11. Compare your result for phase angle with the value given in plot B, Fig. 9, and observe the error introduced by the approximations made in this method, when the Q-factor is small.

17. Circuit of Fig. 8a. $f_0 = 950$ Kcps, $R = 6.91$ ohms, $C = 128 \ \mu\mu f$, $r_p = 800$ K, $g_m = 930 \ \mu$-mhos. (a) Represent this circuit by the equivalent circuit of Fig. 8c and evaluate the impedance components in it. (b) Compute from this circuit the output at 950 Kcps for a signal, e, of 32.0 mv.

18.* Find the amplitude and phase of the output from the circuit of Prob. 17 at 960 Kcps, for the same input.

19. For the circuit of Prob. 17 compute (a) the Q-factor for the load alone, and (b) the Q-factor for the circuit, including the tube. From these Q-factors then compute the width of the resonance curve, $f_1 - f_2$, as defined by Eq. 44, for (c) the load alone, and (d) the entire circuit.

20. Derive Eq. 44.   Suggestion: First show that, when the output is down to 0.71 times the maximum, the admittance of L and C in parallel equals in magnitude the admittance due to the resistors.

21. From the I_p, V_p characteristics of a 6L6 tube (Appendix 5), triode-connected, plot a set of constant-current curves having V_g as y, V_p as x. See Fig. 18, and Fig. 4, Chapter 2.   Take currents of 25, 50, 75, 100, and 125 ma.

22. Plot the transfer characteristic and the operating line for an RF amplifier utilizing a 6L6 pentode under the following conditions. $E_b = 350$ volts, $E_c = -40$ volts, plate-potential trough $= 50$ volts, grid-potential peak $= +5.0$ volts. Follow the procedure illustrated in Fig. 12.

23. (a) From the results of Prob. 22 make an angle (time) plot for I_p and determine from it the average plate current and the first-harmonic amplitude.   (b) Then compute the power input to the plate, the a-c power output, and the plate-circuit efficiency.

24. The following data are taken with a circuit corresponding to Fig. 27. E_b $= 1250$ volts, $R_g = 5430$ ohms, plate-potential trough $(V_m) = 130$ volts, grid-potential peak $(V_h) = 120$ volts, direct current to plate $= 105$ ma, direct current to grid $= 33$ ma, and tank current $= 1.15$ amp rms.   The tube has an amplification factor of 15.0.   From these data compute (a) amplitudes for the alternating voltages to plate and grid, (b) angles of operation for plate and grid currents, (c) the cut-off potentials for plate and grid (at which plate current and grid current become zero).

25. From the data given in Prob. 24 compute (a) the approximate amplitude of the first-harmonic components of plate and grid current, (b) the d-c power supplied to the plate, (c) the power supplied to the grid circuit, and (d) the net power output.

26. From the data given in Prob. 24 compute for the tank circuit, at a frequency of 760 Kcps, (a) the effective series resistance, (b) the reactance X_0, (c) the inductance (L_1 and L_2 in series), and (d) the capacitance of C.

CHAPTER 11

Special Functions

1. Introduction. Amplification is undoubtedly the most important function performed by electron-tube circuits, and the greater part of this book has been given over to consideration of this function and its applications, which include oscillators as well as many types of amplifiers. However, amplification is only one of many functions accomplished by electronic circuits. Among the others are some which depend upon the linear characteristics of electron tubes—are, indeed, amplification functions in disguise—but many are possible only because of *non-linear* characteristics possessed by electron tubes. Rectification, as discussed in Chapter 1, and the operation of gas-tube circuits, are examples of this non-linear class of functions. A survey of the more valuable of these special functions is given in this chapter and in the one following. In this chapter we shall be concerned chiefly with basic functions in their relation to fundamental tube or circuit characteristics, and the applications here considered are incidental, or illustrative of the principles involved. Left over for Chapter 12 is a group of closely related functions, namely modulation, detection, and frequency conversion.

2. Electrical Differentiation. The mathematical processes of differentiation and integration may be performed electrically with a variety of circuits involving resistors, inductors, and condensers. Electron tubes are necessary to such circuits only as amplifiers, to compensate for the attenuation in the process, or as cathode-follower units, for the purpose of changing impedances to more suitable values. We shall confine our attention here to circuits containing resistors and condensers only. Figure 1a shows a simple differentiating circuit. For it we may write

$$e_1 = q/C + iR = q/C + e_2 \tag{1}$$

If we now chose R and C so as to make e_2 very much smaller than e_1 at the highest frequency to be considered, we may neglect e_2 in Eq. 1 and write

$$e_1 = q/C \tag{2}$$

345

Differentiation gives

$$de_1/dt = i/C \tag{3}$$

and

$$e_2 = Ri = RC(de_1/dt) \tag{4}$$

The potential e_2 is thus proportional to the *time derivative* of e_1. The source impedance has been neglected in this analysis. When this

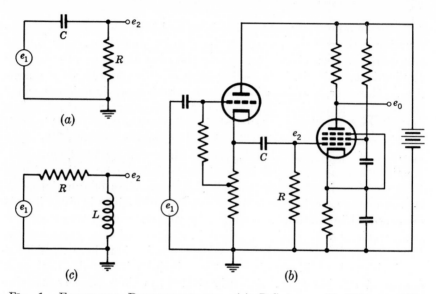

Fig. 1. Electrical Differentiation. (a) R,C type. (b) With amplifier. (c) R,L type.

impedance cannot be neglected we may interpose a cathode-follower unit, as in Fig. 1b. This change provides a small and known resistive source impedance; furthermore, it puts no appreciable load upon the source. Its function might be described as isolating the source from the differentiating circuit. Since e_2 is very small compared with e_1, it is usually necessary to follow the differentiating circuit with an amplifier, as indicated also in Fig. 1b.

Let us now examine the conditions to be met by R and C. If e_1 is periodic, and the *highest* frequency to be considered is f, then the resistance R must be very small compared with the reactance $1/2\pi fC$, or $2\pi fCR$ must be very small compared with unity. A second derivative may of course be taken by following the amplifier of Fig. 1b by a second differentiating circuit of this kind.

3. Electrical Integration.   Integration may be accomplished electrically with the circuit of Fig. 2a.   The equation for this circuit is

$$e_1 = iR + q/C = iR + e_2 \tag{5}$$

If we now choose R and C such that e_2 is always very much smaller

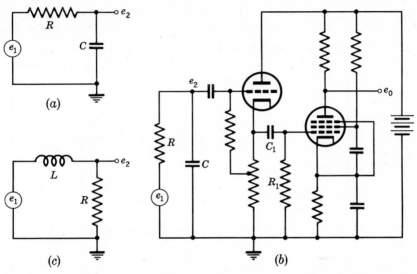

Fig. 2.   Electrical Integration.   (a) R,C type.   (b) With amplifier.   (c) R,L type.

than e_1, at the *lowest* frequency involved, Eq. 5 may be written

$$e_1 = iR \tag{6}$$

and

$$e_2 = \frac{q}{C} = \frac{1}{C} \int i \, dt = \frac{1}{RC} \int e_1 \, dt \tag{7}$$

The potential e_2 thus is proportional to the *time integral* of e_1.   If f is the *lowest* frequency to be considered, the reactance $1/2\pi fC$ must be very small compared with the resistance R, or $2\pi fCR$ must be very large compared with unity.   Contrast this with the condition for differentiation, as expressed in Sec. 2.

The source impedance is less troublesome in this circuit than in the differentiating circuit, unless it is very high.   Instead, the output impedance is critical, and should be infinite.   It is best to put e_2 onto the grid of a cathode-follower unit, followed by an amplifier, as shown in Fig. 2b.

4. Demonstration Experiment 1. One application for such an integrator is to display hysteresis curves on an oscilloscope screen. Connect the winding of an iron-cored choke-coil (or the primary winding of a transformer, with the secondary open) in series with a non-inductive resistance R_2, of low value, to the 60-cps a-c line. See Fig. 3. The input should be variable, by means of an auto-transformer or a series resistor. The potential of the point A is proportional to the magnetizing current, hence to the magnetizing field, H. Connect this point to the horizontal-deflection terminal of the oscilloscope. The

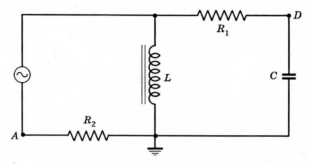

FIG. 3. DEMONSTRATION EXPERIMENT 1.

integrating circuit, R_1, C, is connected in parallel with the choke-coil, as shown, and the point D is connected to the vertical-deflection terminal. (The amplifier in the oscilloscope takes the place of the amplifier in Fig. 2b.) The potential drop across the choke-coil is proportional to dB/dt; hence the potential at point D is proportional to the flux density, B, and the pattern on the oscilloscope screen is a hysteresis loop for the core material. Replace the choke-coil with a pure resistance comparable in value with the choke-coil impedance. If the integration circuit is a good one the pattern then will be a circle when the amplitudes are equal. The value for R_1 should be 50 K or more, and for C, at least 4 mf.

5. Reactance Tubes. A direct application for the differentiation and integration circuits of Secs. 2 and 3 is found in the *reactance tube,* an electronic circuit element whose impedance may be made an almost pure reactance which may be varied electrically, by changing the grid bias. A reactance tube which serves as a variable condenser is diagrammed in Fig. 4a. The currents i, i_1, and i_p are the changes which result from a change, e_1, in the plate potential of the tube. The differentiating element is R_1 and C_1, as in Fig. 1a. If R_1 and C_1 are chosen according to the specifications given in Sec. 2 the current i_1 is practically equal to $C_1 \, de_1/dt$, and e_2 is $R_1 C_1 \, de_1/dt$, as given in Eq. 4. It follows that the current i_p is

$$i_p = g_m e_2 + \frac{e_1}{r_p} = g_m R_1 C_1 \frac{de_1}{dt} + \frac{e_1}{r_p} \tag{8}$$

and

$$i = i_1 + i_p = (C_1 + g_m R_1 C_1) \frac{de_1}{dt} + \frac{e_1}{r_p} \tag{9}$$

It is evident from Eq. 9 that $g_m R_1 C_1$ is equivalent to a capacitance. If

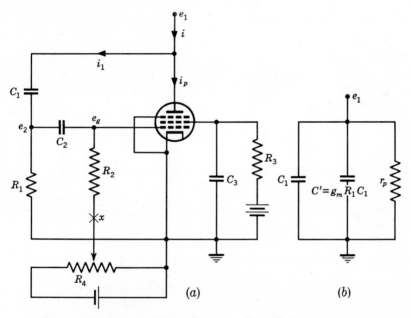

FIG. 4. REACTANCE-TUBE CIRCUIT. Capacitative reactance.

we represent this capacitance by C'

$$C' = g_m R_1 C_1 \tag{10}$$

For example, if R_1 is 1000 ohms, C_1, 50 $\mu\mu f$ (micro-microfarads), and g_m, 2000 micromhos, C' has the value 100 $\mu\mu f$.

An equivalent a-c circuit is shown in Fig. 4b. Since C' is proportional to g_m, and g_m depends upon the grid potential, it is possible to vary C' electrically; the change may be from one steady value to another, made by a change in grid bias, or it may be a periodic change, produced by a low-frequency a-c signal introduced at x, Fig. 4a. Both types of change occur in applications. So far in this discussion we have assumed R_2 and C_2 to be so large as to have no appreciable effect.   When the operation of this circuit is confined to the neighborhood of a single frequency, R_2 and C_2 may be given values which will increase the phase shift, so as to make e_g exactly 90 degrees ahead of e_1 in phase.   It is even possible to make the phase enough greater than 90 degrees to cancel out the resistive term in Eq. 9, thereby making the circuit a pure reactance at that frequency.

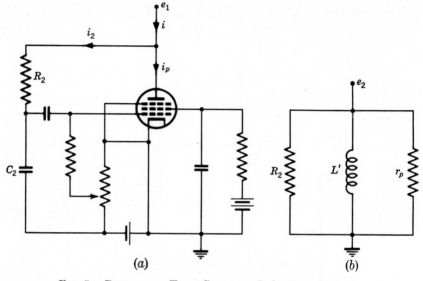

$$(a) \qquad\qquad\qquad\qquad (b)$$

Fig. 5.   Reactance-Tube Circuit.   Inductive reactance.

Figure 5a shows a reactance-tube circuit which is inductive.   In this circuit the grid potential is supplied from an integrating network, R_2 and C_2, and it is evident, by reasoning similar to that employed above, that

$$i = \frac{e_1}{R_2} + \frac{e_1}{r_p} + \frac{g_m}{R_2 C_2} \int e_1 \, dt \qquad (11)$$

or

$$i = e_1 \left(\frac{1}{R_2} + \frac{1}{r_p} \right) + \frac{1}{L'} \int e_1 \, dt \qquad (12)^*$$

The circuit of Fig. 5a is thus equivalent to that of Fig. 5b, and L' is equivalent to

$$L' = R_2 C_2 / g_m \qquad (13)$$

* This equivalence is shown by setting the last term equal to i', multiplying this equation by L', and then differentiating both sides.

For example, if R_2 is 1 megohm, C_2, 150 μμf, and g_m, 1500 micromhos, L' is 0.10 henry.   Since $1/L'$ is proportional to g_m, its value may be varied by changing the grid bias.

For a single frequency, Eqs. 9 and 11 may be written in complex-number notation as

$$I = j\omega(C_1 + g_m R_1 C_1)E_1 + \frac{E_1}{r_p} \tag{14}$$

and

$$I = E_1\left(\frac{1}{R_2} + \frac{1}{r_p}\right) + \frac{g_m}{j\omega R_2 C_2}E_1 \tag{15}$$

Applications for reactance tubes include automatic tuning for radio circuits, and frequency modulation.*

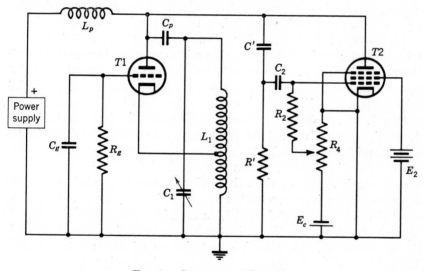

Fig. 6.   Circuit for Exp. 28.

6. Demonstration Experiment 2.   The operation of a reactance tube may be demonstrated with the oscillator circuit of Fig. 6, having a reactance tube in parallel with its tank circuit.   Tune a radio receiver to some radio station (better still, a signal from a RF signal generator), set the grid bias for $T2$, the reactance tube, to some fixed value, and then tune the oscillator to produce a beat-note whistle with the radio-station signal.   Any change in the grid bias of $T2$ will now change the

* L. B. Arguimbau, *Vacuum-Tube Circuits*, p. 467, gives further details concerning these circuits.

oscillator frequency and produce a change in the frequency of this beat-note. If, for example, the oscillator frequency is *above* that of the radio station, the beat-note will rise if the grid bias is made more negative, fall if it is made less negative. The explanation for this change in beat-note frequency shows clearly that the tube reactance is capacitative.

If the differentiating circuit in Fig. 6 is replaced by the integrating circuit of Fig. 5 the reverse changes are observed. Experiment with different values of R_2 and C_2 to find the ones which serve the demonstration best.

7. Experiment 28. Reactance Tube. The circuit of Fig. 6 may be employed to measure the effective capacitance (or inductance) for a reactance tube. For this purpose a calibrated condenser, C_s, of small capacitance (75 to 100 $\mu\mu$f) is connected in parallel with the tank condenser, C_1, and some means is provided to measure the grid bias, V_g. In place of a radio signal it is better to provide a second oscillator of fixed frequency, f_0, and about 5 watts power, and a radio receiver with headphones is best if other experiments are being carried out in the same laboratory. Keep the two oscillators as far apart as possible and still detect the beat-note at some point between them. To minimize frequency drift, hold the d-c supply constant for both oscillators.

Part I. Capacitative Reactance. With the circuit as shown in Fig. 6, set V_g so negative that the plate current is zero. Set C_s to its top value, and tune the oscillator to f_0 (zero beat-note) by means of C_1. Raise V_g until plate current starts, then raise it by equal steps to nearly zero potential. As V_g rises the oscillator frequency falls unless the tube reactance is compensated by changing C_1 or C_s. Leave C_1 fixed (except to correct for drift, as explained later) and decrease C_s at each step to return the oscillator frequency to f_0. The decrease in C_s measures C', the effective capacitance of the reactance tube. Frequency drift may cause some difficulty in making these measurements. If the circuits are well made the drift will be slow, and may be corrected for sufficiently well by frequently checking back to the starting point.

Plot a curve with C' as y, V_g as x. Determine the range of V_g over which the change in C' may be considered linear. Most applications are limited to this range. Obtain the values for C_1 and R_1, and compute g_m for each observation, by means of Eq. 10. Plot a curve with g_m as y, V_g as x.

Part II. Inductive Reactance. Replace the differentiating circuit with the integrating circuit of Fig. 5. Use the circuit constants given in the example in Sec. 5. Start as before with zero current, but with

C_s set to its *lowest* value. As the plate current increases, C_s must be increased to maintain the frequency constant. Prove that L', the equivalent inductance for the reactance tube, equals L_1C_1 divided by the increase in C_s. Obtain values for L_1 and C_1, compute L', and plot a curve with $1/L'$ as y, V_g as x. Again the linear portion of this plot represents the practical working range. Obtain the values for C_2 and R_2, and compute g_m for each observation, by means of Eq. 13. Plot these values along with those obtained from Part I.

8. Mixer Circuits. The *addition* of two emf's may be accomplished electrically, either by putting the two sources of emf in series, or by means of the mixer circuit of Fig. 7, with the sliding contact, S, at the

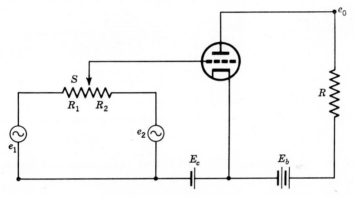

FIG. 7.   MIXER CIRCUIT.

midpoint on the voltage-divider, R_1R_2. The latter arrangement has the advantages that each source has one terminal grounded, and that the emf's may be added in any proportion, depending upon the position of S. The alternating grid potential is given by

$$e_g = \frac{R_2e_1 + R_1e_2}{R_1 + R_2} \tag{16}$$

The electron tube in this circuit serves to amplify the result, and should be operated within its linear range. Its most important function, however, is to serve as a *buffer* tube, to prevent loading of the mixer circuit by presenting to it a very high impedance (the grid impedance). If amplification is not needed, this buffer tube can be operated as a cathode-follower.

If the two sources must be separated electrically it is possible to connect them as shown in Fig. 8a, one in the grid circuit, the other between the cathode and the ground. This arrangement possesses two possible disadvantages: (1) the source connected to the cathode must be capable of supplying power to the circuit, since it is in the cathode circuit, and (2) unless the impedance of this source is zero for current of the other frequency it will cause degeneration for that current. It is possible also to connect one source to the control grid, the other to the screen grid of a pentode, as in Fig. 8*b*. Similar comments apply to the source connected to the screen grid, since there is current in the screen-grid circuit. In both circuits of Fig. 8 there is some coupling between e_1 and e_2 by way of the interelectrode capacitances.

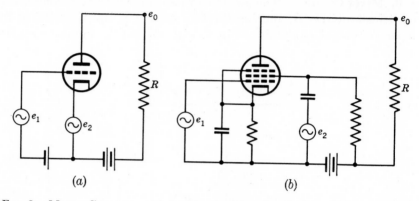

(a)　　　　　　　　　　　　　　　　(b)

Fɪɢ. 8. Mɪxᴇʀ Cɪʀᴄᴜɪᴛꜱ. (a) Inputs at grid and cathode. (b) Inputs at grid and screen grid.

9. Electronic Multiplication. Multiplication of two emf's takes place in any mixer circuit if it is biased to operate over a non-linear portion of its transfer characteristic. Consider, for example, a mixer circuit having the transfer characteristic represented in Fig. 9. If we take the vertical line through the grid-bias value, E_c, as an axis for e_g, the variational part of the grid potential, the equation for this characteristic may be represented by the power series

$$I_p = I_0 + I_1 e_g + I_2 e_g{}^2 + I_3 e_g{}^3 + \text{etc.} \qquad (17)$$

If now e_g is the sum of e' and e'',

$$
\begin{aligned}
I_p = I_0 &+ I_1 e' + I_2 e'^2 + I_3 e'^3 + \cdots \\
&+ I_1 e'' + I_2 e''^2 + I_3 e''^3 + \cdots \\
&+ 2 I_2 e' e'' \\
&+ 3 I_3 (e' e''^2 + e'^2 e'') + \cdots
\end{aligned} \qquad (18)
$$

Unfortunately, the one term in Eq. 18 which contains $e'e''$, the product of the two emf's is intermixed with many others. In certain special cases it is possible to separate this term out electrically from the others;

some of these cases will be considered in Chapter 12.   In general this is difficult, if not impossible, and other means have been sought for electronic multiplication.

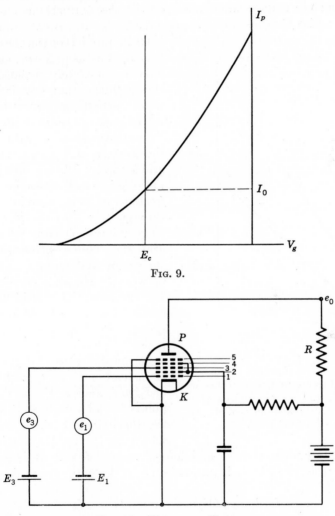

Fig. 9.

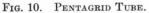

Fig. 10.   Pentagrid Tube.

10. The Pentagrid Tube.   Much better electronic multiplication is produced with the pentagrid tube which has been developed especially for frequency conversion (see Sec. 18, Chapter 12), one of the practical applications of electronic multiplication.   This tube is represented schematically in Fig. 10.   Grid 5 is a suppressor grid, and is connected directly to the cathode. Grids 2 and 4 are connected together and surround grid 3; they serve as a special kind of screen grid, which is held at a constant positive potential, as usual. The two sources of signal emf are connected to grids 1 and 3 respectively, as shown in Fig. 10. Bias for these grids is provided by E_1 and E_3.

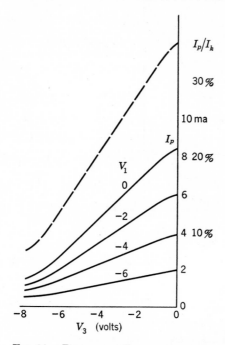

Grids 1 and 2 control the *cathode* current, just as in a pentode; grid 3 is so completely shielded from the cathode that its influence upon the cathode current is effectively zero. A part of the electron stream stops at grid 2, but the greater part passes through grid 2, toward grid 3. The potential of grid 3 now determines what *fraction* of this current passes through grid 3 to the plate, and what fraction is turned back to grid 2. These relationships are shown by the plots in Fig. 11, between I_p, the plate current, and V_3, the potential of grid 3, for a 6SA7 tube. Each plot corresponds to a single value of V_1, the potential of grid 1, and a *constant* value of the cathode current, I_k.

Fig. 11. Pentagrid Characteristics. Plots of I_p and V_3, for various values of V_1. *All* fit broken-line plot of I_p/I_k. 6SA7 tube.

If instead of I_p we plot the *ratio* of I_p to I_k against V_3, we find the points for all values of V_1 falling together along a single line, as shown by the broken line in Fig. 11, except for the highest and lowest values of V_3. It is evident that the ratio of I_p to I_k is a function, p, of V_3 only, over this range. That is,

$$I_p/I_k = p(V_3) \qquad \text{or} \qquad I_p = pI_k \tag{19}$$

Over a considerable range of V_3 the plot of I_p/I_k, in Fig. 11, is nearly straight, so that for this range p may be represented by the equation

$$p = I_p/I_k = p_0 + qe_3 \tag{20}$$

In Eq. 20, p_0 is the value of p when V_3 equals the bias potential, E_3, and e_3 is the variational potential of grid 3, measured from the bias value.   Equation 19 then may be written as

$$I_p = p_0 I_k + q e_3 I_k \qquad (21)$$

In contrast with Eq. 18, for multiplication by a curved transfer characteristic, Eq. 21 contains only two terms: one is the desired current component proportional to the product, $e_3 I_k$, the other is the plate current when e_3 is zero.   Generally the latter may be balanced out.

11. Demonstration Experiment 3.   The multiplication of I_k by e_3 which is represented by Eq. 21 may be demonstrated with the test

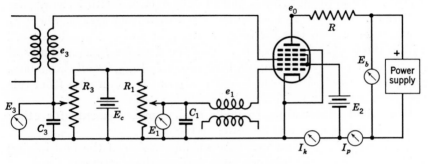

FIG. 12.   PENTAGRID-TUBE TEST CIRCUIT.

circuit in Fig. 12.   For a type 6SA7 tube suitable potentials are: $E_b = 250$ volts, $E_2 = 90$ volts (B-batteries), and $E_1 = -3$ volts. Make R about 10 K, and connect the plate to the oscilloscope.   The a-c signal, e_1, should have about 1 volt amplitude, and produce a good sinusoidal pattern on the oscilloscope screen.   Its frequency may be 60 cps, although 500 to 1500 cps is better.   With no alternating potential on grid 3, vary V_3 by means of the voltage-divider, R_3, and note that the amplitude of the pattern changes with V_3, but its *shape* remains unchanged: all values of I_p are changed proportionally. Next introduce e_3 of the same frequency as e_1.   Since both V_3 and I_k then contain sinusoidal components of the same frequency, the product includes a cosine-squared (or sine-squared) term, which may be resolved into a d-c term plus a second-harmonic term.   Typical second-harmonic distortion then appears in I_p, on the oscilloscope screen.   If e_1 and e_3 are opposite in phase the first-harmonic components at the plate may be made to cancel, by proper adjustment of the magnitudes of e_1 and e_3, leaving only the second-harmonic pattern on the screen.

12. Experiment 29.   Pentagrid Tube Characteristics.   The static characteristics for a pentagrid tube may be studied with the circuit of

Fig. 12. For a 6SA7 tube, fix E_2 at 90 volts (B-batteries) and E_b at about 150 volts, after removing R. Provide meters to measure I_k, I_p, E_1, and E_3. Since there is no current to grids 1 and 3, a single voltmeter may measure E_c, and E_1 and E_3 may be computed from E_c and the readings of calibrated voltage-dividers R_1 and R_3. Note that, when there are no a-c signals, V_1 and V_3 are equal to E_1 and E_3 respectively.

Part I. Observe I_k and I_p as V_1 is varied from zero to the negative value which cuts I_k to zero. Do this for several different values of V_3, and note that V_3 has no effect upon I_k. Plot a curve with I_k as y and V_1 as x. From the data for I_p plot a family of curves with V_1 as x.

Part II. Observe I_p and I_k as V_3 is varied from zero to where I_p becomes zero. Do this for four or five values of V_1, evenly spaced within the working range of V_1. Plot the data for I_p as a family of curves with V_3 as x. Compute the ratio of I_p to I_k for all these data, and plot a curve with V_3 as x and I_p/I_k as y. Determine from this plot the range over which multiplication is satisfactory.

It would be interesting to make similar measurements for other pentagrid tubes, such as 1R5, 6L7, and 6SB7.

13. Electronic Wattmeter.* As an illustration of the multiplying ability of a pentagrid tube we may consider the wattmeter circuit of Fig. 13. For each pentagrid tube the a-c signal, e_1, supplied to grid 1, is a fraction of the potential drop, V, across the load, Z, and the signal, e_3, to grid 3, is proportional to the current in Z. If both e_1 and e_3 are small, so that the change in I_k is linear and Eq. 21 applies, we may write

$$I_k = I_0 + s\,e_1 \tag{22}$$

and

$$I_p = (p_0 + q\,e_3)I_k$$
$$= p_0 I_0 + p_0 s\,e_1 + qI_0\,e_3 + qs\,e_1 e_3 \tag{23}$$

Since the average values of e_1 and e_3 are zero, the d-c plate current *changes* from the quiescent value, pI_0, by an amount qs times the average value of $e_1 e_3$, or by an amount proportional to the average value of VI, the power delivered to Z.

By employing two pentagrid tubes, with the sign of e_3 reversed in the second, it is possible to balance out the quiescent value of the plate potential and measure the d-c change in the plate potential (up at one plate, down at the other) by means of the cathode-follower voltmeter provided by tubes $T3$ and $T4$. Resistors R_7 and R_8, and

---

* See also J. R. Pierce, *Proc. I.R.E.*, Vol. 24, p. 577 (1936.)

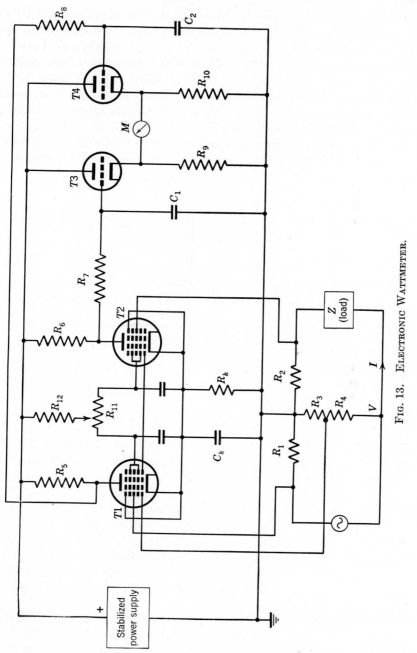

Fig. 13. Electronic Wattmeter.

condensers C_1 and C_2 serve to filter out the a-c components. Meter M reads the d-c potential difference between the cathodes of $T3$ and $T4$, which is almost equal to the d-c potential difference between the plates of T_1 and T_2. The reading of M is adjusted to zero initially by means of the sliding contact on R_{11}. Calibration is made in the usual manner, by means of known current in a pure resistance of known value. The resistances R_1, R_2, R_3, and R_4 should be chosen to keep e_1 and e_3 low, under 1 volt for 6SA7 tubes.

If this circuit is made with two 6SA7 tubes ($T1$ and $T2$), a 6SN7 double triode ($T3$ and $T4$), and a 250-volt power supply, the other

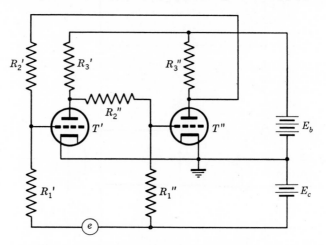

FIG. 14. ECCLES-JORDAN CIRCUIT.

circuit elements may be: R_5, R_6—33 K; R_7, R_8—500 K; R_9, R_{10}— 20 K; R_{11}—a 1-K "potentiometer"; R_{12}—7 K; R_k—approximately 120 ohms (adjust to make the grid bias 3.5 volts); C_1, C_2—0.1 μf; C_k—20 μf; and 4-μf by-pass condensers for the screen grids. The meter, M, should have a range of 1 ma or less and a series resistance of 5 to 10 K. See Chapter 14, Sec. 8, for a discussion of this type of voltmeter. The sensitivity and range of this wattmeter are increased somewhat if R_5 and R_6 are each shunted by a 2-μf condenser, and then the response may be quickened by reducing C_1 and C_2 each to 0.02 μf. A 10-K resistor may be needed in series with each number 3 grid to insure circuit stability.

14. The Eccles-Jordan Circuit. The circuit diagrammed in Fig. 14 appears to be a two-stage, direct-coupled amplifier with positive feedback. Indeed, it does function in that manner if the feedback is kept low enough. In this section, however, we are primarily concerned with its performance when feedback is so great as to render it unstable and useless as an amplifier; it then becomes an Eccles-Jordan circuit, less formally but more descriptively known as a "flip-flop" circuit.

We shall consider here only the symmetrical circuit, with tubes, coupling resistors, and loads the same for each stage as indicated. (For example, R_1 is the common value for R_1' and R_1''.) Let us analyze the operation of this circuit first with coupling so weak that

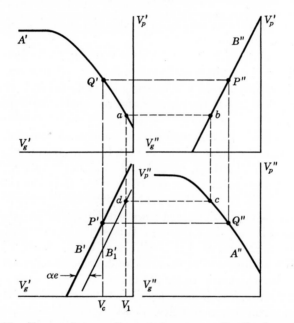

FIG. 15. ECCLES-JORDAN CIRCUIT ANALYSIS.   Feedback small.

it functions as a regenerative amplifier. The V_g, V_p transfer characteristics for tubes T' and T'' are represented in Fig. 15 by plots A' and A''. The coupling between tubes introduces a linear relationship between the grid potential of one tube and the plate potential of the other. Thus V_g'', the grid potential for T'', is given by

$$V_g'' = \frac{R_2E_c + R_1V_p'}{R_1 + R_2} = \alpha E_c + \beta V_p' \qquad (24)$$

The coefficients α and β, which are introduced to simplify later work, have the values

$$\alpha = R_2/(R_1 + R_2) \qquad \beta = R_1/(R_1 + R_2) \qquad (25)$$

Plot B'', Fig. 15, represents Eq. 24. The grid potential V_g', for T'', is similarly related to V_p''. When there is no signal (e is zero)

$$V_g' = \alpha E_c + \beta V_p'' \tag{26}$$

Plot B' represents Eq. 26. If, however, a signal, e, is introduced as indicated in Fig. 14,

$$V_g' = \alpha E_c + \beta V_p'' + \alpha e \tag{27}$$

Plot B_1', which represents Eq. 27, is parallel to B' but displaced horizontally by an amount αe.

Any state of the circuit is represented in Fig. 15 by four points, two of which lie on the A lines, and two on B lines. Thus equilibrium with no signal is represented by points Q', P', Q'', and P''. Furthermore, these four points are at the corners of a rectangle, since Q' and P' have the same abscissas, as do Q'' and P'', whereas the ordinates are the same for Q' and P'', and likewise for Q'' and P'. The effect of a signal e is to change the state of the circuit to that represented by a new rectangle $abcd$. Points a, b, and c remain on lines A', B'', and A'' respectively, but point d lies on B_1'. Note that the change in V_g', from V_c to V_1, is greater than e, as it should be.

The slope of the B lines decreases with increase in feedback, and if the feedback is sufficient to make this slope less than that of the A lines at points Q' and Q'' the equilibrium becomes unstable, like that of a pencil standing on its point. Conditions then are as represented in Fig. 16, in which the rectangle $Q'P'Q''P''$ represents this unstable equilibrium state. It is now possible to construct on these same A and B lines two other rectangles, $u'v'w'x'$ and $u''v''w''x''$, *each* of which represents a *stable* state of equilibrium for this circuit. In the state represented by $u'v'w'x'$ the tube T' is conducting, with V_p' low and V_g' relatively high, whereas current in T''' is zero,* with V_p'' equal to E_b and V_g'' quite negative. In the alternate state, corresponding to $u''v''w''x''$, the conditions in T' and T'' are interchanged, with T''' the conducting tube. This circuit is sometimes referred to as "bi-stable," because of its *two* stable states.

15. Triggering the Eccles-Jordan Circuit. This circuit remains stable about either of these equilibrium states providing that the signal inserted at either grid does not pass the critical "triggering" value. Thus, if the circuit is initially in the state represented by $u'v'w'x'$, with T' conducting, a small negative signal, e, inserted as indicated in Fig. 14, will change its state to that corresponding to $abcd$, Fig. 16, from

---

* It is not necessary for one tube to be cut off, but almost always it is so in practice. Analysis is easier when zero current is assumed.

which it will return to the initial state after e is removed. But if this negative signal exceeds the critical value the circuit will flop almost instantaneously over to the alternate state ($u''v''w''x''$) in which T'' is conducting. A positive signal in excess of a different critical value is then required to return the circuit to its original state. The critical values may be obtained by an extension of the graphical method employed in Sec. 14.

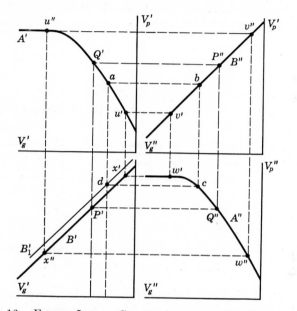

Fig. 16. Eccles-Jordan Circuit Analysis. Feedback large.

Switching occurs in so short a time that the triggering emf may be a pulse of very short duration. If this pulse is introduced by means of a transformer, with its secondary connected in place of e, Fig. 14, the peak of the pulse need not be much higher than the critical d-c value. More often the pulse source is connected between the grid and the cathode of one tube, in series with a small capacitance, so as to be in parallel with R_1. The graphical analysis then does not apply, except for the equilibrium states, and the required switching values are found to be considerably higher. During switching the interelectrode capacitances in the tubes must be considered, and pulse operation is more effective if compensating condensers, C_2' and C_2'', are inserted in parallel with R_2' and R_2'', as shown in Fig. 17. The correct value is found by trial.*

* The effect of these interelectrode capacitances is explained in H. J. Reich, *Theory and Applications of Electron Tubes*, p. 354.

16. Scaling Circuits. The Eccles-Jordan circuit may be converted into a scale-of-two unit which is far quicker in operation than the thyratron type described in Sec. 19, Chapter 9. The example shown in Fig. 17* responds to positive pulses only and produces one positive pulse at the output for every two at the input. The Eccles-Jordan circuit part, provided by tubes T' and T''', differs from the one in Fig. 14 only in the method of biasing, which here is by current in the common cathode resistor, R_4. (This mode of biasing is applicable to most Eccles-Jordan circuits.) This resistor, R_4, serves also as the load

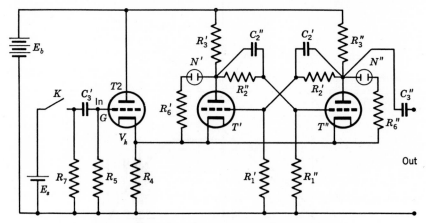

FIG. 17.   SCALE-OF-TWO CIRCUIT.

for $T2$, a cathode-follower tube, when this tube is conducting. Normally $T2$ is not conducting because its cathode potential, V_k, is about 30 volts positive, due to current from T' or T'' alone, and its grid potential is zero. But whenever current is set up in $T2$ by a sufficiently high positive signal at G, this current will always be sufficient to make V_k follow closely the potential at G.

Consider a narrow pulse of positive potential at G, sufficiently high to drive T' and T'' beyond cut-off. After the pulse has passed, V_k returns to its normal value and the Eccles-Jordan circuit returns to either one or the other of its two stable states. Without condensers C_2' and C_2'' the circuit will almost always return to the same state, because of slight differences between its two sides. With these condensers added the circuit will be switched alternately from one state to the other by successive pulses, because of inequalities between the

* For other circuits see H. J. Reich, *Theory and Applications of Electron Tubes*, pp. 623 ff.; Cruft Laboratory Staff, *Electronic Circuits and Tubes*, pp. 850 ff.; and Engineering Research Associates, *High-Speed Computing Devices*, pp. 14 ff.

charges stored in these condensers. Assume that T' is the conducting tube before the pulse acts; C_2' is then charged to a larger potential difference than is C_2'' and this inequality persists during the pulse. As a result the grid potential for T' during the pulse is lower than for T'' and hence the current switches to T'''. Miniature neon lamps, N' and N'', indicate which tube is conducting. Any number of scale-of-two units may be connected in cascade, the output of one to the input of the next, and each unit reduces the count by a factor of 2, as explained in Chapter 9.

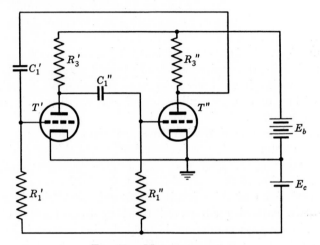

Fig. 18.   Multivibrator.

A pulse-producing unit suitable for demonstrations and testing is provided by E_s, R_7, C_3', and the key K. A small vacuum-mercury switch serves very well for K. A faster-acting key is a tap key modified so as to drive a *clean* platinum wire into a pool of *clean* mercury. Ordinary tap keys and switches are not satisfactory. The time constant for the pulse may be computed from E_s, C_3', and R_5, since the cathode-follower tube isolates the input from the Eccles-Jordan circuit.

17. The Multivibrator. The circuit of Fig. 18 may be regarded as a modified Eccles-Jordan circuit in which condensers C_1 replace the coupling resistors, R_2, in Fig. 14. Like the circuit of Fig. 14, it is violently unstable except for unsymmetrical states in which current is large in one tube, zero (or almost zero) in the other. Unlike the simple Eccles-Jordan circuit, these are states of momentary equilibrium only, and the circuit switches periodically from one extreme to the other and back without the aid of any outside stimulus or signal. The potential changes which make up the cycle are shown by the time plots of Fig. 19. For tube T' these are represented by solid lines, for tube T'' by broken lines. The frequency of alternation may be varied over a wide range by changing the values of R_1 and C_1. If R_1 is much larger than R_3, and E_b and E_c are held constant, the frequency is inversely proportional to $R_1 C_1$.

This circuit has many applications, and its poor waveform is its most valuable asset. For example, it is very useful as a harmonic generator, to "step-up" frequency to an exact multiple of some reference frequency. A unique service, from which it gets its name, multivibrator, is to "step-down" frequency, by operating at a lower or "submultiple" frequency, equal to the reference frequency divided by some exact, integral number. This is accomplished by setting the multivibrator oscillation close to the desired submultiple of the reference frequency, then synchronizing it with the reference oscillation by introducing at the grid of one of the multivibrator tubes a small a-c signal of the reference frequency. This method of synchronization has been described also in connection with the sweep circuit for an oscilloscope, in Sec. 23, Chapter 9. Successive applications of this procedure make it possible to compare very precisely a high-frequency radio signal with the oscillation of the pendulum of a standard clock.

Many variations of this circuit are found. Self-bias is practical, with the two cathodes connected together to a common cathode resistor. No by-pass condenser is needed, since there is current in one tube or the other at all times. Zero bias is also possible. Sometimes the circuit is made unsymmetrical, with different values of resistance, capacitance, and grid bias in the two sides; it then remains for a longer time in one state than in the other. Quite narrow pulses are possible when the dissymmetry is large. Still another variation is a hybrid circuit which flips once. It is switched by an external signal, like an Eccles-Jordan circuit, and flops back to the original state after a short interval.

18. Analysis of Multivibrator Circuit. Let us start with T'' conducting and zero current in T', as represented at the start of the plots in Fig. 19. Initially the grid potential V_g' is below the grid bias, $-E_c$, and V_g'' above $-E_c$, both by considerable amounts, but both potentials are moving toward $-E_c$, because of the electric charge flowing into C_1' (through R_1') and out of C_1'' (through R_1''). The changes in V_g' and V_g'' which are produced by this flow of charges provide the signals to trigger the circuit. The drop in V_g'' is accompanied by a rise in V_p'', as shown, but V_p' remains equal to E_b until V_g' has risen enough to permit plate current to start in T'. Shortly thereafter the circuit switches to the inverse state, with plate and grid potentials for the two tubes interchanged.

The switching requires a time far too short for any measurable charge to flow in either condenser, so that the rise (or fall) of potential for each grid must be exactly the same as for the plate to which the grid is connected by a condenser. Thus the drop in V_g'' is exactly equal to that of V_p', and V_g' and V_p'' rise by exactly equal amounts,

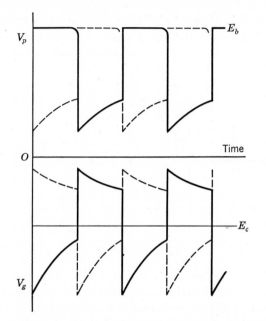

FIG. 19.   MULTIVIBRATOR OSCILLOGRAMS.   Solid line—T', broken line—T''.

as may be seen in Fig. 19.   The process then repeats itself as described above, with the roles of the two tubes interchanged, until a second switching of the circuit returns it to its initial state and completes the cycle.   The time required for each half-cycle is equal to the charge flowing in either condenser divided by the average current in the corresponding grid resistor (R_1' or R_1'') during that time.   Since this charge is proportional to C_1, and the current to $1/R_1$, the period of one oscillation is proportional to $R_1 C_1$, as has been stated in Sec. 17.

19. Experiment 30.   Eccles-Jordan Circuit. In this experiment the performance of an Eccles-Jordan circuit is studied under the various conditions considered in Secs. 14 to 18.   The basic circuit is diagrammed in Fig. 20.   The tube is a 6SN7 twin-triode or a well-matched pair of 6J5 triodes.   Resistors R_1', R_1'', R_2', R_2'', R_3', and

R_3'' must be of good quality, have known values, and be matched to within 1 or 2 percent. Throughout the experiment R_3 is 25 K and E_b is held constant at 250 volts. Voltage-dividers R_5 and R_6 should be of low resistance, not over 5000 ohms for R_5 and 500 ohms for R_6, and R_6 must have a calibrated scale. The voltage V_3, which serves to balance the circuit and also to provide signal emf's, is computed from the reading of R_6 and the sum of E_1 and E_2, which are each about 9 volts.

Part I. Transfer Characteristic. Set R_1 equal to 50 K for each tube and balance the circuit for equal currents (4 or 5 ma) in each tube.

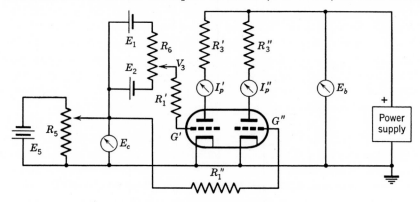

FIG. 20.   CIRCUIT FOR EXP. 30.

Then take data for a transfer characteristic for each tube, by reading plate currents as E_c is varied from zero to current cut-off value. (If there is too much difference between the two tubes, try another pair.) For each tube plot a transfer characteristic having V_g as x and I_p as y.

Part II. Eccles-Jordan Circuit. The circuit of Fig. 14 is made from that of Fig. 20 by adding the resistors R_2' and R_2''; make each 1000 K. If R_1 is left at 50 K the circuit is observed to be symmetrically stable, with equal currents in both tubes. Its condition is then represented by Fig. 15. Observe that a signal, e, produced by changing the setting of R_6, increases the current in one tube while decreasing it in the other, but that the circuit returns to its initial state when e is removed. It is interesting to obtain numerical values for e, $\Delta I_p'$, and $\Delta I_p''$, and to check them against the plot of Fig. 15. Note that $e = \Delta V_3$.

If R_1 is increased to 100 K it is then impossible to have current the same in each tube unless E_c is quite negative, so that both currents are small. As E_c is raised toward zero a point is reached at which current falls in one tube, rises in the other. Observe that, at this point, the slope of the V_p vs. V_g lines (the A lines, Fig. 16) equals $1/\beta$, as predicted in Sec. 16.   Note also that a very small change in V_3 determines which tube gets the larger current when E_c is raised.

In this circuit only E_c, I_p', and I_p'' can be measured directly; plate potentials must be computed from

$$V_p = E_b - I_p R_3 \tag{28}$$

Grid potentials depend upon I_p, and may be read from the plots of Part I. With the larger current in T' set E_c to bring V_g' close to zero, then read I_p' and I_p'' and obtain V_g', V_g'', V_p', and V_p'' in the manner indicated above.   These data now may be checked by means of the graphical construction of Fig. 16.   The A lines are plotted from the data of Part I, and the B lines are plotted from Eqs. 24 and 26.   On these lines locate points u', v', w', and x' according to the data of this part.   If the data are good and the work carefully done these points will lie on the corners of a rectangle.   Explain why. Repeat this procedure with the larger current in T'', and represent these data by a plot of point u'', v'', w'', and x''.

Part III.   Triggering.   Leave E_c at the value set for the latter half of Part II, and show that, if T' is the conducting tube (the tube with the larger current), the circuit cannot be switched to the opposite state by a positive signal at G' but can be switched by a negative signal. Produce these signals by changing V_3, and observe the setting of R_6 at which triggering just occurs.   Observe also the values of current in each tube just *before* the circuit flops over.   Represent this trigger point in the diagram according to Fig. 16 by the four corners of a rectangle.   Note that two corners lie on the A lines and a third on the B'' line, but that the fourth falls on a B_1' line which is displaced by αe from the B' line.   Starting again, with T'' the conducting tube but with all other conditions the same, find the signal that triggers the circuit in the opposite direction.   Take data in the same manner as for the other switching point, and represent this point on the diagram in like manner.

Part IV.   Pulse Triggering.   Triggering the Eccles-Jordan circuit by pulse signals may be studied with either of the pulse-producing units mentioned in Sec. 15 and diagrammed in Fig. 21.   The one of Fig. 21a gives somewhat better agreement with the data of Part III, for reasons stated in Sec. 15.   The transformer must be one designed for pulse operation, with low resistance, and must have a secondary-to-primary turn ratio which is approximately 1:1.   Its secondary is connected in series with R_1'' in Fig. 20.   It can be proved that, if flux leakages and losses in the transformer may be neglected, the height of the pulse produced is approximately

$$E_2 = \frac{N_2}{N_1}\frac{E_7 R_7}{R_7 + R_8} \text{ for closing } K \qquad (29a)$$

and

$$E_2' = (N_2 R_7/N_1 R_8)E_7 \text{ for opening } K \qquad (29b)$$

The time constants are approximately L/R_7 with K open, and L divided by the resistance of R_7 and R_8 in parallel with K closed. The inductance, L, is that of the primary with the secondary open. The unit of Fig. 21b is connected between G', Fig. 20, and ground. For this unit the pulse height on closing K is equal to E_4 but the time constant is indefinite. The pulse on opening K is much lower. The

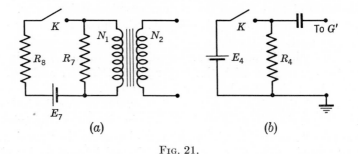

(a)   (b)

FIG. 21.

switch K must be of the type recommended at the end of Sec. 16. The addition of condensers C_2' and C_2'', as shown in Fig. 17, may improve the performance for pulse signals.

If time is available, a study of the scaling circuit of Fig. 17 may be added to this experiment.

Part V. Multivibrator. The circuit of Fig. 20 becomes a multi-vibrator if the grid of each tube is connected to the plate of the other tube by a condenser, as in Fig. 18. A 22-volt battery is sufficient for E_5. Start with 500 K for R_1 and 1.0-μf condensers.* Raise E_c from its most negative value toward zero until current starts; the circuit then should begin to flip-flop, at a rate slow enough to follow with the d-c milliammeters. Observe the range of grid bias over which oscillation occurs, and note how the frequency and amplitude vary with grid bias. For oscilloscopic study both C_1 and R_1 should be variable (by steps). Values may range from 100 K to 1 megohm for R_1, from 0.02 to 0.0005 mf for C_1. Radio resistors and condensers having measured values will serve. Observe and sketch the oscilloscope patterns for the potential at either plate and at either grid, and com-

* These condensers must be good ones, with d-c leakage of not more than 5 μa at 100 volts potential difference.

pare your diagrams with those in Fig. 19.   In practice the grids often
run positive for part of each cycle, and as a result the oscilloscope
patterns are modified considerably from those in Fig. 19.   The frequency may be determined by comparison with the sweep circuit of
the oscilloscope, if the sweep is first calibrated against an audiofrequency signal generator.   If E_b and E_c do not change, a plot made with
f as y and $1/R_1C_1$ as x should be approximately a straight line through

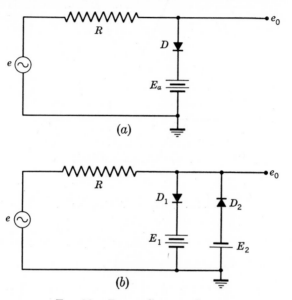

(a)

(b)

FIG. 22.   DIODE CLIPPER CIRCUITS.

the origin.   These observations with the multivibrator also make an
excellent demonstration.

20. Clipper Circuits.   A simple rectifier, such as a thermionic diode
or crystal rectifier, may perform many circuit functions.   The principle underlying many of these functions is called *clipping*.   If we
wish, for example, to set an upper limit to the value of any voltage,
such as the alternating voltage e represented in Fig. 23a, we may do so
with the clipping circuit of Fig. 22a.   Whenever the instantaneous
value of e exceeds E_a, the emf of the battery, the rectifier, D, conducts
and the difference between e and E_a appears as a potential drop across
R (and the internal impedance of the source), not in the output.   The
broken line in Fig. 23a then represents the output, e_0.   Both positive
and negative swings of an a-c voltage may be clipped in this manner
by the circuit of Fig. 22b, the output then appearing as in Fig. 23b.

Clipping is possible also with a triode, by putting a high resistance (R_1, Fig. 24) in series with its grid and driving the grid potential positive, so that there is grid current in R_1. Essentially, the grid is functioning as a diode clipper, the result appearing in the plate circuit, in

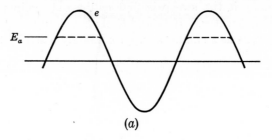

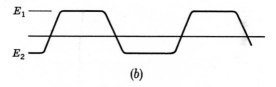

Fig. 23.   Clipped A-C Signals.

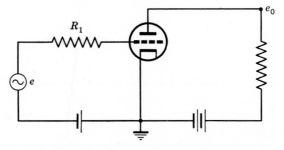

Fig. 24.   Triode Clipper Circuit.

amplified form.   The clipping height is adjusted by means of the grid bias.   Triode clipping in the reverse direction may be produced by driving the grid potential to cut-off value; this is less satisfactory, since distortion becomes large before the plate current is cut off.   Both these clipping methods are possible with a pentode; in addition, the plate potential for a pentode may be limited to a minimum value by a means peculiar to this type of tube.   It may be observed in Fig. 21a, Chapter 5, which represents a typical pentode, that all plate-current lines approach zero along a common curve, so that the intersection between this curve and any load-line represents the maximum possible plate current, and a minimum plate potential, for that load. If the load is large enough this minimum may be reached before the grid potential becomes positive.

21. "Square-Wave" Generator. If a sinusoidal voltage of large amplitude is severely clipped top and bottom, as indicated in Fig. 25a, the result is a voltage which periodically jumps from a positive to a negative value and back again, but holds steady between jumps.

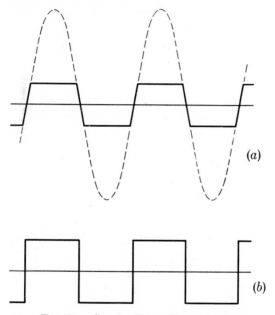

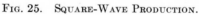

FIG. 25. SQUARE-WAVE PRODUCTION.

The changes may be made very abrupt by having the amplitude for the clipped voltage very much smaller than for the sinusoidal one. If this clipper unit is followed by one or more overdriven amplifier stages, both top and bottom clipping again occurs in each stage and the final output is a "square wave," as represented in Fig. 25b, with practically instantaneous switching from one steady value to the other.

The circuit for a square-wave generator of this type is shown in Fig. 26. It is activated at any desired frequency from a suitable a-c line or signal generator. It is interesting to note that amplitude distortion is relatively unimportant in this circuit, so that pentode clipping is quite satisfactory. Phase distortion, on the contrary, must be avoided, and for this reason the circuit of Fig. 26 is direct-coupled, except for the a-c input to the first grid. The necessary negative-bias values are supplied by a second d-c power supply, of negative polarity, as indicated.   Low output impedance is provided by making the output through a cathode-follower tube, $T3$.   Note that $T3$ and its load, R_9, are connected between the positive terminal of the one d-c supply and the negative terminal of the other, thereby making possible an output which alternates between positive and negative values of equal magnitude.   Adjustment for equality is made by the sliding contact

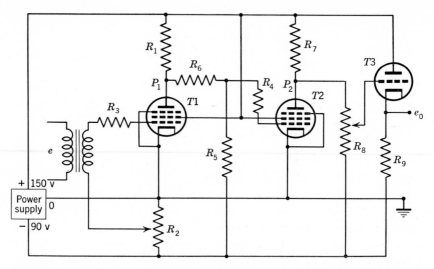

Fig. 26.   Square-Wave Generator.   Sine wave of the desired frequency is introduced as e.

on R_8.   The other adjustment, on R_2, is for equalizing the time intervals for the two parts of the output.   Both d-c sources must be very well regulated; the one of negative polarity may well be a heavy-duty, 90-volt B-battery.

22. Application to Transients.   Many of the uses for square-wave voltages are illustrated in their application to the study of electric transients.   Consider, for example, the charging and discharging of a condenser.   If a condenser C, in series with a resistor R, is connected to a square-wave generator, and if the generator frequency is low enough to allow the transient to die out within the time of one half-cycle, a cathode-ray oscilloscope connected to the terminals of C will show the familiar pattern of Fig. 27a.   In like manner the oscillatory charge or discharge of a condenser C through an inductance L is obtained by connecting C and L in series to the square-wave generator.

The oscillogram of Fig. 27b then may be obtained.   Extension of this method to other combinations of circuit elements is obvious.   Indeed, the transient response of any circuit to a sudden, step-wise change of input may be studied in this manner.   Since, as Heaviside first demonstrated, the frequency response of any circuit is determined by its transient response to a step-wise change of voltage, and may be derived from it mathematically, the square-wave generator may be employed to obtain a quick and complete analysis of the performance of amplifiers, attenuators, all sorts of circuit elements.

(a)   (b)

Fig. 27.   Oscillograms of Transients.

23. Demonstration Experiment 4.   These transient patterns may be demonstrated with any commercial square-wave generator, providing it has a low-impedance output.   A generator may be made according to Fig. 26 if a commercial one is not available.   For many demonstrations a single clipper stage is sufficient, and the second tube in Fig. 26 may be omitted.   Various combinations of R, C, and L may be examined.   Include the filter circuits of Figs. 22, 23, and 24 in Chapter 1.   For this purpose the resistances, capacitances, and inductances have to be made smaller than for a good filter circuit, in order that the transients die away in the time of one-half cycle.   In addition to such built-up circuits, it is interesting to observe the transient response for transformers, amplifiers, delay lines, and any other networks to be found around the laboratory.

24. Electronic Switching.   The output from a pentode may be switched on or off by changing the potential of the screen grid from zero to normal value, or from normal value to zero, and this switching or "keying" may be accomplished by any convenient means.   In the "electronic switch" which serves to superimpose two separate voltage patterns upon a cathode-ray oscilloscope screen these changes of screen-grid potential are supplied by a square-wave generator.   This electronic switch circuit is represented, in simplified form, in Fig. 28.   The potential for each screen grid is supplied from a separate square-wave generator,* the one for the second tube being exactly opposite in phase from the one supplying the first tube, so that the two tubes conduct alternately. The two plates are connected together to a single load, R, and the output to the oscilloscope is from this common plate terminal. Separate signals are applied to each control grid, and the pattern on the oscilloscope screen is produced by whichever tube is conducting at that instant. When the alternations are rapid the two patterns appear superimposed. The switch may be synchronized with the sweep circuit for a sweep frequency of 60 cps or higher. For very low sweep rates the switching may be made quite rapid, so that

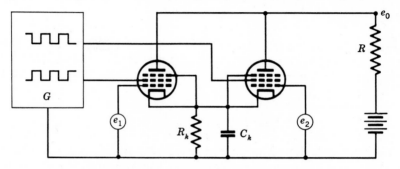

FIG. 28.   ELECTRONIC SWITCHING CIRCUIT.

each pattern appears as a dotted line. Figure 28 shows only the essentials of such a switch; a practical circuit includes means for synchronizing, and for independent adjustment of the position of each pattern on the screen, so that they may appear one above the other, or may overlap by any desired amount.

25. Peaks and Pulses. For applications which require accurate timing, for example, the triggering of thyratron and flip-flop circuits, it is desirable that the signal be sharply peaked rather than sinusoidal, and various methods have been developed for producing such signal peaks. Two of these are shown in Fig. 21 and explained in Sec. 19, Part IV. Another utilizes a saturable reactor, as explained in Sec. 30, Chapter 9. Often the desired signal is a narrow, flat-topped pulse, with quick rise and fall at the beginning and the end, and then a more elaborate circuit, of the kind diagrammed in Fig. 29, is required. The input to this circuit must be a square wave; in Fig. 29 it is produced by the simplest means, a quick-acting switch, S, and a d-c source, E_1. If diodes $D1$ and $D2$ were omitted the potential, V_g, at the grid of the

---

* Two separate clipper sections are supplied from the same multivibrator, one from each tube of the multivibrator, and the multivibrator is usually synchronized with the sweep circuit of the oscilloscope.

amplifier tube would rise sharply at the instant S is switched from y to x, then fall exponentially toward zero.   The diodes serve to clip the top and the bottom of this peak at the levels E_2 and E_3, as represented in Fig. 30a, so that the output from the amplifier is a high negative pulse which is nearly rectangular in form, as represented in Fig. 30b. Only positive input pulses reach the grid; negative pulses, produced by switching S from x to y, are by-passed by the diode $D1$.

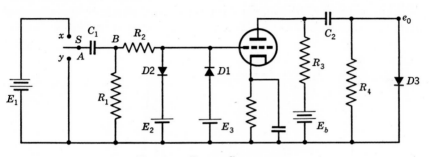

FIG. 29.   PULSE GENERATOR.

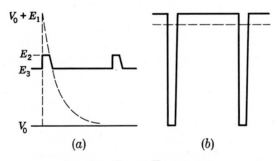

FIG. 30.   PULSE FORMATION.

It is worth while to analyze the operation of this circuit in some details, since it involves processes which have many other applications. In this analysis we shall depart from usual practice and take zero potential at the ground.   When S is at rest in either position, V_g equals E_3, and V_b, the potential at point B, is V_0, equal to $E_3R_1/(R_1 + R_2)$. At the instant S is switched from y to x, V_a jumps from zero to E_1, and V_b jumps to $E_1 + V_0$, then starts to fall exponentially toward V_0, as indicated in Fig. 31a.   As long as V_b is above E_2, diode $D2$ conducts and V_g remains constant at E_2.   The width of this pulse at the top corresponds to the time taken for V_b to fall from $E_1 + V_0$ to E_2.   If R_2 is much greater than R_1 this time is determined by E_1, E_2, R_1, and

C_1, and is approximately

$$t_1 = R_1C_1 \log_e (E_1/E_2) \tag{30}$$

Diode $D2$ no longer conducts after V_b falls below E_2, and V_g then follows V_b down to E_3. Diode $D1$ then becomes conducting and V_g stops at E_3, but V_b continues down to V_0. When E_3 is close to E_2, the signal at the grid is a low, nearly rectangular pulse, which is inverted and increased in height by the amplifier. The third diode, $D3$, is called a "clamping" diode, since its function is to anchor the output at zero value between pulses. Without $D3$ the output would level off so

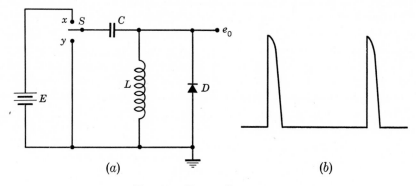

FIG. 31.   PULSE GENERATOR.

that the *average* value would be zero, and the zero line would correspond to the broken line in Fig. 30b. With $D3$ in the circuit the condenser C_2 charges up until the highest portion of the output potential lies on the zero line. (The time constant, C_2R_4, must of course be very large as compared with the time interval between pulses.)

Another means for producing a quite rectangular pulse from a square wave is illustrated in Fig. 31a. If the diode, D, is removed and S is switched from y to x the resonant circuit, L,C, is shock-excited into a damped oscillation such as represented in Fig. 27b, with the first swing positive. With D present the oscillation starts in the same manner when S is switched from y to x, but at the first reversal of potential the diode becomes a conductor which short-circuits L and thereby damps out the remainder of the oscillation. This diode also suppresses *all* of an oscillation which starts in the negative direction (produced by switching S from x to y). The output potential thus consists of positive pulses of the form represented in Fig. 31b. Each pulse is approximately one quarter-cycle long. Its peak may be clipped square with a second diode in series with a suitable battery, as in Fig. 22a, so as to form an almost rectangular pulse. A diode employed as in Fig. 31a to suppress an oscillation beyond the first pulse is called a *damping diode*.

26. Demonstration Experiment 5. The pulse-forming circuits of Figs. 29 to 31 should be demonstrated with an oscilloscope. Generally the amplifier in the oscilloscope is sensitive enough to take the place of the one shown in Fig. 29, and only the input network is needed. Any square-wave generator will provide E_1; a frequency of 60 cps and an amplitude of about 10 volts are recommended. Make R_1 10 K, R_2 100 K, and C_1 variable from 0.01 to 1.0 μf. Obtain E_2 and E_3 from 6 dry cells connected in series. Tap off the middle for E_3; and vary E_2 from 4.5 to 9 volts by means of a 1000-ohm voltage-divider connected across the top 3 cells. Diodes $D1$ and $D2$ may be crystal rectifiers of the 1N34 type.

For the circuit of Fig. 31, L may be an air-core coil such as the one described in Sec. 11, Chapter 10, and C a variable condenser capable of tuning it to between 300 and 1000 cps. The diodes may be of the 1N34 type. A square-wave amplitude of 5 to 10 volts is sufficient, and 1.5-volt clipping is satisfactory.

PROBLEMS

1. In a differentiating circuit (Fig. 1a) C is 300 $\mu\mu$f, R is 2500 ohms, and the input is 25 volts rms at 16,000 cps. (a) Compute the amplitude and phase of de_1/dt. (b) Compute E_2 by the approximate method. (c) Compute E_2 by the exact a-c method. (d) Thence obtain the amplitude error and the phase error for differentiation by this circuit at this frequency.

2. In a differentiating circuit (Fig. 1a) C is 250 $\mu\mu$f, R is 3000 ohms, and E_1 is 18.4 volts rms at 12,000 cps. (a) Compute the output. (b) Assume that the source has an internal resistance of 10 K, and find the amplitude and phase errors due to this source impedance.

3. A differentiating circuit (Fig. 1a) is designed to have E_2 only one-twentieth of E_1 at 15,000 cps. Compute the value for C, if R is 1000 ohms.

4. Verify the following statement: For good differentiation the output, e_2, must always be very small compared with the input, e_1.

5. Show that the circuit of Fig. 1c is a differentiating circuit and derive the equation relating e_2 to de_1/dt. (NOTE: This circuit is much less sensitive to source impedance than the one of Fig. 1a.)

6. Show that the input impedance of the circuit of Fig. 1c is practically independent of frequency over the good working range, whereas the input impedance of the circuit of Fig. 1a is inversely proportional to frequency.

7. In the circuit of Fig. 1c, R is 100 K, L is 0.110 henry, and E is 15.0 volts rms at 8000 cps. Compute (a) the amplitude and phase of de/dt, (b) the current, neglecting L, and (c) E_2, from the approximate current. (d) Redetermine E_2 by exact a-c circuit methods and obtain the amplitude and phase errors of the approximate method at this frequency.

8. Diagram an amplifier circuit suitable for use with the differentiating circuit of Fig. 1c. Consider whether tube capacitances are troublesome factors.

9. In the circuit of Fig. 2a, R is 170 K, C is 0.250 μf, and E_1 is 17.5 volts rms at 50 cps. (a) Compute the amplitude and phase of $\int e_1\,dt$. (b) Compute the current in R, neglecting C. (c) Compute E_2 from this current. (d) Compute E_2 by exact a-c methods and obtain the amplitude and phase errors for (b).

10. (a) Show that the circuit of Fig. 2c is an integrating circuit and derive the equation between e_2 and $\int e_1\,dt$. (b) State the conditions for good integration by this circuit. Cf. the statement made near the end of Sec. 3.

11. Compare the dependence of input impedance upon frequency for the circuits of Figs. 2a and 2c, over the range of good integration.

12. Design an amplifier circuit suitable for use with the integrating circuit of Fig. 2c.

13. In the circuit of Fig. 2b it is assumed that the reactance of C_1 is negligible at the lowest frequency involved. What effect is produced if C_1 does not meet this condition? Discuss this question in terms of integration and differentiation.

14. In the reactance-tube circuit of Fig. 4, R_1 is 12,400 ohms, g_m is 1325 μ-mhos, and the desired "electronic" capacitance, C', is 215 μμf. Find the necessary value for C_1.

15. It is assumed that the reactance of C_2, in the circuit of Fig. 4a, is negligible at the frequency of operation. Discuss the effect of making C_2 too small to meet this condition, and show by vector diagram how it is possible to give C_2 such a value that i is exactly 90 degrees out of phase with e_1, at one frequency.

16. Show that, if the reactance tube in the circuit of Fig. 6 is replaced by the reactance tube of Fig. 5, an increase in g_m will cause an increase in frequency of oscillation.

17. Prove Eq. 16, for the mixer circuit of Fig. 7.

18. In the mixer circuit of Fig. 8a, E_1 is 45 mv at 1800 cps, E_2 is 60 mv at 650 cps, g_m is 1650 μ-mhos, r_p is 12.1 K, and the load is 55 K. Assume that the source of e_2 is of negligible internal impedance. (a) Compute the magnitude and phase with respect to the input, at each frequency. (b) Compute the power input to the circuit by e_2, and compare it with the power output at the same frequency.

19. In the mixer circuit of Fig. 8b the load is 45 K, E_1 is 22.5 mv at 950 cps, and E_2 is 450 mv at 1600 cps. The tube is a 6J7 pentode having the tube factors listed in Sec. 26, Chapter 5. (a) Compute the a-c components of plate current and output voltage for each frequency. (b) Compute the power input to the circuit by e_2 and compare it with the power output at the same frequency.

20. A mixer tube (Fig. 7) is biased to have the transfer characteristic shown in Fig. 9, for which the equation may be taken as

$$I_p = 4.50 + 3.00e_g + 0.48e_g{}^2 \text{ (ma)}$$

Its input is determined by E_1, 500 mv at 450 cps, and E_2, 1500 mv at 60 cps, and the slider is set so that R_2 equals $2R_1$. (a) Compute the first-harmonic currents for each signal. (b) Describe the appearance of the product term and compute its maximum amplitude. (c) Compute the amplitude of the second-harmonic current for each signal.

21. The following data are found for a certain pentagrid tube: For a bias of -3.5 volts on grids 1 and 2 the cathode current, I_k, is 12.5 ma and the plate current, I_p, is 3.30 ma. The change in I_k for a signal on grid 1, with no signal on grid 3,

is 3.00 ma per volt. The change in I_p/I_k for a signal on grid 3, but none on grid 1, is 4.50 percent per volt. Compute the alternating plate current (a) for 0.85 volt (peak value) on grid 1 at 5000 cps, no signal on grid 3; (b) for 1.75 volts (peak) on grid 3, at the same frequency, and no signal on grid 1; and (c) for both these signals acting simultaneously, but 180 degrees out of phase. Describe the product term in case (c), and find the change in direct current which it produces.

22. An Eccles-Jordan circuit (Fig. 14) operates with 6J5 tubes under the following conditions: $E_b = 250$ volts, $E_c = -29.0$ volts, $R_1 = 100$ K, $R_2 = 900$ K, $R_3 = 24$ K. Assume that T' is not conducting and find (a) the current in T'', (b) the grid and plate potentials for T'', (c) the grid potential for T', and (d) the grid potential for T' at which current just starts in T'.

Solution: α and β are (Eq. 25) 0.90 and 0.100. Equation 24 then is

$$V_g'' = -26.0 + 0.100V_p'$$

If T' is not conducting, V_p' is 250 volts and V_g'' computes to be -1.0 volt. Draw a transfer characteristic for each tube and load and read from it I_p'', 6.7 ma for -1.0 grid potential. The corresponding value of V_p'' is computed from E_b, I_p, and R_3 to be 89 volts. Substitution of this figure into Eq. 26 gives $V_g' = -17.1$ volts. The same result may be obtained graphically, by the construction of Fig. 16. According to the transfer characteristic, current starts in T' at about -15.0 volts, and the circuit flops over very close to this point. Hence the trigger potential for these conditions is only a little more than the difference between -15.0 volts and -17.1 volts, or 2.1 volts.

23. An Eccles-Jordan circuit (Fig. 14) operates with 6J5 tubes under the following conditions: $E_b = 300$ volts, $E_c = -80$ volts, $R_1 = 100$ K, $R_2 = 400$ K, $R_3 = 25$ K. (a) Assume T' conducting and find its grid potential and plate current. (b) Find the grid potential for T''. (c) Find the signal at T' to just start current in T''; this is the approximate triggering signal.

24. The input to the clipper circuit of Fig. 22b is 48 volts rms and E_1 is 10.0 volts, E_2 zero volts. (a) Sketch a time plot for the output. (b) Compute the fractional part of each cycle occupied by the slanting portion.

25. In the circuit of Fig. 22b take E_1 and E_2 each to be 5.0 volts, and compute the rms voltage input required to make a square wave with each slanting portion only $\frac{1}{100}$ cycle wide.

26. In the circuit of Fig. 29, E_1 is 15.0 volts, E_2 is 5.40 volts, E_3 is 5.00 volts, R_1 is 800 K, and C_1 is 0.0120 μf. (a) Find the width of the pulse produced, at top and at bottom. (b) Find the height of the pulse if the tube gain is 17.3.

27. In the circuit of Fig. 31, L is 0.078 henry. (a) Compute the value for C to make the width of the pulse at its base 58 μ-sec. (b) Diagram this circuit with a diode clipper unit added so as to clip these pulses to a height of 4.0 volts. (c) For this modified circuit compute the width of pulse at the top, in terms of its base width, if E_1 is 22.0 volts.

CHAPTER 12

Modulation Processes

1. Modulation Processes. In this chapter, which in many ways is a continuation of Chapter 11, we consider a group of electronic processes which are closely related in at least two respects: first, all are essential to the field of radio communication, and second, all involve application of the same fundamental physical process which, for lack of a better name, we shall call the *fundamental modulation process*. The term *modulation* was first applied to the process now called amplitude modulation, whereby an audiofrequency oscillation is represented as variations in amplitude of a radiofrequency signal or wave. These amplitude variations enable a radio receiver to produce, by another process called detection, a replica of the original audiofrequency oscillation. In this chapter we shall see that both these processes are variants of the fundamental modulation process, which includes also frequency modulation, frequency conversion in superheterodyne receivers, and still other processes which have as yet no commercial applications. A better name is needed for this fundamental process, but none other has yet been given it.

2. The Fundamental Modulation Process. Whenever a circuit is made up wholly of linear impedance elements, such as resistors, condensers, and air-cored inductors, and the input is a sinusoidal voltage of a single frequency, f, the output is an exact replica of the input, except for changes in amplitude and phase. If the input is e, the output, e_0, and $2\pi f$ is represented by ω,

$$e = a \cos \omega t \tag{1}$$

$$e_0 = C \cos (\omega t + \phi) \tag{2}$$

If, in addition to the impedance elements listed above, the circuit includes an electronic amplifier tube, biased to operate over its linear range, the output will still be an almost exact replica of the input within the linear range.* If this linear range is exceeded, however, the output will be distorted. Then, as has been explained in Sec. 6, Chapter

---

* A similar statement may be made for a circuit which includes an iron-cored inductor.

4, the result of distortion may be described as the *production* of components of higher frequencies, which are harmonic multiples of the original frequency.   That is,

$$e_0 = C_1 \cos (\omega t + \phi_1) + C_2 \cos (2\omega t + \phi_2)$$
$$+ C_3 \cos (3\omega t + \phi_3) + \cdots \quad (3)$$

If the input to a *linear* circuit consists of *two* sinusoidal components, of different frequencies, f' and f'', the output will contain components of these frequencies only.   That is, if

$$e = a' \cos \omega' t + a'' \cos \omega'' t \quad (4)$$

then

$$e_0 = C' \cos (\omega' t + \phi') + C'' \cos (\omega'' t + \phi'') \quad (5)$$

On the screen of an oscilloscope this output will appear quite different from the input unless C'/a' equals C''/a'' and ϕ'/ω' equals ϕ''/ω''; and these conditions are not met if the circuit, although linear, has reactive components.   Nevertheless, the output is called *undistorted* unless it includes in addition components of frequencies other than those appearing in the input, and the production of these additional components requires a *non-linear* circuit.   Consider for example the mixer circuit of Fig. 7, Chapter 11.   If it is biased to operate as a linear circuit, the output is an almost exact replica of the input, except for magnitude and sign.   If, on the contrary, it is biased to operate over a curved portion of its transfer characteristic, the output will include higher-harmonic components for each frequency component in the input, just as for each separately.   Furthermore, as we shall demonstrate later, it will include components of frequencies equal to the sum and the difference of the original frequencies, together with other combination frequencies involving the harmonics of the original two frequencies.   These new frequencies are the result of distortion; we may say that they have been *generated* as a result of the curvature of the transfer characteristic.   In general, any non-linear characteristic in a circuit will produce components of new frequencies in this manner.   For example, the reception of sound by the human ear is non-linear for loud sounds, so that when two loud sounds of different frequencies enter the ear together, tones are heard corresponding to the sum and to the difference of the original frequencies.   This is perhaps the earliest known example of this phenomenon.

The production of components of new frequencies as a result of non-linear operation of any device is here called the *fundamental modulation process*, and the additional components are called *modulation products*. The new frequencies are always linear combinations of the original frequencies, made by adding or subtracting them in various ways. For example, if the curvature of our mixer-circuit characteristic is parabolic, and the original frequencies are f' and f'', the frequencies of the modulation products include all possible combinations of f' and f'', taken *two* at a time: $f' + f', f' - f', f'' + f'', f'' - f'', f'' + f'$, and $f'' - f'$. These are recognized as second harmonics for each original frequency, sum and difference frequencies, and zero frequencies ($f' - f'$ and $f'' - f''$) which represent d-c components. On the other hand, if the curvature of the transfer characteristic is cubic, so as to produce only third-harmonic distortion for a *single* frequency, the new components have frequencies obtained by combining the original frequencies *three* at a time: $3f', 3f'', 2f' + f'', 2f' - f'', 2f'' + f', 2f'' - f'$, $2f' - f'$, and $2f'' - f''$. The *order* of a modulation product is determined by the number of times the original frequencies are represented in it. Thus for the first example cited above they are second-order modulation products, for the second example, third-order products.

3. Second-Order Modulation. The origin of second-order modulation terms may be demonstrated mathematically as follows. Let the transfer characteristic for the mixer circuit of Fig. 7, Chapter 11, correspond to the following quadratic equation between I_p, the plate current of the amplifier tube, and e, the a-c component of the grid potential.

$$I_p = I_0 + b_1e + b_2e^2 \qquad (6)$$

Now let e consist of two sinusoidal components of different frequencies, as represented by Eq. 4. Then e^2 will include four new frequencies $f' + f'', f' - f'', 2f'$, and $2f''$, as well as two d-c components. To show this start with

$$e^2 = a'^2 \cos^2 \omega't + a''^2 \cos^2 \omega''t + 2a'a'' \cos \omega't \cos \omega''t \qquad (7)$$

By familiar trigonometric relationships, Eq. 7 becomes

$$e^2 = \tfrac{1}{2}a'^2(1 + \cos 2\omega't) + \tfrac{1}{2}a''^2(1 + \cos 2\omega''t)$$
$$+ a'a'' \cos (\omega' + \omega'')t + a'a'' \cos (\omega'' - \omega')t \qquad (8)$$

Hence

$$I_p = I_0 + \tfrac{1}{2}b_2(a'^2 + a''^2)$$
$$+ b_1a' \cos \omega't + b_1a'' \cos \omega''t$$
$$+ \tfrac{1}{2}b_2a'^2 \cos 2\omega't + \tfrac{1}{2}b_2a''^2 \cos 2\omega''t$$
$$+ b_2a'a'' \cos (\omega' + \omega'')t + b_2a'a'' \cos (\omega'' - \omega')t \qquad (9)$$

In Eq. 9 the first line represents direct current, increased by rectification; the second line, the undistorted, first-harmonic components; the third line, the second-harmonic components; and the fourth line, the components whose frequencies are the sum and the difference of the original frequencies. Since e_0 equals the product of $-I_p$ and the load resistance, these same frequencies appear in the output.

4. Demonstration Experiment 1. Build up the mixer circuit of Fig. 7, Chapter 11. The following circuit constants are suggested for

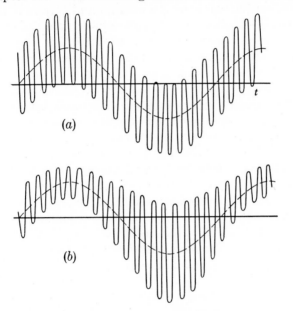

(a)

(b)

Fig. 1.   (a) Mixing.   (b) Modulation.

a 6J5 tube: $R = 25$ K, $E_b = 250$ volts, and E_c variable from 0 to 12 volts.   A 6.3-volt filament transformer will furnish e_1 at 60 cps, and an audiofrequency signal generator, set at about 600 cps, will provide e_2. A 100-K or 200-K radio "potentiometer" serves well for $(R_1 + R_2)$. Connect an oscilloscope to the output.   Set the bias for linear operation and adjust for equal input signals by means of the oscilloscope. When both signals are applied together the oscilloscope pattern appears as shown in Fig. 1a.   Note that the oscillation of higher frequency is swung up and down by the one of lower frequency, but its amplitude remains unchanged.   Next increase the bias negatively until pronounced distortion appears, as shown in Fig. 1b.   Note then that the amplitude for the higher-frequency oscillation varies from a maximum at the bottom of the low-frequency swing, to a minimum at the top. This change in amplitude is modulation, and it may be shown that this higher-frequency oscillation of varying amplitude is equivalent to three components, of frequencies f'', $f'' + f'$, and $f'' - f'$, or 600, 660, and 540 cps for the values assumed above. The modulation may be increased by increasing the amplitude of the low-frequency signal to 2 or 3 times that of the high-frequency one.

This modulation may be demonstrated audibly. Connect the output of this mixer circuit to the input of a speech amplifier and loud-speaker. When the bias is set for minimum distortion both tones will be heard, the 60-cps tone being much fainter than the other because the ear (and perhaps also the speech amplifier) is less sensitive at this frequency. But when the bias is set for distortion such as shown in Fig. 1b the 600-cps tone will sound quite harsh, since it includes the sum and difference tones, as stated above. A trained ear may be able to distinguish the separate tones. That this harshness is due to the 60-cps modulation may be demonstrated by turning off the 60-cps source; the comparatively clear 600-cps tone is again heard. If the experiment is repeated with fairly high frequencies for both e_1 and e_2, say 10,000 and 15,000 cps, the difference tone (500 cps for the frequencies cited) will be audible to everyone, since the ear is more sensitive to it than to the higher tones.

5. Amplitude Modulation. In amplitude modulation the pattern of an audiofrequency signal is impressed upon the amplitude of radio-frequency oscillations, or waves, in the manner represented in Fig. 2. The unmodulated radiofrequency oscillation, of constant amplitude A, is represented by Fig. 2a; the audiofrequency or modulating signal, by Fig. 2b; and the modulated oscillation appears as in Fig. 2c. At any instant the *amplitude*, h, of the modulated oscillation deviates from its average (unmodulated) value, A, by an amount which is proportional to the *instantaneous* value, e', of the modulating signal. If k is the proportionality factor,

$$h = A + ke' \tag{10}$$

In general, e' may have any arbitrary form, as indicated in Fig. 2b. For the present we shall consider it sinusoidal, for frequency f'. That is

$$e' = a \cos \omega't \tag{11}$$

For this value of e'

$$h = A + ka \cos \omega't$$

$$= A(1 + m \cos \omega't) \tag{12}$$

The *modulation factor*, m, has here been written in place of ka/A. The instantaneous value of the radiofrequency voltage is then

$$e_m = A(1 + m \cos \omega't) \cos \omega''t \tag{13}$$

A plot for Eq. 13 is shown in Fig. 2d. We may now expand this equation in the usual manner, obtaining

$$e_m = A \cos \omega''t + \frac{mA}{2} \cos (\omega'' + \omega')t + \frac{mA}{2} \cos (\omega'' - \omega')t \quad (14)$$

In Eq. 14, e_m is shown to be the sum of three sinusoidal components of constant amplitude but different frequency. The first is the "car-

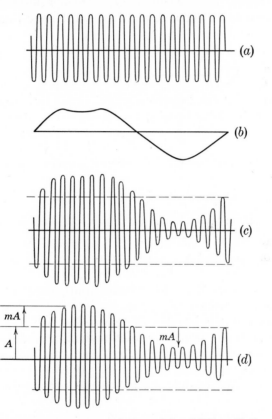

FIG. 2. AMPLITUDE MODULATION.   (a) Unmodulated RF oscillation.   (b) Modulating (audiofrequency) signal.   (c) Modulated RF oscillation.   (d) Sinusoidal modulation.

rier" frequency component. The second and third are called the upper and lower "side-bands." The modulation factor, m, is never greater than unity; this limitation is set by the methods for producing modulation, and for detection, not by theory.   In all practical applications the carrier frequency, f'', is very much higher than the highest value of f', although this also is not required by the theory given above. The side-bands include all frequencies which may be required by the modulating signal; for commercial broadcasting the range is roughly from 50 to 5000 cps to either side of the carrier frequency, which itself lies in the range from 500 to 1500 Kcps. Within this range the carrier and side-band frequencies are so close together that it is very difficult to separate them, even with the sharpest-tuned resonant circuits. The whole band of frequencies comprised by the carrier and two side-bands is relatively so narrow that radio circuits

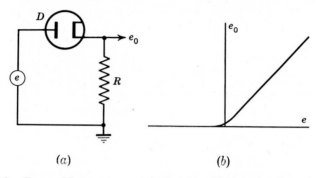

(a) (b)

Fig. 3. Diode Modulator. (a) Circuit. (b) Transfer characteristic.

designed for the carrier frequency pass it as a unit. The audiofrequency signal is absent, but its *pattern* is carried by the variations in amplitude of this band, so that a counterpart of it may be produced in the receiver by another non-linear process called detection. Amplitude modulation is frequently abbreviated to AM.

6. Production of Amplitude Modulation. Amplitude modulation may be produced in many ways, but the underlying principle for all is the fundamental modulation process. In each the carrier-frequency oscillation and the modulating signal are combined in a *non-linear* circuit of some kind, with the generation of numerous modulation products; suitable filter circuits then pass the desired products and reject or block out all others. Consider the example of Sec. 3, and compare Eq. 14 with Eq. 9. Of the seven modulation products appearing in Eq. 9, only three appear in Eq. 14, and these three are so close in frequency that a simple resonant circuit, tuned to the mid-frequency, f'', is a satisfactory filter. This may be shown in the demonstration of Sec. 4, by replacing R, the resistive load, with a condenser and inductance connected in parallel and tuned to 600 cps. (It is better then also to replace the triode with a pentode.) So simple a filter is possible because all other frequencies are either very much lower or very much higher than those in the modulation band. This method for producing amplitude modulation was invented by van der Bijl, and is one of the earliest. More efficient methods are described farther on.

7. Diode Modulation. As another example of modulation produced by a non-linear circuit let us consider the circuit of Fig. 3a, in which

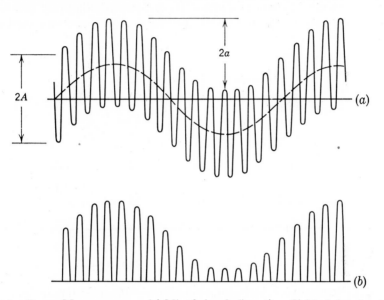

FIG. 4. DIODE MODULATION. (a) Mixed signals (input). (b) Modulated output

the simplest possible non-linear element is employed, namely a crystal or thermionic diode. The transfer characteristic for this circuit is shown in Fig. 3b. When the input voltage is large the curvature of this plot near the origin may be neglected and the characteristic then regarded as two straight lines meeting at the origin. With this approximation the output, e_0, becomes equal to the *positive* part of the input, e. Consider now that e consists of two components, e', of a low frequency, f', and e'', having a frequency f'' very much higher than f'. If the amplitude, A, of e'' is somewhat larger than a, the amplitude of e', the oscillogram for e will appear as in Fig. 4a, and the one for e_0 will be the positive peaks of Fig. 4a, as shown in Fig. 4b.

The output, e_0, includes components of frequencies f', f'', $f'' + f'$, $f'' - f'$, and zero (d-c components), plus many others representing higher orders of modulation. If we neeglct the higher-order products, we might represent this output approximately by

$$y = \left(\frac{A}{2} + \frac{a}{2} \cos \omega' t\right)(1 + \cos \omega'' t) \tag{15}$$

It may be seen that y in Eq. 15 corresponds to e_0 in that its positive peaks coincide with the peaks of e_0 in Fig. 14b, and all its negative peaks touch the time axis. It is only an approximation to e_0, since its loops are quite different in shape from those of Fig. 14b, but yet it serves to indicate the nature of the result produced. Expansion of

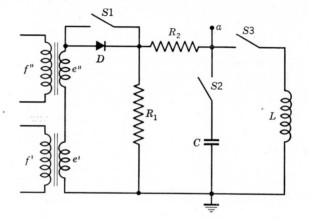

Fɪɢ. 5.   Dᴇᴍᴏɴsᴛʀᴀᴛɪᴏɴ Exᴘᴇʀɪᴍᴇɴᴛ 2.

Eq. 15 shows that it includes a constant term, $A/2$, one of frequency f' with amplitude $a/2$, one of frequency f'' and amplitude $A/2$, and the side-band terms of frequencies $f'' + f'$ and $f'' - f'$, with amplitudes $a/4$. Filtering, as described in Sec. 8, removes all but the three components of amplitude modulation.

8. Demonstration Experiment 2.   The production of modulation by a diode may be demonstrated with the circuit of Fig. 5. The 60-cps line will supply e', through a filament transformer and a variable-output auto-transformer. The higher frequency should be as near as possible to some exact multiple of 60 cps, such as 900 or 1200 cps, and e'' may be supplied from a signal generator, through a second transformer having its secondary in series with the first, as shown. The primary or secondary of an audio transformer will serve as the inductance, L, of the resonant circuit. Radio resistors may be used for R_1 and R_2, which should be about 10 K each.

To display the patterns of Figs. 4a, 4b, and 2d on the oscilloscope screen, connect the oscilloscope to point a, Fig. 5, and set the sweep rate for one or two cycles of e'; synchronize with e' (or the a-c line), *not* the signal.   If f'' is now an exact multiple of f' the high-frequency peaks will be stationary; otherwise they will move across the pattern. If switch $S1$ is closed, with the others open, the pattern seen is Fig. $4a$, the sum of the two emf's.   With all switches open, the pattern is Fig. $4b$, showing simple rectification, and the amplitude-modulation pattern of Fig. $2d$ is produced by then closing $S2$ and $S3$ and tuning the filter unit (L and C) to resonance at f''.   For each pattern observe the changes produced by varying the amplitude of e' so as to change the

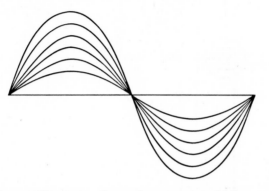

FIG. 6.   MODULATION PATTERN.   Sweep frequency equals the *carrier* frequency.

modulation from zero to 100 percent.   Observe also the effect of over-modulation.   In addition to showing the conventional pattern of Fig. $2d$, produce the pattern of Fig. 6, by increasing the sweep rate until only one or two cycles of e'' appear on the screen.   (This pattern will synchronize with the signal as well as with e''.)   This pattern is particularly instructive, in that it shows how the instantaneous ampli-tude of the modulated voltage varies with the instantaneous value of e'.   Finally, the presence in e_0 of the low-frequency component may be demonstrated by opening $S3$, but leaving $S1$ open and $S2$ closed, and increasing C.   If C is large enough, most of the high-frequency com-ponents are attenuated in R_2 and only the low-frequency component is left.

9. Grid Modulation.   Although the diode (Sec. 7) and the over-biased triode (Sec. 3) serve best to illustrate the fundamental principles of modulation, neither method is practical when much power is required.*   Most practical amplitude-modulation circuits utilize a class C amplifier, or class C oscillator, as the essential non-linear ele-

---

* For low-power modulation systems, balanced modulators, employing crystal diodes, are quite satisfactory.

ment, and vary the amplitude of its output by one or the other of two methods, called grid modulation or plate modulation. The desired modulation products (the carrier and the two side-bands) are selected automatically by the resonant circuit in the output.

The grid-modulation circuit is diagrammed in Fig. 7. Compare this figure with Fig. 14, Chapter 10. The input to the grid is the sum of the audiofrequency signal, e', and a radiofrequency voltage, e'', and is produced by connecting the secondaries of the two transformers in series,

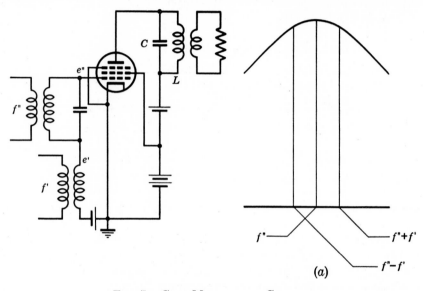

(a)

FIG. 7. GRID-MODULATION CIRCUIT.

as shown. The load is a resonant circuit, L,C, having a resonance curve broad enough at the top to include both side-bands, as indicated in Fig. 7a. The grid bias is set to some value below cut-off (the grid potential at which the plate current is just reduced to zero) and E'', the amplitude of the radiofrequency voltage, is adjusted so that the output voltage without modulation is half the maximum value. The peaks of the grid-potential swings will now lie about halfway between cut-off and maximum value. These relationships are shown in Fig. 8. The amplitude of e'' is then held constant while the audiofrequency (modulation) signal, e', is added. This signal may now be regarded as *changing the bias*, as indicated by the broken line in Fig. 8, thus pushing the grid-potential peaks up toward maximum value, or down toward cut-off, causing the plate current and the output voltage to vary accordingly, in the manner pictured in Fig. 2d. When the circuit is

carefully designed the amplitude of the output voltage is approximately
proportional to the height above cut-off of these grid-potential peaks.

10. Heising ("Plate") Modulation. When the bias for a class C
oscillator is produced by means of a grid resistor and condenser, as in
Fig. 22b, Chapter 10, the amplitude, E_0, of the output voltage is nearly

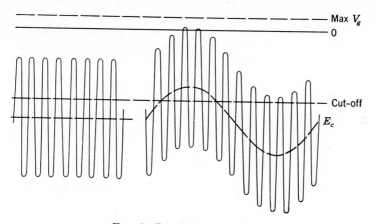

FIG. 8. GRID MODULATION.

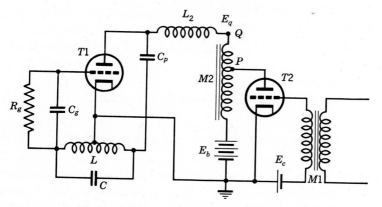

FIG. 9. HEISING MODULATION CIRCUIT.

equal to E_b, and quite closely proportional to it.   If the proportionality
factor is k,

$$E_0 = kE_p \tag{16}$$

Thus the output from an oscillator may be modulated by varying the
plate potential in proportion to the audiofrequency signal.   The
Heising modulation circuit, diagrammed in Fig. 9, operates on this

principle. The tube $T1$ and its associated circuit constitute a Hartley oscillator which receives its plate power from the d-c source, E_b, in series with the auto-transformer, $M2$. Tube $T2$ operates as an audio-frequency amplifier for which $M2$ is the output transformer, and for which the entire oscillator circuit is the *load*. The radiofrequency choke-coil, L_2, serves to isolate the radiofrequency part of this circuit from the audiofrequency part; compare it with coil L_3 in Fig. 22b, Chapter 10.

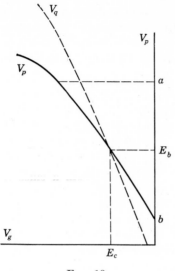

FIG. 10.

Without modulation the amplitude of the oscillator output voltage is steady and equal to kE_b. When the audio amplifier is operating the potential of the point P is the sum of E' cos $\omega't$, the audiofrequency output from $M2$, and E_b. We may now consider a time interval which is very short compared with the period of an audiofrequency cycle, but long enough to contain many radiofrequency cycles. During this interval E_q, the potential at Q, may be considered constant, at the value $E_b + E'$ cos $\omega't$, and the amplitude of the radiofrequency output then will be

$$E_0 = kE_q = k(E_b + E' \cos \omega't) \tag{17}$$

and

$$e_0 = kE_b \left(1 + \frac{E'}{E_b} \cos \omega't\right) \cos \omega''t \tag{18}$$

Compare Eq. 18 with Eq. 13; Eq. 18 evidently represents amplitude modulation, with a modulation factor, m, equal to E'/E_b. The auto-transformer $M2$ is needed to raise the a-c output from $T2$ high enough to make 100 percent modulation possible. Without this increase the output (at P, Fig. 9) would have too short a linear range, as may be seen in Fig. 10, where the potential V_p, at P, is represented by the solid line. With this increase the output V_q, represented by the broken line in Fig. 10, has a linear range extending from zero to $2E_b$, so that full modulation is possible. Other means may be employed to insure full modulation, but this one is the most efficient.

Heising or plate modulation is much more nearly linear than grid modulation, but less economical. The power requirements for the class A amplifier are several times higher than for the oscillator, since (1) the power input to the oscillator is the power output from the amplifier, and (2) the efficiency of class A amplification is very low. The amplifier efficiency may be improved by employing a class B audio amplifier.   Heising modulation may be applied also to class C amplifiers having grid-resistor and condenser bias.   After modulation the radiofrequency power may be further amplified by means of a class B radiofrequency amplifier; see Sec. 20, Chapter 10.

11. Demonstration Experiment 3.   Plate modulation makes an excellent demonstration.   The circuit may be built up according to Fig. 9, with a type 76 triode for $T1$, and a type 6L6 tube, triode-connected, for $T2$.   (The circuit of Exp. 31 will serve even better if it is available.)   Make E_b 250 volts, and bias the 6L6 tube with a 490-ohm resistance and a 10-mf condenser, in place of E_c.   The circuit elements for the oscillator, including L_2, may be the same as for the demonstration oscillator in Chapter 10; find by trial the best value for R_g.   The auto-transformer, $M2$, may be improvised from a class B output transformer.   If each half of the primary winding has approximately the same number of turns as the secondary, connect the primary between E_b and the plate of $T2$, and connect the secondary in series at the plate end, to form the booster coil between the plate and the point P.   The audio input may be made from the a-c line, through an isolation transformer, $M1$, to avoid grounding troubles.

The modulated output may be displayed on the oscilloscope screen by connecting a parallel-resonant circuit to the vertical-deflection terminals of the oscilloscope, coupling it very loosely to the tank coil of the oscillator, and tuning it to resonance.   Unless the amplifier in the oscilloscope is especially designed for radiofrequency operation, it will be necessary to use the oscilloscope without amplification.   The amplitude on the screen may always be varied by changing the coupling between the pick-up circuit and the tank circuit.

If the horizontal deflection of the oscilloscope is actuated by the sweep circuit the modulated pattern will correspond to Fig. 2d.   If instead the horizontal-deflection terminal is connected to P, Fig. 9, the pattern is a trapezoid, as shown in Fig. 11a.   The reason for this trapezoidal form is found if we write the time equations for each coordinate:

$$x = A \cos \omega't \tag{19}$$

$$y = B(1 + m \cos \omega't) \cos \omega''t$$

$$= B\left(1 + m\frac{x}{A}\right) \cos \omega''t \tag{20}$$

The equations for the two diagonal lines in the trapezoid are then found by putting cos $\omega''t$ equal to $+1$ and -1 respectively. They are

$$y_+ = B\left(1 + \frac{mx}{A}\right) \quad \text{and} \quad y_- = -B\left(1 + \frac{mx}{A}\right) \quad (21)$$

If the modulation is truly linear these diagonal lines are straight, as assumed above, and any lack of linearity is revealed by curvature in

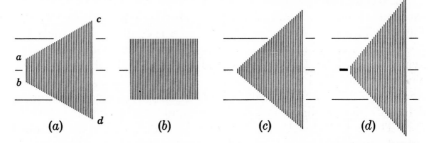

Fig. 11. Modulation Patterns. x—AF signal. y—RF output. (a) Modulation less than 100 percent. (b) No modulation. (c) 100 percent modulation. (d) Over 100 percent modulation.

them.* This trapezoidal figure is commonly used to measure percent modulation. It is easy to show that, for Fig. 11a,

$$m = \frac{cd - ab}{cd + ab} \quad (22)$$

The effects of overmodulation (E' greater than E_p) should be observed, both in the trapezoidal pattern and in the time plot.

The operation of grid modulation may be demonstrated in similar manner, with the circuit of Fig. 7.

12. Experiment 31. Plate Modulation. For quantitative measurements the modulated oscillator circuit of Fig. 9 may be built up as shown in Fig. 12, with a type 45 tube in the oscillator, and a 6N7 twin triode in the class B audio amplifier. The amplifier circuit is that of Exp. 12, except that here the load is the oscillator, and the output is taken directly from one plate of the 6N7 tube. (Only the primary of the output transformer is used.) In order to obtain 100 percent

* If the horizontal deflection is produced by the signal at the grid, phase shift in the amplifier may cause the top and bottom boundaries of this modulation figure to appear elliptical. If we think of the figure as being three-dimensional, made by rolling one audiofrequency cycle of Fig. 2a up into a cylinder, these different aspects of the figure may be easily understood.

modulation, the d-c plate potential for the oscillator is reduced below E_b by the *dropping resistor*, R_1, which should be a 10-watt variable resistor of about 2000 ohms resistance. The d-c source must have good regulation at 300 volts, up to 100 ma. The meters for reading the d-c potential, E_p, and the a-c potential, E', at the point P, must be high-resistance types, at least 1000 ohms per volt.

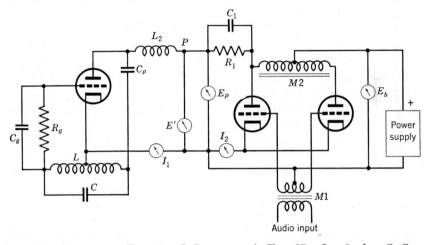

Fig. 12.   Circuit for Exp. 31. L, C—same as in Exp. 27. L_2—5 mh. C_g, C_p—500 $\mu\mu$f, 1000 volts. R_g—50 K.   The reactance of C_1 at the modulating frequency should not exceed 500 ohms.

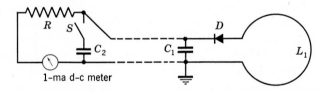

Fig. 13.   Output and Modulation Meter. R—at least 10 K. D—IN34 diode.

The radiofrequency output is measured in relative values by the pick-up circuit of Fig. 13.   The coil, L_1, which is a little larger in diameter than L, is supported about the middle of L, close to the cathode tap.   One or two turns of stiff wire (No. 14 or heavier) should be sufficient.   The crystal detector, D, and a 0.002-μf condenser, C_1, complete the RF part of this circuit.   The rest of the circuit should be mounted in a metal box and placed a foot or so from the oscillator, with the leads to it (represented by the broken lines in Fig. 13) closely twisted together.   If the low-capacity switch, S, is open the meter reading is proportional to the peak value of the RF output, averaged over a complete cycle of modulation, or the height A in Fig. 2d. But if S is closed, so as to put a large capacitance, C_2, in parallel with C_1, the meter reading corresponds to the highest RF peaks, or the height $A + mA$ in Fig. 2d. Call these two meter readings I_a and I_m respectively; then m equals $(I_m - I_a)/I_a$. It is essential that C_2 be large enough to make the product of RC_2 times the modulating frequency at least 20.

Part I. D-C "Modulation." Remove the 6N7 tube, so that only the oscillator is in operation, and observe I_a as E_p is varied from zero to the highest value obtainable (not over 450 volts). Take enough readings for a good plot of I_a as y, E_p as x. If this plot is a straight line through the origin, the modulation with an a-c signal will be linear. At the same time take readings of the d-c plate current, I_1, and plot I_1 as y, E_p as x. Interpret this plot.

Part II. A-C Modulation. Put the entire circuit into operation, adjust E_b to 300 volts, and set R_1 so that E_p is 250 volts. Observe I_1, I_2, and I_a with no modulation. Then modulate the circuit at some frequency between 500 and 1500 cps,* taking readings of all meters at 8 or 10 points between zero and 100 percent modulation. Observe also the effect of modulation in excess of 100 percent. Adjust the value of R_1 to make these observations possible. For each point compute the modulation index m from the output meter readings. Compute also the ratio of the *peak* value of the alternating voltage E' to the d-c voltage E_p, and explain why this ratio is also equal to m. Take a second set of data with R_1 removed, and explain why 100 percent modulation is not possible under these conditions.

Replace R_1, set the modulation to about 60 percent, and then load the oscillator by bringing toward L a coil of 2 or 3 turns of wire connected to a 10-watt, 115-volt lamp. Observe carefully whether I_a and I_m increase proportionally. If a cathode-ray oscilloscope is available check the values of m obtained in the first set of Part II by means of the trapezoidal pattern described in Sec. 11. Finally, explain carefully the operation of each part of the circuits employed in this experiment.

13. Diode Detection. The audiofrequency signal represented by amplitude modulation may be reproduced by another non-linear process called *detection*. A simple diode detector is shown in Fig. 14. When the radiofrequency input, e, is unmodulated this is a simple rectifier circuit, for which the explanation has been given in Sec. 19, Chapter 1. The condenser C then charges up until the potential e_a

---

* If a source of higher frequency is not available the 60-cps line will serve.

is nearly equal to the peak value of e. If the input is modulated this same explanation may be given if it is limited to a time interval over which the amplitude of e remains practically constant, but one still long enough to include many radiofrequency cycles. If the detector circuit is correctly designed, e_a will approach the peak value of e within this interval, and as e fluctuates to follow the modulation pattern, e_a will follow these fluctuations, as illustrated schematically in Fig. 15a.

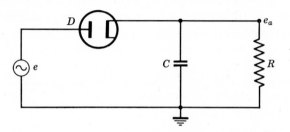

FIG. 14.   DIODE DETECTOR.

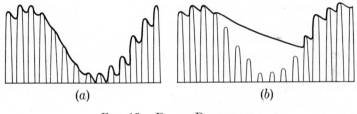

(a)   (b)

FIG. 15.   DIODE DETECTION.

The design of a good detector circuit must take into consideration the following factors.   First, the impedance, R_i, of the source and the diode (when it is conducting) must be as small as possible; the diode impedance is made small by making e fairly large, at least several volts. The time constant R_iC must be small enough to enable C to charge up to e_a in a very small fraction of the shortest audiofrequency cycle.   Next we must consider RC, the time constant for the discharge of the condenser.   For e_a to be close to the peak value of e, RC must be as large as possible, and very much larger than R_iC.   On the other hand, if RC is too large, the condenser will be unable to discharge fast enough to follow the rapid decreases in potential which occur with high-frequency audio signals.   The condenser charges fast enough to follow increasing values of e, but it holds much of its charge from one audiofrequency peak to the next, as represented in Fig. 15b.   Thus

RC must be very large compared with R_iC, but small compared with the period of the shortest audiofrequency cycle.

14. Detection is a Modulation Process. In Sec. 7 it was shown that a diode is a *modulating* device, in that it produces new components, called modulation products, whose frequencies are sum and difference combinations of the frequencies present in the input. *This same function* is performed by the diode in a detector circuit. The frequency f' is *not* present in the input, which contains only the frequencies f'', $f'' + f'$, and $f'' - f'$, but is produced by the non-linear characteristic of the diode, in the second-order modulation products having the *difference* frequencies $(f'' + f') - f''$ and $f'' - (f'' - f')$. The frequencies of *possible* second-order modulation products are $f'' \pm (f'' + f')$, $f'' \pm (f'' - f')$, and $(f'' + f') \pm (f'' - f')$; or $2f'' - f'$, $2f''$, $2f'' + f'$, $2f'$, and f'. These include f', the desired frequency, and the detector load is designed to isolate this component and reject the others.

Note that no harmonics of f' are present in the output from a diode detector. Although these are possible for second-order modulation in general, diode detection does not produce them. For strong signals diode detection is quite free from audiofrequency distortion, or quite "linear." Various other types of detectors are described in radio treatises. Each functions because it includes some non-linear impedance, and may be analyzed most easily by first looking for this essential characteristic. The most thorough analysis of detector action is found in E. L. Chaffee, *Theory of Thermionic Vacuum Tubes*, Chapters XIX to XXII.

15. Demonstration Experiment 4. Diode detection may be demonstrated on the oscilloscope screen with 60 cps for f', and some multiple of this value, such as 1500 or 1800 cps, for f''. The modulated signal may be produced by diode modulation as described in Sec. 8. Indeed, the modulating diode and the detecting diode may be the two halves of a 6H6 tube, thus emphasizing the fundamental identity of the two processes. Two crystal detectors also may be used. To prevent the detector circuit from reacting adversely upon the modulator circuit, the two circuits should be connected through a buffer tube. A suitable circuit is given in Fig. 16. The modulated signal, e, is taken from point a in Fig. 5. The output transformer, M, should be a good audio transformer with low d-c resistance; its primary resistance will probably produce a satisfactory bias for the tube. (If not, Fig. 30, Chapter 6, shows methods of changing the bias.)

When the oscilloscope is connected to point A it shows the modulated signal; when connected to point B, with both switches open, it shows the positive half of this signal. If $S1$ is closed and C_3 has a suitable value the pattern of Fig. 15a is obtained. Experiment with different values of R_2 and C_3 to find the best. The values are somewhat critical in this case, since f' and f'' are much closer than for radio modulation. The pattern of Fig. 15b may be produced by making C_3, R_2, or both quite large. If $S1$ is opened and $S2$ closed, with L_2C_4 tuned to the carrier frequency, the original modulated signal will reappear, with the low-frequency component again eliminated. Also, if L_2C_4 is tuned to the frequency $2f''$, the oscilloscope will reveal the modulated second-harmonic band noted in Sec. 14.

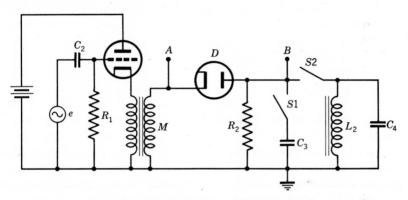

FIG. 16. DEMONSTRATION EXPERIMENT 4.

16. Heterodyne Detection. Another interesting example of the fundamental modulation process is furnished by heterodyne detection. Radio signals which are unmodulated,* for example, CW (continuous wave) radio telegraph signals, must be modulated at the receiver in order to produce audible signals. This result is accomplished by adding to the signal, at the receiver, a locally generated voltage of nearly the same frequency. The process is called *heterodyning.* If now this combined voltage is put into a detector circuit, such as the diode detector of Fig. 14, the detector serves to *modulate* it, generating components of many new frequencies, including the sum and difference of the original two frequencies. The low-pass filter circuit (R,C in Fig. 14) then rejects all components except the one of the difference frequency. The local oscillator is adjusted so that this difference frequency is in the audible range.

* No intelligence may be communicated by radio without *some* type of modulation. In CW telegraphy this modulation is produced by the interruptions which form the dots and dashes, and even this type of modulation produces some frequency changes.

As we have seen earlier, the difference-frequency component results from the *product* of the two input voltages. Let the signal voltage and the local voltage be represented by

$$e_s = a \cos \omega_s t \qquad \text{and} \qquad e_1 = b \cos \omega_1 t \qquad (23)$$

Then

$$e_s e_1 = ab \cos \omega_s t \cos \omega_1 t$$

$$= \frac{ab}{2} [\cos (\omega_s + \omega_1)t + \cos (\omega_s - \omega_1)t] \qquad (24)$$

Thus the amplitude of the difference-frequency component is proportional to the product of the two amplitudes, a and b. It follows that the strength of the audio tone may be increased by increasing the amplitude of the local voltage.

17. Demonstration Experiment 5. The heterodyne process of detection may be demonstrated with a radio receiver (AM broadcast range) and a radiofrequency signal generator to produce the local oscillation. If the receiver is tuned to a distant station (or a near-by station with the gain low, so that the program is barely heard), and then the signal generator is coupled to the antenna lead and tuned to nearly the same frequency, the modulation between the carrier component of the radio signal and the local oscillation will produce a strong, audible tone. As the local frequency passes through the carrier frequency of the radio signal this *beat-note* drops from above audibility down to zero frequency, then rises, and finally becomes again inaudible. By this heterodyne means it is possible to detect radio stations which are so faint that they are not otherwise heard. If the signal generator has strong harmonics the beat-note between its second harmonic and the carrier of the radio signal may be heard when the signal generator is tuned to about half the frequency of the radio signal.

Another interesting result may be observed when the signal generator is tuned exactly to the carrier frequency and the beat-note frequency is zero. If the tuning is exact the audiofrequency output of the modulated signal (the program) is heard much louder. If the tuning is not *extremely* precise the program thus heard will be of very poor quality, but even so the result is astonishing. The explanation is obvious: the local oscillation is reinforcing the carrier voltage, to increase the intensity of the modulation products between the carrier and sidebands. If the frequency of the local oscillation could be controlled precisely enough it would be unnecessary to transmit the carrier at all; only the side-bands, or even one side-band alone, would be sufficient. This is actually the practice for certain types of carrier telephony, in which the side-bands are transmitted as guided waves along a cable. The side-bands are generated by means of a *balanced-modulator* circuit, which suppresses the carrier component.

18. Frequency Conversion. Since the fidelity of the output for a detector, as well as its efficiency, is best when the input to it is fairly high, it is necessary to amplify incoming radio signals before detection. Several stages of radiofrequency amplification may be necessary, and the amplifier must serve the entire band of frequencies we wish to receive. The obvious solution is an amplifier having each stage tunable to the desired frequency, but the tuning of such an amplifier

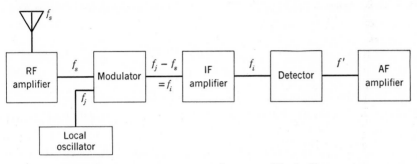

FIG. 17. SUPERHETERODYNE CIRCUIT. Block diagram.

involves many difficulties. It requires skill and patience to adjust each stage separately, and it is almost impossible to construct a circuit precisely enough to permit operation from a single control. An alternate possibility is to *convert* all incoming signals to the same frequency, by heterodyning the incoming signal with a locally generated voltage, and to then build the radiofrequency amplifier with all its stages tuned to that *fixed* frequency. This is the mode of operation in a *super-heterodyne* radio receiver, which is represented in the block diagram of Fig. 17.

Frequency conversion is another modulation process, accomplished by any suitable non-linear device. The radio signal, usually after one stage of RF (radiofrequency) amplification, as indicated in Fig. 17, is added to the locally generated voltage at the input of the *modulator* unit, which is generally called a *mixer*, *converter*, or *first-detector* unit. In Fig. 17 the carrier frequency is designated by f_s and the locally generated frequency by f_j. Among the modulation products there is a component of the difference frequency, $(f_j - f_s)$, and this component is the one passed on to the IF (intermediate-frequency) amplifier. This IF amplifier is tuned to a fixed frequency, f_i, and the frequency f_j is adjusted to make $(f_j - f_s)$ equal to f_i. The RF amplifier circuit and the local oscillator circuit may be designed so that a single control will maintain this relationship for both.

19. Frequency-Converter Circuits. Early frequency-converter circuits employed over-biased triodes, tetrodes, or pentodes, and these circuits were troubled with undesired interactions between the signal and the strong local oscillation. To meet this difficulty special tubes have been developed, of which the pentagrid tube described in Sec. 10, Chapter 11, is typical. The principle of operation for a pentagrid converter circuit is illustrated by the simplified circuit of Fig. 18. Let us assume that the operation of both grids 1 and 3 is limited to their linear ranges. Then the cathode current, I_k, may be written as

$$I_k = I_0 + s_1 e_j$$
$$= I_0 + s_1 E_j \cos \omega_j t$$
$$= I_0 + I_j \cos \omega_j t \tag{25}$$

Note that the coefficient, s_1, is the conductance defined in Sec. 25, Chapter 5. Now, as explained in Sec. 10, Chapter 11, the fraction, p, of I_k which reaches the plate is determined by V_3, the potential of grid 3. Hence, over the linear range of V_3 we may write, from Eq. 20, Chapter 11,

$$p = p_0 + q\, e_s = p_0 + q\, E_s \cos \omega_s t \tag{26}$$

and

$$I_p = p\, I_k = (p_0 + q\, E_s \cos \omega_s t) I_k \tag{27}$$

If we now insert in Eq. 27 the value for I_k given by Eq. 25, we obtain

$$I_p = p_0 I_0 + p_0 I_j \cos \omega_j t + q\, I_0 E_s \cos \omega_s t$$
$$+ q\, I_j E_s \cos \omega_j t \cos \omega_s t \tag{28}$$

We then recognize that the last term of Eq. 28 represents second-order modulation products having frequencies $(f_j + f_s)$ and $(f_j - f_s)$. The frequency-conversion process is completed by adjusting the value of f_j so that $(f_j - f_s)$ equals f_i, the frequency to which the IF amplifier is tuned.

From Eq. 28 we may show that the amplitude for each of these second-order modulation products is

$$I_{js} = \tfrac{1}{2} q\, I_j E_s \tag{29}$$

20. Conversion Transconductance. The ratio of I_{js}, the amplitude of the IF component of the plate current, to E_s, the amplitude of the signal voltage, is called the *conversion transconductance*. It is represented by g_c and defined by

$$g_c = I_{js}/E_s \tag{30}$$

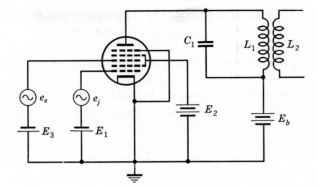

Fig. 18. Pentagrid Frequency Converter. Class A input.

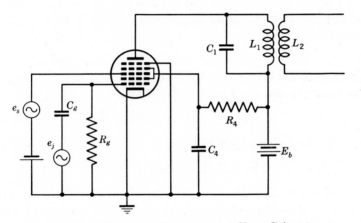

Fig. 19. Pentagrid Converter. Class C input.

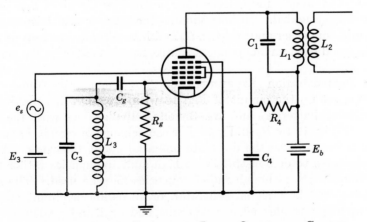

Fig. 20. Pentagrid Converter—Local Oscillator Circuit.

In the example considered in Sec. 19,

$$g_c = \tfrac{1}{2}qI_j \tag{31}$$

In practice, e_j is made much bigger than in this example, and grid 1 is biased so that the cathode current consists of pulses of about half-cycle size. When this is done, I_p includes modulation products of higher order ($2f_j \pm f_s$, $4f_j \pm f_s$, etc.), in addition to those of second order, but these are rejected by the IF amplifier when $(f_j - f_s)$ equals f_i. The advantage of this mode of operation is that it yields a higher value for the conversion transconductance. For this mode of operation I_j is the amplitude of the first-harmonic component of the cathode-current pulses, and g_c is found by inserting this value into Eq. 31. For example, if I_k consists of half-cycle pulses of height H, the first-harmonic component is found by harmonic analysis to be $H/2$, and, *for this example,*

$$g = \tfrac{1}{4}qH \tag{32}$$

This analysis has been made for the carrier frequency, f_s, only. The same frequency conversion takes place for each side-band, so that if

$$e_s = E_s(1 + m \cos \omega't) \cos \omega_s t \tag{33}$$

the input to the IF amplifier will be

$$i_i = I_i(1 + m \cos \omega't) \cos \omega_i t \tag{34}$$

Practical conversion circuits are shown in Figs. 19 and 20. In Fig. 19 the local oscillator is a separate circuit, indicated by e_j, whereas in Fig. 20 it is driven by the converter tube, with grids 1 and 2 serving as grid and anode respectively, for a Hartley circuit. The anode (grid 2) is grounded. In both circuits the bias for grid 1 is obtained by a grid condenser and resistor, C_g and R_g. Usually the bias for grid 3 is supplied from an independent source, here indicated by the battery E_3.

21. Demonstration Experiment 6. To demonstrate these phenomena, set up the circuit of Fig. 18 with a 6SA7 tube, making E_2 90 volts (B-batteries) and E_3, 3 volts. Replace E_1 with the bias shown in Fig. 19 by R_g and C_g. For each change of circuit E_b should be adjusted to make the d-c plate potential about 100 volts. Again it is desirable to demonstrate with high audiofrequencies rather than radiofrequencies, although radiofrequencies may be used. The local oscillator may be a signal generator, or an oscillator circuit may be built up with a triode such as a 6J5 tube, and a coil and condenser large enough to produce a frequency of about 20,000 cps. Its output should be about 10 volts peak. Omit L_2, and connect the oscilloscope to the plate of the tube.

Start with a resistive load of about 50 K, in place of L_1 and C_1, and observe the change in output from a pure sinusoid to peaks as e_j is increased from zero to maximum, with no signal on grid 3. Then replace the resistive load with the parallel-resonant circuit, L_1C_1, and

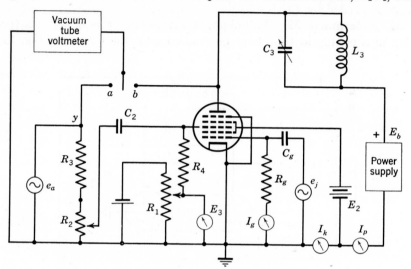

FIG. 21. CIRCUIT FOR EXP. 32.

R_1— 2 K.	C_2, C_g—0.005 μf.
R_2— 5 K.	C_3—0.001 μf max.
R_3— 45 K.	L_3—1250 μh.
R_4—100 K.	E_2—90 volts.
R_g— 20 K.	E_b—100 volts.

VTV (vacuum-tube voltmeter) must be free from frequency error up to 1000 kcps.

set E_j to about 10 volts peak. When the output circuit is tuned to resonance the output is of course sinusoidal, with amplitude proportional to I_j, in Eq. 28. Now put a 60-cps signal on grid 3, and set the sweep frequency to 30 or 60 cps. The typical amplitude-modulation pattern of Fig. 2d is observed. This tube produces excellent amplitude modulation, and this demonstration serves to show the essential identity of this process with the frequency-conversion process.

Next put a signal of about 7000-cps frequency on grid 3, from a signal generator. Unless this signal is too large, the pattern observed with L_1C_1 tuned to f_j is affected very little. (Reduce e_s if necessary, to make this so.) But now, if L_1C_1 is tuned to the intermediate frequency, $f_j - f_s$, or 13,000 cps for the figures cited above, the conversion product will be discovered, with a lower intensity. By further tuning of the tank circuit we may discover the other two components included in Eq. 28, of frequencies f_s and $(f_j + f_s)$ (7000 and 27,000 cps). Since I_k consists of peaks, it should be possible also to detect the higher-frequency modulation products mentioned in Sec. 20. To cover all these frequencies several coils, or a coil with several taps, may be needed for L_1.

22. Experiment 32. Frequency Conversion. Frequency conversion in a pentagrid tube may be studied with the circuit of Fig. 21,

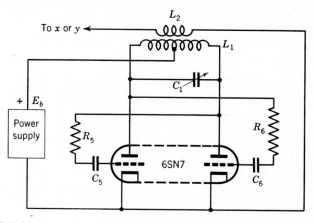

FIG. 22.   RF OSCILLATOR. L_1—50 turns of No. 16 wire on a coil form about 2.75 inches diameter. C_1—500 $\mu\mu$f max. C_5, C_6—0.001 μf. R_5, R_6—100 K.

and the conversion transconductance measured for various conditions. Instructions are for a 6SA7 tube, and radiofrequencies in the AM broadcasting range. The circuit is the same as the one of Fig. 18, with measuring devices added. The d-c power for the screen grid is supplied from an independent source, since the a-c output is quite sensitive to changes in E_2. Oscillators to supply e_j and e_a may be built according to the diagram and specifications of Fig. 22, for frequencies of about 1300 and 1000 Kcps respectively. Coil L_2 is slightly smaller in diameter than L_1 and is placed inside L_1, at its center. The output is varied by changing the d-c supply voltage. The number of turns in L_2 must be determined by trial to give 20 volts maximum. (An alternate method for varying the output is to pivot L_2 about an axis perpendicular to the axis of L_1, so as to change its coupling to L_1.)

The local-oscillator input, e_j, is monitored by observing the direct current, I_g, to grid 1; its amplitude is a little greater than the grid bias, which equals $I_g R_g$. The signal, e_s, is derived from a voltage-divider, a 5-K "linear volume control," R_2, in series with a 45-K resistor, R_3. The precision of the results depends upon the quality of these resistors. The power factor of each must be close to unity, and they should be calibrated at radiofrequency for the resistance *ratio*. The input to this voltage-divider from the 1000-Kcps oscillator, or e_a, is made equal to e_i, the desired output at b, and the signal input is compared with the IF output by the method employed in Exp. 7 for an audio amplifier. The signal, e_s, is adjusted to make the vacuum-tube voltmeter reading the same at a and at b. The *conversion gain*, A_c, is then determined from the resistance ratio.

$$A_c = E_i/E_s \qquad (35)$$

Part I. Conversion Gain. Set the bias for grid 3 at -3 volts, and adjust e_j to make I_g equal to 0.50 ma. Then measure A_c as E_i varies from zero to 3 volts.* Compute E_s for each observation, and plot a curve having E_i as y, E_s as x. From this plot determine the range of linear operation.

Part II. Conversion Conductance. To compute g_c we must know I_i, and this in turn requires us to known R_0, the parallel resistance of $L_3 C_3$. Although there are more precise methods, the following one gives a value of R_0 sufficient for this experiment. (*a*) With the circuit as in Part I, make E_i about 5 volts, and measure A_c. Then put a known resistance in parallel with L_3 and C_3, choosing one by trial which reduces the gain to between 50 and 70 percent of its initial value, and measure the gain, $A_c{}'$, under these conditions. If the added resistance is R,

$$A_c/A_c{}' = (R + R_0)/R \qquad (36)\dagger$$

The added resistor must have close to unity power factor, and its resistance should be measured at f_i. It is possible to use a good radio resistor (*not* wire-wound) and take its d-c resistance as approximately equal to the a-c resistance. Prove Eq. 36, and compute R_0 from your data. Show that

$$g_c = A_c/R_0 \qquad (37)$$

Compute g_c from your data in Part I. If the tube in this experiment is the same one studied in Exp. 31, the value of q in Eq. 31 may be obtained from the slope of the plot of p vs. V_3 made in Exp. 31. Put this value of q, and your value of g_c, into Eq. 31, and solve for I_j. The

---

* Each time a change is made, check the tuning of $L_3 C_3$, to make sure that it is always set at resonance.

† This value of R_0 includes the shunting effect of r_p for the tube, and the value of I_i computed from it is the source current for an equivalent circuit of the current-source type. It is, however, for this current that g_c is properly defined.

result should be comparable with the d-c value of the cathode current. Explain why.

Part III. Dependence of g_c upon I_g and E_3. (a) Starting with conditions as in Part I, hold E_i fixed at about 5 volts and determine A_c and g_c for values of the bias to grid 3 ranging from zero to -10 volts. Represent your results as a plot of g_c as y, grid bias as x.

(b) Starting as in Part (a), hold the bias to grid 3 fixed at -2 volts and measure A_c as I_g is varied from zero to 1.0 ma. Represent the

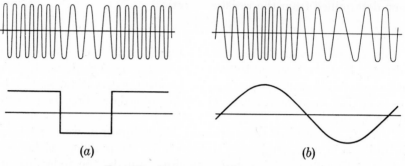

(a)   (b)

FIG. 23. FREQUENCY MODULATION.

results with a curve having g_c as y, I_g as x. Discuss this result in terms of the theory given in Sec. 20.

23. Frequency Modulation. Frequency modulation does not appear to resemble the modulation processes considered earlier in this chapter except in one respect: it enables radio waves to "carry" a telephone or telegraph message so that it may be reproduced at the receiver. The simplest application of FM (frequency modulation) is to CW telephony. In this application the telegraph key changes the frequency of the radio waves, without changing their amplitude, as represented in Fig. 23a, so that the heterodyne beat-note at the receiver changes from an inaudible to an audible frequency. When FM is applied to telephony the amplitude of the waves likewise remains constant, but the *instantaneous* frequency, f, varies from the average value, f_0, by very small amounts (1 part in 500 is an extreme value) so that the difference between f and f_0, *at any instant*, is directly proportional to the *instantaneous* value of the modulating signal. If the signal is represented by y, and k is the proportionality factor,

$$f - f_0 = ky \qquad (38)$$

For example, if the signal is periodic, of frequency f' and amplitude E',

$$y = E' \cos 2\pi f't \qquad (39)$$

and

$$f - f_0 = kE' \cos 2\pi f't \qquad (40)$$

This kind of modulation is represented in Fig. 23b, with the frequency differences greatly exaggerated. From Eq. 40 we see that $(f - f_0)$ varies periodically at the frequency f', the maximum change in f being proportional to E'. If E'' is the amplitude of the radiofrequency voltage, e'', we may write

$$e'' = E'' \sin \theta \tag{41}$$

At this point we must not be misled into putting θ equal to $2\pi f t$. Instead,

$$\theta = \int 2\pi f \, dt = 2\pi \int (f_0 + kE' \cos 2\pi f't) \, dt$$

$$= 2\pi f_0 t + (kE'/f') \sin 2\pi f't$$

$$= 2\pi f_0 t + m_f \sin 2\pi f't \tag{42}$$

and

$$e'' = E'' \sin (2\pi f_0 t + m_f \sin 2\pi f't) \tag{43}$$

The quantity m_f, which stands for kE'/f' in Eq. 43, is called the *modulation* index; it equals the ratio of the peak value of $(f - f_0)$ to f'. If y is expressed as some more general function of time, we must write

$$e'' = E'' \sin 2\pi (f_0 t + k \int y \, dt) \tag{44}$$

From Eq. 40 it might appear that frequency modulation requires only a very narrow band of frequencies. Actually, as may be shown by expanding Eq. 43 into a Fourier series, the frequency band includes an infinite number of side-band components, separated from one another by the modulating frequency, f'. When the modulation index, m_f, is small, all but one or two components on either side of f_0 are of negligible magnitude, but as m_f increases, more and more side-band components must be considered, as shown in Fig. 24.* In this respect,

---

* We may expand the sine term in Eq. 43 as follows:

$$\sin (2\pi f_0 t + m_f \sin 2\pi f't) = \sin 2\pi f_0 t \cos (m_f \cos 2\pi f't)$$
$$+ \cos 2\pi f_0 t \sin (m_f \sin 2\pi f't) \tag{45}$$

When m_f is very small, we may approximate $\cos (m_f \cos 2\pi f't)$ by 1, and $\sin (m_f \sin 2\pi f't)$ by $m_f \sin 2\pi f't$. Then Eq. 43 becomes, approximately,

$$e'' = E'' \sin 2\pi f_0 t + E'' m_f \cos 2\pi f_0 t \sin 2\pi f't$$

$$= E'' \sin 2\pi f_0 t + \tfrac{1}{2} E'' m_f [\sin 2\pi (f_0 + f')t - \sin 2\pi (f_0 - f')t] \tag{46}$$

The modulated wave thus consists of a carrier-frequency term and two side-bands, just as for amplitude modulation, but here the two side-bands have *opposite signs* and are relatively very small. When m_f is larger this expansion is incomplete, and additional side-band components appear, as shown in Fig. 24. For further details, see F. E. Terman, *Radio Engineers' Handbook*, p. 578, or Cruft Laboratory Staff, *Electronic Circuits and Tubes*, Chapter XIX, Sec. 6.

then, frequency modulation comes within the broad definition of the fundamental modulation process: it creates whole bands of new frequency components, by what must be some non-linear process.

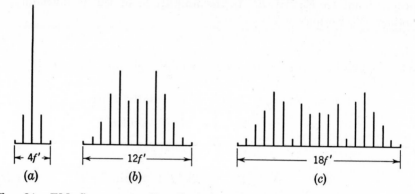

FIG. 24. FM Side-bands (Amplitudes). (a) $m_f = 0.5$ radian. (b) $m_f = \pi$ radians. (c) $m_f = 2\pi$ radians.

24. Phase Modulation. Equation 43 may be interpreted as representing a radiofrequency voltage of constant frequency, f_0, but varying *phase angle*, ϕ, the variations in ϕ being produced by the modulating voltage, y.

$$\phi = m_f \sin 2\pi f't \qquad (47)$$

From this point of view we could speak of this kind of modulation as *phase* modulation as well as frequency modulation. Technically, *phase modulation* is the name given to a type of modulation for which *phase angle*, rather than change in frequency, is proportional to the modulating voltage, y. Let the proportionality factor be $2\pi c$. Then

$$\theta = 2\pi(f_0 t + cy) \qquad (48)$$

It follows that

$$f = d\theta/dt = f_0 + c(dy/dt) \qquad (49)$$

or

$$f - f_0 = c(dy/dt) \qquad (50)$$

Thus change in frequency is proportional to dy/dt for phase modulation, whereas it is proportional to y itself for frequency modulation. When y has the value given by Eq. 39

$$e'' = E'' \cos 2\pi(f_0 t + cE' \cos 2\pi f't) \qquad (51)$$

Except for their manner of dependence upon y, frequency-modulated waves and phase-modulated waves are identical physically, as may be seen by comparison of Eq. 51 with Eq. 43. (The difference between cos $2\pi f't$ and sin $2\pi f't$ is only in initial phase.)   Waves of either kind will operate an FM receiver, and only then may one kind be distinguished from the other; the audio output from the receiver will be a replica of the original sounds for waves which are frequency-modulated, but not for the phase-modulated ones.

25. Production of Frequency Modulation.   The simplest way to produce frequency modulation is to vary the resonant frequency of the tank circuit of an oscillator by means of the "reactance tube" described

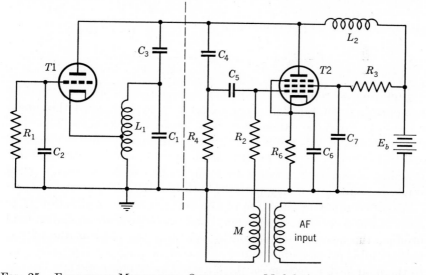

FIG. 25.   FREQUENCY-MODULATED OSCILLATOR.   Modulation is produced by a reactance tube, $T2$.

in Sec. 5, Chapter 11.   This method is illustrated by the circuit of Fig. 25.   A grounded-grid, Hartley oscillator circuit is driven by tube $T1$.   The tank capacitance consists of capacitance C_1 in parallel with the effective capacitance, C', of the reactance-tube circuit to the right of the dotted line.   Comparison will show that this reactance-tube circuit is the same as shown in Fig. 4, Chapter 11.   In Fig. 25 the d-c part of the grid bias for $T2$ is produced by R_6 and C_6, and the audiofrequency part by the modulating voltage, y, through the transformer M.   If the d-c bias is adjusted so that g_m changes linearly with V_g over the desired range of operation, it follows from Eq. 10, Chapter 11, that the change in C', over this range, is proportional to y:

$$\Delta C' = k'y \qquad (52)$$

The resonant frequency of the oscillator circuit also will change by an amount proportional to y, and the output of the oscillator will be frequency-modulated. The proportionality factor, k (Eq. 38), may be found by differentiating the equation for the frequency, f, of the oscillator.

$$f = \frac{1}{2\pi \sqrt{L_1(C_1 + C')}} \tag{53}$$

$$\frac{df}{dC'} = -\frac{1}{4\pi L_1^{\frac{1}{2}}(C_1 + C')^{\frac{3}{2}}} \cong -\frac{f_0}{2(C_1 + C')} \tag{54}$$

Hence $(f - f_0)$ is, approximately,

$$f - f_0 = \frac{df}{dC'} \Delta C' \cong -\frac{f_0 k'}{2(C_1 + C')} y \tag{55}$$

Equation 55 represents frequency modulation, as may be seen by comparison with Eq. 38. If the circuit is well designed this linear relationship may be extended over a considerable range. The chief disadvantage of this method is difficulty in maintaining f_0 constant, and this difficulty may be met by means of a frequency-control system* utilizing a second reactance tube in parallel with the first. (Or a single reactance tube may perform both functions.)

An alternative method for producing frequency modulation is to start with a constant-frequency, crystal-controlled oscillator, and produce the desired modulation by changing the *phase* of the output with suitable phase-shift circuits. If the phase angle, ϕ, is proportional to the modulating voltage, y, the output will be phase-modulated, but if ϕ is made proportional to the *integral* of y, by an integrating circuit of the type described in Sec. 3, Chapter 11, the output will be frequency-modulated. This method has the advantage of stable frequency, but the phase-shift circuits are quite complicated and produce relatively small phase shifts. When this system is employed the modulation must be increased by frequency multiplication; the modulation is applied to a crystal oscillator whose frequency is so much lower than the desired value for f_0 that, when frequency multiplication has raised the mean frequency to the desired value, it has also increased $(f - f_0)$ to a satisfactory value.

26. The Discriminator Circuit. Frequency-modulated signals are usually detected by the *discriminator* circuit shown in Fig. 26. This is a double-detector circuit in which the rectified outputs from the two diodes, $D1$ and $D2$, balance out when the resonant circuit, $L_2 C_2$, is tuned to the frequency f_0. Whenever frequency modulation causes the

* See Cruft Laboratory Staff, *Electronic Circuits and Tubes*, p. 668.

frequency f to differ from f_0, however, the output from one detector is greater than from the other and an audiofrequency output, e_0, appears. The explanation which follows is made in terms of the capital letters which represent amplitudes for the alternating currents and voltages, and throughout it will be assumed that the resonant circuit, L_2C_2, is tuned to the mean frequency, f_0.

The FM signal reaches this circuit as an alternating current, I_1, in the coil L_1, which is a part of the plate circuit in the last stage of a

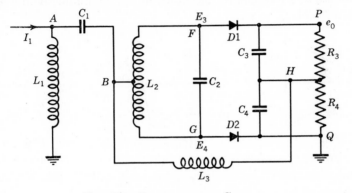

FIG. 26. DISCRIMINATOR CIRCUIT.

RF amplifier. The condenser C_1 serves to block direct current from the discriminator circuit. This alternating current produces an alternating potential, E_1, at the point A, and induces an emf, E_m, in L_2 by mutual induction between L_1 and L_2. The magnitudes of these voltages are

$$E_1 = L_1\omega I_1 \tag{56}$$

$$E_m = M\omega I_1 = (M/L_1)E_1 \tag{57}$$

Both E_1 and E_m lead I_1 in phase by 90 degrees, as represented in the diagrams of Fig. 27.

In the resonant circuit the emf E_m produces a current I_2 which, in turn, produces a potential difference E_2 between the ends of L_2. If the input is of frequency f_0, and unmodulated, I_2 is in phase with E_m, and E_2 leads I_2 by 90 degrees, as shown in Fig. 27a. The magnitudes are

$$I_2 = (1/R_2)E_m = (M/L_1R_2)E_1 \tag{58}$$

$$E_2 = L_2\omega I_2 = (ML_2\omega/L_1R_2)E_1 \tag{59}$$

Since the potential at B is the same as at A, or E_1, the potential E_3 at

F is the *vector* sum of E_1 and $+E_2/2$, and E_4, the potential at G, is the vector sum of E_1 and $-E_2/2$, as represented in Fig. 27.

To simplify this discussion let us consider that the ground connection is made at H. The alternating potential E_3 then appears across the detector $D1$ and its filter circuit, C_3R_3, and C_3 is charged to a d-c potential almost equal to E_3, with P positive. Likewise the a-c potential E_4 appears across $D2$ and L_4C_4, and C_4 is charged to a d-c potential almost equal to E_4, with Q positive. When the input is unmodulated, E_3 equals E_4, as shown in Fig. 27a, and the d-c output, between P and Q, is zero.

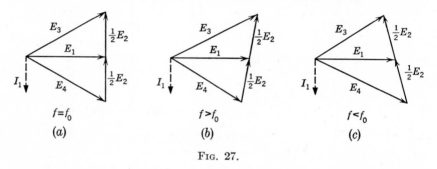

Fig. 27.

Consider next a signal for which the frequency, f, differs slightly from f_0. The magnitude of I_2 is now E_m/Z_2, but the magnitude of Z_2 does not differ much from R_2 over the range of frequency variation encountered in frequency modulation. Hence we may assume that I_2 has the magnitude given by Eq. 58, and consider only the change in phase which is produced by difference in frequency. If f is greater than f_0 the reactance of L_2 and C_2 to I_2 is inductive, and I_2 lags behind E_m in phase. The same change in phase appears in E_2, so that E_3 is greater than E_4 in magnitude, as shown in Fig. 27b, and there is a d-c output, with P positive. If instead f is less than f_0, the reactance is capacitive, I_2 and E_2 advance in phase, as shown in Fig. 27c, and there is a d-c output with P negative. Over a considerable frequency range about f_0 the d-c output is proportional to the frequency difference, as shown by the plot of Fig. 28. The extent of this linear range may be made to conform to the range of frequency modulation by proper design of the circuit.

For a frequency-modulated input the audio output is produced in a similar manner. Since a time interval which is very short compared to the period of an audiofrequency cycle may comprise many radiofrequency cycles, the frequency difference which corresponds to an "instantaneous" value of the audio signal may be regarded as a steady difference in the RF circuits, and the instantaneous audiofrequency output is equal to the corresponding d-c output. The same results follow if the ground connection is moved to Q from H, since all points to the right of $D1$ and $D2$ are at zero potential in so far as the RF voltages are concerned. Note that the RF choke-coil, L_3, is needed in any case to complete the d-c path for each diode.

Various other applications exist for this discriminator circuit. For example, it may be combined with a reactance tube to maintain the output of an oscillator close to the frequency f_0 determined by L_2 and C_2 in Fig. 26. For this application more filter sections are added to

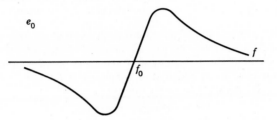

FIG. 28.　DISCRIMINATOR OUTPUT VS. FREQUENCY.

C_3R_3 and C_4R_4, so that the output is a steady d-c potential determined by the average frequency of the input. This d-c output is then fed back to the grid of a reactance tube in the oscillator circuit, in such a direction as to reduce the discriminator output by changing the oscillator frequency toward f_0. With strong feedback the oscillator frequency may be held close to f_0.

27. The Limiter Circuit. A radiofrequency amplifier for FM signals does not differ greatly from those employed for AM signals, except for the addition of a *limiter*. Once the input from the antenna has been amplified sufficiently it may be clipped top and bottom so that the input to the discriminator is at a constant amplitude for all signals. The clipper or limiter may have any of the forms mentioned in Sec. 20, Chapter 11. Since frequency modulation depends upon only the spacing from one wave to the next, *along the axis*, this clipping does not alter the pattern of the signal. It does, however, eliminate the effects of fading, unless the signal drops below the clipping level, and almost eliminates the effects of static and other spurious signals.

PROBLEMS

1. Take the equation for the transfer characteristic of a tube biased for modulation to be

$$I_p = 4.0 + 1.20x + 0.080x^2$$

Let the input, x, be the sum of a signal of 2.00 volts amplitude and 500 cps frequency, and one of 2.50 volts amplitude and 1800 cps frequency, and find the amplitudes and frequencies for all the components appearing in the plate currrent. (Do not solve by formula, but work the problem out, following the procedure shown in Sec. 3.)

2. Assume a transfer characteristic having the equation

$$I_p = 6.0 + 1.60x - 0.0160x^3$$

Take the input the same as for Prob. 1 and solve in the same manner for the amplitudes and frequencies of all the components of I_p.

3. A 1400-Kcps RF voltage, which has an average amplitude of 85 volts, is amplitude-modulated 45 percent. Find (a) the amplitude of the modulating AF signal, (b) the maximum and minimum amplitudes for this voltage, and (c) the amplitudes and frequencies of the side-bands, if the modulating frequency is 500 cps.

4. A 950-Kcps RF voltage is amplitude-modulated so that its amplitude varies from a maximum of 48 volts to a minimum of 6 volts. (a) Find the percent modulation. (b) Find the frequency and amplitude for the carrier component and for each side-band if the modulating frequency is 250 cps.

5. Prove Eq. 22, giving reasons for each step.

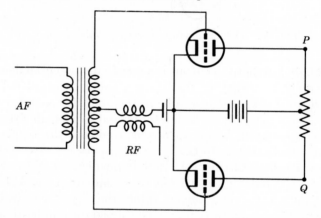

FIG. 29. BALANCED MODULATOR. See Prob. 6. Output includes both side-bands, but not the carrier component.

6. In the balanced-modulator circuit shown in Fig. 29, each tube is biased so that its transfer characteristic is represented by Eq. 6. (a) Note and explain how the RF input produces the same potential at each grid, but the AF potentials are of opposite sign. (b) Show that the output between P and Q is zero with RF input alone. (c) Show that, if both AF and RF inputs are present, the output includes both side-bands, but not the carrier component.

7. Rearrange the input circuit of Fig. 29 so that the output includes the carrier component and the side-bands, but no AF component.

8. Show that a tube operating on a "square-law" part of its transfer characteristic may act as a detector for AM signals. Assume the equation given in Prob. 1, and find the AF output if the input has a mean amplitude of 500 mv, with 50

percent modulation. Take the carrier frequency to be 1450 Kcps, and the modulating frequency as 1600 cps. Include the AF harmonics. SUGGESTION: find the carrier component and the two side-bands; then find the modulation products between these three terms, taken two at a time.

9. Grid modulation is to be applied to a class C amplifier for which the cut-off grid potential is −55 volts, and the peak grid potential is +30 volts. The amplitude of the RF input to the grid is 80 volts. (a) Find the value of the grid bias needed. (b) Find the amplitude of the AF input needed to produce 75 percent modulation.

10. A 650-Kcps radio signal is amplitude-modulated by a 1200-cps note, and this signal is picked up by a radio receiver, along with an unmodulated signal of 651 Kcps, from a signal generator. *Four* AF notes are heard. Explain their origin, and find their frequencies.

11. The cathode current in a pentagrid tube is 8.0 ma d-c, and 8.5 ma a-c at 25,000 cps. The bias for grid 3 is such that 25.0 percent of this current reaches the plate, and this ratio changes by 6.0 percent if the grid potential is changed by 1.00 volt. A signal of 25 mv amplitude and 12,000 cps frequency is put on grid 3. (a) Find the plate current as a product (see Eqs. 27 and 28). (b) Resolve this current into its harmonic components, and find their amplitudes and frequencies. (c) The plate load is a resonant circuit tuned to 37,000 cps, with a parallel resistance of 75 K. Find the output voltage.

12. Find the conversion transconductance for the tube specified in Prob. 11.

13. In a frequency-modulation system the mean frequency is 40.0 Mcps (megacycles per second) and the instantaneous frequency changes 10.0 Kcps for unit change in y, the modulating signal. (a) Obtain the equation for the modulated output having an amplitude of 50 volts, for a signal of 2.70, and frequency 750 cps. (b) Repeat for a signal having the same amplitude but a frequency of 2250 cps. (c) Find the modulation index for each.

14. Assume that the RF voltage specified in Prob. 13 is *phase*-modulated by the same AF signals, and that the modulated output is identical for the 750-cps signal. (a) Find it for the 2250-cps signal. (b) Find the modulation index for each.

15. If the input to a discriminator circuit is phase-modulated, it is apparent from Eq. 48 that the AF output will be proportional to the *time derivative* of the original AF signal. Design a circuit to follow the output of the discriminator, so that the original signal may be heard.

16. A frequency-modulated voltage which fluctuates 60 Kcps to either side of 50.0 Mcps produces a current of 2.50 ma at the input (in L_1, Fig. 26) of a discriminator circuit. Find the amplitude of the AF output, assuming that the detector and filter units read peak values. Take $L_1 = 35$ μh (microhenries), $L_2 = 30$ μh, $M = 0.85$ μh, and $Q = 50$ for L_2C_2.

CHAPTER 13

Ultra-High-Frequency Electronics

1. High-Frequency Operation of Electron Tubes. At low frequencies the reactances associated with an electron tube, such as those due to interelectrode capacitances, are quite negligible, and the only observable phase difference between output and input is the change of sign which always occurs. Unfortunately, this ideal phase relationship between output and input does not continue as the frequency is raised. Somewhere in the upper audiofrequency range it becomes quite necessary to take account of the interelectrode capacitances, as has been explained in Chapter 10, and in the radiofrequency range these factors are so troublesome in triodes as to require special circuits to neutralize their adverse effects. Tetrodes and pentodes were developed originally as means for minimizing the objectionable tube capacitances, so that simpler radiofrequency circuits are possible. Tetrodes and pentodes are satisfactory also for much of the higher ranges of frequency which include FM broadcasting and television.

Difficulties arising from tube reactances increase rapidly as the frequency of operation is raised above the broadcasting range, and ultimately all tube reactances become troublesome, including those due to the connections between the electrodes and the external circuits. The frequency at which this difficulty becomes acute depends upon the type of tube; roughly speaking, it is in the neighborhood of 100 Mcps (megacycles per second). To a considerable degree the adverse effects of these reactances may be compensated by improvements in the associated circuits, such as replacement of the coils and condensers, which form resonant circuits for the lower frequencies, by sections of transmission lines, or by hollow conductors (resonant "cavities") of various shapes and sizes. In addition, triodes and pentodes have been redesigned, as described below, so as to reduce tube reactances to a minimum and to make the most direct connections between the electrodes and the resonant circuits. These modifications are discussed in the sections which follow.

Commercial applications and scientific research both find need for electrical oscillations of higher and higher frequency, and the ultimate limit to high-frequency operation of electron tubes is found to be a factor hitherto disregarded, namely, the *time of flight* for electrons from cathode to anode. Indeed, this factor seriously alters the performance of electron tubes even before the high-frequency limit is reached. In this chapter we shall first consider methods available for reducing flight time in tubes of familiar types, so as to extend their operation into the UHF (ultra-high-frequency) range of approximately 300 to 3000 Mcps. We shall then consider the special types of tubes which have been developed to make operation most effective in this range, as well as to extend operation into the microwave region beyond.

2. Input Impedance. The effect of tube capacitance is most serious in the input circuit. The input capacitance for most pentodes* is in the neighborhood of 2 to 5 $\mu\mu$f (micro-microfarads), and the corresponding reactance, at 100 Mcps or higher, is only a few *hundred* ohms. Even if the tube capacitance is the only capacitance in the input circuit, the inductance needed to tune it to resonance is very small, and the input impedance is far too low for satisfactory operation unless the Q-factor of this inductance is very high. A coil of wire is not very satisfactory, since the losses in it, especially losses by radiation, are quite high at these frequencies. A much better inductance is provided by a short length of transmission line. For a transmission line the losses are relatively small, and the Q-factor correspondingly high, since its conductors are quite large and the electric and magnetic fields are confined close to the conductors. In a coaxial line these fields are entirely inside the outer conductor and the radiation losses are practically zero. Tuning is accomplished for a line section by varying its length, by means of a movable "bridge" or shorting-bar on a parallel-wire line, or a movable plug in a coaxial line. Since the output capacitance for the tube is also low, a section of transmission line may serve also as the output circuit, if it seems desirable.

Figure 1 represents such a UHF amplifier having sections of coaxial line, $T1$ and $T2$, in the grid and plate circuits respectively. The by-pass condensers, C_1, C_2, and C_3, must be placed as close as possible to the tube and the connecting wires made no longer than absolutely necessary. The input from the antenna is made to the inner conductor of $T1$ by a probe inserted through a slot in the outer conductor, and coupling is varied by moving this probe along the line. The line thus serves as a tapped coil or auto-transformer. Output is obtained by means of a similar probe in line $T2$.

* For triodes the grid-to-cathode capacitance is about the same, but the grid-to-plate capacitance introduces additional (parallel) impedance whose nature depends upon the output circuit, as has been explained earlier.

3. Transmission-Line Reactors. At this point let us digress to consider those aspects of transmission lines which we shall need here. A transmission line for UHF purposes may be a pair of parallel wires, as shown in Fig. 2a, or a rod surrounded by a coaxial cylinder or tube, as in Fig. 2b. Less often it may take other forms. All transverse dimensions, such as D in Fig. 2a, or R_2 in Fig. 2b, must be much

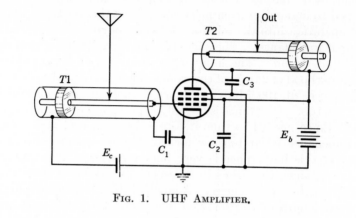

FIG. 1.   UHF AMPLIFIER.

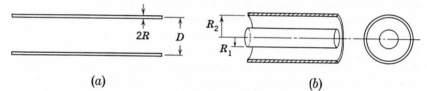

FIG. 2.   TRANSMISSION LINES.   (a) Parallel wires.   (b) Coaxial cylinders.

smaller than the wavelength of the transmitted waves. The speed of guided waves along such a line is very close to c, the speed of light, and may be assumed to have that value. Losses are small and may be neglected for the short sections of line here considered. In what follows we shall be concerned with transmission lines only when one end is terminated by a pure reactance. Perfect reflection then occurs at that end, and *standing waves* exist along the line.

Consider, for example, a parallel-wire line terminated by a metal plate,* as represented in Fig. 3, and let us measure distance x along the line from this short-circuited end. At this end the potential difference, v, between the wires is zero, the current, i, a maximum. Elsewhere

---

* Theoretically, this plate should be of infinite extent, but practically it need be only several times wider than the line spacing.

along the line v and i are given by

$$v = V_0 \sin 2\pi ft \sin 2\pi x/\lambda \qquad (1)$$

$$i = I_0 \cos 2\pi ft \cos 2\pi x/\lambda \qquad (2)$$

From Eqs. 1 and 2 it is seen that v and i are everywhere out of phase by

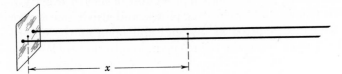

FIG. 3.   SHORTED LINE.   Left end is terminated by a large metal plate.

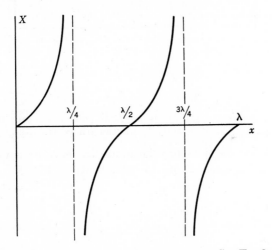

FIG. 4.   REACTANCE OF SHORTED LINE.   See Eq. 3.

90 degrees, so that at any point x the ratio of their amplitudes represents a *reactance*, X_x.   If V_0/I_0 is represented by Z_0*

$$X_x = (V_0/I_0) \tan 2\pi x/\lambda = Z_0 \tan 2\pi x/\lambda \qquad (3)$$

A plot of this equation is given in Fig. 4.

Any section of transmission line of length b, having one end shorted, the other connected to a generator of frequency f, appears to the generator to be a *reactance*, X_b, of value given by Eq. 3 for x equal to b, and λ equal to c/f.   From Fig. 4 it is seen that X_b is inductive for b

* This ratio is the characteristic impedance of the line.   For parallel wires, $Z_0 = 276 \log_{10} D/R$ ohms; for a coaxial line, $Z_0 = 138 \log_{10} R_2/R_1$ ohms.   See Fig. 2 for meanings of symbols.

less than $\lambda/4$, is capacitative for b between $\lambda/4$ and $\lambda/2$, and alternates between inductive and capacitative values for higher values of b.

4. Resonant Lines. A section of transmission line may be tuned to resonance by proper terminations at *both* ends. Thus a line section which is shorted at one end and less than $\lambda/4$ in length may be tuned to resonance by a variable condenser connected to its other end. Resonance will occur likewise in a line section of length exactly $\lambda/2$, with both ends terminated by shorting plates, and also in one approximately $\lambda/4$ in length, if shorted at one end and open at the other. (Stray fields at the open end make the resonant length slightly less than $\lambda/4$.)

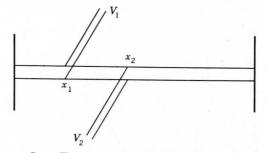

FIG. 5. RESONANT-LINE TRANSFORMER. Both ends of line are shorted by metal plates exactly $\frac{1}{2}$ wavelength apart.

A resonant line section may be made to serve as a voltage transformer, by making connections to it as shown in Fig. 5. If the power transmitted through it is small the voltage ratio is given by Eq. 1, that is,

$$\frac{V_1}{V_2} = \frac{\sin 2\pi x_1/\lambda}{\sin 2\pi x_2/\lambda} \tag{4}$$

5. Electron Flight-Time. Since an electron is such a very light particle the time it takes to travel from the cathode to the anode of an electron tube is very small; hitherto we have regarded it as negligibly small. The order of magnitude of this electron flight-time may be estimated from the following computation for a diode having plane-parallel electrodes. Let the distance between electrodes be s, and the anode potential be V. Then, if we neglect the effect of space-charge, the electric field between electrodes is uniform and equal to $-V/s$, and gives to an electron a constant acceleration eV/ms. If the flight-time is t_1 the laws for accelerated motion give us

$$s = \tfrac{1}{2} \times \text{acceleration} \times t_1{}^2$$

$$= \frac{eV}{2ms} t_1{}^2 \tag{5}$$

or

$$t_1 = \sqrt{\left(\frac{2m}{e}\right)} \frac{s}{\sqrt{V}} \qquad (6)$$

For V measured in volts, and s in centimeters,

$$t_1 = 3.4 \times 10^{-8} \frac{s}{\sqrt{V}} \qquad (7)$$

Space-charge causes the flight-time to be longer, the corresponding value being

$$t_2 = 5.0 \times 10^{-8} \frac{s}{\sqrt{V}} \qquad (8)$$

For tubes with grids the flight-times will be different, and generally longer, but the order of magnitude is indicated by Eq. 8. In any case the flight-time may be reduced by decreasing the spacing between electrodes, and by increasing the effective potential of the anode. The distance from cathode to anode for ordinary receiving tubes is around 1 or 2 mm, and the effective potential of the order of magnitude of 100 volts. For s equal to 2 mm, and 100 volts for V, Eq. 8 gives 10^{-9} sec for t_2, and we may take this figure as representing the *order of magnitude* for the flight-time in ordinary tubes and circuits. In power tubes the electrode spacings must be greater but these tubes are operated at higher potentials, so that for these tubes also the flight-time has roughly the same magnitude.

Let us now inquire into when and why flight-time is important. At low frequencies, when the time of one oscillation is very much larger than the flight-time, we may consider current values in an electron tube at any instant to be the same for instantaneous potentials as for d-c potentials of the same values. This assumption is made whenever the a-c performance of a tube is analyzed from its d-c characteristic curves. For a flight-time of 10^{-9} sec this assumption is good to above 10 Mcps, since 10^{-9} sec is only $\frac{1}{100}$ cycle at 10 Mcps, but when the flight-time becomes an appreciable fraction of a cycle we may no longer neglect it. Then we find that the current lags behind the plate potential because of the *inertia of the electrons*, and if the flight-time exceeds about $\frac{1}{4}$ cycle the tube functions poorly if at all. A flight-time of 10^{-9} sec becomes $\frac{1}{4}$ cycle at a frequency of 250 Mcps.

6. UHF Triodes, Tetrodes, and Pentodes. The first step in reducing flight-time for triodes, tetrodes, and pentodes is to decrease electrode spacing. Since this change by itself increases the interelectrode capacitances, it is then necessary to reduce the other dimensions of the electrodes, the result being miniature tubes such as the "acorn" triode represented in Fig. 6. Thus the cathode-to-plate distance in this triode is less than $\frac{1}{2}$ mm, and the other electrode dimensions are less than 10 mm. Interelectrode capacitances are in the neighborhood of 1 $\mu\mu$f. Leads from the electrodes are brought out radially as shown,

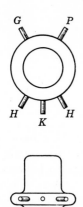

so that they are short and well separated, and their inductances very small. This triode will operate up to 600 Mcps, but its power output is small, less than $\frac{1}{2}$ watt at 300 Mcps. In acorn-type pentodes the cathode-to-plate spacing is comparable to that for the triode, but somewhat larger to make room for the additional grids. In a tetrode electrons spend most of the flight-time between cathode and screen grid, since they have high speed between screen grid and plate. In a pentode electrons lose additional time by being slowed down in the low-potential region around the suppressor grid. For this reason acorn pentodes are limited in use to frequencies below about 400 Mcps. Tetrodes may be operated at higher frequencies, but only triodes will function throughout the UHF range.

FIG. 6. ACORN TUBE (955) (ABOUT $\frac{2}{3}$ SIZE). Terminal pins project radially from a flat glass press.

The "door-knob" tube illustrated in Fig. 7 is made more powerful than the acorn tubes by providing the plate with large cooling vanes, W, which increase greatly its ability to dissipate heat. The plate itself is a cylinder about 3 mm in diameter and 13 mm long, with the cathode a straight tungsten wire along its axis. The grid wires are stretched between end-rings, G, and run parallel to the axis so as to reduce the inductance of the grid to a minimum. The glass bulb is the size and shape of a small door-knob, with the short leads from the electrodes brought out through one of the flattened sides. A power output of 4 watts at 600 Mcps is possible, and the limiting frequency is about 750 Mcps. The same principles are applied to the construction of larger triodes and tetrodes, in which greater electrode spacings may be partially offset by operation at high voltages.

7. Lighthouse Tubes. The UHF triode has reached its highest development in the "lighthouse" or "disk-seal" type of tube illustrated in Fig. 8a. In this tube the electrodes form a plane-parallel structure about 5 mm in diameter, with very close electrode spacings: from cathode to grid is $\frac{1}{10}$ mm, from cathode to plate, $\frac{3}{10}$ mm. The grid is a mesh of fine wires covering a hole in the center of the metal

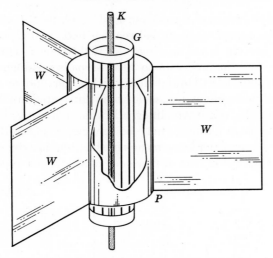

FIG. 7.   DOOR-KNOB TUBE (316-A) (ELECTRODE STRUCTURE ONLY).   *K*—cathode.
P—plate.   *G*—grid.   *W*—cooling vanes.   This structure is enclosed in a glass bulb
the size and shape of a door-knob.

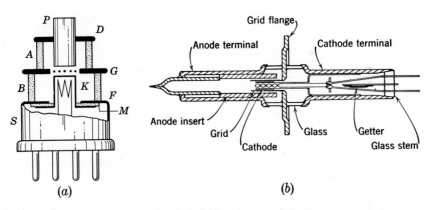

(a)   (b)

FIG. 8.   DISK-SEAL TUBES.   (a) Lighthouse tube (2C40).   *K*—cathode.   *P*—
anode.   *G*—grid and grid disk.   *A,B*—glass cylinders sealed to disks *D,G*, and *F*.
M—mica disk insulating *K* from outer shell, *S*.   (b) Pencil tube (5675).   (Figure
8b used through the courtesy of the Radio Corporation of America.)

disk, *G*.   The anode is the lower end of the metal cylinder, *P*, and the
cathode is the oxide-coated, upper end of the hollow cylinder, *K*.
Short glass cylinders, *A* and *B*, are sealed between the metal disks, *D*,
G, and *F*, to form the evacuated enclosure.   External connections are
made to these metal disks and may be made from all sides, so as to
reduce the lead-in inductances to exceedingly small values.   Capaci-

tances are small, being 1.3 $\mu\mu$f from grid to plate, 2.1 $\mu\mu$f from grid to cathode, and practically zero between cathode and plate. Because of the very close electrode spacings the flight-time is between 10^{-10} and 10^{-11} sec, and operation up to 3000 Mcps is possible. The same type of construction is followed in several larger and more powerful tubes. A modified form of disk-seal tube is illustrated in Fig. 8b.

8. The Grounded-Grid Amplifier. Interaction between input and output circuits of an amplifier may be prevented in the RF range by means of a screen grid, and this means of shielding is extended into the lower UHF range by means of pentodes of the acorn type. For the

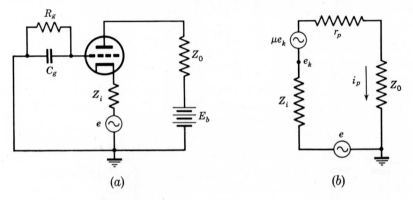

FIG. 9. GROUNDED-GRID AMPLIFIER. (a) Actual circuit. (b) Equivalent circuit.

upper UHF range, in which only triodes will function, other means must be found. One such means is to make the triode grid the grounded electrode, as shown in Fig. 9a, so that this grid provides the necessary electrostatic shielding between input and output. The input is now between cathode and ground, the output between plate and ground, or between plate and grid within the tube. This circuit has certain disadvantages, however, which preclude its use whenever other methods of neutralization are satisfactory. First, since the input source is in the cathode-to-plate circuit, in which there is the alternating plate current, i_p, the input emf, e, must supply power equal to ei_p, in addition to any power supplied to the grid circuit. (This type of amplifier is generally operated class C, with the grid bias supplied by a small grid current in a grid resistance and condenser, R_g and C_g in Fig. 9a.) Second, since the input impedance is in the cathode-to-plate circuit it produces degenerative feedback, as seen in the following analysis.

The equivalent a-c circuit, neglecting grid current, is diagrammed in Fig. 9b; if the circuit is properly adjusted the output and input impedances, Z_0 and Z_i, are nearly pure resistances, as here represented. Since e_g, the potential of the grid relative to the cathode, equals $-e_k$, the equivalent emf, μe_g, equals $-\mu e_k$ and acts upward, in the direction of e_k and e.   The current i_p is also taken in this direction around the circuit.   When the plate circuit is open, e_k is equal to e, but when it is closed, e_k is less than e by the potential drop in Z_i caused by i_p:

$$e_k = e - i_p Z_i \tag{9}$$

From the equivalent circuit we may write

$$i_p(r_p + Z_0 + Z_i) = e + \mu e_k = e + \mu e - \mu i_p Z_i \tag{10}$$

or

$$i_p = \frac{(\mu + 1)e}{r_p + Z_0 + Z_i(1 + \mu)} \tag{11}$$

and

$$e_0 = i_p Z_0 = \frac{(\mu + 1)Z_0 e}{r_p + Z_0 + Z_i(1 + \mu)} \tag{12}$$

It is evident from Eq. 9 that Z_i produces negative feedback, so that the gain represented by Eq. 12 is less than it would be if Z_i were negligible.   Indeed, the gain may be less than unity if Z_i is very large. The power output, P_0, equals $e_0 i_p$; if the power input, P_i, is taken equal to $e i_p$ (neglecting grid current) the power gain is in the same ratio as the voltage gain.   The effective input impedance, R' (neglecting grid current), may be obtained from the input power and Eq. 11.

$$P_i = i_p e = \frac{(\mu + 1)e^2}{r_p + Z_0 + (\mu + 1)Z_i} = \frac{e^2}{R'} \tag{13}$$

Evidently

$$R' = Z_i + \frac{r_p + Z_0}{\mu + 1} \tag{14}$$

It is characteristic of the grounded-grid amplifier that the input impedance must be low, the output impedance high, whereas the reverse is true for an ordinary amplifier.

9. Experiment 33.   Grounded-Grid Amplifier.   Although a grounded-grid amplifier is of value chiefly in the very high-frequency ranges, its performance may be studied more readily, and understood more easily, in an audiofrequency amplifier, where the impedances may be resistances of known values.   Such an amplifier is diagrammed in Fig. 10.   For a 6J5 triode with a d-c supply of about 250 volts, R_0 may be 100 K, and the grid bias adjusted to make the direct current about 1.0 ma.

The transformer $T1$ (of negligible resistance) and resistors R_1 and R_2 are employed to produce a signal source of small emf and known internal impedance.   When there is no tube current in R_2 the potential at K is

$$e = \frac{R_2}{R_1 + R_2} e_1 \qquad (14a)$$

Also, the resistance between K and ground is

$$R_i = \frac{R_1 R_2}{R_1 + R_2} \qquad (14b)$$

It now may be shown* that, when the circuit is operating as an amplifier, this arrangement is equivalent to an emf e in series with an imped-

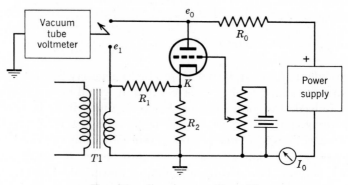

FIG. 10.   CIRCUIT FOR EXP. 33.

ance Z_i equal to R_i, as represented in Fig. 9a.   The transformer may be a filament transformer connected to the 60-cps line, or better to a source of higher audiofrequency.   The value of e_1 should be between 2 and 6 volts.   The resistors should be non-inductive.   Fixed resistors of the values indicated below will serve for R_2, but R_1 must be a variable resistor, either a laboratory resistance box or one having a sliding contact and a calibrated scale.

Part I.   Make R_2 about 1000 ohms and adjust R_1 so that the vacuum-tube voltmeter readings for e_1 and e_0 are approximately the same.   From these voltmeter readings compute e, e_k, and the gain,

* From Thévenin's theorem, which may be stated as follows: "If the potential difference between any two points in a circuit is e and the impedance of the circuit between these points is Z_i, then the current in any additional circuit element connected between these two points is the same as if the element had been connected to a generator of emf e and internal impedance Z_i."   For proof, see A. T. Starr, *Electric Circuits and Wave Filters*, p. 78.

e_0/e. Compute R_i. Check the gain by computing it from Eq. 12; obtain μ and r_p from the tube handbook. Any discrepancies should be due primarily to inexact values for r_p.

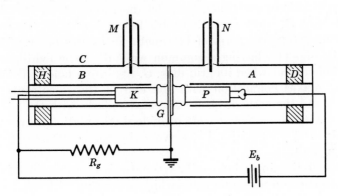

(a)

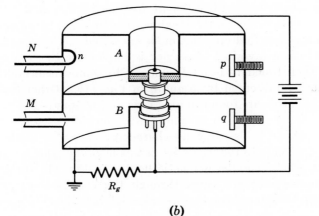

(b)

Fig. 11.   Resonant-Cavity Amplifier.   (a) With pencil tube.   (b) With light-house tube.   B—input cavity.   A—output cavity.

Part II.   Repeat these observations and computations for R_2 equal to 5000 ohms, and 400 ohms.   Compute the value of R_i for which the "gain" would be only unity.

10. Cavity Resonators.   Two grounded-grid amplifiers for operation up to the top of the UHF range for triodes are diagrammed in Fig. 11. In Fig. 11a the resonant "circuits" are sections of coaxial line.   The outer conductor for both, C, just fits over the grid disk, G, of the pencil-type triode (see Fig. 8b) which is designed especially for use with such coaxial lines. The inner conductors, A and B, fit over the pencil-size anode and cathode, P and K, with clearance enough for mica separators to provide d-c insulation between these electrodes and the grounded lines. These lines are tuned by axial displacements of the shorting plugs D and H. For operation with lighthouse tubes the resonant circuits may take the form of two metal inclosures or "cavities," A and B in Fig. 11b, having a common wall, W. The lighthouse tube is inserted so that when its grid disk, G, fits into a hole in W its plate terminal makes connection with the end of the re-entrant part of cavity A and the cathode shell connects similarly with the re-entrant part of cavity B. Mica spacers provide d-c insulation between these electrodes and the cavities, but serve as by-pass condensers for alternating current.

The oscillation in such a cavity resonator is best described in terms of the electric and magnetic fields which are set up within it,* and the frequency of oscillation is determined by the size and shape of the cavity. Many shapes are possible, and any single cavity has many modes of oscillation, with different frequencies for each. Generally the shape of the cavity and the manner of coupling it to outside circuits may be chosen so that only one mode is excited. The re-entrant type of Fig. 11b is a favorite. A cavity is built close to the desired frequency, then tuned to exact frequency by some means such as the screw plugs represented by p and q in Fig. 11b. Other examples of cavity resonators are found in klystrons and magnetrons.

There are no electric or magnetic fields outside a cavity resonator, and the outside walls carry no charges or currents. External connections are made to the inside by means of probes which couple with either the electric or the magnetic field. In Fig. 11a the input and output connections are made through the coaxial lines M and N, which have their inner conductors extended into the cavities as probes to couple with the electric field. External connections are made to cavities A and B in Fig. 11b in a similar manner, except that the probe in cavity A is made by bending the inner conductor of N into a loop, n, and soldering its end to the inner wall of A. This loop probe is oriented so that it interacts with the magnetic field in the cavity.

11. UHF Triode Oscillators. Triode oscillators at UHF and microwave frequencies are essentially the same as for lower frequencies,

---

* An elementary description of such an oscillation is given by T. B. Brown in *Foundations of Modern Physics*, 2nd Ed., p. 97. Fuller treatments are found in many textbooks, including H. H. Skilling, *Fundamentals of Electric Waves;* R. I. Sarbacher and W. A. Edson, *Hyper and Ultra High Frequency Engineering;* and S. Ramo and J. R. Whinnery, *Fields and Waves in Modern Radio.*

except for the greater importance of all tube reactances, and the employment of resonant lines or cavities in place of coils and condensers. The oscillator circuit of Fig. 12 illustrates these differences. The tank circuit is a resonant line, A-B, terminated at one end by the grid-plate capacitance of the tube, at the other by the condenser C. Grid- and plate-supply connections are made at the voltage node, N, of this line. Choke-coils L_1 and L_2 take care of any slight error in

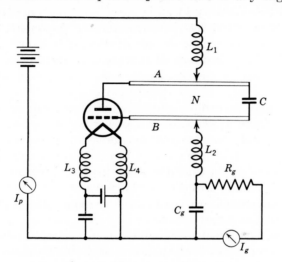

FIG. 12.   500-MEGACYCLE OSCILLATOR.

locating this nodal point. At these frequencies it is found desirable to isolate the cathode by means of choke-coils L_3 and L_4, because of the cathode-grid capacitance. These choke-coils may take the form of quarter-wave resonant lines. Better balanced circuits are obtained with two tubes; in effect such circuits are the same as might be produced by replacing C in Fig. 12 by a second tube, with some other changes of detail. At the highest frequencies attainable with triodes an oscillator is made by providing feedback coupling between the plate-grid cavity and the cathode-grid cavity of an amplifier of the type shown in Fig. 11. This coupling is made by means of a suitable probe extending into both cavities through the boundary wall.

12. Experiment 34. UHF Oscillator. There are few experiments with centimeter wave equipment which are suitable for a single laboratory period. First of all, it takes too much shopwork to assemble a "circuit" for this frequency range; second, the measurements which may be made by any simple means are far too inaccurate to give any quantitative check with theory. There are available commercially several small lighthouse tube oscillators* which serve to give some acquaintance with the general characteristics of such circuits. If the oscillator is one which may be coupled to a transmission line its frequency may be measured in that manner. If, on the other hand, its output is to a dipole in a horn or parabolic "dish," so that a beam of nearly plane-parallel waves may be produced, standing waves may be set up between this source and a metal-plate "mirror," and the wavelength measured by locating successive loops and nodes with a small dipole detector, likewise available commercially. Change of power with various changes of operating conditions may be observed, taking readings of the dipole detector as a measure of relative power. Input power may be measured with a d-c voltmeter and ammeter in the plate-power supply. If the coupling between input and output cavities is variable, explore the effect of such changes and find the adjustment which gives maximum power output. Likewise investigate the effect of changing the output coupling to the transmitting dipole. It is interesting also to introduce a d-c meter in series with the grid resistor to measure the grid current. Then try to find the value for this resistor to make the output greatest. In making these changes do not exceed the maximum values specified for plate current, plate potential, and grid current.

13. Pulsed Operation of Triodes. One means for shortening the transit time in a triode is to operate it at as high a plate potential as possible. Then, to keep the power loss down to what the plate can dissipate, this high voltage must be *pulsed*, or applied intermittently for an interval short compared with the time between pulses, but long enough to include hundreds of oscillations. In practice the pulse is generally about one microsecond long, and repeated about 1000 times per second. The upper limit to the plate potential is set by the peak value of cathode emission for the tube. For example, the type 15-E tube, only slightly larger than the one shown in Fig. 7, is designed for pulsed operation at about 500 Mcps, with a d-c supply of 10,000 volts. Its maximum cathode emission is 6 amperes. During a pulse its power output may reach 10,000 watts, but its average output is 10 watts, with a duty cycle, or ratio of operating time to total time, of 1:000. Note that the potential which determines transit time in a class C amplifier or oscillator is close to the minimum or "trough" value of the plate potential. (See Sec. 26, Chapter 10.) At low radiofrequencies efficiency is gained by making this trough potential

---

* Central Scientific Co., Chicago, Ill., supplies this equipment. Another source is Decimeter, Denver, Colo.

low; in the UHF range it is necessary to keep it high because of transit time, and the efficiency is correspondingly less.

14. Pulse Modulators. This pulsed operation is characteristic of all radar transmission, and various pulsing circuits, or *pulse-modulators*, have been devised. The single example of Fig. 13 must suffice here. The energy for each pulse is stored in an artificial line formed by the tapped inductance, L, and the condensers connected to it. This line is charged from E_b through the high resistance R_2 and the diode $T2$, and discharges through the load and the thyratron $T1$. The circuit is designed so that Z_0, the characteristic impedance of the line, is approxi-

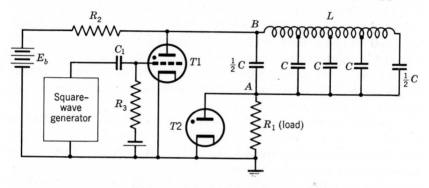

FIG. 13. PULSE MODULATOR.

mately equal to R_1, the resistance of the load. The discharge is triggered by a sharp pulse of positive potential on the grid of $T1$, and the discharge current remains nearly constant at a value equal to $E_b/(R_1 + Z_0)$ while the wave of discharge travels along the line from the end A-B to the open end D, where it is reflected, and back to A-B again. If R_1 is just equal to Z_0 the current then drops to zero, with the line fully discharged. To make sure the current in R_1 then stops, Z_0 is made slightly greater than R_1. Diode $T2$ is required only when the load is an electron tube which will not conduct the charging current; it is not needed for a pure resistance such as R_1. For an ideal line this current pulse is quite flat on top, with sharp rise and fall at its beginning and end, but for an artificial line the top shows small ripples, with a narrow but sharp initial peak. The potential at A is likewise nearly constant over the pulse interval, at a value $-E_bR_1/(R_1 + Z_0)$, or approximately $-E_b/2$.*

* For further information concerning pulse modulators and artificial lines, consult D. G. Fink, *Radar Engineering*, pp. 465–470, and *Principles of Radar* (M.I.T. Staff), 2nd Ed., pp. 2–88 to 2–100 and 6–2 to 6–37.

15. Demonstration Experiment 1. The pulse-forming circuit of Fig. 13 is best explained by demonstration. Tube $T1$ may be a 2050 thyratron. Ground the second grid and bias the first about 6 volts negative. Omit $T2$; instead, connect a gas-type diode between B and ground, with its cathode connected to B. A second 2050 tube, with both grids connected to its anode, will serve. The trigger pulse is provided by a square-wave generator and a differentiating circuit, as indicated in Fig. 13, with a square-wave amplitude of about 10 volts. Make R_2 and R_3 each 500 K, C_1 20 $\mu\mu f$, and E_b 100 volts. The load, R_1, may be a radiofrequency box or a group of radio resistors. Connect the oscilloscope to point A.

A good delay line may be made by winding No. 22 wire into a single-layer coil 40 inches long, on a plastic tube 3 inches in diameter, with taps at 4-inch intervals. Support a heavy wire about 2 inches from the coil and parallel to it, and connect 0.00100-mf condensers between this wire and the coil taps, including the coil ends. The pulse length should be about 20 μ-sec.

Observe the pulse form at A for values of R_1 ranging from 100 ohms to 10 K, with $T2$ removed, and find the value (Z_0) for which no reflection occurs at the input end. When R_1 is greater than Z_0 the potential at A decreases step-wise, without reversal, but it alternates in sign for each reflection when R_1 is less than Z_0. Remove the diode and observe that no change is produced when R_1 exceeds Z_0, but only one pulse is seen when R_1 is less than Z_0. Explain the function of the diode.

16. The Resnatron. Still another solution for the problem of flight-time is to introduce a compensating phase shift into the feedback from the plate circuit to the grid circuit. This principle is applied in the resnatron, a high-power, water-cooled tetrode capable of producing 30 Kw of power continuously at 500 Mcps, and 100 Kw for short periods. Details are given in the references listed in the footnote.*

17. Electron "Bunching." When transit time is an appreciable fraction of a cycle of oscillation it is necessary to analyze the operation of class C amplifiers and oscillators in a manner quite different from that described in Chapter 10 for lower frequencies. It is then necessary to regard the grid as a device which chops up the electron stream into *bunches*, and then to consider how the current in the plate circuit is related to the passage of these bunches through the tube. At lower frequencies the plate current is very closely equal to the rate at which electrons carry charge from the cathode to the anode, but this is far

* W. W. Salisbury, "The Resnatron," *Electronics*, February 1946, pp. 92–97; F. W. Boggs, "The Resnatron," *Westinghouse Engineer*, March 1947, pp. 57–60.

from true at the very high frequencies here considered. At these frequencies a large part of the current to an electrode is accounted for by the flow of charges which are *induced* in it by electrons moving in its neighborhood.

To illustrate this concept let us consider the triode represented schematically in Fig. 14. In order to simplify this example, by having an electron bunch of uniform electron concentration and speed, both the grid, G, and the plate, P, are held at zero potential and the cathode, K, is pulsed. During most the time K is held at a low positive potential, so that no electrons pass the grid; to produce a pulse it is raised to a high negative potential, and during the pulse-time, t_1, electrons travel between G and P in a bunch having a concentration of n electrons per unit volume and a uniform speed, u, determined by the cathode potential. The *electron current, I_e* (per unit area), is then

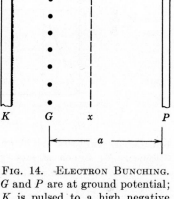
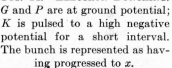

$$I_e = neu \qquad (15)$$

FIG. 14. ELECTRON BUNCHING. G and P are at ground potential; K is pulsed to a high negative potential for a short interval. The bunch is represented as having progressed to x.

In Fig. 14 this bunch is represented as having progressed part-way from G to P, and no electrons have yet reached P. Nevertheless there is current at P from the time the pulse starts, due to the changing value of the positive charges induced in P by the presence of negative charge (electrons) between G and P. This plate current increases as the electron bunch approaches P, as shown by Fig. 15a, and attains the value I_e when the head of the bunch reaches P, and the bunch fills the space between G and P. The time t_0 required for the head of the bunch to cross the distance a between G and P is the flight-time for the electrons, equal to a/u. Once the current at P reaches the value I_e it stays constant until the end of the pulse-time, t_1; then it decreases, as indicated in Fig. 15a, reaching zero at a time t_0 after the end of the potential pulse at K. The effect of electron flight-time is thus to cause the current to start and stop less abruptly and to spread it over a time equal to t_1 plus t_0. If the pulse is so short that t_1 is less than t_0, then the rear of the pulse leaves G before the head reaches P, and the current at P never reaches the value I_e. See Fig. 15b. The current at G is at all times the same as at P, owing to induced currents in G. Mutual repulsions among the electrons tend to lengthen the bunch and thereby to extend still further the time of the current pulse.

In most circuits conditions are more complex than in the one represented by Figs. 14 and 15. In general the grid and plate potentials change during the pulse-time, introducing current components due to electrode capacitances, and neither electron speed nor electron concentration is uniform within the bunch. Nevertheless, whenever electron flight-time is appreciable induced currents such as those dis-

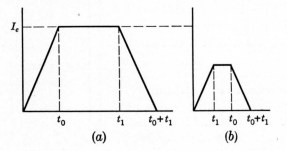

FIG. 15. CURRENT IN THE TUBE OF FIG. 14. (a) Bunch is longer than grid-plate distance. (b) Bunch is shorter than grid-plate distance. t_0—time of flight. t_1—time of pulse.

cussed above constitute an important part of the total current, and lengthen the current pulse in the manner described.

18. The Klystron. The lighthouse tube represents the practical limit in the development of the conventional electron tube for UHF use. It serves at frequencies as high as 3000 Mcps, but to reach this limit it must be made so small that its power output is quite feeble. Even before the development of the lighthouse tube it became apparent that radically different kinds of tubes are needed to generate UHF power, and the *klystron* was invented to meet this demand. The principles upon which the klystron operates are in some respects comparable to those for a triode, but in most respects quite different. Bunching of the electron stream is an essential process, just as for a triode, but the interactions of the electron bunches with the input and output circuits are entirely by means of electrostatic induction, not by direct flow of electrons to any of the electrodes, and flight-time becomes an essential part of the process rather than a factor of difficulty.

The essential features of a klystron amplifier are represented in Fig. 16. The input and output circuits are resonant cavities of the re-entrant type, A and B, tuned to exactly the same frequency. The cathode, K, is similar to the electron gun of a cathode-ray tube, and the electron beam emitted by it passes through grids a_0, a_1, a_2, b_1, and b_2 to the collector electrode, P. The electrons in this beam are accelerated between K, which is at a high negative potential, E, and grid a_0, which is at ground potential. From there on to P the electron speed remains constant if there are no oscillations in the cavities. Since the electron concentration along the beam is likewise constant under these conditions, there is then no interaction between the beam and either cavity.

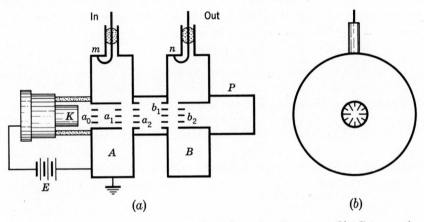

FIG. 16. KLYSTRON AMPLIFIER. (a) Schematic diagram. (b) Cross-section through A, showing grid.

If, however, an electrical oscillation is set up in cavity A by a signal introduced at m, the oscillating electric field between grids a_1 and a_2 acts upon the electrons as they pass through it, so as to bunch them in the manner described in Sec. 19. These electron bunches then induce charges in b_1 and b_2 as they pass through the cavity space between these grids, so as to set up a strong oscillation in cavity B when it is tuned to the bunch frequency. Once this oscillation in B reaches a steady value its phase is always such that each electron bunch, as it passes between b_1 and b_2, moves against the force exerted on it by the electric field of the cavity and thus loses energy to it. The energy which the electrons thus lose to the cavity field serves to maintain the cavity oscillation and supply the power taken from the cavity at n. It should be observed especially that this energy transfer takes place by *induced* current only, without any *electron* current to B. All electrons, except for the very few which may be stopped by the grids, go to P.

19. Bunching in a Klystron.   At ultra-high frequencies a grid is a very inefficient bunching device, and in a klystron a more efficient buncher is provided by the resonant cavity A.   This buncher does not attempt to stop any part of the beam, but only to *modulate its speed* by rather small amounts, by means of the oscillatory electric field between a_1 and a_2.   As the electrons in the beam pass between a_1 and a_2 their speeds are increased when this field is in one direction, decreased when the field is reversed.   Thus, after passing through this field the electrons in the beam no longer travel all with the same speed, but have speeds which vary periodically above and below the average, at the frequency of the input signal.   If the average speed is u_0, and we assume the changes in speed to be sinusoidal, with amplitude u_1, the instantaneous speed, u, may be represented by

$$u = u_0 + u_1 \sin 2\pi ft \qquad (16)$$

These changes in speed are not apparent just as the beam leaves the *buncher* (cavity A), but as the electrons travel along the "drift-space" between a_2 and b_1 those with lowered speed lag behind, while those with higher than average speed gain on the others.   The result is a close bunching of many of the electrons at some distance s from a_2.   It can be shown that this distance s is given approximately by

$$s = u_0{}^2/(2\pi f u_1) \qquad (17)$$

Since u_0 depends upon the cathode potential, whereas u_1 is determined by the signal strength, the value of the cathode potential may be adjusted so that, for any input signal, the distance s is equal to the distance from a_2 to b_1.   Maximum bunching then will occur between b_1 and b_2, where the bunches set up and maintain a strong oscillation in cavity B, in the manner explained above.

It should be noted that a klystron amplifier is comparable with a class C triode amplifier in that it is designed for constant power input and output, at a single frequency.   This frequency may be varied in most klystrons by some method for tuning the cavities, usually by having one wall made flexible so that the spacing between the disks may be varied a small amount.   A klystron amplifier may be operated as an oscillator by coupling the output back to the input, *in the proper phase.* For example, the coupling may be through a length of coaxial cable having a sliding section, like the slide of a trombone, by means of which the length of the return path may be varied so as to obtain the proper phase of feedback.   However, the reflex klystron (see Sec. 21) is preferred as an oscillator, since it has but one cavity to tune.

20. The Bunching Formula. Equation 17 may be derived as follows. Electrons which pass through the buncher when the electric field is zero have the speed u_0 in the drift-space. If we count time as zero when such electrons leave the buncher, they will travel the bunching distance, s, in some time t_s, and

$$s = u_0 t_s \tag{18}$$

For electrons which pass through the buncher at a later time, t_1, the speed is given by Eq. 16. If these electrons catch up with the first group in the distance s then

$$s = u(t_s - t_1)$$

$$= u_0 t_s - u_0 t_1 + (t_s - t_1) u_1 \sin 2\pi f t_1 \tag{19}$$

Combining Eqs. 18 and 19 gives

$$u_0 t_1 = (t_s - t_1) u_1 \sin 2\pi f t_1 \tag{20}$$

These relationships are represented graphically in Fig. 17, as a plot of electron displacement against time. Line A is a plot for electrons which start at time zero with speed u_0, and plot B represents electrons which start at time t_1. These two lines cross at displacement s and time t_s, where the second group of electrons catches up with the first. Equations 16 and 20 apply also to electrons which start at an earlier (negative) time t_1', represented in Fig. 17 by plot C. If we now consider only those electrons which leave the buncher for values of t_1 which are small compared with the period of oscillation we may write $\sin 2\pi f t_1$ as $2\pi f t_1$ and Eq. 20 becomes

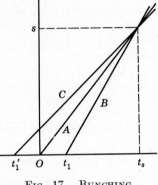

FIG. 17.   BUNCHING.

$$u_0 = 2\pi f u_1 (t_s - t_1) \cong 2\pi f u_1 t_s \tag{21}$$

It follows that, approximately,

$$t_s = u_0/(2\pi f u_1) \quad \text{and} \quad s = u_0^2/(2\pi f u_1) \tag{22, 23}$$

If Fig. 17 is extended to represent a whole series of electron groups starting at equally spaced time intervals the Applegate diagram of Fig. 18 is produced.*

21. The Reflex Klystron. As mentioned in Sec. 19, a klystron amplifier may be converted into an oscillator by suitable feedback, but this involves the difficulty of tuning two cavity resonators very closely to the same frequency, in addition to precise adjustment of phase for the feedback. A much simpler oscillator circuit is possible with a reflex klystron, in which a single cavity serves as both buncher and catcher. A single cavity is made possible by turning the electron

* For a more rigorous analysis of bunching in a klystron, see L. B. Arguimbau, *Vacuum-Tube Circuits*, pp. 626–656; A. H. W. Beck, *Velocity-Modulated Thermionic Tubes;* K. R. Spangenberg, *Vacuum Tubes*, pp. 527–560; or F. E. Terman, *Radio Engineers' Handbook*, pp. 518–521.

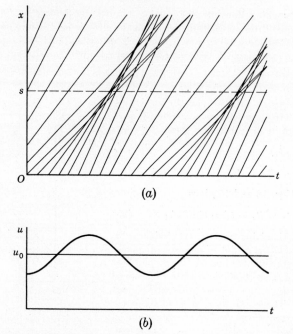

(a)

(b)

Fɪɢ. 18. Aᴘᴘʟᴇɢᴀᴛᴇ Dɪᴀɢʀᴀᴍ. Compare (a) with Fig. 17. (b) Speed of electrons upon leaving buncher, at $x = 0$. s—bunching distance according to Eq. 17 .

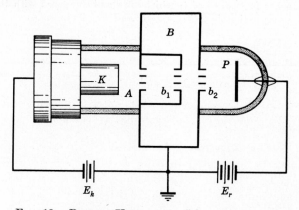

Fɪɢ. 19. Rᴇғʟᴇx Kʟʏsᴛʀᴏɴ. Schematic diagram.

beam back upon itself, so that it traverses the single cavity twice. A reflex klystron is diagrammed schematically in Fig. 19, and two commercial types are illustrated in Fig. 20. After being accelerated between the electron gun, K, and the anode grid, A, the electron beam passes through grids b_1 and b_2 in the cavity, B, toward the repeller electrode, P, which is maintained at a potential more negative than that of K. Before the beam reaches P, however, its motion is reversed by the opposing electric field between b_2 and P; it then passes back through the cavity grids in the reverse order and stops at A.

During the first passage of the electron beam through the UHF field, E, between b_1 and b_2, the electron speeds are modulated as

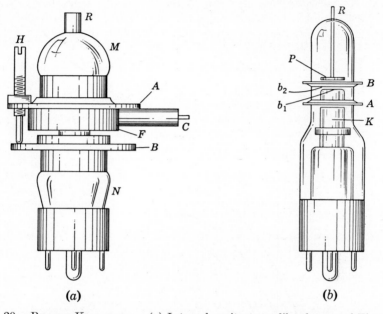

(a)   (b)

FIG. 20.   REFLEX KLYSTRONS.   (a) Integral-cavity type, like the one of Fig. 19. F—flexible diaphragm. A,B—tuning rings. The spacing between A and B is maintained by three tuning screws, only one of which (H) is shown. Springs, which are not shown, hold B tightly against these screws. M,N—glass. C—coaxial cable connection. (b) McNally type, for use with external cavity. The cavity is clamped to the projecting rims of the disk seals, A and B, which carry grids b_1 and b_2.

explained in Sec. 19, and bunching takes place in the region between b_2 and P; the potential of P may be adjusted so that bunching is a maximum when the electrons again enter the space between b_1 and b_2. If the *timing* is also correct, so that the electron bunches move between b_2 and b_1 against the force exerted upon them by E, they will then give up energy to the UHF field so as to maintain the oscillation.

It is important to note that the bunching conditions for a reflex klystron are not the same as for a two-cavity one. In the two-cavity klystron bunching occurs in those parts of the electron beam which pass through the buncher at times t_1, t_1'

in Fig. 21, when the electric force, $-Ee$, is increasing, and in which faster electrons are overtaking slower ones. In the reflex klystron, on the contrary, bunching occurs in those parts of the beam which traverse the buncher at times t_2, t_2' when $-Ee$ is *decreasing*, and faster electrons are ahead of slower ones, because the opposing field between b_2 and P turns back the slower electrons sooner than the faster ones. A time plot of electron displacements between b_2 and P is given in Fig. 22. Plot A represents the displacement of electrons which pass between b_1 and b_2 when E is

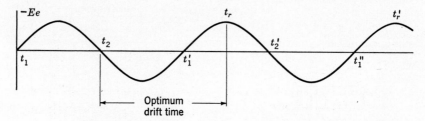

FIG. 21.   TIME PLOT OF THE FORCE, $-Ee$, EXERTED BY THE UHF ELECTRIC FIELD UPON AN ELECTRON AS IT PASSES THROUGH THE BUNCHER.

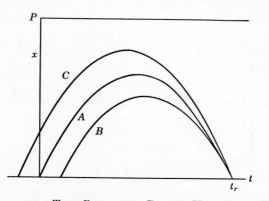

FIG. 22.   DISPLACEMENT-TIME PLOT FOR A REFLEX KLYSTRON. The position of the reflector is indicated by P.

zero and their speed u_0; plot B, electrons which leave the cavity at a later time, with lesser speed; and plot C, those which leave at an earlier time, with greater speed. These three groups of electrons are here represented as coming together at the time t_r, when they have returned to b_2.

If the return passage of the electron beam through b_2 and b_1 is to transfer energy to the oscillation in the cavity the electron bunches must pass between b_2 and b_1 at times when their motion is opposed by the UHF field. If we remember that they now are moving in the opposite direction to their first passage, we see that these times correspond to t_r, t_r' in Fig. 21, and that the drift-time, or the time spent by the electrons in the space between b_2 and P, equals three-fourths of a cycle (plus any whole number of cycles). This drift-time is determined by the potentials of K and P. Once these potentials have been given suitable values the amplitude of the oscillation adjusts itself automatically to the value which makes bunching a maximum. Oscillations of the same frequency may take place for a series of different values of the potential at P; for each the drift-time is $(n + \frac{3}{4})$ cycles, where n is an integral number.   The value of n for which the power output is maximum is determined by the design of the tube.

The reflex klystron, like the two-cavity one, may be tuned mechanically, by changing the distance between b_1 and b_2.   In the McNally (type 707A) klystron the cavity is external to the vacuum tube, and is tuned with screw plugs.   It is possible also to vary the frequency over a small range by changing the potentials of P and K.   The klystron was developed originally to provide a strong source of UHF power, but the multicavity magnetron has now taken over this task.   The main applications for klystrons at present are as amplifiers, as local oscillators in UHF superheterodyne reception, and as steady power sources for laboratory research in the range from 3000 to 30,000 Mcps.   Substantial amounts of power may be produced in the 10,000-Mcps region with the Shepherd-Pierce tube (type 723A/B).   According to a pioneer* in this field the development of applications for klystrons, especially for those of higher power, is only just begun.   Tubes of this type are applicable in many diverse fields where they may be able to compete successfully with triodes and magnetrons, or even exceed them, once the development research has been carried out.

22. Experiment 35.   Reflex Klystron Oscillator.   Experiments with klystrons are disappointing in so far as they concern the electronic principles involved, since so few measurements may be made to check the theory.   Experiments are primarily a study of operating conditions (or a study of the utilization of the output, which is not our concern here).   Klystrons of various kinds are available† and detailed instructions for their operation are furnished by the manufacturers.   A special power supply is required, capable of providing (1) a well-regulated negative voltage for the cathode, with the positive terminal grounded, and (2) a variable potential for the repeller, which is always negative with respect to the cathode.   A fixed cathode potential is sufficient, but a variable potential permits a more detailed study of klystron operation.   Some klystrons have an intensity-control grid, requiring a third potential source, slightly positive relative to the cathode.   Controls must be interlocking, so that the cathode potential cannot be applied before the repeller voltage is turned on.   An S-band (10-cm) klystron, such as the 2K41 type, has more flexibility of adjustment than an X-band (3-cm) one of the 723A/B type.‡

* R. H. Varian, *Electronics*, April 1952, p. 112.

† Sperry Gyroscope Co., Western Electric Co., and others.

‡ Equipment for use with the 723A/B tube is described by G. F. Hull, Jr., in *American Journal of Physics*, Vol. 17 (December 1949), p. 559.

For a 2K41 klystron the load may be a half-wave antenna such as employed in Exp. 34, connected by a short length of coaxial cable to one of the output terminals. The other output terminal should be capped. The power output is strongly influenced by the length of this coaxial line; hence there should be in it a sliding section, or "line stretcher," by which its length may be varied to produce maximum output. The detector employed in Exp. 34 will serve to indicate relative power output for this experiment. Meters must be provided to measure the d-c plate current and the potentials of the cathode and the repeller.

For any fixed cathode potential the repeller potential has a sequence of ranges over which oscillation occurs, each range representing a different mode of operation. The existence and nature of these several modes are explained in Sec. 21. Follow the instructions provided by the manufacturer and find the values of V_r, the repeller potential, at which output is a maximum for each mode, for a fixed value of V_1, the cathode potential. Adjust the load for best output in the mode which yields the most power, and do not change this adjustment thereafter. For each mode determine also the upper and lower limits for V_r. Represent these results graphically, plotting V_r as x and relative output as y.

If V_1 is variable observe how V_r must be changed to maintain optimum output (in any one mode) as V_1 is changed. Do this for the principal mode, and for one or two other modes. It may be possible to show that additional modes appear as V_1 is decreased. Show these results with a plot having V_1 as x, V_r as y. Make another plot with V_1 as x and relative power output as y.

23. The Magnetron Oscillator. The multicavity magnetron oscillator is at present the most powerful source of microwave energy. Like the klystron oscillator, it possesses a resonant-cavity system which is maintained in electrical oscillation by moving electron bunches, but instead of one cavity resonator it has six or more, coupled together. Its greatest difference from other oscillators, however, is its utilization of a strong magnetic field, in addition to electrical fields, to produce electron bunches and to control their movements. The essential elements of an eight-cavity magnetron are shown schematically in Fig. 23. The cathode, K, is cylindrical and oxide-coated. The anode, A, is a hollow cylinder, concentric about K and divided into eight segments by the slots $S_1, \cdots, S_8$, which connect the annular space between A and K with the cylindrical cavities $C_1 \cdots C_8$. This assembly is inclosed by metal walls and highly evacuated. In operation it is placed between the poles of a strong magnet, with the lines of magnetic induction, B, parallel to its axis, and a high negative potential, V, is supplied to K, with A at ground potential. The magnetic field is so strong that, when there are no oscillations, the electron paths are curved lines which do not reach A but bend back toward K again, and there is no current between A and K. For certain values of B and of V, however, electrical oscillations are set up in the cavities and then there is a large current. The manner in which these oscillations take place and are maintained is explained below.

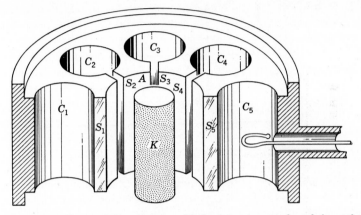

FIG. 23.   EIGHT-CAVITY MAGNETRON.   End plates removed and front half cut away.

24. Motions of Electrons in Crossed Electric and Magnetic Fields. First we must consider how electrons move in the combined electric and magnetic fields encountered in a magnetron. Unfortunately, this cannot be determined with great certainty, because of the effects of space-charge factors hard to analyze. Nevertheless a very useful picture of what occurs may be obtained without considering these factors. Let us consider the very simple case of crossed electric and magnetic fields represented in Fig. 24, the electric field, E, being produced by a potential difference between plane-parallel plates A and K in an evacuated region, with a uniform magnetic field perpendicular to E and to the plane of the figure. If an electron is at P and is moving with a speed u_0, as indicated, the electric force on it is $-eE$, the magnetic force, Beu_0.* If these two forces are opposed and equal, as indicated, the electron will continue to move at constant speed along the straight, dotted line, parallel to the plates. This condition is

$$Beu_0 = eE \qquad (24)$$

The speed is

$$u_0 = E/B \qquad (25)$$

* In these equations B is in gauss, e in abcoulombs, and E in abvolts/cm. For e in coulombs, E in volts/cm, these forces are $-10^7\, eE$ and $Beu_0/10$.

A situation closer to the one met in a magnetron is represented in Fig. 25, in which the electric field is caused by a potential difference between cylindrical electrodes A and K in an evacuated region, and B

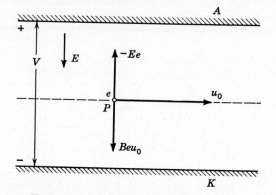

Fig. 24.   Crossed Electric and Magnetic Fields. B is into the plane of the figure.   Forces on an electron are shown.

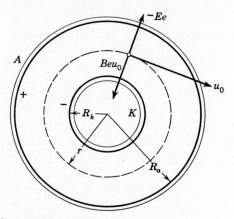

Fig. 25.   Axial Magnetic Field Crossed with a Radial Electric Field. B is into the plane of the figure.

is parallel to the axis and into the plane of the figure.   The path of an electron at P will be a circle as shown if

$$Beu_0 = eE + (mu_0{}^2/r) \tag{26}$$

Equation 26 differs from Eq. 24 only by the term $mu_0{}^2/r$, which represents the inertia reaction of the electron mass moving in a circle of radius r.   Under conditions commonly existing in magnetrons this term is small compared with the other two.

25. Cycloidal Paths. In the crossed fields shown in Fig. 24, and again in Fig. 26, an electron may, in general, be at some point having coordinates x and y, and have a velocity whose x- and y-components are dx/dt and dy/dt respectively. With E and B directed as

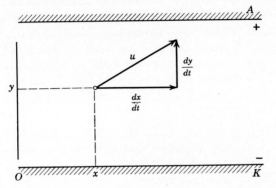

FIG. 26.   MOTION OF AN ELECTRON IN CROSSED FIELDS.   Fields are the same as in Fig. 24.

in Fig. 26 the x-component of the force acting on this electron is given by

$$m(d^2x/dt^2) = Be(dy/dt) \tag{27}$$

Likewise the y-component is

$$m(d^2y/dt^2) = eE - Be(dx/dt) \tag{28}$$

A solution for these equations is given by

$$x = g + a\omega t - b \sin \omega t \qquad y = h - b \cos \omega t \tag{29, 30}$$

The corresponding derivatives are

$$dx/dt = a\omega - b\omega \cos \omega t \qquad dy/dt = b\omega \sin \omega t \tag{31, 32}$$

$$d^2x/dt^2 = b\omega^2 \sin \omega t \qquad d^2y/dt^2 = b\omega^2 \cos \omega t \tag{33, 34}$$

If Eqs. 31 to 34 are substituted into Eqs. 27 and 28 it is found that

$$\omega = \frac{Be}{m} \qquad \omega a = \frac{E}{\omega}\frac{e}{m} = \frac{E}{B} \tag{35, 36}$$

Note particularly that the *average* value for dx/dt is ωa, which, according to Eqs. 36 and 25, is the same as for an electron moving with uniform speed in this region, as represented in Fig. 24. The values of b, g, and h are determined by initial conditions. For example, if the electron starts from the surface of K with zero speed we may take x,

y, dx/dt, and dy/dt all equal to zero when t is zero. Substitution of these values in Eqs. 29 to 32 then gives $b = a$, $g = 0$, and $h = a$, or

$$x = a(\omega t - \sin \omega t) \qquad y = a(1 - \cos \omega t) \qquad (37, 38)$$

The electron path represented by Eqs. 37 and 38 is a *cycloid*, and may be reproduced by rolling a disk of radius a along a straight line with an angular velocity ω. The center of this disk moves parallel to the line, with the speed ωa, or E/B, and the point on its rim which touched the line at the start traces out the cycloidal path, as indicated in Fig. 27. The general motion of an electron in the fields represented

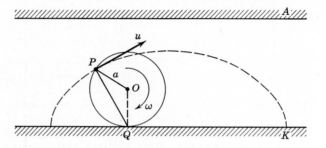

FIG. 27.   CYCLOIDAL PATH.

in Fig. 26, and given by Eqs. 29 and 30, may be described in corresponding fashion as the resultant of revolution in a circle of radius b, with angular velocity ω, and linear motion of the center of the circle with the speed E/B.

In like manner the motion of an electron in the interaction space between cathode and anode of a cyclotron *which is not oscillating* may be described approximately as the resultant of revolution in a circle of radius b, with angular velocity ω equal to Be/m, and movement of the center of this circle about a larger circle whose center is on the axis of the magnetron. The speed with which this center point moves along the circumference of this larger circle is given approximately by Eq. 26.

26. The Cavity Resonators. The type of oscillation taking place in a slot-and-hole cavity of the type illustrated in Fig. 23 is represented in Fig. 28. At the phase represented in Fig. 28a the current is zero and the electric field is a maximum. It is strongest in the slot, although there is some electric flux inside the hole and a small but very important part of it bulges into the interaction space between the anode and the cathode. A quarter-cycle later the flux is entirely magnetic, with the lines of magnetic flux threading through the holes as shown in Fig. 28b. An important difference between these cavities and those employed with the lighthouse tube and the klystron is now apparent;

these cavities are open at the ends and the magnetic flux extends out through these ends and returns outside the hole, through the copper block and through the adjacent holes. This stray flux then constitutes a flux linkage which couples each cavity to its neighbors, so that oscillations must take place in all together, and not in one alone. The oscillations may alternate in phase, with a phase difference of π radians from one cavity to the next, and this mode of oscillation, which is called the π mode, is the one desired for all practical magnetron operation. However, other modes also are possible, the number depending

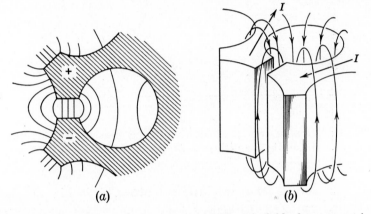

(a)   (b)

Fig. 28.   Fields in Cavity Oscillation.   (a) Electric field when current is zero. (b) Magnetic field one quarter-cycle later.   Note magnetic coupling between cavities.   I—current.

upon the number of cavities. For example, the eight-cavity magnetron diagrammed in Fig. 23 might oscillate in a $\pi/2$ mode, corresponding to the standing-wave pattern produced by two identical running waves traveling in opposite directions around the ring of cavities, with a phase difference of $\pi/2$ radians from one cavity to the next. For this mode the oscillations in cavities 1, 2, 5, and 6 are identical, with those in cavities 3, 4, 7, and 8 also identical but in exactly opposite phase. Oscillations in a $\pi/4$ mode also are possible, with half the cavities (1, 2, 3, and 4) in one phase, the other half in the opposite phase; in this case the amplitude of oscillation would be greater in cavities 2, 3, 6, and 7 than in the others. Special precautions are taken in the design of magnetrons and the associated circuits to insure oscillations in only the desired π mode.*

* See J. B. Fisk, H. D. Hagstrum, and P. L. Hartman, "The Magnetron as a Generator of Centimeter Waves," *The Bell System Technical Journal*, Vol. 25 (1946), pp. 167–348.

27. Oscillations. Oscillations are set up and maintained in this resonant system by interactions between the electrons which are moving in the interaction space, and the portion of the RF electric flux which bulges out of each slot into this space. (See Fig. 28a.) The nature of these interactions is represented in Fig. 29. Here again it is convenient to represent the cathode and anode as parallel planes instead of concentric cylinders. If the magnetron is not oscillating

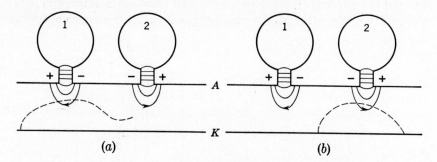

(a)   (b)

FIG. 29. INTERACTION OF ELECTRONS WITH CAVITY FIELDS. *B* is into the plane of the figure. *A*—anode, *K*—cathode. Arrows show direction of RF electric-field force on electrons.

the electron path is then cycloidal, as represented in Fig. 27, and the electrons return to the cathode, *K*; but when oscillations are present the path is altered by the RF electric field. If at the instant the oscillation phase is as represented in Fig. 29 an electron passes slot 1 as shown, it is deflected toward the anode, *A*, so that its average distance from *K* is increased and it does not return to *K*. On the contrary, an electron passing under slot 2 at this same instant is deflected toward *K* and returns to *K* sooner than in the absence of oscillations. These two electron paths are illustrated by Figs. 29a and 29b respectively.

These changes in orbit are produced by the part of the RF electric field which extends into the interaction space around the slots. When this field *opposes* the motion of an electron, as shown under slot 1, Fig. 29a, the electron speed, *u*, is decreased, the magnetic force, *Beu*, is thereby weakened, and the electron path is deflected away from *K*. Furthermore, since this electron is moving against the force exerted on it by the RF field, *it gives energy to that field*, to build up and maintain the electrical oscillations. On the contrary, an electron passing slot 2 at this same instant gains speed from the RF field, the magnetic force on it is thereby strengthened, and its path is bent toward *K*. This electron *takes energy away from the field*.

If there were as many electron interactions of the second kind as of the first, as much energy would be taken away from the oscillations by the second kind of interaction as would be given them by the first kind, and the magnetron could not function. Fortunately, an electron makes but one interaction of the second kind before it returns to the cathode, whereas an electron interaction of the first kind leaves the electron free to repeat the process whenever conditions are favorable. If the average speed of the electrons carries them from one slot to the next in the time of one half-cycle, an electron which interacts with the electric field in the manner shown under slot 1 in Fig. 29 will keep pace with the changing phase of the field, so as to repeat this type of interaction under each slot it passes, each time giving energy to the oscillations, until the succession of radial deflections removes it from circulation by taking it to A.

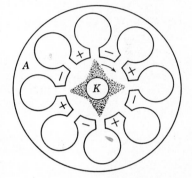

FIG. 30. ELECTRON BUNCHES IN A MAGNETRON. (Schematic diagram.)

28. Bunching in Magnetrons. Since, as shown in Fig. 29, the electric field alternates in phase from one slot to the next, electron bunches are formed under every other slot by the electrons which interact favorably with the electric field and thus escape from the cathode. These bunches somewhat resemble the spokes of a wheel, as indicated in Fig. 30, and revolve around the cathode at a rate which is determined by the oscillation frequency and the number of cavities. If the frequency is f and there are N cavities, the bunches make $2f/N$ revolutions per second. We may then ascribe the maintenance of oscillation in the cavities to the charges *induced* in the anode by these electron bunches as they sweep past.

29. Conditions for Oscillation. If oscillations are to be set up and maintained in a magnetron a definite relationship must exist between the magnetic induction, B, and the d-c potential difference, V, from cathode to anode, to insure that the electron bunches revolve about the cathode in step with the oscillations in the cavities. An approximate equation for this relationship may be derived by considering only the part of the electron motion which is at right angles to the radial electric field, and assuming this to be, *on the average*, motion at constant speed in a circle midway between the cathode, K, and the anode, A. Let the radii of A and of K be R_a and R_k respectively. Then the radius of this average path is equal to $(R_a + R_k)/2$, and the electrons must circle this path $2f/N$ times per second, with a speed u_0 given by

$$u_0 = (2f/N) \times \pi(R_a + R_k) \tag{39}$$

We may now assume that u_0 satisfies Eq. 26, from which we may evaluate the radial electric field, E. That is, *approximately*,

$$E = Bu_0 - (mu_0^2/er) \tag{40}$$

or

$$E = \frac{2\pi fB}{N}(R_a + R_k) - \frac{2m}{e}\left(\frac{2\pi f}{N}\right)^2 (R_a + R_k) \tag{41}$$

Let us now take V as equal to E multiplied by $R_a - R_k$, the distance from A to K. Then

$$V \cong E(R_a - R_k)$$

$$\cong \frac{2\pi fB}{N}(R_a^2 - R_k^2) - \frac{2m}{e}\left(\frac{2\pi f}{N}\right)^2 (R_a^2 - R_k^2) \tag{42}$$

In volts,

$$V \cong 6.3 \times 10^{-8}\,\frac{f}{N}\,B(R_a^2 - R_k^2)$$

$$- 4.4 \times 10^{-14}\left(\frac{f}{N}\right)^2 (R_a^2 - R_k^2) \tag{42a}$$

Equation 42 is the same as one derived by Hartree,[*] except for R_k^2 in the last term, which does not appear in Hartree's equation.

A minimum value for B is set by the height of the cycloidal loops, which must be considerably less than the gap between A and K. For this condition it is sufficient to employ the equations derived for plane electrodes. The height of the first loop is $2a$, and from Eqs. 36 and 25,

$$2a = 2E/B\omega = 2u_0/\omega \tag{43}$$

We may now insert the values of u_0 and ω given by Eqs. 39 and 35, and obtain

$$2a = \frac{4\pi m}{e}\,\frac{f}{N}\,\frac{R_a + R_k}{B} \tag{44}$$

or

$$B = \frac{4\pi m}{e}\,\frac{f}{N}\,\frac{R_a + R_k}{2a}$$

$$= 7.2 \times 10^{-7}\,\frac{f}{N}\,\frac{R_a + R_k}{2a}\ \text{gauss} \tag{45}$$

---

[*] See J. B. Fisk, H. D. Hagstrum, and P. L. Hartman, "The Magnetron as a Generator of Centimeter Waves," *The Bell System Technical Journal*, Vol. 25 (1946), p. 197.

Let us apply these equations to a typical magnetron having 8 cavities and oscillating at 3000 Mcps. For this magnetron $R_a = 0.8$ cm, $R_k = 0.3$ cm, and the gap is 0.5 cm. If we take $2a = 0.2$ cm, Eq. 45 gives $B = 1500$ gauss. The recommended value is 1600 gauss, and the corresponding value for V, as given by Eq. 42a, is 17.4 Kv. Hartree's equation gives 16.8 Kv, and the experimental value is 16 Kv.

30. Practical Considerations. The magnetic field for a magnetron must be quite uniform over the entire interaction space between

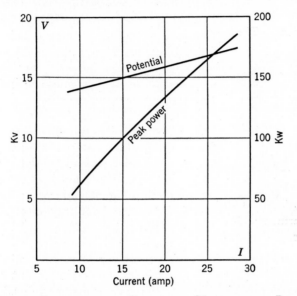

Fig. 31.   Typical Characteristic Data for a Magnetron. $B = 1600$ gauss. Data correspond to magnetron analyzed in Sec. 29.

cathode and anode, and must be held very steady. It may be produced by an electromagnet, but most commonly a permanent magnet is employed. Characteristic data for a magnetron equipped with a permanent magnet are shown in Fig. 31. Although Eq. 42 indicates that the d-c potential, V, should be constant for any fixed value of B it is seen in Fig. 31 that V increases slightly as the current increases, in most part because of the space-charge. With B constant the efficiency is nearly constant, but both power output and efficiency increase as B and V are increased. The upper limit for B is set by the available magnet materials. To increase the frequency the cavities must be made smaller and increased in number; in a magnetron for generation of 1.25-cm waves there are eighteen cavities, and the magnetron body is less than half an inch in diameter.

The lower limits to practical operation are set by several factors. First is the lower limit for B, discussed in Sec. 28, which sets also a lower limit for V. Next, operation is unsatisfactory below a certain current limit. Below this limit, which is several amperes for the magnetron represented by Fig. 31, oscillations will occur for several modes simultaneously, and the output will contain components of these several frequencies. Thus it is impractical to operate a magnetron of this type below a rather large minimum value of power, and the waste power which must be dissipated under these conditions

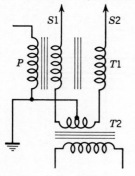

would burn the magnetron up very quickly if it were operated continuously. Pulsed operation is absolutely necessary. This is true also for almost all magnetrons. The exceptions are a few very special ones, most of which are operated at quite low microwave frequencies. Fortunately, pulsed operation is also necessary for radar applications, and not a serious objection for most other applications. The usual pulse rate is 1000 per second, each pulse being about one microsecond long. The *average* power is then a thousandth of the peak power represented in Fig. 31 and the waste power may be dissipated without difficulty by radiating fins attached to the magnetron body.

F I G . 3 2. P U L S E
TRANSFORMER.

31. Power Supply for Magnetrons. The power-supply circuit for a pulsed magnetron oscillator is essentially the same as discussed in Sec. 13 for pulsed operation of triodes. One simple but suitable circuit is diagrammed in Fig. 13. There are many others.* Most are considerably more complex, in order to operate more efficiently. For many practical reasons the anode must remain at ground potential and a *negative* pulse be supplied to the cathode. It follows that some provision must be made to allow the potential of the heater to follow that of the cathode, and one means by which this may be accomplished is a heater transformer having its secondary winding of large diameter and well separated from the primary and the core at all points, as well as highly insulated. Another ingenious means is the special pulse transformer represented in Fig. 32. Secondary windings $S1$ and $S2$ act in parallel to supply the pulse potential to the cathode and simultaneously to raise the heater to the same potential. These windings are of heavy wire and offer little impedance to the heater

* See *Principles of Radar* (M.I.T. Radar School), Chapter VI, or D. G. Fink, *Radar Engineering*, Chapter IX.

current from the transformer $T2$.   The secondary of $T2$ remains at ground potential at all times.

32. Output Circuit.   The power output from a magnetron may be into a coaxial cable, of large enough diameter to handle the peak power.   Power is extracted from the cavity-resonator system by means of a suitable probe.   In Fig. 23 this probe is represented as a simple loop inserted into one of the cavities so as to couple with the magnetic field in that cavity; it corresponds to the loop employed for magnetic coupling of an antenna to the tank circuit of a triode oscillator.*   Since all the cavities are coupled together, extracting power from one takes power from all.   For operation at 3-cm wavelength or shorter the output is generally into a wave guide.   The probe may be a loop, as in Fig. 23.   At 1.25-cm wavelength power is extracted directly into the wave guide, through a narrow slot cut in the back of one cavity.

Many practical details concerning the design and operation of magnetrons have been omitted from this discussion, such as methods for insuring that a magnetron will oscillate in the π mode and not in others.   These details are given in the references listed under Sec. 31.

33. Experiment 36. Magnetron Principles.   Radar magnetrons do not lend themselves to simple laboratory experiments.   Fortunately, a miniature magnetron has been developed† which is admirably suited to laboratory use.   Its cathode and anode are concentric cylinders, as in radar magnetrons, and the anode is divided into eight segments or strips.   Alternate strips are connected together to form two electrodes of four strips each.   The resonant circuit is separate from the tube and may have any desired form, at any frequency up to 1000 Mcps.   Furthermore, d-c connections may be made to these electrodes so that the static characteristics of magnetrons may be studied.   The tube comes with a permanent magnet rigidly attached.

Part I.   Cut-Off Relationship.   Connect both anodes together, to a variable d-c source and a milliammeter of 25-ma range.   Include also a current-limiting resistor of about 2000 ohms.   As the anode potential, V, is raised the electron current, I, remains very small until the cut-off potential is approached; it then rises sharply.   Obtain data for a plot of I as y, V as x, taking data close together where the current change is

---

* It is quite important that the effective impedance of the probe be matched to the impedance of the line and load; suitable matching elements are built into the magnetron between the probe and the coaxial line connection.

† By the General Electric Co.   It is designated by the number Z-2061, and is described by D. A. Wilbur, P. H. Peters, and H. W. A. Chalberg in *Electronics*, January 1952, p. 104.

rapid. Ideally the current should rise to its space-charge limited value as soon as the cut-off potential is exceeded, and be zero below cut-off. Deviations from this ideal behavior are accounted for by various factors, such as non-uniformity of the magnetic field and non-uniformity of electric field and of electron flow near the ends of the electrode structure.

Part II. Negative Conductance. In the circuit of Fig. 33 a separate d-c source is provided for each anode, so that the anode potentials, V_1 and V_2, can be varied independently. Starting with V_1 and V_2 each equal to 70 volts, take voltage and current readings as V_1 and V_2

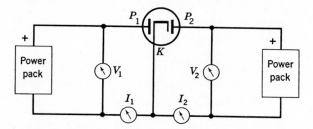

FIG. 33. CIRCUIT FOR EXP. 36-II.

are changed in opposite directions, keeping the average value, $\frac{1}{2}(V_1 + V_2)$, constant at 70 volts. Cover the range of zero to 140 volts for V_1. Represent these data by curves plotted with V_1 as x, and I_1 and I_2 as respective y-values. The strange behavior exhibited by these data is explained qualitatively in Sec. 27.

Plot a third curve having the same abscissae but having as ordinates the current I_b, which is the deviation of I_1 from the average value of I_1 and I_2.

$$I_b = \tfrac{1}{2}(I_1 - I_2) \tag{46}$$

The negative slope of the middle portion of this plot represents a *negative conductance.* Note that all these results occur for an average anode potential *below cut-off.* Observations may be taken in the same manner for an average anode potential of 90 volts.

Part III. Negative-Conductance Oscillations. The negative conductance characteristic displayed in Part II enables the magnetron to set up and maintain oscillation in a resonant circuit connected to it as shown in Fig. 34. For this experiment an audiofrequency is best, and a center-tapped coil of about 0.2-henry inductance, with a capacitance of 0.05 mf, is suitable. Observe V, I, and the amplitude of oscillation, as V is increased; do not let I exceed 15 ma. The amplitude may be measured with a vacuum-tube voltmeter or a cathode-ray oscilloscope.

Oscillations may be generated in this manner at any frequency up to about 100 Mcps, but the efficiency is low.   Transit time becomes a significant factor above 100 Mcps, making this type of oscillation

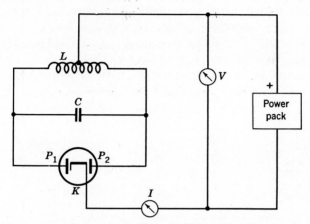

FIG. 34.   MAGNETRON OSCILLATOR (EXP. 36-III).   Negative conductance type.

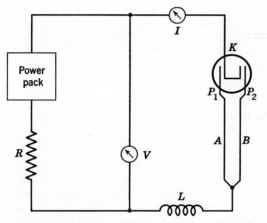

FIG. 35.   MAGNETRON OSCILLATOR (EXP. 36-IV).   "Traveling-wave" type.
V—150-volt meter.   I—25-ma meter.   R—5 K.   L—30 turns No. 20 wire,
½ inch diameter coil.   Do not couple L to AB.

difficult and very inefficient.   At these higher frequencies, however, it becomes possible to set up oscillations of the type described in Part IV.

Part IV.   UHF Oscillation.   The "traveling-wave" type of oscillation employed in radar magnetrons may be studied with the circuit of Fig. 35.   The resonant circuit is a length of transmission line, less then one-quarter wavelength long, shorted at the d-c input end and having the other end connected as directly as possible to the anode terminals. It may be made by bending brass or copper rod, ⅛ inch in diameter, into a hairpin about 5 cm long and 8 mm wide. Oscillation may be demonstrated by the lighting of a 0.06-amp, 1.5-volt, lamp bulb connected to a small loop of wire which is coupled magnetically to AB. The output may be measured, in relative values, with the circuit of Fig. 36a, loosely coupled to AB.

Slowly raise the d-c potential, V, until oscillation begins. The current, I, then increases rapidly with further increase in V, and the

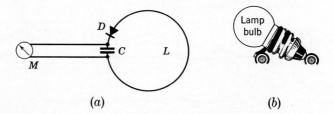

(a)   (b)

Fig. 36 (a) Detector for Exp. 36-IV. D—crystal detector. C—15 $\mu\mu$f, mica. M—1-ma meter. L—circle of No. 14 wire about 5 cm in diameter. (b) Cross-section of Lecher-wire bridge.

detector indicates RF output of increasing intensity. These results are in agreement with Fig. 31, which shows a relatively small change in V accompanying a large change in current and power output. (Simple theory indicates a constant value for V.) Note that the potential at which this oscillation occurs is well below cut-off, so that only the small leakage current exists in the absence of oscillation, and compare this observation with the theory devloped in Secs. 27 to 29. Represent your data by plots of V as y and I as x, and detector current as y, I as x. If the length of AB, Fig. 35, is made variable it can be shown that the range for V depends upon frequency, being higher or lower according to whether the frequency is higher or lower, in qualitative agreement with Eq. 42.

The frequency may be measured with a Lecher-wire system, a resonant transmission-line section of variable length. This line is made by stretching on a wood frame a pair of No. 16 copper wires about 120 cm long and 12 mm apart. One end of this line is terminated in a small loop which is coupled magnetically to the oscillator. The sliding bridge for tuning the line is made from two pieces of brass tubing about 5 cm long, which slide side by side along the wires. These tubes are slotted lengthwise, as indicated in Fig. 36b, so that they may be slipped on or off the wires, and at the end farthest from the coupling loop they are connected by a cross-bar soldered to them. At the other end they are connected by a 0.06-amp, 1.5-volt lamp bulb. The base of the lamp is screwed into a wire loop soldered to one tube, and the tip is soldered to the other tube. Points of resonance are indicated by glowing of the lamp, and the distance between two adjacent resonant points is one-half wavelength.

34. Traveling-Wave Tube.* The traveling-wave tube represented in Fig. 37 is a UHF amplifier which utilizes many of the principles already discussed in this chapter. The electrode structure in this device is a helical coil of wire, H, which is fitted closely into the evacuated glass tube, E. A beam of electrons from the electron gun, K

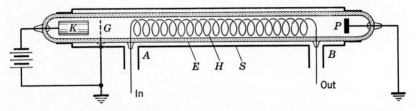

Fig. 37. Traveling-Wave-Tube Amplifier. (Schematic diagram.)

passes along the axis of this helix to the collector electrode, P; it is kept from spreading by means of a strong axial magnetic field which is produced by direct current in a solenoid (not shown in Fig. 37) which surrounds the tube. In Fig. 37 the input and output are shown through coaxial cables A and B, with the inner conductors of these cables connected to the ends of the helix.

The input signal travels along the helix as a guided electromagnetic wave. Its speed along the length of the wire is essentially the speed of light, c, but its speed along the axis of the helix is less in proportion to the pitch of the helix. Thus, if the wire is 15 times as long as the helix, the axial speed is $c/15$. The potential of K may be adjusted to make the speed of the electrons in the beam only a little greater than the speed of the waves along the helix.† Then the output is found to

---

* A fuller treatment is given by J. R. Pierce in his *Traveling-Wave Tubes* and in *Bell System Technical Journal*, Vol. 29, pp. 1, 189, 608 (1950).

† The initial speed of the electrons is the same as the axial speed of the guided waves when the electron beam is absent. The interaction between the electron beam and the wave fields distorts the waves in a manner which may be described mathematically as equivalent to three wave components moving forward, and one backward, with phase speeds which differ slightly from the speed of the undisturbed waves. The component which interacts with the electron beam so as to receive energy from it is traveling more slowly than the beam, as is described above.

be considerably larger than the input: the tube is operating as an amplifier. Furthermore this amplifier, unlike the klystron, is not limited to one frequency, but will operate over a wide frequency range. Gains up to 30 db are possible, and power output of over a kilowatt has been obtained with some types.

35. Bunching in a T-W Tube. Amplification in a traveling-wave tube results from interactions between the beam electrons and the RF electric field inside the helix. These interactions first produce bunching of the electrons in the beam; the bunches then interact with the field to increase the RF energy. Both these interaction processes are very similar to those occurring in a klystron or a magnetron.

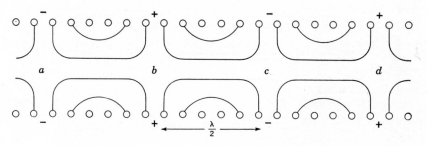

FIG. 38.   ELECTRIC FIELD IN A TRAVELING-WAVE TUBE.

The general nature of the RF field is indicated in Fig. 38. Since both the field and the electrons are traveling to the right with nearly the same speed we may represent the RF field as standing still and the electron beam as moving *slowly* to the right, with a speed equal to the excess of its speed above the traveling-wave speed. Let us assume first that the electron beam has the *same* speed as the waves. Then those electrons at *a*, *b*, *c*, and *d*, which start out in regions of zero field, will remain at rest with respect to the field. In Fig. 38 they are represented as stationary. Electrons between *a* and *b* have their speeds increased by the action of the electric field, so that their relative motion is toward *b*, while those between *b* and *c* are slowed down so that their motion relative to the waves is also toward *b*. Thus a bunch of electrons will build up at *b*, and at all similar points, such as *d*. However, when the electron speed equals the wave speed the bunches which are thus formed have no further interaction with the RF field; they remain in the zero-field regions in which they are formed. No amplification takes place, since the energy gain to the field in the regions corresponding to *b*-*c* in Fig. 38 is just canceled by the energy taken away from the field in regions corresponding to *a*-*b*.

36. Amplification in a T-W Tube. If the electron speed is somewhat greater than the wave speed, bunching occurs in a similar manner, and the bunches form in the neighborhood of the same points. But the bunches then move on into the regions of retarding field ahead of these points (the region b-c, for a bunch formed near b) where they lose energy *as a group*, and this energy is not canceled out by losses elsewhere, but goes to increase the intensity of the output. The amplification should be greatest when each bunch is just able to finish its passage through the retarding segment of the field in which it is formed by the time the wave reaches the output end of the tube.

37. Microwave Applications. The major applications for microwave equipment are in radio communication, television, and radar. In the radio and television fields a very important service is to provide relay links between distant points. Coast-to-coast transmission of television programs in this manner was initiated in 1951. Relay-station towers placed "line of sight" distances apart from a line connecting the distant points, and interconnected microwave transmitters and receivers at each tower pick up signals from the neighboring tower on one side, amplify these signals, and then transmit them to the next station on the other side. Applications are being found, however, in many other fields, including most fields in which electrical oscillations and waves of lower frequency are employed. For example, magnetron-generated waves of 3000-Mcps frequency prove to be very effective for diathermy, that is, for heating body tissues by radiation.

In the laboratory, studies of dielectric constants and other electrical properties of matter at very high frequency are made possible with microwave equipment, and much valuable information concerning molecular forces and vibrations is obtained by these means. As early as 1923 Nichols and Tear* produced *damped* electromagnetic waves of only a few tenths of a millimeter wavelength, thereby overlapping the long-wave end of the infrared optical spectrum. It is the ambition of present-day workers in the microwave field to reach or pass this mark with *continuous* electromagnetic waves. The microwave field is one of the frontiers of electronic research.

PROBLEMS

1. A type 954 "acorn" pentode, which has an input capacitance of 3.4 $\mu\mu$f, is operated as an amplifier at a wavelength of 100 cm. (a) Compute its input reactance. (b) Compute the magnitude of the inductance needed to tune the

* E. F. Nichols and J. D. Tear, "Joining the Electric Wave and Heat Wave Spectra," *Annual Report of the Smithsonian Institution*, 1923, pp. 175–185.

input to resonance.   (c) Compute the Q-factor which this inductance must have to produce an input impedance of 120 K.

2. The inductance for Prob. 1 is produced by a section of transmission line, shorted at its far end.   (a) Compute the length of line needed if the characteristic impedance of the line is 375 ohms.   (b) This line is made with parallel wires 4.0 mm in diameter.   Compute the spacing between wires to produce this impedance.

3. A line having a characteristic impedance of 375 ohms is terminated by a flat metal plate.   When standing waves are set up in it the first nodal point (zero potential) occurs at 27.8 cm from the plate.   If the metal plate is replaced by a small reactance across the end of the line, the first nodal point is at 35.2 cm.   (a) Is the reactance inductive or capacitative?   (b) Compute its value.

4. Compute the electron flight-time between cathode and anode of a "light-house" diode, if the electrode spacing is 0.0070 inch and the potential of the anode is 45 volts.   Neglect space-charge effects.

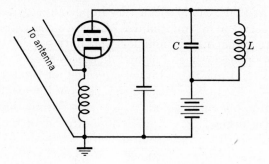

Fig. 39.   See Prob. 7.

5. In the tube described in Sec. 17, the cathode is pulsed to 120 volts for an interval of 0.050 μ-sec.   (a) Compute the length of the electron bunch produced. (b) Compute the electron flight-time between grid and anode, if this distance is 12.2 mm.   (c) Compute the total time of duration for current at P.

6. A type 6J5 triode is operated as a grounded-grid amplifier, with a load of 250 K.   The input source has an internal impedance (resistance) of 1400 ohms and an emf of 80 mv.   (a) Diagram the circuit, and the equivalent circuit.   (b) *From the equivalent circuit* find the a-c plate current and the output voltage.   (c) Compute the input power and the output power.

7. Figure 39 is the circuit diagram for a grounded-grid preamplifier.   The antenna connection may be considered to be an emf e between the cathode and ground, in series with a resistance of 550 ohms.   For the output circuit at resonance take the Q-factor to be 95 and the reactance of either L or C to be 400 ohms.   For the tube take $g_m = 4000$ μ-mhos and $\mu = 70$.   (a) Diagram the equivalent a-c circuit.   (b) Compute the voltage gain.

8. Figure 40 shows a grounded-grid amplifier with a cathode-follower input directly connected through a common resistor, R_3.   (This combination provides a high-impedance input.)   Assume a type 6SN7 double triode, and take $R_1 = R_2 = 400$ K, $R_3 = 50$ K.   (a) Resistor R_1 is included to make the plate potential the same for each triode.   Explain carefully the function of the large condenser, C_2. (b) Compute the output voltage and output impedance for the cathode-follower stage, with the amplifier stage disconnected.   (c) Consider the result of Part (b)

as the input to the grounded-grid amplifier, and compute the output of the amplifier. (Apply Thévenin's theorem.)

9. A klystron is operated at 2850 Mcps, with a cathode potential of -1250 volts. (a) Compute the average speed of the electrons in the drift-space. (b) Compute the distance between bunches.

10. In the klystron of Prob. 9 the catcher grid is 13.5 mm from the buncher grid. (a) Determine the phase difference between the oscillations in the catcher and the buncher. (b) Compute the length of delay line needed to produce optimum feedback coupling when the klystron is operated as an oscillator.

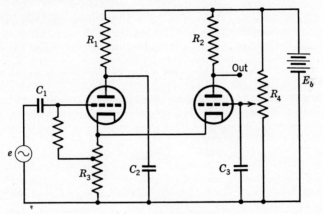

FIG. 40.   See Prob. 8.

11. Compute the value of u_1, the peak change in speed for the electrons in the klystron of Probs. 9 and 10, to produce maximum bunching in the drift-space distance of 13.5 mm.

12. Compute the amplitude of the a-c emf* acting between the grids of a klystron buncher to produce 8 percent velocity modulation, if the cathode potential is -975 volts.

Solution: Let the accelerating potential be V_0, the emf between the grids be x, the average electron speed be u_0, and the amplitude of the speed modulation be u_1. The change in speed from u_0 to $(u_0 \pm u_1)$ requires work equal to

$$\tfrac{1}{2}m(u_0 \pm u_1)^2 - \tfrac{1}{2}mu_0^2 = \pm xe$$

from which

$$mu_0u_1 \cong xe$$

But

$$\tfrac{1}{2}mu_0^2 = V_0e$$

Dividing

$$2u_1/u_0 \cong x/V_0 \quad \text{or} \quad x \cong (2u_1/u_0)V_0 = 16 \text{ percent of } V_0$$

13. A reflex klystron is operated at 1400 Mcps, with a cathode potential of -970 volts. The repeller electrode is 7.5 mm from the resonator grid, and its potential is -1260 volts. Assume the electric field between the repeller and grid

_____

* The potential difference between these grids is always zero, since both are at ground potential.

to be uniform. (a) Compute the average speed of the electrons as they leave the grid. (b) Compute the distance they travel toward the repeller before being turned back. (c) Compute the time of flight between leaving the grid and returning to it. (d) Is this time favorable or unfavorable to maintenance of oscillations at 1400-Mcps frequency? Explain your answer carefully, with diagrams.

14. An electron is moving with a speed u in a uniform magnetic field, in a plane normal to the field. There is no electric field in this region. (a) Show that this electron is revolving in a circle with angular velocity ω given by Eq. 35. (b) Compute ω if B is 1200 gauss. (c) Compute the energy of the electron, in electron-volts, if the diameter of the circle is 4.0 mm.

15. In Fig. 24, take $B = 1500$ gauss, $V = 18,000$ volts, and the electrodes 8.0 mm apart. (a) Compute the speed electrons must have, to move in a straight line parallel to the electrodes. (b) An electron starts from rest at the cathode, as in Fig. 27. Compute the height and the length from cusp to cusp of the cycloidal electron path. (c) Compute the forces acting on the electron at the top of this path, and explain why they are not equal.

The next five problems relate to a hypothetical magnetron having 24 cavities, with anode diameter 32.0 mm, cathode diameter 22.0 mm. In these problems approximations may be made as in the text. Work these problems from fundamental relationships, using Eqs. 42 and 45 only as a check.

16. Compute the speed at which an electron must move in a circle midway between K and A (Fig. 28) if $E = 14.0$ Kv per cm, and $B = 900$ gauss.

17. Assume $B = 1300$ gauss and compute the potential between K and A so that electrons may circle about K, halfway between K and A, at the rate of 250 million revolutions per second.

18. (a) Compute the mean speed of an electron in this magnetron, to maintain oscillations in the π mode with a frequency of 3000 Mcps. (b) Compute the value of B required to make the cycloidal height 2.0 mm. (c) Compute the corresponding value of the cathode potential.

19. Describe the six possible modes of oscillation for this magnetron, and identify each by the phase shift from one cavity to the next for the running waves. NOTE: The frequencies of these modes do not form a harmonic series.

20. (a) Compute the mean speed for an electron in this magnetron, to maintain oscillations in the $\pi/3$ mode. Assume a frequency of 1300 Mcps. (b) Compute the value of B required to make the cycloidal height 2.0 mm. (c) Compute the corresponding value of the cathode potential.

21. The helix in a traveling-wave tube has 5 turns per centimeter and is 0.70 cm in diameter. (a) Compute the speed of the traveling waves along this helix. (b) Compute the accelerating potential needed to give approximately this speed to electrons in the beam.

CHAPTER 14

Electronic Instruments

1. Applications. Applications for electronics range far outside the fields of communication and radio in which this branch of physical science had its genesis. Indeed, there is hardly any field of science or technology in which some application of electron tubes and circuits does not play an essential part. Even if we confine our attention to those applications in which the fundamental principles of electronics here studied are directly concerned we must include X-ray tubes, electron microscopes, mass spectrographs, cyclotrons, betatrons, and many other devices of comparable importance. It is evident that we must leave most applications to other books. The applications which have been considered from time to time in earlier chapters have been introduced primarily to illustrate principles being studied. The further applications considered in this chapter are for the most part those having to do with physical measurement.

2. Electronic Instruments. Electronic measuring instruments represent an outstanding contribution to many fields of science and engineering, in addition to being indispensable in the electronics laboratory. With them measurements and observations may be made which are impossible otherwise. A considerable number of these instruments have already been considered in the foregoing chapters. In this chapter we shall survey this field of electronic instrumentation, reviewing those instruments already considered and including others not previously mentioned. Foremost among these instruments are the cathode-ray oscilloscope and vacuum-tube voltmeters.

3. Cathode-Ray Oscilloscope. The cathode-ray oscilloscope probably has wider application than any other electronic instrument. Its essential element is the oscilloscope tube which is described in Sec. 6 of the Introduction, which includes also a description of the other elements encased with this tube to make up a complete oscilloscope, such as power supplies, amplifiers, and the sweep circuit. The requirements imposed upon oscilloscope amplifiers are particularly severe; not only must they be essentially free of amplitude distortion over a wide frequency range, but they must also show negligible phase shift over that range. Although phase distortion is not detectable by the ear it is quickly perceived on the oscilloscope screen. The power output from these amplifiers is not large, but the potential swing may be several hundred volts, so that their design involves the principles discussed in Chapter 4. In the best oscilloscope amplifiers tubes are employed in pairs, in push-pull or balanced circuits: see Figs. 18 to 20, Chapter 4. Suitable feedback helps to maintain linearity of output and negligible phase shift. A further refinement often added to oscilloscopes is a "z-axis" control, which varies the potential of the intensity-control grid so as to alter the brightness of the fluorescent spot, or even blank it out.

4. Cathode-Ray Oscilloscope Applications. Any phenomenon which can produce an emf or current may be represented on the screen of an oscilloscope. For example, many medical and biological phenomena, such as heart beats, may be thus displayed, with compact electrical pick-ups replacing the cumbersome mechanical devices formerly employed to detect and record such phenomena. Applications in physics and electrical engineering laboratories need no elaboration here, and applications to the study of mechanical vibrations of all kinds are almost as familiar. The *transducers* employed to generate the necessary emf's, proportional to the motion parameter under study, may themselves be electronic devices. Thus there is an electron tube* whose plate is connected through a flexible diaphragm to an external stylus, so that minute motions of the stylus may produce proportional changes in the electrical output of the tube. One noteworthy use for the oscilloscope is for balancing any a-c bridge (cf. Secs. 22 to 24, Chapter 2), where it provides the most reliable means for detecting a balance at the fundamental frequency in the presence of other harmonics.

Several types of fluorescent screens are available. For very high-frequency operation the screen must be practically free from any phosphorescence, but a screen of longer persistence but greater efficiency may be employed at lower frequency. For the observation of transient phenomena a screen having a long-time phosphorescence serves to hold the image until it may be observed. In oscilloscopes designed for viewing transients there are controls provided to keep the electron beam off the screen until just before the transient starts, and to remove it immediately afterward. The sweep circuit likewise is blocked until the beam spot appears on the screen.

5. Electronic Switching. Simultaneous events may be represented on the same screen if the cathode-ray tube has two electron guns, and tubes of this kind are invaluable for the study of many transient

* RCA type 5734.

phenomena.* A simpler way to view simultaneous *periodic* events, such as current and voltage in a circuit, is with an electronic switch of the kind shown in Fig. 28, Chapter 11, and described in Sec. 24 of that chapter. An interesting variation of this device is shown in Fig. 1, which represents the switching part of a commercial instrument. In this circuit switching is accomplished by varying the cathode potential of the amplifier tubes, $T2$ and $T3$, by means of the cathode-follower

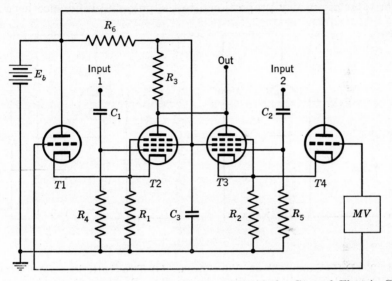

Fig. 1. Electronic Switch. Part of the circuit of the General Electric Co., Type YE-9 electronic switch.

stages $T1$ and $T4$. A multivibrator circuit, MV, supplies square-wave signals of opposite signs to the grids of $T1$ and $T4$ so that one or the other is always conducting. If $T1$ is conducting the current in R_1 is so large that the cathode of $T2$ is biased to cut-off. At the same time $T4$ is *not* conducting and R_2 (the counterpart of R_1) serves as cathode-bias resistor for $T3$, which then operates as an amplifier with cathode-resistor degeneration. When the multivibrator input reverses, $T2$ operates as an amplifier and $T3$ is cut out. A common load resistor, R_3, serves both amplifier tubes and the output is taken from the common plate connection. The multivibrator is synchronized with the sweep circuit so that the output alternates from $T2$ to $T3$ and back at the sweep frequency.

6. D-C Vacuum-Tube Voltmeter. For many purposes the vacuum-tube voltmeter comes close to being the ideal voltmeter, capable of

* The RCA color television tube has three electron guns.

reading potential difference with negligible disturbance to the circuit into which it is connected.   A voltmeter impedance of many megohms is possible.   One of the simplest types of d-c vacuum-tube voltmeters is represented in Fig. 2.   Compare it with Fig. 16, Chapter 3.   The reading of the meter M is reduced to zero for zero input by varying R_1, which is many times larger than the resistance of M.   [This balance is reached when the IR-drop in $(R_1 + R_2)$ equals E_1.]   Readings of M thereafter are nearly proportional to the potential difference between

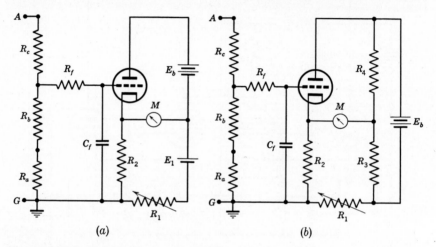

(a)   (b)

Fig. 2.   D-C Vacuum-Tube Voltmeter.   (a) Two batteries.   (b) Common battery.   A *low*-resistance voltage-divider, $R_3 - R_4$, across E_b, provides E_1.

A and G, over a grid-potential range of 1 volt or less.   Resistors R_a, R_b, and R_c provide a voltage-divider, or multiplier, whereby the input range may be extended.   The sensitivity of this meter depends upon the range of M, and may be made quite high by employing a galvanometer for M.   The limit is determined by the stability of the circuit balance: if high-quality resistors and batteries are used the full-scale reading may represent only a few millivolts.   Unfortunately, the calibration of this type of meter changes with the tube characteristics, so that good accuracy requires frequent checking of the calibration, as well as of the zero balance.   Since a high-impedance d-c voltmeter is quite sensitive to a-c fields it is customary to add to all d-c vacuum-tube voltmeter circuits a filter to by-pass a-c input from a little below 60 cps upward.   In Fig. 2 this filter is provided by C_f and R_f.

7. Cathode-Follower D-C Voltmeter.   The cathode-follower voltmeter circuit of Fig. 3 possesses greater stability, far higher intrinsic input impedance, and very much less dependence upon vacuum-tube characteristics than the one of Fig. 2. For effective cathode-follower operation the meter, M, must have a resistance which is comparable with R_1 and large in comparison with the resistance of R_2 and R_3 in parallel. Then the potential drop which is produced across M by the input between A and G is nearly equal to that input, and also close to the corresponding change in the potential difference between K and S. The readings of this meter are quite exactly proportional to the input voltage, and are changed very little by changes in g_m for

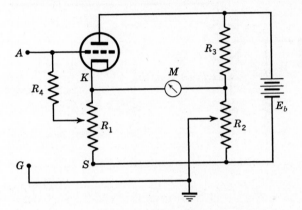

FIG. 3.   CATHODE-FOLLOWER D-C VOLTMETER.

the tube. A reversing switch, or a zero-center meter, makes possible readings of either sign.

High input impedance is provided by the grid-bias connection shown in Fig. 3, as explained in Sec. 18, Chapter 6. Because of this connection a double zero balance is required. First, with A connected to G, the sliding contact on R_2 is set to give zero reading. Then, with A disconnected, the sliding contact on R_1 is adjusted for zero reading. Thereafter only the first adjustment is necessary to correct for slight shifts in balance. The balance is quite stable with respect to small changes in E_b, but, like all other vacuum-tube meters, this one is sensitive to changes in cathode-heater power.

8. Balanced-Circuit Voltmeters. Figure 4 represents a d-c voltmeter circuit favored by many manufacturers. At first sight it appears to be a cathode-follower circuit comparable to that of Fig. 3, having the added advantage of a symmetry which makes it more independent of power-supply variations. Actually it is a modification of the circuit of Fig. 2 and subject to errors caused by changes in tube characteristics. Exact analysis gives the following relation between the input, E, and the meter current, I_m.

$$\frac{E}{R_2 I_m} = 1 + \frac{1}{\mu} + \frac{2}{g_m}\left(\frac{1}{2R_1} + \frac{1}{R_2}\right) \tag{1}$$

From Eq. 1 it is seen that the output cannot be made relatively independent of g_m unless the last term is very small, and this may be accomplished only by making the resistance between the two cathodes,

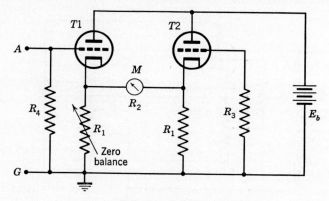

FIG. 4.   TWO-TUBE D-C VOLTMETER.

which is R_2 in parallel with $2R_1$, much larger than $2/g_m$. Unfortunately this requirement is frequently neglected in commercial circuits. Indeed, if the grid bias is taken over all of R_1, as indicated in Fig. 4, it is impossible to make R_1 large enough to meet this condition. A true cathode-follower circuit of this balanced type is diagrammed in Fig. 5. Note the means employed to produce grid bias for both tubes, so that it is only a fraction of the potential drop across R_1. Equation 1 still holds but now R_1 and R_2 may be made large enough to insure linearity and relative freedom from errors due to variations in tube characteristics. This circuit is also very insensitive to changes in E_b.

9. Grid Current in Vacuum-Tube Voltmeters. As explained in Sec. 27, Chapter 2, there is always a small grid current in a vacuum tube, and this current may affect the reading of a vacuum-tube voltmeter if the source impedance is high. Fortunately for this application the grid current in most tubes reverses at some negative potential not too far below zero, and may be held to a minimum by fixing the bias near this potential. The double balance for the circuits of Figs. 3 and 5 may be adjusted to meet this condition, and in these cathode-follower circuits this advantage may be maintained over a considerable input range, since the change in grid potential is but a small fraction of the input.   If this adjustment is carefully made the grid-bias resistor may have a very high value and the input resistance, for small input voltage, may approach infinity.   In this connection read again the description of the so-called electrometer tubes, in Sec. 18 of Chapter 3. The input impedance for one of these tubes may be a million megohms or higher.

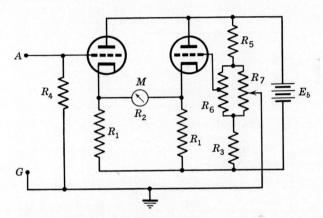

Fig. 5.   Two-Tube Cathode-Follower D-C Voltmeter.   For a 6SN7 tube, suitable values are:

R_1—10 K. R_5—22 K, 4 watts.
R_2—about 20 K (adjust to make M R_6—1 K, center-tapped.
   direct-reading). R_7—1-K "potentiometer."
R_3—10 K. E_b from 130 to 250 volts.
R_4—15 megohms.

10. A-C Voltmeters.   Electronic a-c voltmeters include invariably some form of rectifier circuit, followed by some means for measurement of the d-c output.   The simplest type consists of a diode in series with a high resistance and a sensitive d-c meter.   A crystal diode is best for low voltage, since a thermionic diode has a small internal bias which must be balanced out in some manner.   This type of meter reads the "average value" of the a-c voltage, that is, the average taken with all values assumed positive.   It is necessary of course that the a-c source provide a complete d-c path; otherwise the diode cannot function, as has been explained in Chapter 1.   This limitation precludes the insertion of a series condenser to block out any direct current from the source.   The commonest type of average-value a-c voltmeter has four crystal diodes arranged in a "bridge" circuit, as illustrated in

Fig. 30, Chapter 1, and explained in Sec. 27 of that chapter. This diode bridge gives full-cycle rectification and also provides the necessary d-c path. Generally the scales of average-value meters are graduated to read the equivalent rms values, on the assumption that the a-c voltage being measured is sinusoidal.

11. "Peak-Value" A-C Voltmeters. The d-c output from a diode-detector circuit having a large time constant is equal to the *peak value* of the input voltage. It may be measured by a d-c milliammeter in

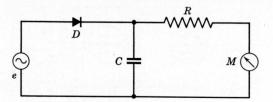

Fig. 6.   Peak-Value A-C Voltmeter.

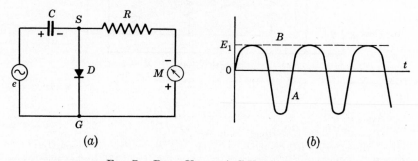

Fig. 7.   Peak-Value A-C Voltmeter.

series with the resistor, as represented in Fig. 6, or even better with a d-c vacuum-tube voltmeter connected to the condenser terminals. For this circuit also the a-c source must provide a d-c path. When it does not the circuit must be modified to provide the d-c path within itself. In the usual peak-voltmeter circuit, which is shown in Fig. 7a, this condition is met by making the filter condenser serve also as a blocking condenser, in series with the input. If the source impedance includes a series condenser the d-c potential from S to G is divided between this condenser and condenser C.

The operation of this circuit may be explained as follows. Let the alternating voltage be represented by plot A in Fig. 7b. During the first few cycles the condenser, C, charges up, with signs as shown, until the potential drop across it practically equals E_1, the *positive* peak of the a-c voltage. The distance from the x-axis to line B, drawn tangent to the peaks of A, represents this potential difference. Thereafter the potential at S is always negative or zero (except for the slight positive potential needed to maintain the charge in C) and is represented in Fig. 7b by plot A if line B is taken as the x-axis. (The diode is functioning as a *clamping* diode, to hold the potential at S to a maximum value of zero.) The meter M reads only the d-c component of the potential difference between S and G, or E_1. If E_1 is read by a vacuum-tube voltmeter connected between S and G it is very necessary to interpose an a-c filter, since the a-c potential difference between these points is equal to the full value of the input voltage. This circuit is found in most a-c, d-c electronic voltmeters.

In this type of a-c meter also the scales generally are graduated to read equivalent rms values, on the assumption that the a-c input is sinusoidal. If the a-c voltage is badly distorted the readings of an average-value meter, a peak-value meter, and a true rms meter all will be different, even though all are graduated to read alike for sinusoidal voltage. Furthermore, reversal of the input connections to a peak-value meter will give a different reading whenever the distortion is unsymmetrical, as shown in Fig. 7b.

Although the peak-value a-c voltmeter is a favorite for commercial electronic meters it has several serious faults. In addition to those mentioned above it possesses a very poor input impedance. The input current consists of narrow pulses of relatively high peak value, and whenever there is appreciable resistance in the a-c source this current peak will produce a considerable potential drop in the peak input voltage *at the time that the voltage is being measured*. This effect is strikingly shown in Exp. 2, Part III, in which a similar circuit is studied. It follows that the effective input impedance for the peak-value voltmeter is many times less than the resistance in series with the d-c meter.

It is often argued that the input impedance to the detector circuit is approximately $\frac{1}{2} R$ (Fig. 7a), and this is true in so far as it concerns the load on the a-c emf supplying the input, if the input is sinusoidal. Harmonic analysis shows that I_1, the peak value of the first-harmonic component of the current pulse in D, is approximately equal to twice the average value, or equal to $2E_1/R$. If the a-c input is now assumed to be sinusoidal, with peak value equal to E_1, it follows that the input impedance is E_1/I_1, or $R/2$. But E_1 is determined by *all* components of the current pulse, and *all are in phase* when the diode conducts. Hence any resistance R_i in the a-c source causes E_1 to drop below the peak value by far more than I_1R_i, and the effective *transfer* impedance (a-c in to d-c out) for the circuit is far less than $R/2$.

12. RMS Voltmeters. The readings of a thermocouple current meter may be made closely proportional to the *square* of the current, and hence give true rms values regardless of waveform, from zero frequency up to high radiofrequency. The sensitivity is low, however, so that thermocouple voltmeters are not practical except as standards for calibration. On the other hand a triode, biased to operate on a suitably curved portion of its transfer characteristic, may have excellent square-law characteristics and good sensitivity, plus the high input impedance characteristic of all electronic meters. Its

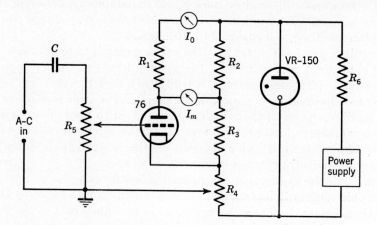

FIG. 8. RMS VACUUM-TUBE VOLTMETER: CIRCUIT FOR EXP. 37.

chief drawback is need for frequent checking of its calibration. A practical circuit is shown in Fig. 8. Suitable operating conditions are found experimentally so that the meter current, I_m (which is balanced to zero with no input), is directly proportional to the square of the input voltage. The extent of this range is generally limited to about 1 volt rms at the grid, but the input range for the meter may be extended indefinitely by means of the multiplier, R_5. The resistance in series with the meter for I_m must be of low impedance compared to R_1, and both E_b and the cathode-heater power must be well regulated. Since this circuit requires occasional recalibration it is a better laboratory meter than shop tool. Nevertheless it is an excellent instrument having many uses.

13. Experiment 37. Square-Law Voltmeter. The performance of the voltmeter circuit of Fig. 8 is to be studied; instructions are given for a type 76 tube. The d-c source may be provided by a laboratory power supply, with a VR-150 tube in parallel with R_2-R_3-R_4 to maintain E_b constant at about 150 volts. Be sure to include a suitable dropping resistor, R_6, between the power supply and the VR tube. The cathode heater is best supplied by a storage battery. Make R_2 2 K, R_3 5 K, R_4 a 500-ohm potentiometer, and R_5 2 megohms. Several values may be tried for R_1; start with 15 K. The meter for I_m should have a range of not over 500 μa. The a-c input may be measured most precisely if supplied from a potentiometer connected to a fixed a-c voltage (e.g., from a 2.5-volt filament transformer). Monitor this fixed voltage with an ordinary a-c voltmeter.

Connect the grid to the top of R_5 and balance the circuit with the input terminals connected together. Then take readings from zero up to the a-c input which gives full-scale reading for I_m. Space the observations uniformly along the scale of I_m. From these data make a plot with I_m as y, the square of the a-c grid potential as x. This plot should fit to a straight line over a considerable range upward from zero. Draw this straight line and determine from it the working range of the meter for not over 1 percent deviation from this line, and the meter calibration for this range. Repeat measurements for other values of R_1. Try 10 K and 25 K. From the plots for each set of data determine the value of R_1 which represents the longest range. In your report explain carefully how this circuit functions.

14. Cathode-Follower Input for A-C Voltmeters. Any a-c voltmeter may be connected through a cathode-follower stage to the points between which potential difference is to be measured, as shown in Fig. 9. The effective input impedance then has the very high value characteristic of cathode-follower circuits; the impedance from the cathode-follower into the a-c voltmeter is characteristically low. The a-c voltmeter may be the rectifier-bridge type shown in Fig. 9, or any of those illustrated in Figs. 2 to 5 and 8. Careful design is required, to insure that the a-c swing in the output does not exceed the working range of the tube (see the graphical analysis in Sec. 17, Chapter 6). It is necessary also to keep the load impedance, including the meter, well above r_p in order to gain the desired high input impedance. The values given in Fig. 9 are suitable for a meter of about 10 volts rms input range. All types of a-c voltmeters may be preceded by one or more stages of amplification to produce increased sensitivity, and negative feedback may be employed in the amplifier to compensate for distortion and to stabilize gain. The design of such precision amplifiers is discussed in Sec. 9, Chapter 6.

15. A-C Bridges. The most precise electrical measurements are made with null methods in which a balance is obtained between points on two parallel circuits. The Wheatstone bridge and the potentiometer are familiar examples of d-c null methods. Many more null methods have been developed for a-c measurement, including bridges for comparing all kinds of impedances and circuits for determining frequency. Details concerning these circuits are found in all manuals of a-c measurements. In the electronics laboratory null methods include also circuits to measure small variations of non-linear quantities, such as those described in Chapter 2 for measurement of μ, g_m, and

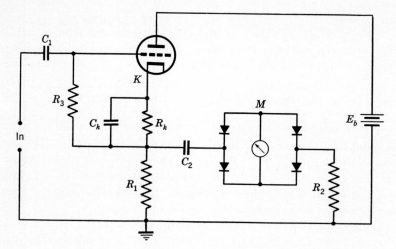

Fig. 9. Average-Value A-C Voltmeter with Cathode-Follower Input.
For 15-volt range with 6J5 tube:

R_1—15 K. $\qquad$ C_1—0.005 μf.
R_2—15 K. $\qquad$ C_2—2.0 μf.
R_3—2 megohms. $\qquad$ C_k—20 μf.
R_k to make d-c potential at K 65 volts,
$\quad$ with 150 volts for E_b.

r_p. And a-c bridges are needed in the chemistry laboratory to measure the conductance of solutions, since direct current produces polarization at the electrodes.

For all these a-c null methods the balance detector was originally a sensitive pair of headphones, but this detector is now almost entirely replaced by a variety of electronic devices, aided by electronic amplifiers. The cathode-ray oscilloscope and vacuum-tube voltmeters are foremost among these detectors, but the electron-ray tube (Sec. 16) is very convenient, as well as inexpensive, where the highest precision is not required, and a differential amplifier* meets the need in certain difficult situations.

* See Matthew Conrad, "Differential Amplifier Null Detector," *Electronics*, February, 1950, p. 96.

16. Electron-Ray Tube. The electron-ray tube, which was designed originally as a radio tuning indicator, is represented in cross-section in Fig. 10a. A shallow metal cup, T, is coated inside with fluorescent-screen material which glows by electron bombardment if there is a potential difference of 200 to 250 volts between T and the cathode, K, which projects into this cup through a hole in its bottom. The lower

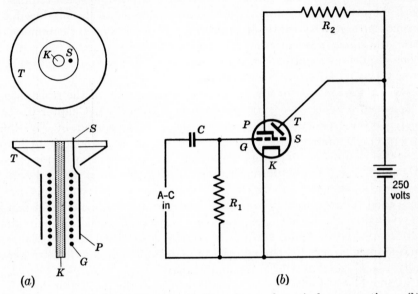

(a)   (b)

FIG. 10. ELECTRON-RAY TUBE. (a) Top view and vertical cross-section. (b) Circuit for balance detector.

half of K is surrounded by the grid, G, and plate, P, of an amplifier tube, and P supports a straight rod, S, which projects into T alongside K. The amplifier circuit is shown in Fig. 10b. Since the potential of S is that of P, and lower than the potential of T, S shields electrically a portion of the fluorescent screen, thus producing an angular shadow whose width increases or decreases as the potential of S falls or rises. A small change in grid potential is amplified at S and produces a noticeable change in shadow angle.

For a-c bridge balancing the amplifier must be preceded by a rectifier circuit such as the one included in Fig. 10b. The diode rectifier is provided by the triode grid, which is initially at zero potential, and the grid current produces a potential difference across C which is approximately proportional to the a-c input voltage, with the grid side negative. Balance of the bridge, or zero input, is indicated by maximum shadow angle.   An a-c amplifier may be placed ahead of the rectifier for greater sensitivity.

17. Low-Frequency Signal Generators.   Electronics has supplied laboratories with a-c generators of great convenience and flexibility of operation.   Available oscillation frequencies range from close to zero up above 10 billion cps, and any frequency may be controlled with great exactness.   High purity of waveform is possible when required, but distortion of any kind (e.g., square waves) may be produced at will.   Although kilowatts of power may be generated for commercial use, the *signal generators* employed in the laboratory are of low power. The important requirements are steadiness of power and of frequency, together with exactness of waveform.

Signal generators for low frequency are generally of the resistance-capacitance type, such as those described in Sec. 24, Chapter 6.   A typical low-frequency signal generator is diagrammed in Fig. 26, Chapter 6; commonly its frequency is continuously variable from 20 to 20,000 cps, in three overlapping ranges.   A separate set of condensers, C_1 and C_2, is provided for each range, and within each range the frequency is changed by varying R_1 and R_2.   If this circuit is well designed the amplitude is almost the same at any frequency, and there is very little distortion.   Several other resistance-capacitance circuits are employed in signal generators, as well as at least one resistance-inductance circuit.*   The addition of a suitable clipper circuit makes any signal generator also a square-wave generator.   (See Sec. 21, Chapter 11.)   If only square waves are desired the oscillations may be generated by a simpler circuit of the multivibrator type described in Sec. 17, Chapter 11.†

18. Radiofrequency Signal Generators.   The resonant circuit in a radiofrequency signal generator is invariably an inductance and a capacitance in parallel, maintained in oscillation by one of the circuits described in Chapter 10.   Its frequency should be as independent as possible of tube characteristics and of variations in the power supply, and a prime requisite to meeting these requirements is class A or near class A operation.‡   A circuit capable of delivering considerable

---

* P. G. Sulzer, "Wide-Range R-C Oscillator" (20 cps to 2 Mcps), *Electronics*, September 1950, p. 88; P. G. Sulzer, "Single-Band Audio Generator," *Electronics*, January 1952, p. 95; A. Hershler and B. Carlin, "Bridge Oscillator Has Linear Tuning" (resistance-inductance circuit), *Electronics*, August 1952, p. 134.

† See G. W. Gray, "Inexpensive Square-Wave Generator" (50 cps to 1 Mcps), *Electronics*, February 1952, p. 101.

‡ Circuits particularly useful for laboratory work are described in F. E. Terman, *Measurements in Radio Engineering*, Chapter 12.   See also F. E. Terman, *Radio Engineers' Handbook*, Sec. 13, Par. 6, and Sec. 6.

power with excellent frequency stability is diagrammed in Fig. 11. It may be seen that each tube is capable of driving the circuit by itself, and that the two tubes working together provide the equivalent of class A operation with one tube. Low-μ tubes, such as types 45 and 2A3, are best. The circuit will operate without the choke-coil, L_2, since the center tap in L_1 is at zero RF potential; L_2 cares for any small unbalance between the two tubes. The entire circuit should be

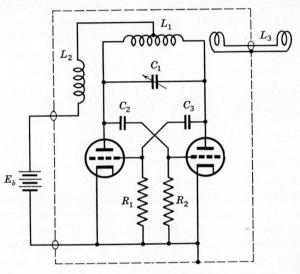

FIG. 11.   LABORATORY OSCILLATOR.

shielded by a heavy metal case. Radiofrequency connections to the outside are made by a loop connector, L_3, closely coupled to L_1 at its midpoint. The tank coil, L_1, plugs in, and several coils should be provided to cover a series of overlapping ranges.

19. Crystal Control of Oscillation. For frequency control with highest precision an electrically driven mechanical oscillator may be employed as a frequency standard. At very low frequency this standard may be a pendulum. In order of increasing frequency then come tuning forks, magneto-striction rods, and quartz crystals. For the highest frequency yet controlled in this manner the standard is provided by the vibration of the NH_3 (ammonia) molecule, in the so-called atomic clock.* Oscillations of each type are maintained electrically by suitable coupling of the oscillator to an amplifying circuit.

Plates of crystal quartz are especially valuable as frequency stand-

---

* See Harold Lyons, "The Atomic Clock," *The American Scholar*, Vol. 19 (1950), p. 159.

ards over a large part of the radio frequency spectrum, since they may be cut so that their frequency of oscillation is practically independent of temperature. In general these plates are approximately square, with a thickness determined by the vibration frequency and the orientation of the plate faces with respect to the crystallographic axes of the quartz. Special orientations are designated by various letters, such as X, Y, AT, and CT. The modes of vibration for a plate depend upon this orientation. Consider for example an X-cut plate, which can vibrate in the direction of its thickness, with longitudinal standing waves having a nodal plane midway between the two

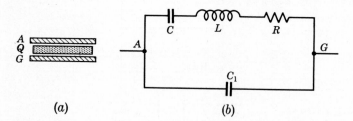

(a)   (b)

Fig. 12. Quartz-Crystal Resonant Unit. (a) Mounting. A, G—metal plates. Q—quartz-crystal plate. Small projections at the corners of A and G support Q. (b) Equivalent circuit.

faces. The velocity of these waves (for the direction in quartz determined by this cut) is 5720 meters per second, and the wavelength is twice the thickness of the plate. Thus if the thickness is 2.00 mm the frequency of this vibration is 1430 Kcps. The effect of temperature upon frequency depends upon the type of cut, and a plate may be cut in such a manner as to have practically zero temperature coefficient for frequency.*

The piezoelectric properties of quartz provide the means whereby a quartz plate may be maintained in oscillation electrically. The procedure is to mount the plate between flat metal electrodes which almost touch its faces, as indicated in Fig. 12a. An alternating electric field between these electrodes now produces mechanical forces within the crystal, and if the field has the proper frequency these forces set up and maintain resonant oscillations of the crystal plate. Conversely, mechanical oscillations of the plate produce electric charges on its two faces and, by induction, on the two electrodes, and the reaction of these charges with the electric field makes the crystal plate and its electrodes

* For further details concerning these properties of quartz see F. E. Terman, *Radio Engineers' Handbook*, pp. 488–498, and W. G. Cady, "Crystals and Electricity," *Scientific American*, December 1949, p. 47.

equivalent electrically to the circuit of Fig. 12b. Two possible oscillator circuits controlled by this quartz-crystal assembly are diagrammed in Figs. 13 and 14. Before analyzing these circuits, however, we must consider the electrical characteristics represented in Fig. 12b.

20. Electrical Characteristics of a Quartz-Crystal Assembly. In Fig. 12b the electrical capacitance between electrodes in Fig. 12a, with the quartz plate as dielectric, is represented by C_1, whereas the mechanical properties of the quartz plate account for C, L, and R. Since the elastic forces and density are both large for quartz, C is very small, L remarkably large. The most significant characteristic of this oscillator, however, is its Q-factor, which is exceedingly large if the plate is properly supported. Oscillation then dies away very slowly and the frequency of oscillation is practically unaffected by changes in the circuit to which the electrodes are connected.

At a frequency f_1 this circuit is series-resonant, with zero reactance and a very low resistance equal to R. This frequency is the natural vibration frequency of the crystal, and is related to L and C by

$$f_1 = 1/(2\pi \sqrt{LC}) \tag{2}$$

At a slightly higher frequency f_2 the circuit is parallel-resonant, with zero reactance and a very high resistance R_2.

$$f_2 = f_1 \sqrt{\frac{C + C_1}{C_1}} \tag{3}$$

and

$$R_2 = 1/(C_1{}^2\omega_2{}^2 R) \tag{4}$$

At frequencies above f_2 and below f_1 the impedance of this circuit is reactive and negative (capacitive). But at frequencies between f_1 and f_2 it is equivalent to an inductive reactance which has a very high value just below f_2. Frequency f_2 is very close to f_1 and may be brought still closer (at the sacrifice of a reduction in Q-factor) by putting additional capacitance in parallel with C_1.

21. Crystal-Oscillator Circuits. The two principal crystal-oscillator circuits are diagrammed in Figs. 13a and 14a. The equivalent circuits are represented in Figs. 13b and 14b. In each circuit the crystal oscillates at a frequency somewhere between f_1 and f_2 such that the crystal assembly is equivalent to a high inductive reactance, represented by X_a in Figs. 13b and 14b. In the Miller circuit (Fig. 13) the resonant circuit $L_2 C_2$ is tuned above the oscillation frequency so that it also functions as an inductive reactance, X_b in Fig. 13b.

The circuit of Fig. 13b may be recognized as a Hartley-type oscillator, in which the tank circuit is formed by X_a, X_b, and C_3. It differs from the usual Hartley circuit in that there is no coupling between X_a and X_b. The interelectrode capacitance between grid and plate of the tube may suffice for C_3, although better frequency stability may be obtainable by adding a small external capacitance.

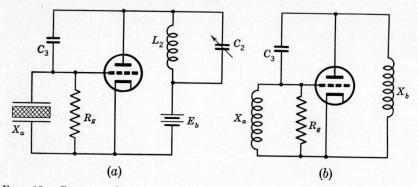

(a)   (b)

FIG. 13. CRYSTAL OSCILLATOR: MILLER CIRCUIT. (a) Actual circuit. (b) Equivalent circuit (a-c parts only).

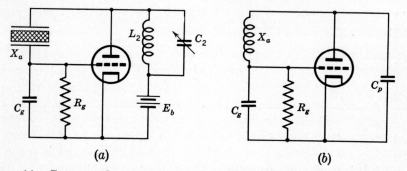

(a)   (b)

FIG. 14. CRYSTAL OSCILLATOR: PIERCE CIRCUIT. (a) Actual circuit. (b) Equivalent circuit (a-c parts only).

In the Pierce circuit (Fig. 14) the inductive reactance X_a is between grid and plate of the tube, and capacitative reactances then are required between the cathode and both grid and plate. The circuit is thus a Colpitts oscillator, as seen in Fig. 14b. In this circuit $L_2 C_2$ is therefore tuned below the oscillation frequency to make it equivalent to a capacitance C_p. The capacitance C_g may be the input capacitance of the tube, augmented if necessary by a small external capacitance.*

* A more detailed analysis of these circuits is given by J. E. Anderson in *Electronics*, August 1938, pp. 22–24.

The circuits of Figs. 13 and 14 may be modified for pentode (or tetrode) operation, with the advantage that the output does not disturb the oscillator. A pentode modification of the circuit of Fig. 14 is shown in Fig. 15. Note that the screen grid, which serves as plate for the oscillator, is at ground a-c potential, with the cathode at an a-c potential determined by the *capacitative* reactance produced by tuning L_2C_2 below resonance. The output is from the plate, and is electrically shielded from the oscillator part by the grounded screen grid. The circuit L_3C_3 may be tuned to the resonant frequency, for output at

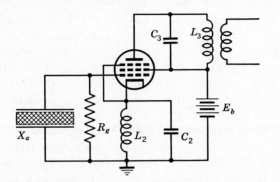

FIG. 15.   CRYSTAL OSCILLATOR: PENTODE CIRCUIT.

the fundamental frequency, or it may be tuned to a higher harmonic, thereby achieving frequency multiplication. For other crystal-oscillator circuits see F. E. Terman, *Radio Engineers' Handbook*, p. 496, and the *Radio Amateurs' Handbook* (new edition yearly).

22. Frequency Measurement. Oscillation generators of precise frequencies make possible very accurate frequency measurements and frequency standards. Low frequencies (up to several hundred cps) may be determined by actually *counting* cycles with an electric-clock mechanism driven by the oscillation generator. Higher frequencies must be determined by a process of comparison with some frequency in the counting range, by a series of steps if the frequency ratio much exceeds 10. Such comparison may be made most readily with a cathode-ray oscilloscope. If signals of the two frequencies are applied to the x and y terminals of the oscilloscope a Lissajou figure characteristic of the frequency ratio appears on the screen. If the two frequencies are commensurable the pattern is stationary and the frequency may be determined from the figure. An alternate plan is to view the time plots of the two signals simultaneously by means of an electronic switch (Sec. 5).

Consider for example the rating of a 100-Kcps oscillator against a standard clock. Three intermediate oscillators may be employed, of frequencies 10,000, 1000, and 100 cps, and these oscillators may be multivibrator circuits, employed in the manner described in Sec. 18, Chapter 11. The first multivibrator is triggered by the oscillator being rated, so as to operate at exactly one-tenth of the oscillator frequency. The ratio is checked in the manner described above. Each multivibrator then triggers the one following, so as to maintain an exact 10 to 1 ratio between them. The final multivibrator operates an electric-clock mechanism whose motion may be timed by a standard clock, over a time interval long enough to yield the desired accuracy. If the 100-Kcps oscillator is crystal-controlled to exact frequency, the combination becomes a crystal-controlled clock, or frequency standard. Since each multivibrator generates more than 100 detectable harmonics, such a frequency standard provides many frequencies of accurately known values with which other oscillations may be compared, by beats or otherwise.

23. D-C Power Supplies. Although d-c power supplies cannot be classed as measuring instruments they are an essential part of most such instruments and hence qualify for discussion here. Storage batteries fill the need for steady d-c sources of low voltage, and in earlier days were employed for high voltage, up to 100,000 volts. At the present time their place has been taken, for all but the lowest voltages, by a-c to d-c rectifier power supplies, the basic forms of which are discussed in Chapter 1, Secs. 19 to 25. Practical circuits are diagrammed in Figs. 22, 23, 24, and 26 of Chapter 1. Oxide or selenium rectifiers may take the place of hot-cathode diodes whenever they meet the current and voltage requirements.

For precise work it is desirable, and often necessary, to have d-c sources of steady emf and low internal impedance. The simple VR-tube circuit of Fig. 9a, Chapter 8, serves well for many purposes, and VR tubes of different voltage characteristics, alone or in series, provide a wide range of output voltage. If the current required exceeds that which may be controlled by VR tubes alone, circuits of the type represented in Figs. 12 and 13, Chapter 8, may be employed. The operation of these circuits is explained in Sec. 19, Chapter 8. A practical circuit for a laboratory power supply, variable from zero to about 250 volts, with 50 ma maximum current, is given in Fig. 16. Since the waste power must be dissipated by the power tube the current is limited to a maximum value determined by the allowable power dissipation at the plate of the tube, at the plate potential corresponding to the lowest output voltage. Two or more tubes may be connected in parallel to increase the current output.

24. Electronic Voltage Regulation. By adding an amplifier to the circuit of Fig. 12, Chapter 8, we may obtain much closer regulation of its d-c output. A typical circuit is shown in Fig. 17. The cathode potential for the amplifier tube, $T2$, is fixed by the VR tube, $T3$, and

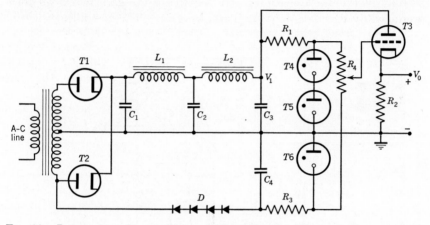

FIG. 16. LABORATORY POWER SUPPLY. For 250 volts, 50 ma maximum output, and 350 volts at V_1:

R_1—6 K.	$T5$, $T6$—VR-105.
R_2—100 K.	D—4 half-wave rectifiers, 150 volts,
R_3—15 K.	65 ma.
R_4—70 K.	C_1, C_2, C_3—8 μf.
$T1$, $T2$—type 80 double diode.	C_4—4 μf.
$T3$—6L6, triode-connected.	L_1, L_2—5 or 10 henries.
$T4$—VR-150.	

the grid potential for $T2$ is derived from the voltage-divider, R_1, across the output. The grid potential for the power tube, $T1$, is determined by the potential drop across R_2, which is the plate load for $T2$. Hence any change in output potential, V_0, causes a proportional change in potential at the grid of $T2$, and the amplified output of $T2$ then shifts the grid potential of $T1$ in a direction to oppose the change in V_0. The effective internal resistance of the power supply may in this manner be reduced to only a few ohms. If A is the gain in $T2$, g_m the mutual conductance of $T1$, and r the resistance of the part of R_1 between G and S, the effective internal resistance of the power supply is approximately

$$R_0 = R_1/(Ag_mr) \qquad (5)$$

In this circuit the screen grid in $T2$ is utilized to keep V_0 independent of any fluctuations in the d-c input, V_b. If V_b increases the screen-grid potential increases also, in the ratio of R_4 to $(R_3 + R_4)$, and the consequent increase in current in R_2 causes a drop in potential at the grid of $T1$, in opposition to the increase in its plate potential. To hold V_0 constant, the ratio of $(R_3 + R_4)$ to R_4 is made equal to the product of the amplification factor for $T1$ by the gain in $T2$ which is produced by signals applied to its screen grid. The best adjustment is

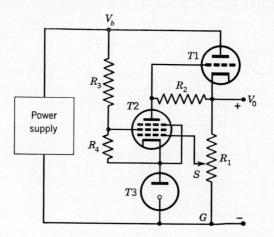

Fig. 17. Electronic Regulation. This circuit is employed in the Lambda Model 25 Regulated Power Supply. (Lambda Electronics Corp., Corona, N.Y.)

found experimentally. The fundamental principles upon which all d-c voltage stabilizers operate have been analyzed by Hunt and Hickman.*

25. Miscellaneous Power Supplies. Power-supply circuits have been devised to operate without transformers, by cascading diodes. The circuit diagrammed in Fig. 18 serves to illustrate this principle. Either thermionic or oxide-type diodes may be used. These circuits are of value chiefly when small current is needed and space or weight is at a premium. Filtering circuits may be made much smaller and lighter for any power supply if a-c power is available at higher frequency than 60 cps, for example 400 to 1000 cps.

For certain high-voltage applications RF circuits are employed to boost power from the 200 to 300 volts produced by the ordinary power supply to thousands of volts. The advantages gained are small weight

* F. V. Hunt and R. W. Hickman, "On Electronic Voltage Stabilizers," *Review of Scientific Instruments*, Vol. 10 (January 1939), p. 6.

and easier insulation, made possible by small filter condensers and no iron-core transformers. A circuit of this type is shown in Fig. 19. It is a Tesla-coil circuit, driven by the oscillator tube, $T1$. The secondary coil, L_2, has many turns and is designed to have a suitable self-resonant frequency (due to coil capacitance). The tank circuit is

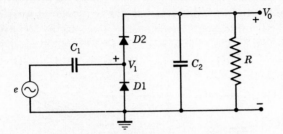

Fig. 18.   Voltage-Doubler Power Supply.

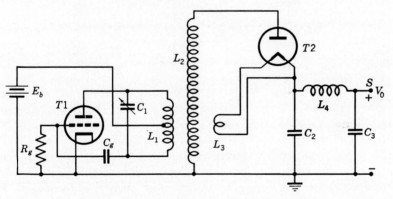

Fig. 19.   D-C Power Supply Having RF Input.

tuned to this frequency and loosely coupled to L_2, the degree of coupling being determined to give the highest output. The ratio of the d-c output at S to the d-c supply, E_b, is roughly proportional to the *square* of the turn ratio between L_2 and L_1. Observe that the diode filament is heated by RF power, obtained by coupling L_3 loosely to L_1.*

26. Ionization "Vacuum" Gauge. Certain types of measurement have been made possible by the development of highly specialized electron tubes. An example is the measurement of pressure, or density, of the residual gas in a highly evacuated vessel. For pressure

* See also P. G. Sulzer, "Series-Resonant High-Voltage Supply," *Electronics*, September 1952, p. 156.

measurements down to about 10^{-5} mm Hg there has long existed a very satisfactory instrument, the McLeod gauge, but below this limit the ionization gauge takes over.* This gauge is a triode, very similar to a radio triode in construction, but it is operated in quite a different manner. It is sealed into the vacuum system by a connecting tube, so that the gas density in its bulb is as near to that in the vacuum system as possible, and all occluded gas is driven from the electrodes and bulb by suitable heat treatment. The circuit for operating it is shown in Fig. 20. A positive potential of 100 to 200 volts is put on the *grid*, G, and I_e, the electron current to G, is held constant by careful

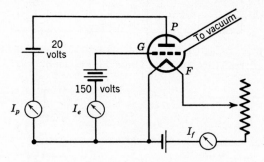

FIG. 20. IONIZATION VACUUM GAUGE.

regulation of the heating current to the cathode, which is a pure tungsten filament. A negative potential of about 20 volts on the plate, P, prevents any electrons from reaching it, although many electrons pass between the grid wires and into the space between P and G before returning to G. If now there is any gas in this space it will be ionized by these electrons, and a positive-ion current, I_p, will be set up to P. At pressures below about 10^{-3} mm Hg relatively few electrons produce ions, and practically none make more than one ionizing collision. (Contrast this behavior with the cascade process: see Sec. 9, Chapter 8.) No plasma is formed; the positive ions are produced in a strong electric field and are quickly collected by the plate. From these considerations it follows that, for pressures below about 10^{-3} mm Hg, the positive-ion current to P is directly proportional to the gas density and to the electron current to G. Unfortunately, it depends also upon the kind of gas present. This gauge must therefore be calibrated for the gas being used, by

* For descriptions of both these gauges see C. H. Bachman, *Techniques in Experimental Electronics,* Chapter 4; and J. Strong, *Procedures in Experimental Physics,* pp. 138–144.

comparison with a McLeod gauge within the pressure range in which the two gauges overlap. The ionization gauge then may be extrapolated to lower pressures according to the theoretical considerations given above.

The lowest pressure measurable with the ionization gauge is reached when the positive-ion current to P is comparable with the background current having other origins. Almost all this background current is now known to be the photoelectric emission of electrons from P, caused by soft X-rays excited by the electron bombardment of G. For gauges of the construction described above this limit is about 10^{-8} mm Hg. Alpert and Bayard* have lowered this limit to below 10^{-10}

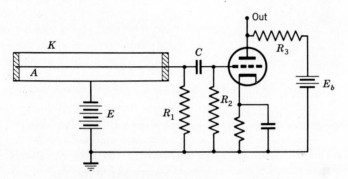

FIG. 21.   GEIGER-MÜLLER TUBE CIRCUIT.

mm Hg by redesigning the ionization gauge, putting the cathode outside the grid, the collector, P, inside. The collector, which is a thin wire along the axis of the grid, gathers in all the positive ions formed inside the grid but has so small a surface area that it intercepts only a small fraction of the X-rays emitted by the grid.

27. G-M Counter Tubes. The G-M (Geiger-Müller) counter tube is an even more highly specialized electron tube designed for a particular kind of measurement. Its essential features are represented in Fig. 21. The negative electrode is a metal cylinder, K; the positive electrode, a fine wire along the axis of this cylinder. These electrodes may be sealed into a glass tube, or the cylinder may be made gas-tight by insulating plugs which support the axial wire, as indicated in Fig. 21. The inclosed space contains a suitable gas, usually at a pressure less than atmospheric. The emf E is so large that a single ionizing particle

---

* D. Alpert and R. T. Bayard, "Extension of the Low-Pressure Range of the Ionization Gauge," *Review of Scientific Instruments*, Vol. 21, (June 1950), p. 571.

passing through this gas is sufficient to set off a discharge which, if the circuit resistance is low, will build up to a high-current, self-sustaining glow discharge. To prevent this occurrence a resistance, R_1, of several hundred megohms is put in series with the tube so that, as the current increases, the potential difference between its terminals falls low enough to quench the discharge. Each ionizing particle passing through the tube then produces a short, sharp pulse of current in R_1, and a consequent pulse of negative potential at the grid of the amplifier tube, $T1$. The corresponding pulse at the plate of $T1$ is amplified and positive in sign.

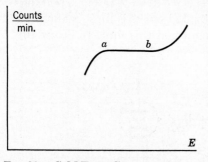

Fig. 22.   G-M Tube Characteristic.
Plateau is from a to b.

If this G-M tube is exposed to a fixed source of ionizing particles the response of the circuit is found to depend upon E in the manner shown in Fig. 22. Over the "plateau" from a to b the response is almost constant, and represents a true count of all ionizing particles passing through the tube. In addition, an oscilloscope shows that all pulses are of the same height, regardless of the type of particle, if the tube is operated in this range. X-rays, gamma rays, and cosmic rays penetrate the walls of the tube, but a thin window must be provided for beta particles. A quartz window will allow photons of ultraviolet light to be counted. The pulses produced in this range are so large that the output from the amplifier tube will trigger a thyratron tube, so that it is possible to count the pulses with an electrically operated counter in the plate circuit of the thyratron. At voltages above the plateau the count is increased by self-excited pulses, and not too far above, the tube breaks down into a continuous glow discharge.

The discharge which occurs in the plateau region is a cascade process, similar to the one described in Sec. 9, Chapter 8. The mean free path is short, the electric field very strong, so that the electron-multiplying process is repeated many times before the anode is reached. The increase in current is finally checked by the large reduction in the potential difference between A and K which takes place as the current builds up in R_1. The duration of the pulse depends upon the time required by the slower-moving positive ions to reach K. Even though the electrons reach A very quickly they are held on the surface of A by the positive-ion space-charge and flow along this wire, as current in the circuit, only as fast as this positive-ion space-charge is removed at K.*

28. Computing Machines. Electron tubes and circuits find extensive application in modern computing machines. All computing machines fall into two classes: (1) digital computers, (2) analog computers. Digital computers are essentially counting devices, as the name suggests. The Chinese abacus is the simplest example, the adding machine the most familiar. In analog computers the problem is set up in terms of measurable quantities such as lengths, angles, current, or voltage, whose variations reproduce the conditions of the problem. The slide rule is a simple example of an analog computer employing lengths, whereas a familiar electrical example is the representation of a problem in dynamics by an electric circuit in which current corresponds to velocity, inductance to mass, etc. Any detailed consideration of computing machines is far outside the scope of this chapter,† and we shall here discuss only briefly the points at which they may utilize electronic elements. It is obvious from the examples cited above that none are essentially electronic in nature, although electronic components contribute largely to their speed and practicability. Amplification is employed extensively in both types of computers, to maintain workable energy levels throughout. In digital computers electron tubes also perform a variety of switching operations, and in analog computers some use is made of the non-linear characteristics of electron tubes, for example for multiplication.

As an example of the amplifier function consider an analog computer designed to integrate any function. The essential circuits are described and illustrated in Chapter 11, Sec. 3 and Fig. 2. Only one additional element is needed, namely a device to produce the input emf, e_1, which represents the function to be integrated. This emf might be produced mechanically, by moving the contactor of a voltage-divider back and forth in suitable fashion, that is, by means of a cam. The analog computer then would be purely an electro-mechanical

* Figure 21 shows the simplest circuit. The following references describe circuits producing quicker and more positive quenching, and hence capable of very rapid counting: J. Strong, *Procedures in Experimental Physics*, Chapter VII; A. L. Hughes, "Experiments with Geiger-Müller Counters and Associated Circuits," *The American Physics Teacher* (now *American Journal of Physics*), Vol. 7 (1939), p. 271. See also B. Rossi, *Ionization Chambers and Counters*.

† The following references may be consulted: E. C. Berkeley, *Giant Brains;* D. R. Hartree, *Calculating Instruments and Machines;* Engineering Research Associates Staff, *High-Speed Computing Devices;* G. A. Korn and T. M. Korn, *Electric Analog Computers*.

device, with the electronic amplifier serving only to raise the energy level of the output. Alternatively the input emf could be produced electronically, with a phototube, lamp, slit, and a moving strip of photographic film upon which the function is represented by light and dark areas. This method is familiar in the production of sound from the sound-track along the edge of moving-picture film. Although this electronic procedure is not essential to the computer it may be very convenient. Still another method of "storing" the function to be integrated is to record it as variations in the magnetic state of a wire,

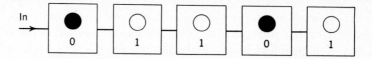

Fig. 23. Binary Counter. Open circles—lighted indicator lamps. Black circles—dark lamps. The binary number represented is 10,110 (decimal number 22).

tape, or sheet of magnetic material. Integrating circuits may be employed for multiplication, by making use of the following identity.

$$xy = \int d(xy) = \int x \, dy + \int y \, dx \qquad (6)$$

The design of electric analog computers capable of more complex mathematical operations follows the same general pattern. The prime requisite is an electric network capable of representing the desired mathematical process. If the computation involves several steps the intermediate results may be stored for transmission to the next operation.

29. Binary Counter. Digital computers may be operated with electro-mechanical switches, or relays, and such relay-type computers employ electron tubes only as amplifiers. Faster switching is possible with electron tubes, biased below cut-off except when a positive grid signal "closes" them to permit current. Electronic switching possesses the added advantages of small size, low input power, and greater versatility. As an example of a very simple electronic digital computer consider the *binary* counter represented schematically in Fig. 23. Each rectangle represents a scale-of-two unit of the type shown in Fig. 17, Chapter 11. As explained in Sec. 16, Chapter 11, a negative input pulse to any one of these units switches plate current from one tube to the other, and two input pulses are required to produce one negative output pulse, as input to the next unit. If all the units are initially in the same state, with the second tube conducting, then the total number of pulses introduced into the first unit may be deter-

mined from the consequent states of the several units. The state of
any unit may be indicated by the glow lamp, N' (Fig. 17, Chapter 11),
in the plate circuit of its first tube.   Initially all lamps are dark.   The
first pulse lights the first lamp, the second pulse lights the second lamp
and extinguishes the first, the third relights the first lamp, etc.   If a
lighted lamp is represented by the digit 1, a dark lamp by 0, and these
digits are written down in reverse order, last first, the successive
combinations of states may be represented by *binary numbers*.*   For
the first ten pulses these binary numbers are

Pulses	1	2	3	4	5	6	7	8	9	10
Binary number	1	10	11	100	101	110	111	1000	1001	1010

Note that 1 represents 2^0, 10 $- 2^1$, 100 $- 2^2$, etc.   Thus 110 represents $2^2 + 2^1$, or 6.

It is evident that this counting device, like the ordinary adding
machine, may be employed to add and to multiply numbers.   Procedures also can be devised whereby subtraction and division may be
carried out.   Various other indicators may be used in place of glow
lamps to display the count, to record it, or to store it for use in subse-
quent computations.   Binary counters require a relatively large
number of units as compared with decimal counters.   Thus a count of
1000 requires 10 binary scaling units, and 20 units are required for
six-digit decimal numbers.   Nevertheless, the simplicity and reliability
of counting devices having only two states (e.g., relays) have strongly
favored binary counting systems for digital computers.

30. Harmonic Analyzer.   Some familiar electrical instruments may
be classed as analog computers.   Thus a wattmeter, which computes
the product of current and voltage in a circuit, might serve to compute
the average product of any two periodic quantities if one can be represented by a voltage, the other by a current.   For example, the first-
harmonic component for a voltage of complex waveform may be
found with a wattmeter, by connecting the voltage source to the
potential terminals of the wattmeter and a source of pure sinusoidal
current of the same frequency to the current terminals.   The indicated power equals the product of the rms values of the current and of
the first-harmonic component of the voltage, times a power factor
which may be made unity by properly phasing the two inputs.   If
there is a slight difference in frequency between the two inputs the
indicated power will fluctuate slowly between maximum positive and

---

* Binary numbers are written with 2 symbols only, namely 0 and 1.   Compare
them with *decimal* numbers employing 10 symbols.   For more detailed information, see the references under Sec. 28.

negative values as the phase changes. The principle involved here is explained in Sec. 6, Chapter 4. Higher harmonics may be measured in like manner, with pure sinusoidal current of the corresponding higher frequencies. The electronic wattmeter of Fig. 13, Chapter 11, serves even better than the ordinary type, since it does not possess the frequency limitations of the electrodynamic meter. For this application it may be modified to work with sinusoidal voltage instead of current.

A somewhat simpler circuit is possible if the product taken is not of zero frequency but of a frequency somewhat higher than the highest harmonic to be measured. The circuit then becomes essentially the same as the frequency-conversion circuit of Fig. 18, Chapter 12. It must be operated with small-signal input to both grids 1 and 3, and the output circuit must be a tuned amplifier having a pass-band so narrow that all modulation products other than the one desired are rejected. If the frequency to which this amplifier is tuned is f_i and the fundamental frequency is f, the sinusoidal voltage needed to measure the nth harmonic must have the frequency f_1 given by

$$f_1 = f_i \pm nf \tag{7}$$

Means must be provided for measuring the amplitude and frequency of the sinusoidal voltage, and the apparatus must be calibrated with known sinusoidal inputs to both grids. The harmonic analyzer made by the General Radio Co.* employs this same method, but uses a balanced-modulator circuit instead of a pentagrid tube to produce the required multiplication. In order to cover fundamental frequencies from 20 to 16,000 cps this apparatus has an output frequency of 50,000 cps, with a pass-band only 4 cps wide.

In this chapter we have considered applications of many of the fundamental principles treated elsewhere in this book. Over and above the importance of these applications themselves is their value in illustrating how such applications are developed. Much of the work in applied electronics involves devising circuits and instruments to meet new needs. It may be possible to find a solution by adapting to the task an instrument or circuit already developed, or to work by analogy to known circuits, but the most successful workers are those who have learned to analyze circuits in terms of *fundamental* principles, and to develop new circuits directly from those principles. It has been the aim of this book to develop this understanding and ability in those who study it.

* L. B. Arguimbau, *General Radio Experimenter*, Vol. 7 (June 1933), p. 12.

PROBLEMS

1. In the d-c voltmeter circuit of Fig. 2a, take: $R_2 = 400$ ohms, $E_1 = 22.0$ volts, $E_2 = 90$ volts, $\mu = 19.0$, $g_m = 2100$ μ-mhos, plate current with zero input and zero meter reading $= 5.00$ ma, and meter resistance $= 300$ ohms. (a) Compute R_1. (b) Compute the d-c input at the grid to produce a current of 1.00 ma in M. (c) Take $(R_a + R_b)$ to be 1.00 megohm, and compute R_c to make the calibration 5.00 volts per ma.

2. In the circuit of Fig. 2b take: $R_1 = 9.5$ K, $R_2 = 500$ ohms, $R_3 = 3.5$ K, $R_4 = 6.5$ K, meter resistance $= 300$ ohms, $\mu = 19.0$, $g_m = 2100$ μ-mhos. (a) Find the potential above ground of the cathode if M reads zero. (b) Find the plate current for this condition. (c) Find the d-c input, e, at the grid to produce a current of 1.00 ma in M. NOTE: First diagram the equivalent *variational* circuit, having μe_g as the emf. Observe that removing E_b puts R_3 and R_4 in parallel. Then solve for e_g, e_f (feedback voltage), and e.

3. Derive Eq. 1.

4. In a commercial meter of the type represented in Fig. 4 the circuit constants are: $R_1 = 1500$ ohms, $R_2 = 1000$ ohms, $\mu = 20.0$, and $g_m = 1250$ μ-mhos. (a) Compute the meter current for 2.50 volts input. (b) Find the change in meter current (which requires a change in calibration) for a 10 percent change in g_m.

5. The circuit of Fig. 5 is balanced at zero input; then an emf e between A and G produces a current of 0.250 ma in M. Take: $\mu = 20.0$, $g = 1250$ μ-mhos, $R_1 = 10.0$ K, $R_2 = 16.0$ K. (a) Compute e. (b) For this same e compute the meter current if g_m changes by 10 percent.

6. In the peak-value voltmeter circuit of Fig. 6 take: $R = 20.0$ K, meter current $= 0.450$ ma, and source emf $= 6.72$ volts rms. (a) Compute the peak value of the diode current, assuming the emf to be sinusoidal and following the method outlined in Sec. 19, Chapter 1. (b) Compute the source resistance (including the diode in this resistance) from this peak value and the peak value of the emf.

7. Compute the source impedance for the data of Prob. 6, on the assumption discussed in the fine print of Sec. 11.

8. In the circuit of Fig. 8 assume the resistance values given in Sec. 13, with R_1 equal to 15.0 K. (a) Compute the current in R_1 and the tube when I_m is zero. (b) Assume the transfer characteristic to be

$$I_p = 3.90 + 1.22x + 0.232x^2$$

in which x is the instantaneous value of the input. Find the *average* change in I_p for an input of 1.15 volts rms. (c) Find the value of I_m for this input. NOTE: Neglect the meter resistances, and assume that R_2 and R_3, in *parallel*, are in series with the I_m meter. Explain why this may be assumed.

9. In the equivalent circuit of Fig. 12b take: $L = 2.50$ henries, $C = 0.080$ $\mu\mu$f, $C_1 = 6.0$ $\mu\mu$f, and $R = 12.0$ K. Compute (a) the series-resonant frequency, (b) the parallel-resonant frequency, (c) the impedance at parallel-resonance. (d) Compute the impedance at a frequency 0.50 percent above series resonance.

10. In a parallel-resonant circuit, L is 65.0 μh, C is 350 $\mu\mu$f, and the Q-factor at resonance is 100. Compute (a) the resonant frequency, (b) the reactance X_0, and (c) the impedance at resonance. (d) Compute the frequency at which the reactance is 15.0 K.

11. Analyze the operation of the voltage-doubler power supply of Fig. 18, and make a time plot for the potentials V_1 and V_2.

12. As explained in Sec. 11, the detector in the electron-ray tube circuit of Fig. 10b functions best if the a-c source has low impedance. Design a preamplifier circuit for this detector, having one stage of amplification direct-coupled (see Fig. 21, Chapter 6) to a cathode-follower unit. Use a 6SN7 twin triode. Compute the a-c input to change the shadow angle 5 degrees, if this change in angle is produced by 0.20 volt d-c change at the grid of the 6E5 tube.

APPENDIX 1. LABORATORY PROCEDURES

1. General. Every student should read Sec. 13 of the Introduction, in which the essential part served by laboratory work in the study of electronics is discussed. He should read it often enough to be thoroughly familiar with its content. In the performance of laboratory experiments certain rules and procedures must be agreed upon and followed, to avoid confusion and to obtain best results. To some extent these rules are arbitrary and differ from one laboratory to another. In large part, however, they represent what has been found by years of experience to be good laboratory practice. As an example the rules followed in the George Washington University laboratory are given below.

2. Records. A record is kept of the experiments performed by each student, including the dates and the particular pieces of apparatus assigned for each experiment. This record is kept on a ruled 4-in. by 6-in. card having the student's name at the top. At the left side of the card are two columns, one for the date, the other for the number of the experiment, and at the right side is a column for the number of the "station" or place in the laboratory at which the experiment is performed. In the body of the card is listed all apparatus having identifying numbers—meters, tubes, etc. In general the record for each experiment is kept to one line. The student receives this card as he enters the laboratory, fills it out, and returns it to the instructor before he starts work.

3. Circuits and Wiring. Setting up a good circuit is often the most important part of an experiment. It starts with proper placing of the parts on the table, so that the several circuit loops are as well separated as possible and involve the least intertangling of wires. Generally the arrangement shown in the circuit diagram is suitable for the layout of apparatus on the laboratory table.

Wire up the circuit systematically, completing each circuit loop before starting the next. Consider an amplifier circuit for example. Connect first the heater to the filament transformer, keeping the two wires, in which the current is oppositely directed, parallel and close together or even loosely twisted together. Make these wires fairly long and place the filament transformer well away from the rest of the circuit. Next wire up the d-c loop of the plate circuit, from the plate

499

to the cathode.   This loop includes the d-c power supply,* the d-c part of the load, the cathode-biasing resistor, and the d-c plate-current meter.   Place the current meter between the cathode and the negative terminal of the power supply, where the d-c potential is low.   Add the d-c voltmeter last.   Then wire the a-c parts of the plate circuit. Finally, add the grid circuit, d-c part first.   Keep the grid-circuit loops as far as possible from the plate-circuit loops and keep all loops small in area, running wires carrying currents in opposite directions close and parallel as far as possible.   This loop method of wiring a circuit is simpler and surer than most other methods, since each loop serves a definite *function*.   Observe that the instructor always checks a circuit loop by loop.   In making circuits follow these rules.

(*a*) Never make connections to *batteries* or *power lines* until after your circuit has been approved by an instructor.   This prohibition includes C-batteries; any battery may cause damage to meters or tubes when improperly connected.   Both leads to a battery may be fastened to the same terminal of a battery (e.g., the negative terminal) until after the circuit has been checked.   Connections may be made to the terminals of transformers and power supplies if the a-c input is disconnected from the power line.

(*b*) *Turn off all power immediately* if anything goes wrong or does not appear right, and have your circuit inspected before turning power on again.

(*c*) Never make any change of circuit without first turning off the power in all parts of the circuit affected by the change.   If a major change is made, have the circuit re-inspected before turning power on again.

(*d*) Never make more than one connection to a *meter* binding-post. It should always be possible to remove or exchange any meter without otherwise disrupting the circuit.

(*e*) If additional apparatus is needed, do not "borrow" it from another station; ask an instructor for it.

4. Observations and Data.†   The performance of an experiment, once the apparatus is readied, involves manipulating the apparatus, observing its performance, and recording data in a data sheet or notebook.   Although these procedures might be carried out by following instructions "cook-book" fashion, they will profit you only if you perform them with full understanding of what you are doing, and are always alert to observe everything that happens, the unexpected as well as the expected.   Make yourself acquainted with the plan and

---

* See instruction (*a*).

† *Data* is the plural of *datum*.

purpose of each experiment *before* starting it. No student should be permitted to work otherwise.

Data are the recorded results of observations. Most data are numerical, but all data involve units and must be labeled. Some very important data may be purely descriptive. Follow the rule of making a record of everything you observe, whether you expect to need it or not. Surplus data are easily discarded, but missing data may require repetition of the experiment. Record data systematically, do not crowd them, and always specify clearly the conditions under which observations are made. Good data can be interpreted a year from now as well as today; poor data may be undecipherable at the end of the laboratory period. Follow these rules.

(*a*) Arrange data in neat, tabular form, and label all observations clearly. Put successive observations of the same quantity one below the other in a column, with the name of the quantity and its units at the head of the column. Thus successive plate-current readings might be tabulated in a column headed *plate current, ma.* RULE: name columns, number rows.

(*b*) Record observations *exactly* as read, in *ink*, before performing the simplest computations. For example, if the range of a voltmeter is doubled by means of a series resistance (multiplier) record the meter readings directly and label the column *meter reading*. The reduced value (twice the meter reading in this example) is tabulated in the next adjacent column and labeled *volts*.

(*c*) If data are identified by symbols, include a key to these symbols on the same sheet. This key may be a table in which each symbol is named and described fully, a circuit diagram on which the symbols appear, or a sketch of the apparatus on which dimensions are indicated.

(*d*) Go over your data carefully before leaving the laboratory and add any information overlooked, such as units, statement of conditions of test, etc.

(*e*) If you finish early spend the rest of the period computing data. Sometimes you will find that additional observations are desirable.

(*f*) At the end of the period take down the circuit and return meters, tubes, and other special parts to the stockroom.

5. Reports. The culmination of an experiment is a report. A good report reads logically from front to back, and presents a clear picture of the experimental work done, the results attained, and the interpretation of these results. It should be concise but complete. Pages should be numbered and cross references made by page number. Tabulate computed data and numerical results on data sheets and add explanation sufficient to make these data sheets tell a fairly complete story of the work. Likewise make plotted curves and other diagrams as self-explanatory as possible. In writing a report keep in mind the objectives stated in Sec. 13 of the Introduction. A report is below average in quality if it does no more than present data, taken as directed, curves plotted according to instructions, and results computed from formulae with no evidence of original study, analysis, and interpretation of results.

Pass reports in on time. (At George Washington University they are due not later than one week after data are taken. A penalty of 10 percent per week late is levied on late reports, and if a student has more than one report late his work is stopped until his reports are up to date.) There are several obvious reasons for this requirement. In particular, each report completed adds to your ability to do good work in the laboratory, and to understand what is being done.

When reports are returned to you examine them carefully, so as to profit by your mistakes and by the suggestions made in them by the instructor. If you are given opportunity to correct mistakes, realize the advantage this affords you, not only to earn a higher grade, but also to obtain a better understanding of the principles involved.

6. Partners. It is the custom in most laboratories to have students work in pairs. This practice has advantages and disadvantages. Each student in a pair must guard against the disadvantage of letting his partner do most the work, to the detriment of his own understanding of it. It is a waste of opportunity to divide the labor, one student manipulating the apparatus and reading the meters, the other recording data. Instead, each student should participate in every part of the operations, and each should read every meter and record observations independently. This procedure pays off if a mistake in reading is made: a check against the partner's data may catch the error. It should not be necessary to add that each of a pair should write his own report, quite independently of the other.

APPENDIX 2. PLANNING AND EQUIPPING
AN ELECTRONICS LABORATORY

1. Experiments. The first step in planning an electronics laboratory course is to choose a list of experiments. If the laboratory meets once a week it has been found best in our laboratory to limit the list to 11 experiments in a 15-week term. For a class of 18 students, working in pairs, 9 sets of apparatus are required each period. Experiments such as Nos. 1 and 4, which require no special equipment, may be done in concert, all students doing the same experiment. Most experiments, however, require some special equipment and then it is more economical of time and equipment to have several experiments carried out simultaneously. For example, provision might be made for 18 students, working in pairs, with 3 sets of apparatus for each of 3 different experiments. The students are rotated from one experiment to the next until each has done all 3 experiments.

2. Apparatus. Although the equipment for a course in electronics may be as elaborate as the budget can afford, it is possible to do most experiments and demonstrations outlined in this book with relatively simple and inexpensive equipment, and much of it may be assembled from radio parts. Students may be very helpful in assembling such equipment and keeping it in repair. The general equipment for each laboratory station includes a d-c power supply, a filament transformer, and a tube socket. The power supply must be continuously variable from 0 to 250 volts. A suitable circuit is shown in Fig. 16, Chapter 14. It may be assembled from radio parts, or an inexpensive amplifier power supply may be modified to include the control parts. The tube socket is mounted on a wood base and wired to binding-posts or Fahnstock clips, with the terminals clearly numbered. It is well to add two extra binding-posts to serve as junction points. Filament transformers are likewise mounted on wood bases, the primary terminals being connected to a cord and plug to connect to the a-c line, the secondary terminals wired to binding-posts. If the secondary supplies much over 6.3 volts when connected to a tube a rheostat may be added to reduce this voltage. If this rheostat is screwdriver-adjusted it may be preset for the type of tube in use.

At least 18 sq ft of desk space is needed for each station, and a few experiments, such as those with phototubes, require considerably more. Each station must have two or three 60-cps a-c outlets, and it is

very desirable that each station be protected by individual fuses.   A
ground line should be run along the skirt of the tables, fastened to
Fahnstock clips 2 or 3 ft apart.   For many experiments there is need
for a low-voltage source of several hundred cps.   This need might be
supplied by a signal generator at each station, but it is cheaper to
install a low-power, 110-volt motor-generator of a frequency between
400 and 1000 cps and wire it to outlets at the stations.   Ordinary
filament transformers serve as satisfactory step-down transformers
for the very little power required in these experiments.

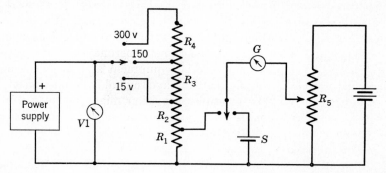

Fig. 1.   D-C Voltmeter Calibration. R_1, R_2, R_3, R_4—volt-box.   Values
might be: R_1—1000, R_2—9000, R_3—90,000, and R_4—100,000 ohms. R_5—potentiometer. S—standard cell. G—galvanometer. $V1$—Voltmeter being calibrated.

3. Meters.   A fairly large number of meters are required.   At least
one d-c voltmeter of 250-volt range and one milliammeter of 15-ma
range are needed for each station, and if 3 sets of apparatus are provided for each experiment at least 3 meters are required of each of the
following ranges: 1 ma, 5 ma, and 50 ma.   There are also required 3
each of d-c voltmeters of 10- and 2-volt ranges, and a-c voltmeters of
150-, 10-, and 3-volt ranges.   The 150-volt a-c voltmeters should be of
the high-resistance (1000 ohms per volt) rectifier type.   One or two
spare meters of each type are desirable.   Satisfactory d-c voltmeters of
any range may be made by adding to a 1-ma meter a multiplier (series
resistor) of suitable value and good quality.

Inexpensive 3-inch radio meters are quite satisfactory for this work,
if means are available for checking their calibration.   D-c voltmeters
are checked easily with a potentiometer* and a volt-box.   A satisfactory volt-box may be made with ½- percent, 1-watt fixed resistors
of the resistances indicated in Fig. 1.   The scales of most meters of this

* "Student" potentiometers, such as are made by Central Scientific Co., Leeds
and Northrup Co., and Rubicon Co., are suitable.   Also suitable are the decade
voltage-dividers mentioned in the footnote on page 505.

type are close enough to linear to permit giving the calibration as a
constant by which the meter reading may be multiplied to obtain the
true value.   Milliammeters also may be checked with a potentiometer
and a standard resistor capable of carrying the current.   For meters
up to 15-ma range place a ½ percent, 1-watt, 100-ohm resistor in
series with the meter and measure the potential drop across this
resistor with the potentiometer.   Obviously 10 times the potential
drop, in volts, is numerically equal to the current in milliamperes.

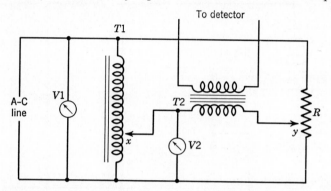

FIG. 2.   A-C VOLTMETER CALIBRATION. $V1$—standard voltmeter. $V2$—voltmeter under test. $T1$—auto-transformer. $T2$—isolation transformer. R—see
text.   Detector may be an oscilloscope, an electron-ray tube (see Sec. 16, Chapter
14), or headphones.

A-c voltmeters of any range may be checked against a standard
voltmeter with the circuit of Fig. 2.   Since the standard voltmeter, $V1$,
reads the line voltage only, it may be any voltmeter whose calibration
is known in the neighborhood of 115 volts.   Slider x on the Variac-
type auto-transformer, $T1$, is adjusted to the desired reading of $V2$,
the meter under test; slider y then is adjusted to balance the circuit for
zero reading of the detector, and the true voltage at $V2$ is computed
from the reading of the voltage-divider, R.   The ratio between the
voltages at $V1$ and $V2$ equals the ratio of the total resistance of R to
the part of it up to y.   The voltage-divider must be capable of safe
operation at 120 volts and be accurately calibrated.*

4. Other Equipment.   Quite a few experiments call for voltage-
dividers of about 1000 ohms, which must be quite linear and provided
with finely divided scales (at least 50 divisions full-scale).   It is easy
to obtain wire-wound "potentiometers" which are sufficiently good
for this purpose, but it is difficult to obtain satisfactory scales.   The

* Suitable decade voltage-dividers are made by the Daven Co., General Radio
Co., and Shallcross Manufacturing Co.

best scales are hand-made, the exact positions for the scale lines being located by means of a Wheatstone-bridge circuit. Several experiments specify a cathode-ray oscilloscope as a balance indicator. One is needed for each set of apparatus for these experiments, or 3 for the three-set plan mentioned earlier. At least one good oscilloscope is needed for lecture demonstrations; the others may be of the inexpensive type obtainable in kits.

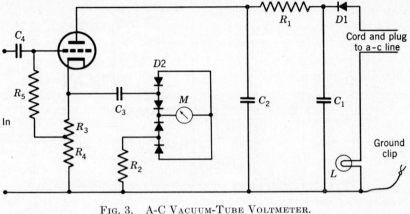

FIG. 3.   A-C VACUUM-TUBE VOLTMETER.

R_1—5 K.	$D2$—Full-wave meter rectifier.
R_2—4 K.	L—115-volt, 7-watt lamp.
R_3, R_4—2 K.	C_1, C_2—8 μf.
R_5—5 megohms.	C_3—1 μf (5 μf for 60 cps).
M—1-ma meter.	C_4—0.005 μf.
$D1$—150-volt, 65-ma, half-wave oxide rectifier.	Mount in metal case.

Several experiments (e.g., 7, 14, and 32) require a-c vacuum-tube voltmeters of about 5 volts range. Commercial voltmeters may be purchased, or meters may be built according to Fig. 9, Chapter 14. Figure 3 shows a compact, a-c-operated circuit of suitable range. It must always be plugged in so that its ground terminal is at the ground side of the a-c line, and this is assured by the ground-clip and the lamp L. The ground-clip is fastened to the ground-line before the plug is inserted in the a-c socket, and the correct position for the plug is such that the lamp does not light.

Some experiments require special parts which are described in detail in the instructions. See for example Exps. 5, 7, 10, and 11. Most of this equipment must be home-made or assembled. Circuits for such equipment should be made up bread-board fashion on a wood base, and spread out enough to permit easy tracing of the connections.

5. Demonstrations. Much of the equipment needed for lecture demonstrations may be borrowed from the laboratory. A 5-inch oscilloscope is satisfactory for a class of 50 students or less, although a larger one is more impressive. Additional equipment needed includes an audiofrequency signal generator, a radiofrequency generator, and several isolation transformers. Additional items required for particular experiments are specified in the descriptions of these experiments. Much of this equipment can be assembled from inexpensive parts, and some of it is not obtainable otherwise. Demonstration experiments may be assembled as needed, but time is saved over a period of years by building bread-board circuits. More interest is created if the students assist in the demonstrations. It may even be possible for students to take over the set-up and presentation of many experiments.

It is quite desirable to have meters visible to the class, and for a large class the best type is a projection meter, made by mounting the movement of a 3-inch, 1-ma meter in a transparent case, with a transparent scale. Such a meter is obtainable from the Central Scientific Co. It may be used in the lecture-room projector, but it is more convenient if equipped with its own projecting system. Shunts, multipliers, and meter rectifiers enable this basic instrument to serve for any a-c or d-c measurement.

6. A Half-Year Course. The content of this book is sufficient for a year course with laboratory. If the electronics course must be limited to a half year a suitable program might include Chapters 1 to 9, with deletions of Secs. 21 to 28 in Chapter 4, Secs. 24 to 29 in Chapter 5, Secs. 17 to 25 in Chapter 7, and Secs. 32 to 36 in Chapter 9. This program would cover the basic principles of electronics and the low-frequency applications of electron tubes. The accompanying experiments could be Nos. 1, 2, 4, 5, 7, 10, 11, 14, 16, 19, and 25.

APPENDIX 3.   UNITS AND CONSTANTS

1. Units.   Systems of units, like clothing, should be chosen to suit the work at hand.   At present there are five systems of electrical units in general use: electromagnetic (emu), electrostatic (esu), practical or commercial, Gaussian, and meter-kilogram-second (mks).   All are related through the universal constant c (numerically equal to the velocity of light) and various powers of ten.   The quantity 4π is also involved in relating the rationalized mks units to the other systems. In this book the electromagnetic system has been chosen as best suited to the development of theory for the motions of electrons in space, whereas practical electrical units are employed in circuit problems.

2. Unit Conversions.   The emu, esu, and practical systems of units are related as follows (taking c equal to 3.00×10^{10} cm/sec.):

Practical	*emu*	*esu*
1 joule	$= 10^7$ ergs	$= 10^7$ ergs
1 watt	$= 10^7$ ergs/sec	$= 10^7$ ergs/sec
1 coulomb	$= \frac{1}{10}$ abcoulomb	$= 3 \times 10^9$ statcoulombs
1 ampere	$= \frac{1}{10}$ abampere	$= 3 \times 10^9$ statamperes
1 volt	$= 10^8$ abvolts	$= \frac{1}{300}$ statvolt
1 ohm	$= 10^9$ abohms	$= (\frac{1}{9}) \times 10^{-11}$ statohm
1 henry	$= 10^9$ abhenries	$= (\frac{1}{9}) \times 10^{-11}$ stathenry
1 farad	$= 10^{-9}$ abfarad	$= 9 \times 10^{11}$ statfarads
1 $\mu\mu f$		$= 0.900$ statfarad
Dielectric constant for a vacuum	9×10^{20}	Unity
Permeability for a vacuum	Unity	9×10^{20}

The electron-volt (ev) is a convenient energy unit for certain electronic problems. $1 \text{ ev} = 1.600 \times 10^{-12}$ erg $= 1.600 \times 10^{-19}$ joule.

3. Constants. Below are listed the physical constants needed most frequently in the problems. Values are given to but three significant figures, since greater accuracy is not needed here. A table of more accurate values is given in Appendix II of T. B. Brown, *Foundations of Modern Physics*, 2nd Ed.

Symbol	Value	Name
c	3.00×10^{10} cm/sec	Speed of light in a vacuum.
e	4.80×10^{-10} statcoulomb	Elementary electric charge, or
	1.600×10^{-20} abcoulomb	electron charge.
	1.600×10^{-19} coulomb	
m	9.11×10^{-28} gram	Electron mass.
h	6.62×10^{-27} erg sec	Planck's quantum constant.
T_0	$273°$K	Freezing point of water on the absolute (Kelvin) scale.
k	1.380×10^{-16} erg/degree	Boltzmann's constant, or gas constant per molecule.
N_0	6.02×10^{23} molecules per mole	Avogadro's constant.
N_1	26.9×10^{18} molecules per cm^3 at standard temperature and pressure.	

APPENDIX 4. THE SCHOTTKY EFFECT

As stated in Sec. 10, Chapter 7, Schottky showed that the increase in saturation current from a thermionic cathode with increase in anode potential results from a decrease in the work-function of the surface caused by the electric field, E, at the surface of the cathode, and that this decrease in work-function equals $\sqrt{Ee^3}$. His proof is given below.

Let the ordinates, f, in Fig. 1 represent the forces acting on an

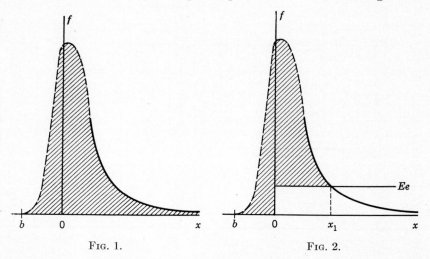

Fig. 1.   Fig. 2.

electron as it escapes through the surface. Then w_0, the work-function with zero external field, is equal to the integral of f from the interior of the cathode, where f is zero, to a point of zero force outside (mathematically at infinite distance).

$$w_0 = \int_b^\infty f\,dx \tag{1}$$

This integral is represented by the shaded area in Fig. 1. If a large anode potential is required to produce saturation current there is then an electric field, E, in front of the surface and all forces acting on the electron outside the surface are thereby reduced by an amount Ee. The reduced forces may be represented by drawing a horizontal line in Fig. 1 at a height Ee, as shown in Fig. 2, and measuring forces *outside* the surface from this line as a new axis. The force on the electron now

510

becomes zero at the point x_1 where this line intersects the plot for f, and the work-function becomes

$$w = \int_b^0 f\, dx + \int_0^{x_1} (f - Ee)\, dx \qquad (2)$$

or

$$w = \int_b^\infty f\, dx - \int_{x_1}^\infty f\, dx - \int_0^{x_1} Ee\, dx$$

$$= w_0 - Eex_1 - \int_{x_1}^\infty f\, dx \qquad (3)$$

This integral is represented by the shaded area in Fig. 2.

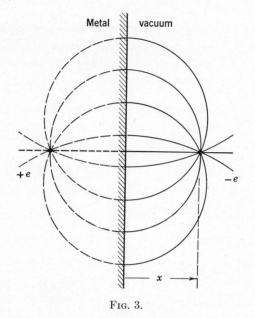

Metal   vacuum

$+e$ $-e$

x

Fig. 3.

Schottky then assumed that from x_1 outward the force f, whatever may be its nature closer to the surface, and inside, reduces to the simple electrical attraction between the negatively charged electron and the positive charge which it *induces* in the surface of the cathode. If the cathode surface is assumed to be smooth and flat the lines of force appear as drawn in Fig. 3 and correspond to those between the point charge, $-e$, on the electron and an imaginary positive point charge, $+e$, called the electrical *image* of $-e$, which is as far behind the surface as the electron is in front of it. The "image force" is then

$$f = e^2/(2x)^2 \qquad (4)$$

Starting from this assumption, we may evaluate x_1 and integrate the last term in Eq. 3.   That is, at x_1

$$Ee = e^2/4x_1{}^2 \tag{5}$$

Hence
$$x_1 = \tfrac{1}{2} \sqrt{e/E} \tag{6}$$

And
$$\int_{x_1}^{\infty} f \, dx = \int_{x_1}^{\infty} \frac{e^2}{4x^2} \, dx = \frac{e^2}{4x_1} \tag{7}$$

Substitution of Eq. 7 into Eq. 3, along with the value of x_1 given by Eq. 6, gives

$$w = w_0 - \sqrt{Ee^3} \tag{8}$$

The experimental verification of Eq. 8 is discussed in Sec. 10, Chapter 7, and these experiments show that it is correct to assume f to be the *mage force* even when the external field is very strong.

APPENDIX 5. TUBE DATA

These data and charts are for tubes to which problems and experiments refer, and are reproduced from the *RCA Tube Handbook*, with the permission of the Radio Corporation of America. No large-power tubes are included since all principles are just as well illustrated by low-power tubes. For further tube data see the various handbooks, such as the *RCA Tube Handbook*.

Tube Type	Cathode Volts	Amperes	Base Type	Description	Char
2A3	2.5	2.5*	4-pin	Power amplifier triode.	1
6A3	6.3	1.0*	4-pin	Power amplifier triode.	1
6F6	6.3	0.7	Octal	Power amplifier pentode.	2
6J5	6.3	0.3	Octal	Triode. $\mu = 20$.	3
6SN7	6.3	0.6	Octal	Twin-triode. Each tube same as 6J5.	3
6L6	6.3	0.9	Octal	Power amplifier beam tube.	4
				Triode connection. $\mu = 8.0$.	5
6N7	6.3	0.8	Octal	Class B twin-triode.	6
6P5-G	6.3	0.3	Octal	Triode. $\mu = 13.8$.	7
76	6.3	0.3	5-pin	Otherwise same as 6P5-G.	7
6SJ7	6.3	0.3	Octal	Sharp-cutoff pentode.	8
				Triode connection: similar to 6J5. $\mu = 19$.	
6SK7	6.3	0.3	Octal	Remote-cutoff pentode.	9
6H6	6.3	0.3	Octal	Twin diode. For each diode: 48 ma peak current, 330 volts insulation between anode and cathode.	
5Y3	5.0	2.0*	Octal	} Full-wave rectifier. For each diode: 400 ma peak current, 280 μ-amp/(volt)$\frac{3}{2}$ perveance.	
80	5.0	2.0*	4-pin		
6SA7	6.3	0.3	Octal	Pentagrid converter. For separate excitation (circuit of Fig. 19, Chapter 12) and the following conditions, the conversion transconductance is 450 μ-mhos. Plate: 250 volts, 3.5 ma. Screen grids: 100 volts, 8.5 ma. Grid 3: -2 volts. Grid 1: Rectified current in R_g (2 K), produced by local oscillator, is 0.5 ma.	

* Filament-type cathodes. All others are heater-type.

APPENDIX 5

RCA-2A3
Average Plate Characteristics

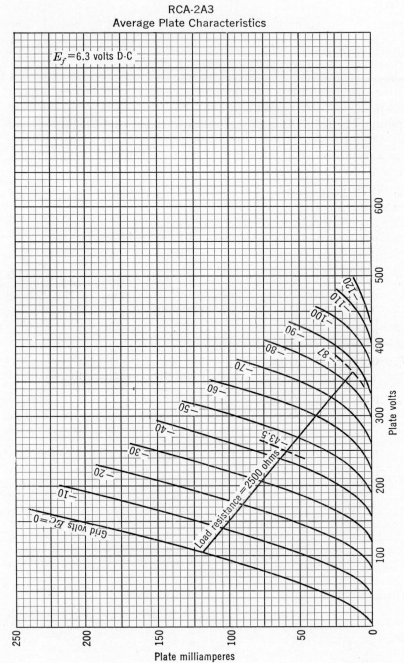

E_f=6.3 volts D-C

Grid volts Ec=0

0 -10 -20 -30 -40 -50 -60 -70 -80 -90 -100 -110 -120

Load resistance = 2500 ohms

43.5

87

Plate volts

100   200   300   400   500   600

Plate milliamperes

0   50   100   150   200   250

CHART 1.

6F6
Average Plate Characteristics
Pentode Connection

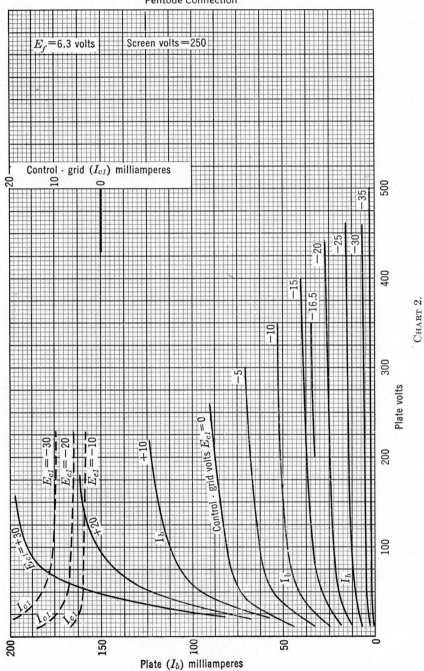

E_f=6.3 volts   Screen volts=250

Control - grid (I_{c1}) milliamperes

Plate volts

Plate (I_b) milliamperes

CHART 2.

6J5
Average Plate Characteristics

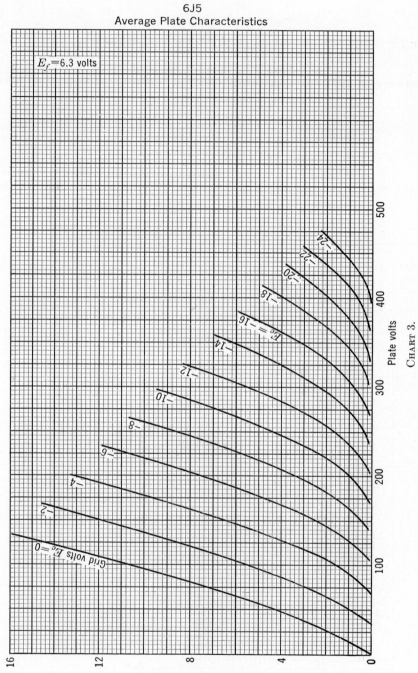

$E_f=6.3$ volts

Grid volts $E_c=0$
-2
-4
-6
-8
-10
-12
-14
$E_c=-16$
-18
-20
-22
-24

Plate volts

CHART 3.

Plate milliamperes

16
12
8
4
0

100   200   300   400   500

6L6
Average Plate Characteristics
With E_{c1} as Variable

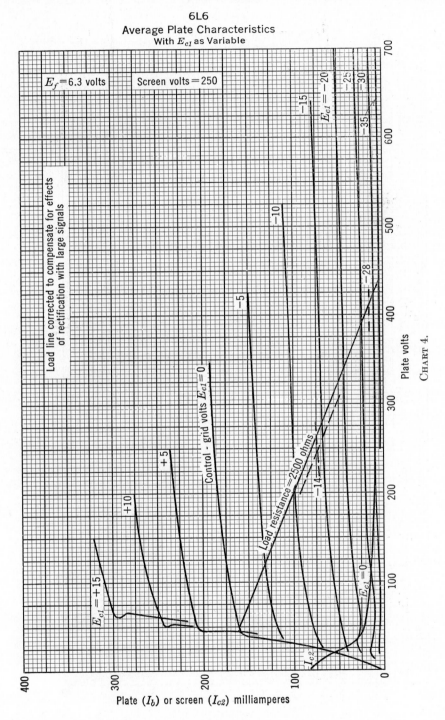

$E_f = 6.3$ volts   Screen volts $= 250$

Load line corrected to compensate for effects
of rectification with large signals

Control - grid volts $E_{c1} = 0$

Load resistance $= 2500$ ohms

$E_{c1} = +15$

$+10$

$+5$

-5

-10

-14

-15

$E_{c1} = -20$

-25

-28

-30

-35

$E_{c1} = 0$

I_{c2}

Plate volts

CHART 4.

Plate (I_b) or screen (I_{c2}) milliamperes

6L6
Average Plate Characteristics
Triode Connection

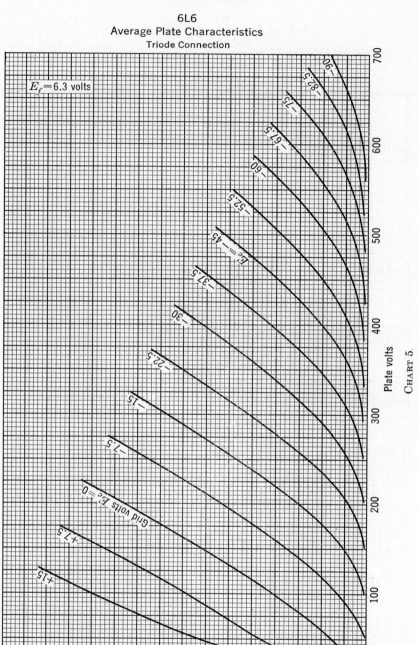

E_f = 6.3 volts

Plate volts

CHART 5.

Plate milliamperes

6N7
Average Plate Characteristics
Each Triode Unit

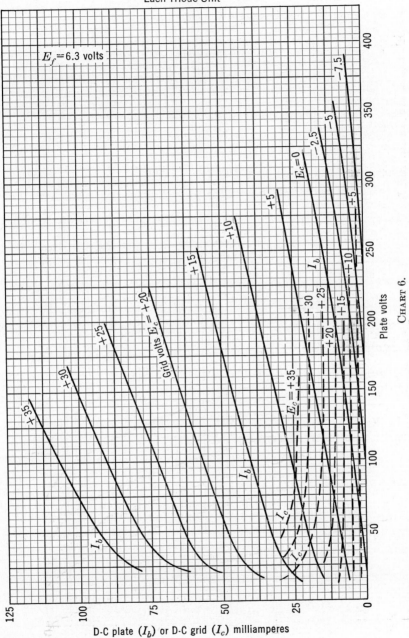

$E_f = 6.3$ volts

Grid volts $Ec = +20$

$E_c = +35$

$E_c = 0$

Plate volts

Chart 6.

D-C plate (I_b) or D-C grid (I_c) milliamperes

6P5G and 76
Average Plate Characteristics

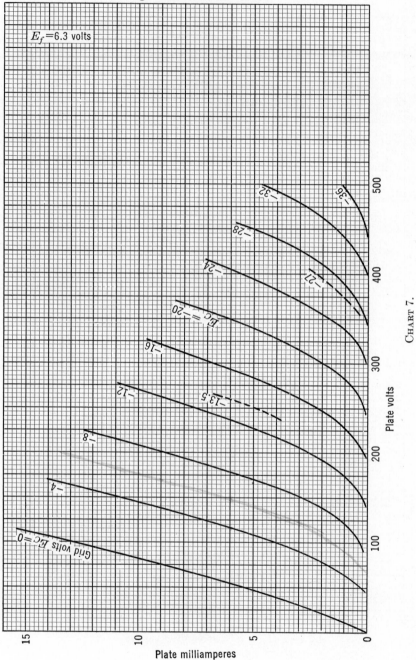

E_f=6.3 volts

Grid volts Ec=0

Ec=-20

Plate volts

Plate milliamperes

CHART 7.

6SJ7
Average Plate Characteristics
Pentode Connection

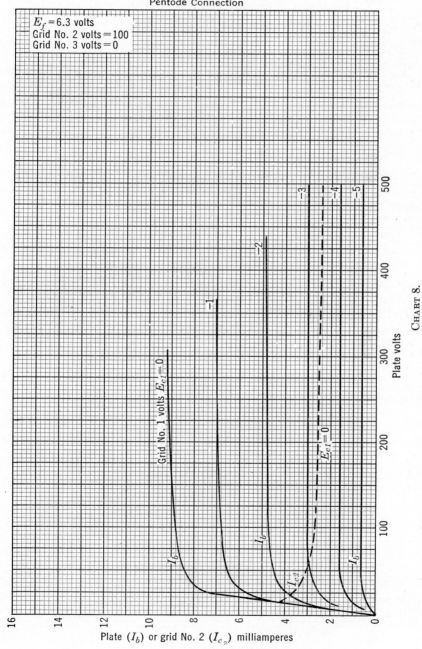

$E_f = 6.3$ volts
Grid No. 2 volts $= 100$
Grid No. 3 volts $= 0$

CHART 8.

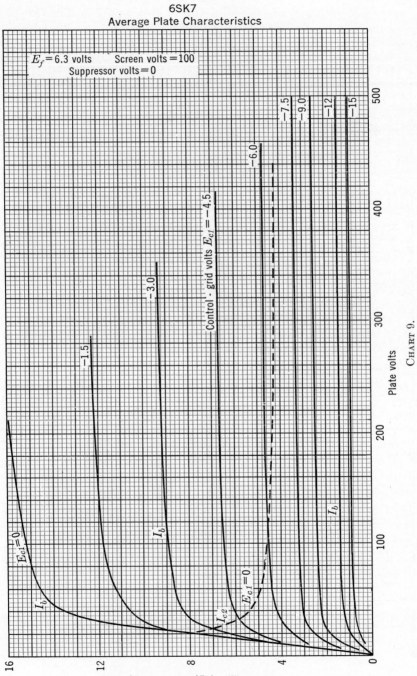

6SK7
Average Plate Characteristics

E_f = 6.3 volts   Screen volts = 100
Suppressor volts = 0

Control - grid volts E_{c1} = −4.5

−1.5

−3.0

−6.0

−7.5

−9.0

−12

−15

E_{c1} = 0

I_b

I_{c2}

E_{c1} = 0

I_b

I_b

I_b

Plate (I_b) or screen (I_{c2}) milliamperes

Plate volts

0   4   8   12   16

0   100   200   300   400   500

CHART 9.

APPENDIX 6.   CRYSTAL RECTIFIERS AND TRANSISTORS

1. Introduction.   The crystal diode is older than the vacuum tube as a rectifying device: contact between a pointed wire and a crystal of galena constituted one of the earliest detectors of radiofrequency current, in the pioneer radio receivers.   Carborundum and several other substances of the class known as semi-conductors (see Sec. 25, Chapter 7) also served in crystal detectors.   Since not all areas of the galena crystal are sensitive, and a sensitive area is easily destroyed by too strong current, manual adjustment of the "cat-whisker" or wire point was required to discover a sensitive area and make proper contact with it.   In the modern crystal diodes the crystal is silicon or germanium and the point contact is adjusted and sealed in at the factory.   The same physical principles are involved in the disk-type rectifiers in which the semi-conductor is a film of cuprous oxide on copper, or of selenium on iron.*   Applications of crystal diodes are mentioned in Sec. 26, Chapter 1, and elsewhere in this book.

The crystal triode, or *transistor*, is a low-power device which is capable of many operations similar to those performed by electron tubes, and within this power range it operates with very high efficiency, being in this respect far superior to electron tubes because it requires no power for cathode heating.   For this same reason a transistor circuit has much less bulk and weight than the smallest vacuum-tube circuit of comparable output.   Thus the transistor makes possible great improvements in many small-power devices such as hearing aids, proximity fuses, and switching circuits for computing machines.   In addition it has stimulated a new interest in the physical properties of semi-conductors and has also provided a new tool for the study of these properties.

2. Semi-Conductors.   To understand the functioning of the devices mentioned in Sec. 1 we shall need to consider the electrical properties of semi-conductors.   First of all the electrical conductivity of these substances is very low, as their name indicates, and changes with temperature in just the opposite direction as for a good conductor such

---

* Copper oxide rectifiers are described by L. O. Grondall and P. H. Geiger, in "A New Electronic Rectifier," *Transactions of A.I.E.E.*, Vol. 46 (1927), p. 357. For selenium rectifiers see C. A. Clarke, "Selenium Rectifier Characteristics, Application and Design Factors," *Electrical Communication*, Vol. 20 (1941), p. 47.

as copper. However, the applications mentioned in Sec. 1 depend upon the manner in which conduction takes place in semi-conductors rather than upon its magnitude, and the nature of this conduction has not been easy to discover. Now, however, as a result of a vast amount of research, particularly with single crystals of germanium, it is possible to describe fairly simply this type of conduction. To be explicit this description will be made for germanium. Germanium atoms, like carbon atoms, have a valence 4 and form crystals in which each atom is surrounded by 4 others which lie at the corners of a circumscribed tetrahedron. Diamond has the same structure. The two-dimensional diagram of Fig. 1 illustrates some of the characteristics of this three-dimensional structure. Each germanium atom is bonded to its 4 nearest neighbors by a pair of electrons as indicated in Fig. 1. Thus all the valence electrons serve as bonds between atoms, and none is free to produce electrical conduction unless some of these bonds are broken. At very low temperatures pure germanium is an insulator, like diamond.

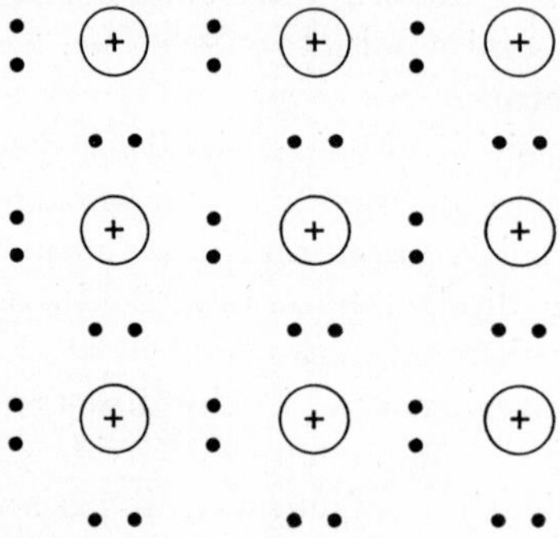

FIG. 1. CRYSTAL STRUCTURE OF GERMANIUM. Two-dimensional simulation. Circles represent atoms; black dots, electrons.

3. Electrons and Holes. At temperatures somewhat above room temperature a few valence electrons may be liberated by thermal agitation of the atoms, and the crystal becomes weakly conducting. Two kinds of conduction now must be recognized. The obvious carriers are the liberated electrons which are free to move about among the atoms. An equal number is provided by the "holes" or places in the crystal lattice which are vacated by the liberated electrons. If a hole is filled by the jump of a near-by electron into it, a new hole appears in the place vacated by that electron; in effect the original hole has moved from one position to the other. In this fashion a hole may wander throughout the crystal until it chances to be filled by a liberated electron. In the absence of an electric field the motions of both holes and liberated electrons are entirely at random, but if electrodes connected to a battery are placed in contact with the two sides of the crystal the liberated electrons will drift toward the positive electrode, and the holes will drift toward the negative electrode just as if they were positively charged particles. The number of liberated electrons and holes increases with temperature, thus increasing the conductivity of the crystal.

The properties which make possible the applications mentioned in Sec. 1 are not possessed by absolutely pure germanium but result from impurities, even though the amount of foreign substance required may be too small to be detected chemically. Let us consider the effect of adding to germanium an infinitesimal amount of an element of valence 5, such as antimony, arsenic, or phosphorus. The foreign atoms take the place in the crystal lattice of an equal number of germanium atoms, leaving the crystal structure unchanged. Only 4 of the 5 valence electrons are required, however, to complete the crystal-lattice bonds, so that the fifth must be disposed of otherwise. At very low temperatures the fifth electron is bound to the foreign

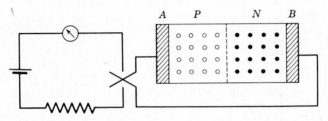

FIG. 2.   JUNCTION RECTIFIER.   ● electrons.   ○ holes.

atom as a satellite, but this bonding is weaker than the crystal-lattice bonds and is easily severed by thermal agitation at room temperature. The liberation of this electron leaves the foreign atom with a positive charge but does not leave a movable hole, since this electron is not a part of the crystal lattice. In a crystal which has this type of impurity we may consider conduction to be by free electrons only. Although, as a result of thermal agitation, there are a few electrons released from the lattice and an equal number of holes, these are relatively unimportant unless the temperature is high. Such a crystal is said to be a negative or *n*-type crystal. If the foreign atom is one of valence 3, for example aluminum, a lattice bond will be missing around each foreign atom and these *holes* will make the crystal conducting in the manner explained above. The result is a positive or *p*-type crystal. In actual crystals both kinds of impurities may exist and the crystal is *p*-type or *n*-type according to which predominates.

4. Rectification. Let us consider a single crystal of germanium of rectangular form as represented in Fig. 2, in which one end is made *p*-type, the other *n*-type. Electrodes are fastened* to the ends of this crystal and connected to a battery, current meter, and resistor through a reversing switch, as shown. If the switch is closed so as to make *A*

* Contact is made in a manner such that rectification does not take place between the electrodes and the crystal.

positive and B negative a large current results with only a small drop in potential across the crystal, since conduction across the p-n junction between P and N can take place by electrons moving to the left and also by holes moving to the right.   If the switch is reversed the current will be zero for a junction between perfect n and p-type crystals, since the holes are pulled toward A, the electrons toward B, and none cross the p-n boundary.   The displacement of electrons in N leaves a positive space-charge layer next the boundary, due to positively charged foreign atoms, and a corresponding negative space-charge layer of foreign ions is produced on the opposite side of the boundary, in P, by displacement of holes.   Displacements of holes and

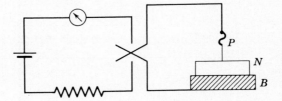

FIG. 3.   POINT-CONTACT RECTIFIER.

electrons cease when the potential difference produced across the boundary by this double layer of space-charge equals the emf of the battery.   The crystal thus functions as a perfect rectifier.   In real crystals there is of course always some reverse current (see Fig. 27, Chapter 1) since in a real crystal a few carriers of opposite sign are always present.

5. Point-Contact Rectifiers.   The junction-type rectifier described above is a fairly recent development.   Most crystal rectifiers are of the point-contact type, in which a fine metal point touches the surface of a suitable crystal as represented in Fig. 3.   The other electrode makes contact with the crystal over a relatively large area and is non-rectifying.   Let us consider the crystal to be n-type germanium.   If the external connections are such that the point, P, is positive, the *base*, B, negative, conduction is easy, but for reversed polarity the current is very small.   It is not so easy to account for rectification in this device, since there are free electrons in both P and N.   For some reason, however, there is a potential barrier at the surface of the semiconductor which opposes electron flow from the metal into the crystal. As the potential of P is made negative with respect to B this surface potential changes with it so as to maintain a nearly constant potential difference between P and the surface of N, with the surface negative. The only current is due to the presence of a few holes in N whose flow to P is aided, not opposed, by this potential barrier.   In the forward direction (P positive) conduction is by electrons leaving N for P. In addition, the radial field from P into N is able to extract some lattice (bound) electrons which join the flow of free electrons into P, so that holes appear in a small region about the point of contact and flow away from it into the interior of the crystal.   The point is then said to *inject holes* into the crystal, and these injected holes play a vital part in the functioning of the point-contact transistor.   (See Sec. 7.)   A point-contact rectifier may also be made with a p-type crystal, with

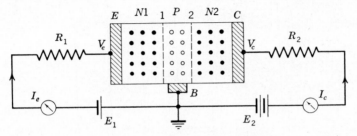

FIG. 4.   JUNCTION TRANSISTOR. E—emitter. C—collector. B—base.   • electrons.   ○ holes.   Direction indicated for I_e is according to convention adopted; I_e actually goes in opposite direction.

conduction then in the opposite direction.   For either type the direction of easy flow is that in which the carriers (electrons or holes) may leave the crystal for the metal.

   6. Junction Transistor.   In 1948 the Bell Telephone Laboratories announced the invention by Bardeen and Brattain* of a three-electrode semi-conductor device which possesses characteristics resembling an electronic triode but does not require a hot cathode.   They gave it the name *transistor*.   This transistor may be made almost microscopically small and operated with high efficiency at very low voltage. Power output is ordinarily quite small, although power transistors are being developed, and an output of several watts has been achieved. Two types have been developed, the point-contact type and the junction type.   Although the point-contact type was developed first, the junction type is explained more easily and has the simpler characteristics.

   The junction transistor is represented schematically in Fig. 4.   A single-crystal bar of germanium is n-type at both ends, but has a thin p-type section across its middle so as to form two p-n junctions, 1 and 2, as shown.   Electrodes are fastened to the ends and middle, with

* J. Bardeen and W. H. Brattain, "The Transistor, a Semiconductor Triode," *Physical Review*, Vol. 74 (1948), p. 230.

non-rectifying contacts; these are called the emitter, E, the collector, C, and base, B. The whole assembly may be very small; a typical one, including the plastic in which it is imbedded, is less than 8 mm long. Either junction by itself is a rectifier and conducts when its end electrode (E or C) is negative relative to B. Thus if V_c, the potential of C relative to B, is positive as indicated in Fig. 4, the current I_c is very small as long as there is no current to E. But if there is an

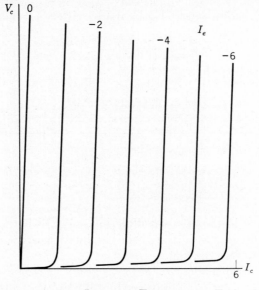

FIG. 5. CHARACTERISTIC FOR JUNCTION TRANSISTOR. Each plot represents a constant value of I_e.

emitter current I_e across junction 1 the collector current rises to a value nearly equal to I_e. The collector current is almost independent of V_c, as shown by the plots in Fig. 5. The increase in I_c may be explained qualitatively by observing that conduction across junction 1 carries holes into N_1, free electrons into P. If C is insulated these electrons must go to B, but with N_2 at a positive potential and P thin enough most of these free electrons entering P from N_1 diffuse across P and are pulled across junction 2 into N_2. Although there is no current gain it is possible to obtain large voltage and power gains, since the load resistance, R_2, may be made very large without appreciably decreasing I_c, whereas the input resistance and voltage are quite small. decreasing I_c, whereas the input resistance and voltage are quite small. Power gains of 45 to 50 db have been obtained with junction transistors.

7. Point-Contact Transistors. In the point-contact transistor represented schematically in Fig. 6 the emitter, E, and collector, C, are two fine metal points which make rectifying contacts very close together on a crystal of n-type germanium. The base, B, makes a large-area, non-rectifying contact with the opposite side of the crystal. For the circuit connections shown in Fig. 6 conduction is good between E and the crystal, poor (for C acting alone) between C and the crystal. Current across the emitter junction causes an increase in collector current, just as in the junction type, but in a point-contact transistor

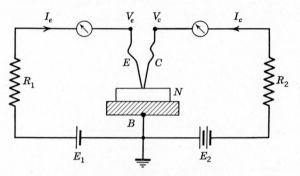

FIG. 6.   POINT-CONTACT TRANSISTOR.

the increase in I_c may be several times larger than I_e, so that current amplification is possible. The current-amplification factor, α, is defined as

$$\alpha = -\left.\frac{\partial I_c}{\partial I_e}\right)_{V_c \text{ constant}} \tag{1}*$$

The operation of this transistor is explained in terms of the holes injected into the crystal at the emitter junction. See Sec. 5. These holes diffuse into the crystal and follow the electric field to the neighborhood of the collector junction, where they reduce the potential barrier and allow a greater flow of electrons across this junction.

Characteristic curves for this type of transistor are shown in Fig. 7. Note that all potentials are referred to the *base* as the point of zero potential, and currents are positive if their direction, *inside* the crystal, is toward the base, or is the direction corresponding to a positive potential on the end electrode concerned. Thus V_c, the collector potential, is negative and the collector current, I_c, is also negative. These plots show that, although there is a current gain, the other

* The minus sign is required because, according to the convention of signs stated in the next paragraph, I_c is negative and I_e positive.

characteristics are not as good as for the junction-type transistor. Power and voltage gains are much lower.

8. Transistor Circuits. Although we may speak of a transistor as a substitute or replacement for the vacuum tube, in the sense that transistor circuits may perform many of the operations formerly made possible only by vacuum tubes, such as amplification, oscillation, and modulation, it is evident from the characteristics noted in the fore-going section that transistors and vacuum tubes function quite differently in several fundamental respects. To be specific let us consider

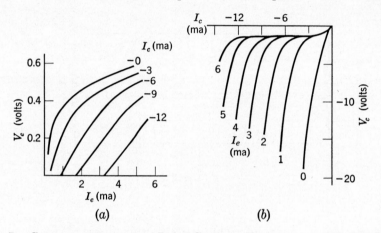

FIG. 7. CHARACTERISTIC FOR A POINT-CONTACT TRANSISTOR. Bell Telephone Laboratory M1729.

amplifier circuits. First of all, a vacuum tube is a voltage-operated device, with grid current almost negligible except at very high frequency, whereas a transistor is current-operated, with emitter voltage comparatively negligible. Thus a vacuum-tube amplifier has high input impedance and operates best from a high-impedance source, but a transistor amplifier has low input impedance and requires a source of quite low impedance. Also, since current is the important variable at the input of a transistor it is natural to regard both emitter current and collector current as independent variables, the corresponding potentials as the dependent variables. Characteristic curves are plotted in this manner (see Figs. 5 and 7) and the amplification factor α is defined as a ratio of currents (Eq. 1). The output impedance of a transistor is always high, in this respect making a transistor comparable with a pentode. This resemblance is clearly seen if the plots of Figs. 5 and 7 are reversed and turned so that V_c is the abscissa. Figure 5 then closely resembles the curves for an ideal beam tube. The next difference to be noticed concerns the relative phase of input and output in transistor amplifiers. A positive increment of V_e causes a positive increase in I_e, and the consequent increase in magnitude of I_c (in the negative direction) causes V_c to rise. Hence for a-c operation of a transistor amplifier the output and input are *in phase*, instead of being 180 degrees out of phase as in an electron-tube amplifier.* Still another important difference is in the dependence of I_e and V_e upon I_c, as seen in Fig. 7a. This dependence represents an internal *positive* feedback from the collector circuit to the emitter circuit.

9. Equivalent Circuit. If we confine our attention to small variations in emitter and collector current and potential in the neighborhood of some Q-point, as we have done for vacuum-tube circuits, we may represent a transistor by the circuit elements shown in Fig. 8.†

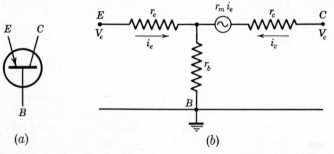

(a)   (b)

FIG. 8.   (a) Symbol for Transistor.   (b) Equivalent A-C Circuit.

Small letters i_e, i_c, v_e, and v_c represent small variations in I_e, I_c, V_e, and V_c respectively. Feedback is represented by the common resistor, r_b, and the effect of i_e upon the collector circuit, in addition to the forward feedback through r_b, is represented by an emf equal to the product of i_e and a fictitious resistance, r_m, called the *mutual resistance*. From Fig. 8 we may write the following small-variations equations.

$$v_e = i_e(r_e + r_b) + i_c r_b \tag{2}$$

$$v_c = i_e(r_m + r_b) + i_c(r_c + r_b) \tag{3}$$

* An exception is to be noted in the grounded-grid amplifier described in Chapter 13, Sec. 8. The grounded-grid amplifier has also the low input impedance noted above for a transistor. This resemblance, which was first noted by Shockley, is especially good for a junction transistor, for which α is nearly unity, but poorer for point-contact transistors having α greater than unity.

† For several other equivalent circuits in addition to this one, see R. M. Ryder and R. J. Kircher, "Some Circuit Aspects of the Transistor," *Bell System Technical Journal*, Vol. 28 (July 1949), p. 367. Another approach to transistor circuitry is found in R. L. Wallace, Jr., and G. Raisbeck, "Duality as a Guide in Transistor Circuit Design," *Bell System Technical Journal*, Vol. 30 (April 1951), p. 381.

The values of these variational resistances are given by the following partial derivatives, taken at the Q-point.

$$\frac{\partial V_e}{\partial I_e} = r_e + r_b \qquad \frac{\partial V_e}{\partial I_c} = r_b \tag{4,5}$$

$$\frac{\partial V_c}{\partial I_e} = r_m + r_b \qquad \frac{\partial V_c}{\partial I_c} = r_c + r_b \tag{6,7}$$

Note that two of these partial derivatives (Eqs. 4 and 7) equal the slopes at the Q-point of the plots in Fig. 7. The other two represent slopes in plots of V_e vs. I_c with I_e as parameter, and of V_c vs. I_e with I_c as parameter respectively. The values needed for these plots may be read from Fig. 7. It can also be shown, by the same method of reasoning employed to show that μ equals $g_m r_p$ for an electron tube (Chapter 2, Sec. 16), that

$$\alpha = (r_m + r_b)/(r_c + r_b) \tag{8}$$

We may employ these concepts to design transistor circuits for small-output operation. Consider the amplifier circuit of Fig. 6. First of all the source of signal must be suitable. With a source such as a phototube a transistor would develop less voltage output than could be obtained without it, by putting a high resistance in series with the phototube. On the other hand a low-impedance microphone is an excellent source. The high output impedance of a transistor indicates that a high load resistance may be used to obtain high voltage amplification. If the load is R_2 the output, V_c, equals $-i_c R_2$. Putting this value in Eq. 3 we obtain

$$-i_c R_2 = i_e(r_m + r_b) + i_c(r_c + r_b) \tag{9}$$

or

$$i_c = -i_e \frac{r_m + r_b}{R_2 + r_c + r_b} \tag{10}$$

By means of Eq. 8 we may transform Eq. 10 into

$$i_c = -\alpha i_e \frac{r_c + r_b}{R_2 + r_c + r_b} \tag{11}$$

and

$$v_c = -i_c R_2 = \alpha i_e \frac{(r_c + r_b)R_2}{R_2 + r_c + r_b} \tag{12}$$

Equation 12 says that v_c equals the product of a current αi_e and the resistance of R_2 in parallel with $r_c + r_b$.

10. Feedback. Since i_c is opposite in sign to i_e, as shown by Eq. 10, the last term in Eq. 2 is intrinsically negative and represents positive feedback in that it aids v_e. To find the magnitudes involved, substitute into Eq. 2 the value of i_c given by Eq. 11. The result is

$$v_e = i_e \left[r_e + r_b - \alpha r_b \frac{r_c + r_b}{R_2 + r_c + r_b} \right] \tag{13}$$

From Eq. 13 we see that the circuit becomes unstable if α is enough greater than unity and R_2 small enough to make the impedance in the

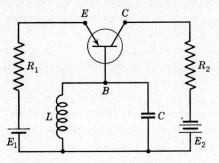

FIG. 9. OSCILLATOR CIRCUIT.

bracket become zero or negative. Thus many of the earlier point-contact transistors were unstable with low or zero impedance output. Resistance introduced externally in series with B will serve the same as internal resistance in producing instability. On the other hand, any resistance in series with E adds to r_e in Eq. 13 and increases the stability. Equations 1 to 13 apply to either type of transistor. For junction transistors, however, although feedback exists it cannot produce instability since for this type α is slightly less than unity.

11. Oscillator Circuits. A resonant circuit may be maintained in oscillation by means of a transistor if there is proper feedback from the collector to the emitter. The operation is the same in principle as that in vacuum-tube oscillators, except for two important differences in detail. One of these is the relative phase of output to input, the other is the requirement of current rather than voltage feedback. Both these differences are described in Secs. 9 and 10. If feedback is supplied by a pick-up coil, as illustrated in Chapter 10, Fig. 20, this coil should have few turns and be closely coupled so as to supply the current needed. Another possible circuit for a transistor oscillator is shown in Fig. 9 compare it with the Hartley oscillator of Fig. 22, Chapter 10. In Fig. 9 one end of the tank coil is connected to the base, the other end to *both* the emitter and the collector, whereas in a

Hartley circuit grid and plate are connected to *opposite* ends of the tank coil. The difference results of course from the inherent *positive* feedback in the transistor. It may improve the output to connect the emitter to an intermediate tap on the coil. Resistors R_1 and R_2 need be only large enough to maintain d-c stability in the circuit.

12. Other Circuits. Cascade amplifiers are practical with transistors if each stage is coupled to the one following by a step-down transformer (or its equivalent) so that the high output impedance of one stage may be matched to the low input impedance of the other. Satisfactory matching is of course impossible with R-C couplings. Point-contact transistors may be operated in radio circuits up to 10 Mcps or higher, but the junction type is limited to lower frequencies by the capacitance across its junctions. The grounded-base circuits of Figs. 4 and 6 are generally employed, although some successful circuits are made with the signal input to the base and the emitter grounded. When the latter connection is employed with a junction transistor the input impedance is much higher than for the grounded-base connection, since the input current for this connection is the difference between plate and emitter currents and is quite small for junction transistors.

Other important transistor circuits are those which, like the Eccles-Jordan "flip-flop" circuit, have two stable states between which they may be switched quickly by a suitable signal pulse. The positive feedback which is produced in a transistor by resistance in series with its base makes possible the construction of such "bi-stable" circuits with only one transistor, and circuits of this kind find many applications, especially in computing machines. The search for more and better transistor circuits represents one of the most promising fields of electronic research.

At the present time most advantages over vacuum tubes which may be claimed for transistors are due to their smallness—in size, in weight, and particularly in power requirement. In addition they have very long life and extreme ruggedness to mechanical shock and vibration. Disadvantages still encountered are changes produced by temperature (good operation occurs over a quite limited temperature range) and variability of characteristics from one unit to another of the same type. In addition, the electronic noise level is high. Much progress has been made in overcoming these faults during the few years since the transistor was invented, and much greater improvement can be expected in the next few years. Improved transistors and new circuits will lead to many more applications, but it is reasonable to believe that the low-power field will continue to be the region of greatest utility for transistors, and that the high-power field of electronics will remain the realm of electron tubes.

13. References.   A selected list of articles on the transistor and related topics is given below.   The first group consists of popular or elementary articles, the second of more advanced articles and research papers.

Group I.   (Popular)

1. "A Revolution in Electronics," L. N. Ridenour, *Scientific American*, August 1951, p. 13.
2. "Holes and Electrons," W. Shockley, *Physics Today*, October 1950, p. 16.
3. "The Junction Transistor," *Electronics*, November 1951, p. 82.
4. "The Junction Transistor," M. Sparks, *Scientific American*, July 1952, p. 28.
5. "New Transistors Give Improved Performance," J. A. Morton, *Electronics*, August 1952, p. 100.
6. "Germanium Transistors," J. S. Saby, *General Electric Review*, Vol. 55 (September 1952), p. 21.

Group II.   (Advanced)

7. "The Transistor, a Semiconductor Triode," J. Bardeen and W. H. Brattain, *Physical Review*, Vol. 74 (1948), p. 230.
8. "The Transistor," J. A. Becker and J. N. Shive, *Electrical Engineering*, Vol. 68 (March 1949), p. 215.
9. "The Theory of *p-n* Junctions in Semiconductors and *p-n* Junction Transistors," W. Shockley, *Bell System Technical Journal*, Vol. 28 (July 1949), p. 435.
10. "Physical Principles Involved in Transistor Action," J. Bardeen and W. H. Brattain, *Bell System Technical Journal*, Vol. 28 (April 1949), p. 239; also *Physical Review*, Vol. 75 (April 1949), p. 1208.
11. "Some Circuit Aspects of the Transistor," R. M. Ryder and R. J. Kricher, *Bell System Technical Journal*, Vol. 28 (July 1949), p. 367.
12. "Hole Injection in Germanium," W. Shockley, G. L. Pearson, and J. R. Haynes, *Bell System Technical Journal*, Vol. 28 (July 1949), p. 344.
13. "Duality as a Guide in Transistor Design," R. L. Wallace and G. Raisbeck, *Bell System Technical Journal*, Vol. 30 (April 1951), p. 381.
14. "The *p-n* Junction Transistors," W. Shockley, M. Sparks, and G. K. Teal, *Physical Review*, Vol. 83 (July 1951), p. 151.
15. "Present Status of Transistor Development," J. A. Morton, *Bell System Technical Journal*, Vol. 31 (May 1952), p. 411.

Index

Diode circuits, graphical analysis, 26
Diode current, *demonstration experiment*, 13
Discriminator circuit, 414
Disk-seal tubes, 426
Displacement current, 68
Distortion, 102
  reduction with negative feedback, 178
    demonstration experiment, 181
  second-harmonic, 107
  third-harmonic, 109
Door-knob tube, 426
Double layer, space charge, 262
Drift space in a klystron, 440, 444
Dynode, 233

Eccles-Jordan circuit, 360
  pulse triggering, 363
  scaling circuit, 364
  triggering, 362
Edison voltage, 17
Efficiency, amplifier, class A, 119
    class B, 130
    class C, 328
Einstein's photoelectric equation, 214
Electrode capacitance, 421
Electrodes, symmetrical, 15
Electrometer tubes, 91
Electron, 2
  electric force on, 3
  free, 3
  initial speeds, 22
  in a metal, 2, 231
  kinetic energy, 3
  magnetic force on, 3
  motions in crossed fields, 447
  thermal energy, 15
Electron bunching, 436
  in a klystron, 440
  in a magnetron, 453
  in a traveling-wave tube, 462
Electron emission, 210
  cold-cathode, 237
  "field," 237
  photoelectric, 211
  poisoning, 222
  secondary, 144, 232
  thermionic, 216
Electron gas, 3
Electron "holes," 524

Electronic instruments, 467
Electronic multiplication, by a pentagrid tube, 355, 357
  by a triode, 354
Electronic phenomena, 1
Electronic switch, 469
Electronic switching, 375, 468
Electronic wattmeter, 358
Electronics, scope, 1
Electron mechanics, 3
Electron-multiplier tube, 233, 234
Electron-ray tube, 479
Electron refraction, 229
Electron temperature in a plasma, 260, 276, 303
Electron-velocity distribution, 225
Electron volt (ev), 215, 508
Emitter (in transistor), 528
Energy levels in an atom, 242
Equivalent circuit, constant-current source, 154
  constant-emf source, 60
  including grid input, 85
  for a pentode, 153
  for a triode, 60
Equivalent diode, 49
Equivalent-diode theorem, 50
Excitation energy, 242
Excited state, atomic, 242
Experiment schedules, 507

Faraday dark space, 252
Feedback, 172
  cascade amplifiers, 176
    demonstration experiment, 183
  cathode-resistor, 172, 206
  current, 173
  equation, 176
  parallel, 209
  pentode circuits, 185
  positive, 200
  ratio (*b*), 174
  screen-grid circuit, 186
  transistors, 533
  voltage, 174
Fermi potential, 232
Field emission, 237
Field tank, 45
  demonstration experiments, 47, 139
Filter circuits, 35